# A Letter to Instructors

It started as a simple suggestion, and ended up taking on a life of its own. In March of 2014, I attended the NCMATYC conference in a town called, charmingly enough, Hamlet, North Carolina. I was there to speak about *Pathways to Math Literacy*, our book designed for a Math Literacy course that replaces both developmental algebra courses in the curriculum for students not traveling the path to calculus. But I also hoped to gather some information on a new project I was kicking around; more on that in a bit.

It turns out that there were some nice folks in the audience who are familiar with my liberal arts math book, *Math in Our World*. After the talk, more than one person suggested that I should write a version of *Math in Our World* in the format of *Pathways*.

Interestingly, I and my team at McGraw-Hill had been wrestling with the idea of what exactly a quantitative reasoning (QR) course should look like, and what differentiated this growing course area from liberal arts math. I was trying to talk to as many instructors as I could to pick their brains, which was my other motive for making the epic journey from suburban Cincinnati to rural North Carolina.

Then the proverbial ton of bricks hit me: the NCMATYC suggestion was exactly what we were looking for, and it was right under our noses. I actually left a happy-hour gathering early that evening, which is quite unusual for me, because I was so excited about the idea that I wanted to put together a sample section. And that night, *Math in Our World: A Quantitative Reasoning Approach* was born.

Since our partnership had resulted in what we think is a fine product in *Pathways*, I asked my partner in crime, Brian Mercer, to keep the team together for this new project, and we set about changing the way quantitative reasoning is treated in the publishing world. Our previous thoughts on QR were along the lines of what we're seeing from a lot of publishers these days: a minor tweak here and there to a liberal arts math book, put "Quantitative Reasoning" on the cover, and call it a revolution. But the project was slow to get off the ground (and by "slow" I mean "I had done nothing") because I didn't feel good about that approach at all.

So what really distinguishes QR from liberal arts math? It's not the topic list—the mathematical content covered is very similar, if not identical. It's about learning style, and the way the course is taught. It's about focusing on context 100% of the time. It's about asking students to take responsibility for their own learning. It's about encouraging discovery learning, and being there to support and encourage. It's about using technology in ways that allow us to focus on understanding and interpretation rather than using formulas and crunching numbers. It's about students working collaboratively, helping each other to learn and finding that learning in a group can be fun and engaging. And most importantly, it's about fostering critical thinking and problem-solving skills that will carry through higher education into a lifetime of intellectual development.

These are the goals of *Math in Our World: A Quantitative Reasoning Approach*. We're serious about building this new course into something that can enrich the college math experience for non-STEM students in ways that we couldn't have imagined in the Jurassic days when college algebra was the default choice for students not headed to calculus. We hope that students using our book will say "Wow, this doesn't seem like a normal math course." And we ultimately hope that students whose position has been "I don't like math" and "When will I ever use this?" will look back on the course and say "Now I FINALLY get it."

The backbone of any well-designed math course is content, so let's have a look at the content that we've chosen as the vehicle for reasoning quantitatively.

# Brief Contents

# Math in Our World: A Quantitative Reasoning Approach

**Dave Sobecki**
*Associate Professor of Mathematics*
*Miami University Hamilton*

**Brian Mercer**
*Professor of Mathematics*
*Parkland College*

Mc
Graw
Hill
Education

1 2 3 4 5 6 7 8 9 0  DOW  21 20 19 18 17 16

ISBN 978-1-259-82757-0
MHID 1-259-82757-7

ISBN 978-1-259-82768-6 (Annotated Instructor's Edition)
MHID 1-259-82768-2

Chief Product Officer, SVP Products & Markets: *G. Scott Virkler*
Vice President, General Manager, Products & Markets: *Marty Lange*
Vice President, Content Design & Delivery: *Betsy Whalen*
Managing Director: *Ryan Blankenship*
Brand Manager: *Adam Rooke*
Director, Product Development: *Rose Koos*
Product Developer: *Vincent Bradshaw*
Product Development Coordinator: *Caitlyn Fuller*
Director of Marketing: *Sally Yagan*
Marketing Coordinator: *Annie Clarke*
Director of Digital Content Development: *Cynthia Northrup*
Associate Digital Product Analyst: *Adam Fischer*
Director, Content Design & Delivery: *Linda Avenarius*
Program Manager: *Lora Neyens*
Content Project Manager: *Peggy J. Selle*
Assessment Project Manager: *Emily Windelborn*
Buyer: *Sandy Ludovissy*
Design: *Tara McDermott*
Content Licensing Specialist Photo: *Carrie Burger*
Content Licensing Specialist Text: *Lori Slattery*
Cover Image: *© Pixdeluxe/Getty Images (farmers); © Fuse/Getty Images (chopping vegetables); © Lisovskaya Natalia/Getty Images (plate)*
Compositor: *SPI-Global*
Typeface: *10/12 Stix Mathjax MAIN*
Printer: *LSC Communications*
All credits appearing on page or at the end of the book are considered to be an extension of the copyright page.

**Library of Congress Cataloging-in-Publication Data**

Names: Sobecki, Dave. | Mercer, Brian A.
Title: Math in our world : a quantitative reasoning approach / Dave Sobecki,
     Professor of Mathematics, Miami University, Hamilton [Ohio], Brian Mercer,
     Professor of Mathematics, Parkland College.
Description: 1e [first edition]. | New York, NY : McGraw-Hill Education,
     [2017] | Includes index.
Identifiers: LCCN 2016030482 | ISBN 9781259827570 (alk. paper)
Subjects: LCSH: Mathematics—Textbooks. | Mathematics—Study and teaching
     (Higher)
Classification: LCC QA39.3 .B5974 2017 | DDC 510--dc23 LC record available at https://lccn.loc.gov/2016030482

mheducation.com/highered

# About the Authors

## Dave Sobecki

Dave was born and raised in Cleveland, and in spite of starting college with a major in creative writing, he somehow ended up with a Doctorate degree in math. Go figure. Dave is a tenured professor of math at the Hamilton campus of Miami University in southwest Ohio. He has won a number of teaching awards in his career, and has written or co-authored either nine or sixteen books, depending on how you count them. He's also working on his first novel. When not teaching or writing, Dave's passions include Ohio State football, Cleveland Indians baseball, heavy metal music, travel, golf, collecting fine art, and most importantly spending time with his wife Cat and over-attached retrievers, Macleod and Tessa.

Courtesy of Dave Sobecki

## Brian Mercer

Brian is a tenured professor at Parkland College in Champaign, Illinois, where he has taught developmental and transfer math courses for 18 years. He began writing in 1999, and has currently co-authored six textbooks, with others in the planning stages. Outside of the classroom and away from the computer, Brian is kept educated, entertained, and ever-busy by his wonderful wife Nikki and their two children, Charlotte, 9, and Jake, 8. He is an avid St. Louis Cardinals fan and enjoys playing softball and golf in the summertime with colleagues and friends.

Courtesy of Brian Mercer

# Table of Contents

## Unit 1: EVERYONE HAS PROBLEMS

## Unit 2: MANAGING YOUR MONEY

# Unit 3: PLACE YOUR BETS

# Unit 4: STATISTICALLY SPEAKING

## Unit 5: BUILDING MODELS

## Unit 6: THE JOY OF SETS

## Unit 7: UNCOMMON SENSE

# Unit 8: HOW DO YOU MEASURE UP?

# A Letter to Students

This book has the term "Quantitative Reasoning" in the title, so we probably ought to begin by describing what that means. But nothing is for free in this course, so before we do that, we're going to ask you to think about an answer to this question: Why are you taking this class? For that matter, why are you in college at all? It would be great if "To get an education" was your answer, or at the very least crossed your mind. It might be even better if you thought "To get smarter." That should be the goal of everyone that's going to school, really.

So can you actually get smarter? OF COURSE YOU CAN. You almost certainly know that you can get stronger and more fit than you currently are by exercising your body. Then why in the world wouldn't you think you can get smarter by exercising your brain? You can, but not if you occupy a chair and expect your professor to just magically fill your head with math. That's not mental exercise. True mental exercise requires challenging yourself to think, to solve problems, to make connections, and to explain your understanding of concepts. Which brings us back to our part of the bargain, a description of what quantitative reasoning means.

At its core, this course is about exercising your brain by challenging you to really LEARN, not just to memorize formulas or mimic step-by-step procedures. When you hear the word "reasoning," it probably brings to mind something like "figuring stuff out." By including the term "Quantitative Reasoning" in the title of this book, we're simply pointing out the fact that we're not going to just ask you to do a bunch of calculations, simplify a bunch of expressions, or solve a bunch of equations. Instead, the focus is going to be practicing your reasoning skills by studying situations where mathematical thinking can help you be smarter and more successful, both as a student and as a citizen of 21st-century planet earth.

Certainly being comfortable with numbers is important in a monetary society. But it goes beyond that: someone once told us that nobody is going to pay people to solve problems that have already been solved, and that kind of became a framework for this course. We gathered as much information as we could about what employers want college graduates to be able to do these days, and three things consistently jumped out at us: being able to work effectively in groups, being able to solve problems and figure stuff out without always being told what to do, and being able to use technology well. It's those three things that became the key principles of this book.

## The Approach: What Truly Makes This Course Different

The thing that makes this a course in quantitative reasoning, rather than a survey of mathematical topics, is the way the material is presented, and more importantly, how we expect you to interact with the material. If you're dead-set on sitting in the back of the room and being talked at for an hour, you'll find out pretty quickly that you're in the wrong place: active participation is required. You won't find a bunch of solved examples in this book, like you're probably used to seeing in math texts. What you will find is a series of activities designed to encourage (and by "encourage" we mean "force") you to take responsibility for your own learning. Discovery learning and productive struggle are the key phrases that describe our philosophy.

Discovery learning is the process of learning new ideas on your own, rather than having them presented to you. That doesn't mean that you're expected to "teach this course to yourself." Your professor is by far the most valuable resource you'll have on this journey. But his or her job is to help you to learn, not to show you exactly what to do. In a very real sense, the goal of this course is to help you become mathematically literate. We can define mathematical literacy as the quantitative and reasoning skills anyone should have to be successful in society. Think about literacy in the reading sense. You can't teach someone to read by just reading to them: at some point you have to guide them through reading on their own, and that's the role of your professor in this course.

Productive struggle is described really well by the exercise analogy from earlier: the best way to really learn something, and to make your brain stronger in the process, is to have to work at it. If you get every question in this book right on the first try, then we've failed as writers, to be honest. Life can be a hard place, especially when you're responsible for your own care and feeding, and we can promise you that you will get NOWHERE in this world if you give up every time you encounter some resistance. In our view, the single most valuable skill you'll practice in this course is GRIT: the ability to overcome obstacles, and keep trying until you reach a goal.

Because working effectively in groups is so important, the book has been designed as a series of in-class activities for you to work through in a group setting. There are two things you need to do in order to maximize your chance for success in this course: be willing to put in a lot of work, and be willing to learn with and learn from your group mates, as well as to help teach them from time to time. If we were pure evil and decided to kidnap you and dump you out in the wilderness somewhere, you surely would appreciate not being alone, right? As you wander the path toward an adult education, having peers there with you should be comforting, and should be a resource that you take advantage of whenever possible.

Once class is over, there will be a lot of work you're expected to do on your own, in a variety of different settings. If you turn ahead to one of the pages in the book marked "Portfolio," you can see the different categories of homework, and no doubt your professor will talk about them on the first day of class. If you keep thinking back to the exercise analogy, you'll have a much easier time getting motivated to keep up with the homework. Why are you in this class? To get smarter. That will happen if you work hard toward the goal, and are never, ever afraid to think on your own. You were smart enough to make the decision to further your education in college, so you're smart enough to think, learn, and succeed in quantitative reasoning. Set a goal, work toward it, and believe in yourself. And don't be afraid to drop us a line if you have questions about the book, suggestions for improvement, or just want to share your thoughts on how the course is going.

davesobecki@gmail.com
bmercer51@gmail.com

# The Content

The backbone of any well-designed math course is content, so let's talk about the content that we've chosen as the vehicle for becoming quantitatively literate.

## Unit 1: Mathematical Reasoning and Problem Solving

In our view, the ideal way to begin this course is to explicitly talk about the different kinds of reasoning that humans do, and to define and practice the types of problem-solving skills that will form the backbone of the course. We also encourage students to practice graph interpretation and estimation skills that should be (but are not) possessed by everyone in a technological and monetary-based society.

## Unit 2: Consumer Math

Did we mention that we live in a monetary society? Consumer math is kind of the low-hanging fruit of quantitative reasoning content: everyone who's ever spent their own money on anything has a natural understanding of how financial literacy is important. The focus of this unit isn't "here's how to do financial calculations"; it's "let's understand the concepts and situations that lead to important financial considerations." While we absolutely will study formulas that calculate interest, loan payments, and the like, we certainly will not just provide the formulas, ask students to plug a bunch of numbers in, and call that education. Instead, students are asked to think like consumers, and develop a true understanding of the math that serves us well in navigating the rocky financial waters of modern society.

## Unit 3: Probability and Counting Techniques

Almost everything that we do is governed at least in part by chance and probability, so a book devoted to quantitative reasoning should go beyond simply calculating probabilities and odds: the focus should be on being able to interpret the story told by those calculations. We certainly feel that performing probability calculations is important, as long as the focus is on understanding rather than formulas. But we also believe that it's important to move beyond simple probability calculations, incorporating technology to allow us to study complex outcomes in a complex world.

## Unit 4: Statistics

The logical follow-up to a study of probability is continuing the mindset by developing key ideas in the study of basic statistics. The focus is different methods of gathering, organizing, and interpreting data. Anyone can find the average (whatever that means) of a list of numbers, but that's a hollow exercise without the ability to interpret the story told by that statistic. While we don't feel that quantitative reasoning necessarily requires high-level statistical analysis, we do feel that our society will be much the better if everyone has experience with sifting through the mountain of information they're exposed to every day, and separating the gold nuggets from the cow pies, if you will. So a major focus of, and the culmination of the unit, is recognizing ways that statistics can be manipulated to tell a story that has at best a passing resemblance to the truth. While politicians and advertisers may not appreciate these efforts, we think that students interested in getting an education will.

## Unit 5: Mathematical Modeling

It's the sad truth that most college math students honestly believe that algebra was developed as a completely abstract field, with applications following along at some later point. We know, of course, that this is completely backward, but traditional curriculum design tends to foster this all-too-common misconception. In Unit 5, we cover important algebra topics from an applied approach, hopefully allowing students to finally see how the algebra that they've learned in the past is useful and relevant.

## Unit 6: Set Theory

Humans have a natural tendency to categorize things in groups, from numbers to people. In a very real sense, the fundamentals of set theory are central to pretty much everything we do in math. So we study set theory both as an accessible way to apply mathematical thinking to our world and as a vehicle for thinking about the type of organized thought that's useful in any math-related field.

## Unit 7: Logic

Digging further into the fundamentals of mathematical and scientific thought, we cover formal logic in a way that helps students to always remember that the $p$s and $q$s they're working with aren't letters, but statements about the world in which they live. We feel like the way to keep students engaged in the study of truth values for statements and validity of arguments is to ask them to build the rules for truth values through examples, rather than providing and illustrating the rules. All of us hope that through math, students learn to think logically and analytically: an explicit study of logical thought helps to foster that type of thinking.

## Unit 8: Measurement and the Geometry of Size

Measuring sizes is not only one of the oldest applications of math; it's also one of the most common even today. The study of mathematics should, of course, be part of any college program for a variety of reasons; in terms of direct application to many fields of study, working with measurement and units ranks highly. Ask any instructor of general sciences how much more they could accomplish if they didn't have to spend weeks covering key ideas in measurement and unit conversion, and you'll gain an appreciation for how useful this topic can be for your students.

One of the best things about a course of this nature is that the material is not completely linear. It's perfectly possible for instructors to choose the content that's most relevant for his or her students, and reordering of some of the topics is reasonable as well. We've devised an ordering that works well for us, but colleges or instructors can certainly choose a topic list and order that best meets the needs of their student populations.

# Acknowledgments

So many people were involved in bringing this project to life that it's tempting to just thank the whole world and move on, but some folks deserve special recognition. We sincerely hope we didn't omit anyone in this category. If we did, blame it on Dave and he owes you some beverages of your choice.

We spent the better part of two years traveling all over the country visiting conferences and campuses, and conducting focus groups and symposia. We thank everyone who attended and shared their ideas on improving college math for non-STEM students. You are the main reason this project exists.

Elizabeth Betzel
*Columbus State Community College*

Colleen Bye
*Utah Valley University*

Erin Cooke
*Perimeter College at Georgia State University*

Steven Cosares
*LaGuardia Community College*

Jodi Cotten-Konsur
*Westchester Community College*

Lisa Creighton
*Central Piedmont Community College*

Tim Delworth
*Purdue University, West Lafayette*

Raina J. Eckhardt
*Manchester Community College*

Jennifer Fitzgerald
*Northern Essex Community College*

Debra Hall
*James Madison University*

Julie Hartzler
*Des Moines Area Community College*

Lori Heymans
*Northern Essex Community College*

Barbie Hoag
*Oakland Community College*

Heather Howington
*University of North Georgia*

Gretta Johnson
*Amarillo College*

Rachel King
*Northern Essex Community College*

Kurt Klopstein
*Bakersfield College*

Bernadette Kocyba
*J. Sargeant Reynolds Community College*

Kelly Kohlmetz
*University of Wisconsin–Milwaukee*

Chris Mansfield
*Durham Technical Community College*

Susan McLoughlin
*Union County College*

Linda Murphy
*Northern Essex Community College*

Jonathan Oaks
*Macomb Community College*

Rebecca Rose
*Northern Essex Community College*

Robin Rufatto
*Ball State University*

Mike Sieve
*Ridgewater College*

Jim Sullivan
*Northern Essex Community College*

Prudence York-Hammons
*Temple College*

Our deepest appreciation goes to all of our friends in North Carolina who inspired and supported this project. In particular, Paula Savich from Mayland Community College was the first person who suggested a version of *Math in Our World* in a group project–based format. Chris Mansfield from Durham Tech went above and beyond, working with us on developing a content plan. Several instructors provided feedback on the various drafts of the manuscript.

Kari Arnoldsen
*Snow College*

Jordan Bertke
*Central Piedmont Community College*

Cindy Box
*Perimeter College at Georgia State University*

Kyle Carter
*The University of West Georgia*

Erin Cooke
*Perimeter College at Georgia State University*

Wendy Davidson
*Perimeter College at Georgia State University*

Maria DeLucia
*Middlesex County College*

Holly Dickin
*Ball State University*

Julie Gunkelman
*Oakland Community College*

Debbie Hanus
*Brookhaven College*

Barbie Hoag
*Oakland Community College*

Kelly Kohlmetz
*University of Wisconsin–Milwaukee*

Crystal Lorch
*Ball State University*

Vikki Maurer
*Linn-Benton Community College*

Kevin McLeod
*University of Wisconsin–Milwaukee*

LeAnn Neel-Romine
*Ball State University*

Eric Neumann
*Community College of Philadelphia*

Kathy Pinzon
*Georgia Gwinnett College*

Linda K. Schmidt
*Spartanburg Community College*

Jennifer Stanley
*West Georgia State*

Donna Toll
*Ball State University*

Erin Wilding-Martin
*Parkland College*

Janet Yi
*Ball State University*

Prudence York-Hammons
*Temple College*

We were very lucky to put together a board of advisors, listed below. The board's thoughtful discussions and detailed content reviews helped to shape our somewhat rough-hewn early attempts into the shiny product you're looking at now.

Nikki Armstrong
*Southwestern Oregon Community College*

Jordan Bertke
*Central Piedmont Community College*

Cindy Box
*Perimeter College at Georgia State University*

Erin Cooke
*Perimeter College at Georgia State University*

Wendy Davidson
*Perimeter College at Georgia State University*

Debbie Hanus
*Brookhaven College*

Barbie Hoag
*Oakland Community College*

Julie Gunkelman
*Oakland Community College*

Kelly Kohlmetz
*University of Wisconsin–Milwaukee*

Vikki Maurer
*Linn-Benton Community College*

Kevin McLeod
*University of Wisconsin–Milwaukee*

Lori Murphy
*Rockingham Community College*

Dawn Peterson
*Itawamba Community College*

Erin Wilding-Martin
*Parkland College*

We also had the rare opportunity to have the following courageous instructors class testing the book as we wrote it: Deb Hanus, Nikki Armstrong, Barbie Hoag, and Marcus Szwankowski (Front Range Community College).

At McGraw-Hill Higher Education, we thank: Managing Director Ryan Blankenship for supporting us as we sailed off into uncharted waters, and Brand Manager Adam Rooke for piloting the ship; Product Developers extraordinaire, Vincent Bradshaw and Elizabeth O'Brien, who provided so much more than what their job description calls for; Tara McDermott and her design team, who continue to amaze with their fresh ideas for visual appeal; Director of Digital Content Rob Brieler (we ask for new features, and he says "I think we can do that"); Marketing Director Sally Yagan, who will NEVER settle for "good enough"; accuracy checker Dawn Peterson—yet another member of the team that did far more than what was expected; copy editors Pat Steele and Julie Kennedy, who never make fun of our silly mistakes; and project manager Peggy Selle who kept it all together.

# Supplements

 **Connect Math® Hosted by ALEKS**

Connect Math Hosted by ALEKS Corp. is an exciting assignment and assessment ehomework platform. Starting with an easily viewable, intuitive interface, students will be able to access key information, complete homework assignments, and utilize an integrated, media rich eBook.

**SMARTBOOK®**  SmartBook

SmartBook is the first and only adaptive reading experience available for the higher education market. Powered by the intelligent and adaptive LearnSmart engine, SmartBook facilitates the reading process by identifying what content a student knows and doesn't know. As a student reads, the material continuously adapts to ensure the student is focused on the content he or she needs the most to close specific knowledge gaps.

**create™**  CREATE

With **McGraw-Hill Create™**, you can easily rearrange chapters, combine material from other content sources, and quickly upload content you have written such as your course syllabus or teaching notes. Find the content you need in Create by searching through thousands of leading McGraw-Hill textbooks. Arrange your book to fit your teaching style. Create even allows you to personalize your book's appearance by selecting the cover and adding your name, school, and course information. Assemble a Create book, and you'll receive a complimentary print review copy in 3–5 business days or a complimentary electronic review copy (eComp) via email in minutes. Go to www.mcgrawhillcreate.com today and experience how McGraw-Hill Create™ empowers you to teach your students your way.

## Instructor's Testing and Resource Online

This computerized test bank, available online to adopting instructors, utilizes TestGen® cross-platform test generation software to quickly and easily create customized exams. Using hundreds of test items taken directly from the text, TestGen allows rapid test creation and flexibility for instructors to create their own questions from scratch with ability to randomize number values. Powerful search and sort functions help quickly locate questions and arrange them in any order, and built-in mathematical templates let instructors insert stylized text, symbols, graphics, and equations directly into questions without need for a separate equation editor.

## Videos

Introduce concepts, definitions, theorems, formulas, and problem-solving procedures to help students comprehend topics.

# Unit 1
# Everyone Has Problems

© Robert Voets/CBS Photo Archive/Getty Images

**Outline**

Lesson 1: Be Reasonable (Inductive and Deductive Reasoning)

Lesson 2: More or Less (Estimation and Interpreting Graphs)

Lesson 3: You Got a Problem? (Problem Solving Strategies)

1

# Math In   Criminal Investigation

In traditional cops-and-robbers movies, crime fighters use guns and fists to catch criminals, but in real life, often it's brain power that brings the bad guys to justice. That's why the TV show *CSI* marked a revolution of sorts when it debuted in October 2000: it featured scientists fighting crime, not tough guys. Solving a case is intimately tied to the process of problem solving: investigators gather and organize as much relevant information as they can, then use logic and intuition to formulate a plan. Hopefully, this will lead them to a suspect.

This same strategy is the essence of problem solving in many walks of life other than criminal justice. Students in math classes often ask, "When am I going to use what I learn?" The best answer to that question is, "Every day!" Math classes are not only about facts and formulas: They're also about exercising your mind, training your brain to think logically, and learning effective strategies for solving problems. And not just math problems. Every day of our lives, we face a wide variety of problems: They pop up in our jobs, in school, and in our personal lives. Which computer should you buy? What should you do when your car starts making an awful noise? What would be a good topic for a research paper? How can you get all your work done in time to go to that party Friday night?

Unit 1 of this book is dedicated to the most important topic we'll cover: an introduction to some of the classic techniques of problem solving. These techniques will prove to be useful tools that you can apply in the rest of your education. But more importantly, they can be applied just as well to situations outside the classroom.

And this brings us back to our friends from *CSI*. The logic and reasoning that they use to identify suspects and prove their guilt are largely based on problem-solving skills we'll study in this unit. In preparation for this unit, talk over the following questions with your group. Don't worry if you don't know how to answer them: If you knew all the answers in advance, you wouldn't need college! The idea is to start thinking about some of the concepts we'll study in the lessons in this unit, and maybe learn a bit in advance about why these topics are useful. When you've completed this unit, you should come back to these questions. If all goes well, you'll have a much better time with them, allowing you to track your progress.

All of the situations below are based on episodes of *CSI*. In each case, evidence was gathered that led the investigators to a suspect or suspects. But . . .

1. Is there a difference between evidence that can help identify a suspect and evidence that will lead to that suspect being convicted in court? Discuss.

2. Are you familiar with the term "circumstantial evidence"? If not, look it up. Then talk about what makes evidence "circumstantial," and whether you think it's right to send people to prison based on this type of evidence.

Now let's look at the cases. Your job is to apply what you talked about in Questions 1 and 2 to analyze the evidence from a juror's perspective. In each case, is the evidence circumstantial? Was the type of reasoning used inductive or deductive? (If you're not familiar with these terms, that's fine: You will be very shortly.) Most importantly, do you think it's (A) legal, and (B) appropriate to use the evidence to convict the suspect?

3. After a violent crime, the investigators identify a recently paroled suspect living in the area who had previously committed three very similar crimes.

4. A homeless man is found dead from exposure after being roughed up. His wrists look like he had been handcuffed, and fingerprints on his ID lead them to a local police officer.

5. A murder victim grabbed a pager from the killer while being attacked and threw it under the couch. With the suspect identified, the investigators found that his DNA matched DNA found under the victim's fingernails.

6. A series of five bodies are found posed like mannequins in public places. The lead suspect is an artist that is found to have sketches matching the poses of all five victims.

## Lesson 1-1   Prep Skills

This is a short review of skills that will come in handy in the next lesson. In each case, answer the question, then rate your confidence level by checking one of the boxes. If you feel like you're struggling with these skills, consult the online resources provided by your instructor for extra practice.

**SKILL 1: RECOGNIZE PATTERNS IN NUMBERS**

1. Fill in the blanks with the most likely next two numbers.

   7, 11, 15, 19, 23, _____, _____

2. Fill in the blanks with the most likely next two numbers.

   1, 2, 4, 8, 16, _____, _____

**SKILL 2: IDENTIFY DIVISIBILITY OF NUMBERS**

3. Which of the following numbers are divisible by 3?

   12, 14, 19, 21, 36, 40

4. Which of the following numbers are divisible by 5?

   25, 36, 55, 70, 100, 111

**SKILL 3: SIMPLIFY ALGEBRAIC EXPRESSIONS**

5. Simplify the expression: $2(3a + 7) - 4a + 2$

6. Simplify the expression: $5y + 6 - 7(2y - 4)$

## Lesson 1-1 **Be Reasonable** (Inductive and Deductive Reasoning)

### LEARNING OBJECTIVES

☐ 1. Explain the difference between inductive and deductive reasoning.

☐ 2. Use inductive reasoning to make conjectures.

☐ 3. Use deductive reasoning to prove or disprove a conjecture.

© Royalty-Free/Corbis

*The difference between science and the fuzzy subjects is that science requires reasoning while those other subjects merely require scholarship.*
　　　　　　　　—Robert A. Heinlein

A big part of being an adult is making decisions on your own—every day is full of them, from the simple, like what to eat for breakfast, to the critical, like a choice of major or career. If you make every decision based on a coin flip, you won't get very far in life. Instead, it's important to be able to analyze a situation based on logical thinking. What are the possible outcomes of making that decision? How likely is it that each choice will have positive or negative consequences? We call the process of logical thinking **reasoning.** It doesn't take a lot of imagination to understand how important reasoning is in everyone's life. So in this lesson, we'll study the process of reasoning, which I think we can all agree is a perfectly reasonable thing to do.

**0.** After reading the opening paragraph, what do you think the main topic of this lesson will be?

## 1-1 | Class

Consider this scenario: A friend invites you to check out their new apartment a few blocks away from where you live. It's a nice day, so you decide to walk over. On the way, you notice a dog loose in someone's yard, but it seems like a nice doggie so you don't think much of it—until the dog runs over and bites you on the leg. Owwww!

**1.** Discuss whether or not you'd be likely to take the same path the next time you visit your friend. Include both an argument for why you would take the same route, and an argument for why you would not.

Courtesy of David Sobecki

*Answers vary. Sample argument in favor: isolated incident, unlikely to happen again. Sample argument against: you could get bitten again if you walk by the same house.*

2. Suppose that you decide to take the same path the next day. When passing by the same dog at the same house, he again runs over and bites you on the leg. Discuss how this might affect your thoughts on this particular route to your friend's apartment.

   *Answers vary, but you would certainly think that most folks would decide not to take that route anymore.*

   Assuming that you would find a different way to get to your friend's place next time, you have used what we call *inductive reasoning*.

   **Inductive reasoning** is the process of reasoning that arrives at a general conclusion based on the observation of specific examples.

In this case, you are using two specific events (the dog bites) to draw a general conclusion (that walking along a different route would be a good idea). That's what makes this way of thinking inductive reasoning.

   Now let's think about another scenario. You're still walking on the shortest path to your friend's new apartment, but on one street, you notice that there's a big hole in the sidewalk where construction is being done, with no way to get around it.

3. Discuss whether or not you'd be likely to take the same path the next day. Would you have to fall into the hole to decide?

   *You would certainly hope not, on both counts.*

© Jim Reed/Science Source

There's a clear difference between these two scenarios: In the second, you wouldn't need to fall into the hole twice to decide that a different route would be a good idea. At least I hope you wouldn't. Instead, you would deduce from a known principle (I like to call it "gravity") that walking along this sidewalk wouldn't work. The use of the word "deduce" was important there: We call this type of reasoning *deductive reasoning*.

Deductive reasoning is the process of reasoning that arrives at a conclusion based on previously accepted general statements. It doesn't rely on specific examples.

Before we start using these two methods of reasoning to draw conclusions, let's make sure you understand the difference between the two. In Questions 4–8, decide whether inductive or deductive reasoning was used to draw the conclusion, and explain your choice in your own words.

4. The last six times we played our archrival in football, we won, so I know we're going to win on Saturday.

    *Inductive reasoning. The conclusion is based on six specific instances—the six previous games.*

> Even though this is in the Class portion of the lesson, it's a good idea to let students discuss these in pairs or in groups before going over them in class.

5. There is no mail delivery on holidays. Tomorrow is Labor Day so I know my student loan check won't show up.

    *Deductive reasoning. The fact that mail doesn't get delivered on legal holidays is a known rule.*

6. The syllabus states that any final average between 80 and 90% will result in a B. I got 80 and 82 on my first two tests, and if I get 78% on my final, my overall average will be 80.1%. That means I'll get a B.

    *Deductive. Don't be misled by the specific scores being given. The conclusion is based on the stated premise that a final average between 80 and 90 will result in a B.*

7. Everyone I know in my sorority got at least a 2.5 GPA last semester, so I'm sure I'll get at least a 2.5 this semester.

    *Inductive. The conclusion is based on the specific experiences of some number of people.*

8. All birds can fly. An ostrich is a bird. Therefore, ostriches can fly.

*Deductive. It doesn't matter that the conclusion is false; it's based on the premise that all birds can fly, not specific examples.*

> You can lay some groundwork for our study of logic here if you like. The conclusion here isn't true, but it was still drawn using deductive reasoning. It just so happens that the "known rule" here is incorrect.

### Did You Get It?

Try this problem to see if you understand the concepts we just studied. The answer can be found at the bottom of the portfolio page.

1. Decide whether inductive or deductive reasoning was used to draw each conclusion.
   a. I've never met a golden retriever with a nasty disposition. I bet there aren't any.
   b. An apple a day keeps the doctor away. I eat an apple every day, so Dr. Phil has never come to my house.
   c. Today is Friday, so it will be Monday in three days.

## 1-1    Group

1. Numerous studies have shown that one of the best ways to do better in college classes is to study in pairs or groups. To help you get started, if you feel comfortable sharing contact information, exchange the information in the table below. The group you're in now will be your small group for the first unit of this course. When you get used to meeting in class, you'll likely find that meeting outside of class to study and work on homework is a good idea as well, so include some study times that would be convenient for you to meet.

| Name | Phone Number | Email | Available times |
|---|---|---|---|
|  |  |  |  |
|  |  |  |  |
|  |  |  |  |
|  |  |  |  |
|  |  |  |  |

> This marks the first time students will formally introduce themselves to their groups and work on the Group portion of a lesson. Set the tone for the class by walking around, asking the groups questions about their work, and encouraging groups that are not working together. Make sure they're not rushing through the problems without really thinking about them.

In inductive reasoning, we're drawing conclusions based on observing specific examples or occurrences. An important aspect of being able to do this effectively is recognizing patterns. So we'll start there in our study of using inductive reasoning. Consider this list of numbers:

3, 6, 9, 12, 15

If you were asked to make an educated guess as to what number might come next on the list, a good place to start would be to recognize that after the first number, all others come from adding 3 to the previous number on the list. In that case, the most logical guess for the next number comes from adding 3 to 15, of course getting 18.

> **Math Note**
>
> The word **conjecture** is basically a synonym for "educated guess." So we would say that we *conjectured* that the next number on the list 3, 6, 9, 12, 15 would be 18.

2. Use inductive reasoning to make a conjecture about the next number on this list:

   1, 2, 4, 5, 7, 8, 10, 11, 13

   Explain how you decided on your answer.

   *14. The pattern is add one, then add two, then go back to adding one and repeat. The last number added was 2, so this time it'll be 1.*

3. Make a reasonable conjecture for the next figure in this sequence, and briefly describe your reasoning.

   *The next figure will be the same shape, but have the flat side facing to the left. Also, the circle inside will be white. With each successive picture, the figure rotates a quarter-turn clockwise. The first four had a black circle inside, and the next four should have a white circle.*

4. Think of a way that you have used inductive reasoning recently to draw a conclusion of some sort, and describe that thought process. Each member of the group should come up with their own example.

   *Answers vary.*

## Did You Get It?

Try this problem to see if you understand the concepts we just studied. The answer can be found at the bottom of the portfolio page.

2. Make a reasonable conjecture for the next two items on each list.
   a. 0   −2   4   −6   8   −10
   b. 26   y   24   w   22   u   20   s
   c.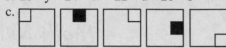

You could make a very real case that inductive reasoning is the essence of where scientific advances come from. You make some observations, then use inductive reasoning to draw a conclusion, and test to see if it seems to hold true. Let's see how this works.

5. If you add two odd numbers together, what will the result look like? Use inductive reasoning to make a conjecture.

   *The best approach is to pick several pairs of odd numbers and add them together. Some samples:*

   $3 + 7 = 10, 11 + 15 = 26, 1 + 3 = 4, 19 + 111 = 140, 51 + 51 = 102$

   *The only connection between the sums is that they're all even.*

6. How sure are you that your conjecture is true? Discuss.

   *Not particularly. I tried five pairs of odd numbers, and it worked each time. But there are infinitely many pairs to choose from, and I tested FIVE. That doesn't give me a ton of confidence.*

   Here's the problem with your conjecture: You're guessing that the sum of EVERY pair of odd numbers has a certain property. But there's no way that you can actually test every pair of numbers, because (of course) there are infinitely many to test. And that's the big issue with inductive reasoning: It's an incredibly useful tool in decision making, but since in most cases you can't verify a conclusion for every possible case, you can't be 100% certain that your conclusion is valid. We'll come back to your conjecture later in the lesson. For now, we'll look at a different problem.

Suppose that your history professor gives a surprise quiz every Friday for the first four weeks of class. At that point, you might use inductive reasoning to conjecture that you'll have a quiz every Friday. But you can't look into the future and know for sure, so it's entirely possible that your conjecture is not true. In fact, the first time you DON'T have a quiz on Friday, your conjecture has proven to be false.

This is a really useful observation: While it can be difficult to prove that a conjecture is true, it's much simpler to prove that one is false. All you need to do is find one specific example that contradicts the conjecture (like the first Friday without a quiz). This is known as a **counterexample.**

7.  This conjecture is false (Trust me, I'm a doctor.): A whole number greater than 10 can be divided by 3 with no remainder if the last two digits can be divided by three with no remainder. Find a counterexample that proves it's not true. (Hint: Pick some random numbers whose last two digits can be divided evenly by three.)

    *103 is the smallest number that works as a counterexample.*

A chord is a line connecting two points on a circle. If you draw a chord connecting two points, it divides the circle into two sections. With only one point, there's no chord to draw, and the circle has just one section:

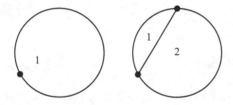

8.  Using the diagrams below, count the number of sections a circle is divided into by chords connecting 3, 4, and 5 points. Numbering the sections as you count them is a big help.

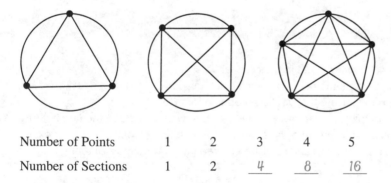

| Number of Points | 1 | 2 | 3 | 4 | 5 |
|---|---|---|---|---|---|
| Number of Sections | 1 | 2 | *4* | *8* | *16* |

**9.** Use your results from Question 8 to make a conjecture as to the number of sections with 6 points. Explain your reasoning.

*The most logical guess is 32, as the number of sections appears to keep doubling.*

**10.** Use the diagram to check your conjecture. What does that tell you about conjectures made using inductive reasoning?

*There are 31 sections. Oops. It's entirely possible you can think logically and make what seems to be a correct conjecture, but it can still turn out to be false.*

> This is easily one of the most important questions in the lesson. Every human being should understand that you can't prove something is true by looking at a handful of specific examples.

Question 10 illustrates the essence of math and science we mentioned earlier: We have an idea that something might be true, and we use inductive reasoning to test it. But the result shows why inductive reasoning can't be used to prove results: What appears to be true after looking at several examples can still turn out to be false. We'll explore this idea more in the Technology part of tonight's homework. Doing so will require using formulas to perform calculations in Excel; if you're not familiar with how to do this, these directions will help.

## Using Technology: Entering a Formula in Excel

To enter a formula in Excel:
1. Set up a separate column for each quantity involved in the calculation.
2. Identify the column where you want to store the result of the calculation.
3. In the first cell of that column, type = to indicate that you're entering a formula.
4. Type the calculation that you want completed after the = sign. When you want to include the number in a particular cell as part of the calculation, you can either type the column and row of that cell (A3, for example), or you can use the cursor to click on the cell and it will be entered into your formula automatically.
5. When you've completed the formula, press ENTER.

*See the Lesson 1-1 video in class resources for further Instruction.*

> It's a good idea to take some class time to demonstrate Excel procedures, especially early in the class. Some students will have no familiarity with spreadsheets.

## Did You Get It?

Try this problem to see if you understand the concepts we just studied. The answer can be found at the bottom of the portfolio page.

3. Find a counterexample to prove that each conjecture is false.
   a. No month has more than eight letters in it.
   b. The sum of any two positive numbers with two digits also has two digits.

11. When you prove that a conjecture is false using a counterexample, are you using inductive or deductive reasoning? Discuss.

*This is an interesting question to discuss. The answer is deductive: it's a known rule that something is not ALWAYS true if there's at least one case where it's not.*

So inductive reasoning can be used to give you a really good idea that something may be true, but most often cannot be used to *prove* that it's true. Our next step will be look at how inductive and deductive reasoning can work together to both make a conjecture, and then prove it.

12. Pick a random number, and add 50 to it. Then multiply by 2 and subtract the original number. What is the result?

*Answers vary depending on the number, of course. Sample calculation: $33 + 50 = 83$; $83 \cdot 2 = 166$; $166 - 33 = 133$. The result is 100 more than the original number.*

13. Repeat Question 12 for several other beginning numbers until you're able to use inductive reasoning to make a conjecture as to what the result will always look like.

*It appears that the result always works out to be 100 more than the original number.*

Now let's use deductive reasoning to prove your conjecture. So far, you've used *specific* numbers in developing your conjecture: That's what makes what you've done so far inductive reasoning. In order to turn the same idea into deductive reasoning, you need to do these calculations on a number that's nonspecific. Sounds impossible, right? Not so fast, my friend. Rather than use another specific number, we'll use a symbol (a letter in this case) to stand in for ALL possible numbers. If that sounds like a variable to you, you're absolutely right! Good job. The letter we choose will represent a quantity (the number we pick) that can VARY. We want our symbol to stand for any old number, so let's use the letter *a*.

14. Add 50 to our variable number. The result will be an **algebraic expression,** which is a combination of numbers and variables using operations like addition, subtraction, multiplication, division, powers, and roots.

    $a + 50$

15. Next, multiply your answer to Question 14 by 2. Please don't forget that the distributive property exists.

    $2(a + 50) = 2a + 100$

16. Finally, subtract the original number from your answer to Question 15. What is the result?

    $2a + 100 - a = a + 100$    *This is 100 more than the original number.*

# 1-1    Class (Again)

1. Explain why Questions 14–16 in the Group portion prove the conjecture, while Questions 12 and 13 just indicated that it was likely to be true.

   *In Questions 12 and 13, we were using specific numbers. There's no way we could test the conjecture using EVERY number, so we can't prove the conjecture that way. In Questions 14–16, however, we used a symbol that represents EVERY number because it's not specific. So deductive reasoning then tells us that the conjecture is always true.*

> This is where we really bring home the key idea between having a pretty darn good idea that something is true and PROVING that it's true, which is why we labeled the remainder of the lesson as class.

## Did You Get It?

Try this problem to see if you understand the concepts we just studied. The answer can be found at the bottom of the portfolio page.

4. Think of any number. Multiply that number by 3, then add 30, and divide the result by 3. Next subtract the original number. What is the result?
   a. Use inductive reasoning to make a conjecture for the answer.
   b. Use deductive reasoning to prove your conjecture.

Now let's get back to your earlier conjecture about adding odd numbers. You DID conjecture that the result is always even, right? Good job. Go buy yourself a muffin or something. To prove this, we'll need to think about what exactly makes a number even or odd. First, even: A number is even exactly when it can be written as 2 times some other whole number. So we know an even number is one that looks like this: $2n,$ where $n$ is a whole number.

2. Every odd number is exactly ____$1$____ less than an even number.

3. So if any even number looks like $2n,$ then any odd number looks like _$2n - 1$_.

4. Write two arbitrary odd numbers using your answer to Question 3. Use the symbol $n$ in one, and the symbol $m$ in the other.

   $2n - 1$ and $2m - 1$

5. Use algebra to add those two numbers together, then combine like terms, and factor a 2 out of your result.

   $2n - 1 + 2m - 1 = 2n + 2m - 2 = 2(n + m - 1)$

> Students are likely to need some help here, especially with the idea of factoring, and then recognizing why the result has to be even.

6. Explain why this proves your conjecture.

   The result is the sum of ANY two odd numbers, and we were able to write it as 2 times a whole number. So the result has to be even.

7.  The owner of a growing business has noticed that as she hires more employees, the company's weekly profit grows. She hires a consultant to run some numbers, and he informs her that the formula below is a good model of the profit in dollars she can expect to make each week. The variable $x$ represents the number of employees. If she started with 6 employees, use inductive reasoning to investigate whether or not the weekly profit will keep going up if she keeps hiring more employees. Write your conclusion in the form of a sentence.

$$-10x^2 + 480x + 308$$

*Answers should vary depending on what number of employees they choose to test for. The function is designed so that the profit increases up until 24 employees, where it reaches a max. and then begins to decrease.*

I actually prefer when students leave with the impression that this conjecture is true, leaving them to find out otherwise in the Technology assignment. So if they say true, let it go and tell them they'll have a chance to confirm their conjecture in the homework.

## 1-1 Portfolio

Name _____

Check each box when you've completed the task. Remember that your instructor will want you to turn in the portfolio pages you create.

### Technology

1. ☐ Spreadsheets can be a hugely useful tool for using inductive reasoning since you can set up a spreadsheet to test the results of calculations for many different values quickly. We'll be using a spreadsheet to test some of the conjectures from this lesson. The goal will be to use formulas to test conjectures for many different values, similar to the sample below. A template to help you get started can be found in the online resources for this lesson, along with detailed instructions.

| | A | B | C | D |
|---|---|---|---|---|
| 1 | Original number | Add 50 | Multiply by 2 | Subtract original number |
| 2 | 56 | 106 | 212 | 156 |
| 3 | | | | |

*Source: Microsoft*

### Online Practice

1. ☐ Include any written work from the online assignment along with any notes or questions about this lesson's content.

### Applications

1. ☐ Complete the applications problems.

### Reflections

Type a short answer to each question.

1. ☐ Describe the difference between inductive and deductive reasoning in your own words.
2. ☐ Which type of reasoning (inductive/deductive) do you prefer, and why?
3. ☐ Why can inductive reasoning never be used to PROVE a conjecture?
4. ☐ Take another look at your answer to Question 0 at the beginning of this lesson. Would you change your answer now that you've completed the lesson? How would you summarize the topic of this lesson now?
5. ☐ What questions do you have about this lesson?

### Looking Ahead

1. ☐ Complete the Lesson 1-2 Prep Skills and read the opening paragraph in Lesson 1-2 carefully, then answer Question 0 in preparation for that lesson.

### Answers to "Did You Get It?"

**1. a.** Inductive **b.** Deductive **c.** Deductive **2. a.** 12 −14 **b.** 18 q **c.** ▢▢

**3. a.** September has nine letters. **b.** If you pick two numbers with a sum more than 100, the sum has more than two digits. **4. a.** The result is always 10.

**b.** $3a \Rightarrow 3a + 30 \Rightarrow \frac{3a + 30}{3} \Rightarrow \frac{3a + 30}{3} - a = a + 10 - a = 10$

## 1-1    Applications

Name _____

In Questions 1–4, decide whether inductive or deductive reasoning was used to draw a conclusion. Briefly explain your choice. An actual sentence or two would be nice.

1.  The last four congressional representatives from this district were all Republicans. I don't know why the Democratic candidate is even bothering to run this year.

    *Inductive reasoning. Based on four specific elections, this draws a general conclusion.*

2.  Working as a nurse in a hospital requires at least a two-year degree in this state, so when I was in the emergency room last week I asked the nurse where he went to college.

    *Deductive. If it's a rule or law that a degree is required, then the nurse must have gone to college.*

3.  Experts say that opening email attachments that come from unknown senders is the easiest way to get a virus on your computer. Shauna constantly opens attachments from people she doesn't know, so she'll probably end up with a virus on her system.

    *Deductive. Whether or not the premise set forth by 'experts' is true, the conclusion is drawn from a rule that is being accepted, not specific instances.*

4.  Every time Beth sold back her textbooks, she got about 10% of what she paid for them; so this semester she realized it wouldn't be worth the effort to sell back her books at all.

    *Inductive. Beth is basing her conclusion on her own past experiences.*

## 1-1 | Applications

Name _____

For each conjecture in Questions 5–7, if it's false, provide a counterexample. If it's true, use deductive reasoning to prove it.

**5.** The square of every real number is greater than the number itself.

*This is false. Any number between zero and one will provide a counterexample.*

**6.** Pick two even numbers and subtract the larger number minus the smaller number. The result is even as well.

*True. If the first is 2n and the second is 2m, then the difference is 2n − 2m. We can factor out 2 and get 2(n − m), which shows that the result is even because n − m is a whole number.*

**7.** When an even number is added to the product of two odd numbers, the result will be even.

*This is false. 3(11) + 4 = 37, which of course is not even.*

## 1-1     Applications

Name _____

8. Suppose that you drive a certain distance at 20 miles per hour, then turn around and drive back the same distance at 60 miles per hour. Choose at least four different distances and find the average speed for the whole trip. Then use inductive reasoning to make a conjecture as to what the average speed is in general. (Hint: You'll need the formula distance = speed times time repeatedly!)

Distance: 60 miles. It will take 3 hours out and 1 hour back in, for a total of 4 hours. Average speed is

120 mi/4 hr = 30 mi/hr.

Distance: 120 miles. It will take 6 hours out and 2 hours back in, for a total of 8 hours. Average speed is

240 mi/8 hr = 30 mi/hr.

Etc. It always works out to be 30 mph.

9. Use algebra to prove your conjecture from Question 8. (Hint: Use the exact same steps you did for each calculation in Question 8, but use a variable for the distance rather than a distance you chose.)

Distance: d miles. It will take d/20 hours out and d/60 hours back in. Total time is

$$\frac{d}{20} + \frac{d}{60} = \frac{4d}{60} = \frac{d}{15} \, hr$$

$$Average \; speed \; is \; \frac{2d \, mi}{\frac{d}{15} \, hr} = 2d \, mi \cdot \frac{15}{d \, hr} = 30 \frac{mi}{hr}$$

# Lesson 1-2    Prep Skills

This is a short review of skills that will come in handy in the next lesson. In each case, answer the question, then rate your confidence level by checking one of the boxes. If you feel like you're struggling with these skills, consult the online resources provided by your instructor for extra practice.

### SKILL 1: RECOGNIZE PLACE VALUES

1. For the number 87.23, list the digit in each place value.

   Tens place          Ones place

   Tenths place        Hundredths place

### SKILL 2: ROUND NUMBERS

2. Round each number to the designated place value.

   8,431 to the nearest ten

   11.46 to the nearest tenth

   $84.76 to the nearest dollar

### SKILL 3: PERFORM MENTAL ARITHMETIC

3. Perform each calculation without using a calculator or computer.

   $12 \times 8$        $300 \times 6$        $25 \times 8$

   $120 + 80$        $95 + 15$        $1,400 + 800$

## Lesson 1-2 **More or Less** (Estimation and Interpreting Graphs)

### LEARNING OBJECTIVES

☐ 1. Review basic percents and rounding rules.

☐ 2. Use rounding and mental arithmetic to estimate the answers to applied problems.

☐ 3. Use estimation to obtain and interpret information from various types of graphs.

*The key to good decision making is evaluating the available information—the data—and combining it with your own estimates of pluses and minuses.*
                                    —Emily Oster

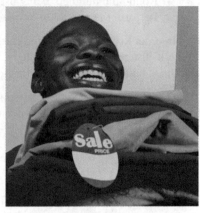

© Digital Vision/Punchstock RF

Everyone likes buying items on sale, so we should all be familiar with the idea of finding a rough approximation for a sale price. If you're looking at a pair of shoes that normally sells for $70 and the store has a 40% off sale, you might figure that the shoes are a little more than half price, which would be $35, so they're probably around $40. We will call the process of finding an approximate answer to a math problem **estimation.** Estimation comes in handy in a wide variety of settings. When the auto repair shop technicians look over your car to see what's wrong, they can't know for sure what the exact cost will be until they've made the repairs, so they will give you an estimate. When you go to the grocery store and have only $20 to spend, you'll probably keep a rough estimate of the total as you add items to the cart. (Imagine buying a week's worth of groceries and keeping track of every price to the penny on your cell phone. Who has time for that?) If you plan on buying carpet for a room, you'd most likely measure the square footage and then estimate the total cost as you looked at different styles of carpet. You could find the exact cost if you really needed to, but often an estimate is good enough for you to make a sound buying decision.

**0.** After reading the opening paragraph, what do you think the main topic of this lesson will be?

## 1-2 Group

Rounding numbers is going to play a very significant role in our study of estimation, so we'll begin with a quick review of the rules for rounding. But of course, we'll do so in the context of an applied problem. (As you may have already noticed, that's kind of the point of this course.) Let's say you're planning a group outing, with lunch included. The lunch is supposed to cost $3.95 per person, and 24 people sign up. Would $94.80 be a reasonable bill?

**1.** Round the price per person to a dollar amount that's easier to work with. Then round the number of lunches to something that's easy to multiply by the rounded dollar amount. Does $94.80 sound about right? Describe your procedure.

*$4 per person, 25 people, gives us $100. We rounded both up, so $94.80 is very reasonable.*

Question 1 does a nice job of illustrating a good, reliable procedure for doing estimation with numerical calculations:

    1. Round the numbers being used to numbers that make the calculation simple.
    2. Perform the operation or operations involved.

    In order to practice rounding rules, we'll start with a very quick review of percents. This topic is covered in detail in Unit 2, so we'll just review the basics here. Percents are used to describe certain portions of a whole. As you know, 50% of some amount is half of it. We can use this idea and estimation to get a rough idea of certain percentages without needing a calculator.

**2.** There are about 38 million people in the U.S. between the ages of 12 and 20. About half of them are female. Estimate the number of females between the ages of 12 and 20.

    *Half of 38 is 19, so there are about 19 million females between 12 and 20.*

> Emphasize that when estimating there is no single correct answer, and that if you use a calculator to get an estimate, you might as well just compute an exact value. The point is to do the arithmetic mentally.

**3.** Of those females, the National Survey on Drug Use and Health reports that roughly 24% drank alcohol at least once in the last month. Notice that 24% is pretty close to half of 50%. Use this to estimate the number of females in the 12–20 age group that used alcohol once in the last 30 days.

    *Half of the 19 million would be 9.5 million, which we can estimate at 10 million. Then half of that is about 5 million. We rounded 9.5 million up, and 24% is a bit less than half of 50%, so let's say somewhere around 4.7 million.*

**4.** For males in that age group, the reported rate of alcohol use is closer to 30%. About how many males between 12 and 20 used alcohol in the last 30 days?

    *Of the 19 million males, half of a half would be somewhere close to 5 million. Thirty percent is more than that, so an estimate around 5.5 million sounds okay.*

    We often use the word "nearest" when talking about rounding numbers. If we're dealing with currency, we typically will want to round either to the ones place (which is dollars), or the hundredths place (which is cents). In that case, we'll use the terminology in Questions 5–7.

**5.** The purchasing manager for a hotel places an order for 943 new towels at $7.49 each. Use a calculator to find the exact cost, then round that to the nearest dollar.

    *943 · $7.49 = $7,063.007, which rounds down to $7,063.*

**6.** The general manager of the hotel wants to know the amount of the expense to the nearest hundred dollars. What is it?

    *To the nearest hundred dollars, the expense is $7,100.*

7. A one-year investment in a certificate of deposit (CD) draws 2.1% interest, which mathematically means that to find the new value after one year, you multiply the original investment by 1.021. If the beginning balance of an investment is $8,412.35, find the value at the end of one year, rounded to the nearest cent.

*1.021 · $8,412.35 = $8,589.00935, which rounds to $8,589.01.*

One of the key concepts involved in rounding is *accuracy*. For our purposes, we'll define accuracy as how far off from the exact value of some quantity an estimate is. For the calculation in Question 7, you could round the initial investment to $10,000, and that would make the computation considerably easier. But because $10,000 is quite a bit different from the actual amount, your estimated value would be very different from the actual value. In that case, we'd say that your answer was inaccurate.

In short, when using rounding and estimation, it's always important to think about the level of accuracy as well as the difficulty level of getting an estimate.

8. The owner of an apartment complex needs to buy six new refrigerators. She's considering choosing a model that costs $579.95 each. By rounding the cost to the nearest hundred dollars, estimate the total cost.

*Rounding to $600, we get 6 · $600 = $3,600.*

9. Instead of rounding to the nearest hundred dollars, round to the nearest ten dollars and estimate the cost. Then discuss the pros and cons of rounding to the nearest hundred as opposed to the nearest ten.

*Rounding to $580, we get 6 · $580 = $3,480. Since there was less rounding, the result is going to be more accurate. But the trade-off is that the computation was more difficult to do mentally. And if you need to use a calculator to get the estimate, there's no point in estimating!*

## Did You Get It

Try this problem to see if you understand the concepts we just studied. The answer can be found at the bottom of the portfolio page.

1. When shopping for his books this semester, Arlen has $400 in financial aid money allocated. He needs two paper books at $147 each, an e-book costing $79, and an online homework system access code for $82. Rounding each value to the nearest ten dollars, estimate if Arlen's aid will cover his expenses.

Questions 8 and 9 bring up an interesting point: How do you know what digit to round to when estimating? The correct answer is "five." Just kidding—there IS no correct answer. It depends on the individual numbers. Deciding on how much to round is really a trade-off: ease of calculation versus accuracy. In most cases you'll get a more accurate result if you round less, but the calculation will be a little harder. Since there's no exact rule, it's important to evaluate the situation and use good old-fashioned common sense. And remember, when you are estimating, there is no one correct answer.

10. Suppose that you're considering a new cell phone plan where you have to pay $179 up front for the latest phone, but the monthly charge of $39.99 includes unlimited data, talk, and text. A different plan gives you the phone you want for free (aside from sales tax of $12.53, which you are responsible for), and the unlimited data, talk, and text plan is $61.20 per month. Use the type of estimation we've practiced to decide which is the better choice. Are there factors other than total cost you might consider? Explain your calculations and your decision.

*Answers will vary on the most important part, but here's the computation for one year:*
$180 + 12 \cdot $40 = $180 + $480 = $660. *Compare to* $10 + 12 \cdot $60 = $730.
*Notice also that the first is an overestimate because of rounding up, while the second is an underestimate.*

Notice that this question is intentionally very open-ended. No time frame is specified, so it's up to each group to decide how they want to estimate costs.

© moodboard/SuperStock RF

11. Is the estimate that you did in Question 8 greater or less than the actual cost? How can you tell?

*It's greater. We kept the number of items the same and rounded the costs up from $579.95 to $600.*

Whether an estimate is too large (**overestimate**) or too small (**underestimate**) is often an important consideration. And since rounding is important in estimation, you get to choose whether your estimate is an overestimate or an underestimate!

12. Fill in each blank with one of the boldface terms from the above paragraph: If you round numbers up before doing an estimated calculation you will get an ___*overestimate*___ . If you round down, you'll get an ___*underestimate*___ .

13. Suppose that when you're shopping, you use estimation and rounding to keep rough track of the total cost of the items you're buying. Would you rather have an overestimate or an underestimate? Discuss.

*You'd much rather have an overestimate. First, if you know how much you can or are willing to spend, you'd want to stay at or below that. Second, nobody likes an unpleasant surprise at the register.*

**14.** What if you're working over the summer to make money for the amount you think you'll need to pay for tuition and expenses in the fall. During the summer, you keep a rough estimate of how much money you've made. Would you prefer an overestimate or an underestimate of that amount? Discuss.

*You'd want an underestimate, so that the amount you make is at least as much as your expenses, and probably more.*

## 1-2 | Class

In the information age in which we live, it's very common for interesting or useful information to be displayed in graphical form, rather than just listing out numbers. Why? Because this almost always makes it easier to get a quick overall view of what that data is telling us. Here's an example: The table below shows the percentage of electricity that was generated by nuclear energy in the five countries most reliant on nuclear power, as well as in the United States, as of April 2015.

| Country | % of Power From Nuclear |
|---|---|
| France | 76.9% |
| Slovakia | 56.8% |
| Hungary | 53.6% |
| Ukraine | 49.4% |
| Belgium | 47.5% |
| United States | 19.5% |

There is absolutely nothing wrong with this table. It's positively delightful. And if you want to read it line by line and concentrate on the percentages, you can get a very accurate comparison of how reliant these nations are on nuclear power. But let's compare that to a **bar graph** representing the same data.

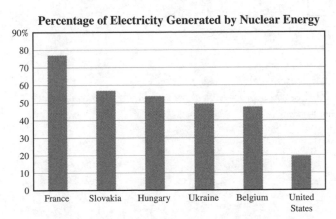

**Percentage of Electricity Generated by Nuclear Energy**

*Source: Nuclear Energy Institute*

Bar graphs are used to compare amounts or percentages using either vertical or horizontal bars of various lengths; the lengths correspond to the amounts or percentages, with longer bars representing larger amounts.

The graph makes it pretty easy to get an overall picture of what the data in the table indicates. First, we can easily see that France is way more reliant on nuclear energy than any other country. We can also see that the next four countries on the list have percentages that are reasonably similar, and that the United States is far less reliant on nuclear power than the top five.

So what does that have to do with estimation? In looking at the graph, we're visually estimating the percentages based on the heights of the bars, rather than getting an exact percentage like we did from the table.

1. Without looking at the table, use the bar graph on page 27 to estimate the percentage of electricity generated by nuclear power for each country shown. Then compare your estimates to the exact percentages shown in the table. You should give some thought to how accurately you think you can reasonably round the percentages based on the graph.

   *Sample answers: France 77%, Slovakia 57%, Hungary 52%, Ukraine 50%, Belgium 48%, U.S. 20%.*

> ## Math Note
>
> Sometimes a graph will contain labels that provide the exact values of the data illustrated. In this case, we could have put the exact percentages at the top of each bar.

2. The same information is shown on the next bar graph. But we've altered the scale on the vertical axis. Describe several ways that this can change your perception of the differences in percentage for these countries.

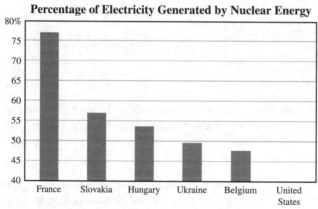

**Percentage of Electricity Generated by Nuclear Energy**

*Source: Nuclear Energy Institute*

*Answers can vary. The most noticeable effects are the fact that the U.S. now appears to be at zero, and that France's percentage looks more than twice as much as the next closest, when that's not the case.*

### Did You Get It

Try this problem to see if you understand the concepts we just studied. The answer can be found at the bottom of the portfolio page.

2. Use the second bar graph describing nuclear energy production to estimate the percentages for the three top producers. Then describe your confidence in how accurate your estimates are compared to the ones you made from the first bar graph.

A **pie chart,** also called a **circle graph,** is constructed by drawing a circle and dividing it into parts called sectors, according to the size of the percentage of each portion in relation to the whole. The next series of questions will be based on the pie chart below, which illustrates the breakdown of different types of fatal workplace injuries in 2013.

3. What percentage of workplace fatalities were caused by transportation incidents?

   41%

4. What percentage of workplace fatalities were not due to exposure to substances or contact with objects and equipment?

   77%

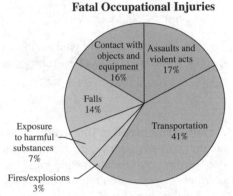

**Fatal Occupational Injuries**

*Source: U.S. Bureau of Labor Statistics*

5. There were 4,585 workplace fatalities in that year. Use rounding and estimation to estimate how many were due to either falls or contact with objects and equipment. Explain how you got your estimate.

   One possible approach: those two categories add up to 30%. We can round up the fatalities to 5,000, and 30% of that is 1,500. So something less than 1,500 is a good estimate.

**6.** Use a calculator to find the exact number of deaths caused by either falls or contact with objects and equipment. Discuss the accuracy of your estimate, and why it was either too low or too high

*30% of 4,585 is 1,375.5. This rounds up to 1,376, although you could make a case that since half a person is silly, you should round down to 1,375. We can see that our estimate was too high, which it should have been since we rounded the total number of fatalities up to 5,000.*

## Did You Get It

Try this problem to see if you understand the concepts we just studied. The answer can be found at the bottom of the portfolio page.

3. Were there more fatal accidents resulting from transportation, or from the next three highest causes? What was the difference in percentages for these causes?

A **time series graph** or **line graph** shows how the value of some variable quantity changes over a specific time period. These are the types of graph you're most likely to remember working with in algebra classes. And maybe you always wondered, "Why does anyone care about drawing graphs in algebra?" The answer to that question is exactly the point of studying different types of graphs. Graphs aren't just bad art; they're used to conveniently display useful numerical information.

The last handful of questions in this portion of the lesson are based on the time series graph below, which illustrates the median selling price of all existing homes in the United States from 1990 to 2014.

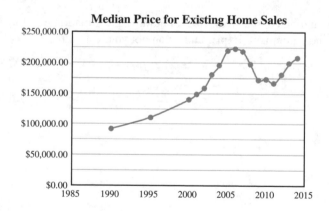

**Median Price for Existing Home Sales**

7. Estimate the median selling price in 1990 from the graph. Don't forget to consider how "rounded" you think your answer should be.

   *About $90,000*

   **Math Note**

   Median is a measure of average that we'll study in Unit 4. It's kind of like the midpoint if you list out an entire string of numbers.

8. When did the median price reach its highest point? Estimate the highest median price, and write a brief explanation of how you decided on your answers.

   *Around 2006 the median price reached very close to $225,000. The height of each point on the graph represents the median price, so we find the highest price by finding the highest point on the graph.*

9. Housing prices rose dramatically as the economy flourished in the early 2000s, but there were many issues that led to a major economic downturn. The period of increase later became known as the housing bubble. How long did it take for the median price to drop by $25,000 when the housing bubble burst? How about $50,000? Explain your answers.

   *It took about 2 years to drop by $25,000, and then only one more year after that to reach $50,000. The goal is to find the year corresponding to the first point on the graph after 2006 with height less than $200,000, then the first point after that with height less than $175,000.*

10. What does the graph tell us about what the median price will be for 2015? Talk about this with your group, and give it some serious thought.

    *It doesn't TELL us anything. We can make a guess based on the pattern of the graph, in which case something around $215,000 would be reasonable. But as what happened after 2006 shows, the pattern could have completely changed after 2014, in which case it wouldn't be useful in predicting the height of the point for 2015.*

# 1-2   Group (Again)

Now that we've studied three different types of graph, we'll wrap up the lesson by thinking about the types of situations for which each type would be most appropriate. In Questions 1–4, some information is discussed. Write which type of graph—bar graph, pie chart, or time series graph—that you think would be most appropriate to display that information. There's not necessarily a right answer, so make sure that you explain why you made your choices.

1. A CNN/*USA Today* poll is conducted in Iowa to decide which of seven Republican presidential candidates voters plan to vote for in the upcoming primary.

   *Pie chart would be an ideal choice here. Since nobody can vote for more than one candidate, the goal will be to compare different parts of a whole.*

   > While we mentioned within the lesson what type of information is best illustrated with each type of graph, we also wanted students to have an opportunity to think about it and discuss among themselves. Encourage them to refer back to our descriptions of each type within the lesson.

2. CNBC reports on the amount of money that had been raised by each of those candidates up to that point in the election.

   *This is classic bar graph territory. A pie chart would be a bad choice here, because the amounts are not parts of some bigger whole. The bar chart will visually illuminate which candidates raised the most and the least money very quickly.*

3. A CBS Evening News profile on one of the top candidates describes how his polling numbers have changed from the time he announced his candidacy to the beginning of the primary season.

   *This is exactly what a time series graph is designed to do: illustrate the change in some single quantity over a period of time.*

4. The supporters of one controversial candidate are broken down demographically, by race, income level, and education level.

   *This one takes a lot of thought, but the best approach is probably three separate pie charts, one for each characteristic. While Questions 1–3 were designed specifically to fit a certain type of graph well, this one is most definitely open to interpretation.*

## 1-2 Portfolio

Name _____

Check each box when you've completed the task. Remember that your instructor will want you to turn in the portfolio pages you create.

> If at all possible, spend a bit of class time demonstrating the basics of making graphs in Excel. This would be a nice supplement to the support documents and videos in online resources.

### Technology

1. ☐ Spreadsheets are FANTASTIC at creating the types of graphs we studied in this lesson. In fact, all of the graphs printed in the lesson were created by little old me using Excel. Go online and find some information on a topic that interests you. Use a spreadsheet to illustrate that information, using at least two of the following types of graphs: bar graph, pie chart, or time series graph. Then discuss which type of graph that you think is most appropriate for the chosen information. Include the source where you found your data. You will find both documents and videos in online resources to help you create your graphs.

### Online Practice

1. ☐ Include any written work from the online assignment along with any notes or questions about this lesson's content.

### Applications

1. ☐ Complete the applications problems.

### Reflections

Type a short answer to each question.

1. ☐ What did you learn in this lesson that you think will be helpful in your daily life? Be specific, and provide one or two examples of where you think you'll use your newly acquired mathematical skills.
2. ☐ Look back at the very beginning of this lesson, and discuss some pros and cons of illustrating the nuclear power data graphically, as compared to in table form.
3. ☐ In what type of situations is estimation helpful, and when might estimation actually be harmful?
4. ☐ Take another look at your answer to Question 0 at the beginning of this lesson. Would you change your answer now that you've completed the lesson? How would you summarize the topic of this lesson now?
5. ☐ What questions do you have about this lesson?

### Looking Ahead

1. ☐ Complete the Lesson 1-3 Prep Skills and read the opening paragraph in Lesson 1-3 carefully, then answer Question 0 in preparation for that lesson.

### Answers to "Did You Get It?"

1. Arlen will need roughly $460, so he's going to come up short.
2. France 77%, Slovakia 57%, Hungary 54%. The finer scale allows us to make a more accurate estimate.   3. The next three highest causes at 47%, which is 6% more than transportation.

## 1-2   Applications

Name _____

1. In 12 months, you're planning a trip to either Miami or San Francisco, whichever is a more likely vacation destination for you. Use the Internet to estimate the cost of transportation and the cost of a hotel. Then estimate the total amount of money you'd need for a five-day trip including food, beverages, and entertainment. Include all details, including what level you're rounding to.

   *Answers vary.*

Use the information shown in the graph for Questions 2 and 3. The graph represents a survey of 1,385 office workers and shows the percent of people who indicated what time of day is most productive for them.

**When Office Workers Feel That
They're Most Productive at Work**

Last few office hours 13%

Before office hours 25%

Late morning/ early afternoon 22%

After office hours 9%

First few office hours 31%

*Source: USA Today*

2. Estimate the number of people who feel they are most productive outside normal office hours. Show details, and discuss if you think you made an overestimate or underestimate.

   *We can round the combined percentage of 34% down to 33%, which is about a third, and the number of people surveyed up to 1,500. This gives us about 500 people who feel they're most productive outside of normal office hours. Because we rounded one number up and one down, it's hard to tell if the estimate is too big or too small.*

# 1-2   Applications

Name _____

**3.** How many more people feel they're most productive in the first few office hours compared to those that feel they're most productive in the last few office hours? (Exact answer this time.)

*First few: 31% of 1,385 is 429 people. Last few: 13% of 1,385 is 180. So 249 feel they're more productive in the first few hours.*

The two bar graphs on this page describe Internet access by continent. The first shows the NUMBER of people that have Internet access in the place where they live, in millions. The second shows Internet penetration, which is the PERCENTAGE of people on each continent that have Internet access where they live. Use the graphs to answer Questions 4–7.

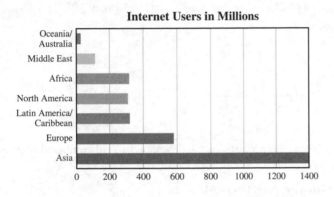
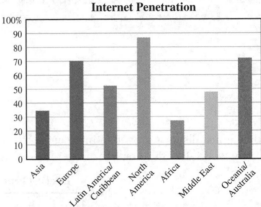

*Source: www.internetworldstats.com*

**4.** Which continent has the most people with Internet access at home? The least?

*Asia has the most by far, Oceania/Australia has the least.*

**5.** If you picked a person at random from each continent, on which continent would it be most likely that the person has Internet access at home? Least likely?

*Most: North America. Least: Africa*

## 1-2 Applications

Name _____

6. What do you think accounts for the fact that North America has the longest bar on the second graph, but is middle of the pack on the first one?

   *North America is middle of the pack in terms of NUMBER of users, but number 1 in percent of the population having access. That tells us that the population of North America is far less than some of the other continents.*

7. Does Asia have more Internet users than the rest of the world combined? Justify your answer.

   *Asia does not. The bar for Asia has length 1,400. Europe is roughly 600 and the next three are all right around 300. This already sums to 1,500 without considering the remaining two continents.*

Our final graph displays growth in Internet penetration from 1998 to 2014 in the developed world compared to growth in the developing world. Use this graph to answer the remaining questions.

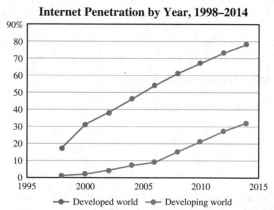

**Internet Penetration by Year, 1998–2014**

*Source: International Telecommunications Union*

## 1-2  Applications

Name _____

8.  By how much did the percentage change from 1998 to 2014 in the developed world? What about the developing world?

    *In the developed world the percentage went up by just about 60%. In the developing world it was very close to a 30% increase.*

9.  Is the gap between the developed and developing worlds getting bigger or smaller? Discuss.

    *Looking at all of the data, starting in 1998, the gap is getting wider. But over the last eight to ten years, it's staying pretty consistent.*

10. Which had a more significant increase between 1998 and 2014, the developed or developing world? Explain how you decided.

    *This is an opinion question. If you look at strictly the amount of increase, you'd choose the developed world. But if you went with percent (or relative) increase, it would have to be the developing world.*

# Lesson 1-3   Prep Skills

This is a short review of skills that will come in handy in the next lesson. In each case, answer the question, then rate your confidence level by checking one of the boxes. If you feel like you're struggling with these skills, consult the online resources provided by your instructor for extra practice.

### SKILL 1: GET INFORMATION FROM A DIAGRAM

1. Find the perimeter of the rectangle.

   12 ft
   4 ft

2. The perimeter of the figure is 59″. What is the length of the missing side?

   13″
   10″
   10″
   8″

3. The total width of the room diagrammed below is 48 ft, and the spaces between the tables are all the same. How far apart are the tables?

   4 ft
   2 ft
   2 ft
   2 ft
   2 ft
   4 ft

# Lesson 1-3   You Got a Problem?  (Problem-Solving Strategies)

## LEARNING OBJECTIVES

☐  1. Identify the four steps in Polya's problem-solving procedure.

☐  2. Apply Polya's procedure to solving problems.

☐  3. Solve problems using different strategies: trial and error, drawing a diagram, using algebra, and comparing different outcomes.

*If you only have a hammer, you tend to see every problem as a nail.*
                    —Abraham Maslow

© Royalty-Free/Corbis

Here's an idea that can help you understand your math classes better: Once in a while, think about what some of the math words you take for granted actually mean in English. For example, have you ever thought about why we call math problems "problems"? In real life, when a problem confronts you, you probably think about different strategies you might use to overcome an obstacle and then decide on the best course of action. So why not use that same approach to solving math problems? This is probably the single biggest reason why taking math classes is useful to anyone: math is all about learning and practicing problem-solving strategies. While we'll study a general framework for problem solving, as the quote above suggests, thinking too rigidly can be a big detriment to solving problems effectively. The more strategies you develop, the more types of problems you'll be able to solve—not just in this course, but in the big, wide world outside the classroom door.

**0.** After reading the opening paragraph, what do you think the main topic of this lesson will be?

> Like most lessons in this book, this one is divided into Class and Group portions. This is always just a general guideline to let instructors know which portions we think might need a little extra guidance, but in this case you should consider treating the entire lesson as "group." The absolute BEST way for students to improve problem-solving strategies is for them to work together and struggle on different types of problems.

## 1-3  Class

To begin the lesson, we're going to dive right in and try to solve a problem, with a little bit of guidance. Then we'll pause for a bit and summarize some important ideas that can be learned from our first problem.

**Problem 1:** Marcus plans to do some of his Christmas shopping this year at an electronics reseller, which sells gently used Blu-ray discs for $8 each, and video games for $14 each (tax included). He plans to buy one item each for 8 friends and relatives, and hopes to spend around $95. How many of each item can he buy?

**1.** The first thing we should do is make sure that we understand the problem. This entails both clearly identifying what we're being asked to accomplish, and what information we're provided that might be useful in accomplishing that goal. Write down the important information provided in the text of the problem, and write a sentence clearly identifying what you're being asked to do.

Blu-ray discs: $8 each

Video games: $14 each

Want a total of 8 items, want the total cost to be close to $95.

We're asked to find how many of each item he should buy to keep the cost close to $95.

2. Remember that when solving problems in your life, you don't just do a bunch of random stuff. Instead, you think about the situation and try to devise a plan of action. In this case, it might be helpful to try out some potential solutions, and see if they fit the given conditions. We'll figure out the cost of different combinations, and see if we can find the one that fits the criteria best. First, find the total cost if Marcus goes with 1 video game and 7 Blu-ray discs. Is this the best choice? Why not?

*One video game at $14 plus 7 discs at $8 each ($56 for all 7) is a total of $70. Not a great choice because he had planned on spending quite a bit more.*

3. Now we've decided on a potential approach. The next logical step to take is applying our strategy to try and solve the problem. In this case, fill in the table to work out the cost of several different combinations of items. We started the table for you, but you'll need to decide on further combinations to try.

| # of games | # of Blu-ray | Total Cost |
|---|---|---|
| 1 | 7 | $70 |
| 2 | 6 | $76 |
| 3 | 5 | $82 |

| # of games | # of Blu-ray | Total Cost |
|---|---|---|
| 4 | 4 | $88 |
| 5 | 3 | $94 |
| 6 | 2 | $100 |

4. Which is the best combination? Why?

*Five video games and three Blu-ray discs, at $94, comes closest to the amount Marcus wanted to spend.*

5. When solving any type of problem, your last step should be a reality check. Does your answer make sense? Does it solve the problem, and fit the parameters that were established? Discuss your solution, focusing on realism in the situation, fitting what you were asked to do, and matching the provided information.

*The solution is realistic, since there's nothing odd about buying 5 games and 3 movies. It fits the situation because a total of 8 items are purchased and close to $95 was spent, and it fits what we were asked to do because it describes the number of each item that Marcus should buy.*

> Once the steps for Polya's method have been described on the next page, encourage students to look back at how the steps were executed in Questions 1–5, and how they helped students find a solution.

### Did You Get It

Try this problem to see if you understand the concepts we just studied. The answer can be found at the bottom of the portfolio page.

1. When shopping for a campus event, two representatives of a student organization are given a budget of $120 to buy bags of candy ($9 each) and packages of cupcakes ($12 each). Based on the expected attendance, they'd like to have a total of 10 or 11 items. How many of each should they buy? (An interesting, absolutely true note about organizational budgeting: when you're given a certain amount to spend, if you don't spend it all, next time you need money for something, you'll get less than you're asking for.)

One thing we can get from the experience of solving problem 1 is that the process of **trial and error**—trying different potential solutions and adjusting until you find an acceptable solution—can be a really useful strategy. But there's actually something much deeper embedded in the first five questions of this lesson: a general problem-solving strategy that can be applied to almost any situation.

A Hungarian mathematician named George Polya did years of research on the nature of problem solving in the first half of the 20th century. His biggest contribution to the field was an attempt to identify a series of steps that were fundamental to problem-solving strategies used by great thinkers throughout human history. Polya's strategy isn't necessarily earth-shattering: Its brilliance lies in its simplicity. It provides four basic steps that can be used as a framework for problem solving in any area, from math to home improvements.

### Polya's Four-Step Problem-Solving Procedure

**Step 1.** *Understand the problem.* The best way to start any problem is to write down information that's provided as you come to it. Especially with longer word problems, if you read the whole thing all at once and don't DO anything, it's easy to get overwhelmed. If you read the problem slowly and carefully, writing down information as it's provided, you'll always at least have a start on the problem. Another great idea: Carefully identify and write down what it is they're asking you to find. This almost always helps you to devise a strategy.

**Step 2.** *Devise a plan to solve the problem.* This is where problem solving is at least as much art as science— there are many, many ways to solve problems. Some common strategies: making a list of possible outcomes; drawing a diagram; trial and error; finding a similar problem that you already know how to solve; and using arithmetic, algebra, or geometry.

**Step 3.** *Carry out your plan to solve the problem.* After you've made a plan, try it out. If it doesn't work, try a different strategy! There are many different ways to attack problems. Be persistent!

**Step 4.** *Check your answer.* It's always a good idea to think about whether or not your answer is reasonable, and in many cases you'll be able to use math to check your answer and see if it's exactly correct. If not, don't forget what we learned about estimation in Lesson 1-2—that can be a big help in deciding if an answer is reasonable.

The goal of this lesson is to use this framework to solve a variety of different problems, using different general strategies. The first of those was trial and error. In our second problem, we'll see the value of drawing a diagram.

**Problem 2:** A private college is given a grant from a wealthy alumnus to build a sculpture garden, where statues of the first eight presidents of the college will be installed in a straight line from earliest to most recent. Each statue will be eight feet tall and two feet wide, and the sculptor decides on a consistent distance of twelve feet between statues to reflect the twelve decades since the school was founded. How much space will be needed between the first and last statues?

6. First instinct, without thinking about it too much, what do you think the solution is?

   *Almost everyone multiplies the number of statues by the space in between to get 96 feet. Some will add 16 for the width of the statues to get 112 feet.*

7. Step 1: Understand the problem.

   a. What exactly are you being asked to find?

      *The distance from the first statue to the last.*

   b. What information is given that will help you to solve the problem?

      *We know that there will be 8 statues, that they'll be installed in a straight line, that each is 2 feet wide, and that there will be 12 feet of space between any two consecutive statues.*

   c. There's some information in the problem that is *extraneous:* that is, it's not needed to solve the problem. What is it?

      *We were told that the statues will be eight feet tall. This is not relevant to how much horizontal distance will be covered.*

8. Step 2: Devise a plan. Explain why drawing a diagram is a good idea in this case.

   *First, a diagram is EXACTLY what the sculptor would have drawn to design the area. Better still, it will allow us to see exactly how much space is needed by counting up the total distances on the diagram.*

9. Step 3: Carry out the plan. I'll make you a deal: I'll supply a really lame but usable diagram if you label it, then use the results to find how much space is needed. Write your final answer as a sentence, please.

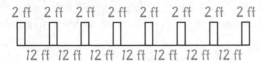

Now we can see that there are seven spaces in between, and 7 times 12 is 84. Adding the 16 feet for the statue widths, we get 100 feet.

10. Step 4: Check your answer. How does it compare to your first instinct? If your first instinct was wrong, why? Why is your answer in Question 9 reasonable?

Answers vary depending on first instinct answer.

---

### Did You Get It

Try this problem to see if you understand the concepts we just studied. The answer can be found at the bottom of the portfolio page.

2. An architect is designing a rectangular sunken bathtub with dimensions 5 feet by 8 feet. She wants to have 2-inch rectangular tiles installed around the outside of the tub as a border. How many tiles will be needed?

## 1-3  Group

Now that we've identified and practiced the four steps in Polya's problem-solving procedure, your group will solve a few other types of problems, keeping Polya's framework in mind. The first is another example of a problem for which a diagram is a big help.

**Problem 3:** A campus group is setting up a rectangular area for a tailgate bash. Since adult beverages will be served, city regulations require the area to be enclosed and access-controlled. They have 100 feet between two roads to use as width and 440 feet of fence to use. What length will use up the total amount of fence and therefore enclose the biggest space?

1. *Understand the problem.* Write down the important information provided in the text of the problem, and write a sentence clearly identifying what you're being asked to accomplish.

   *Build a rectangular area with width 100 feet. We have 440 feet of fence to use. We want to find the length that uses all 440 feet of fence.*

© Nice One Productions/Corbis RF

2. *Devise a plan to solve the problem.* Why is a diagram likely to help? What should your diagram contain?

   *Drawing a diagram will allow us to fill in the information we know for sure—the width of 100 feet—and make it easier to decide on the other dimension.*

3. *Carry out the plan.*
   **a.** Draw a diagram of the tailgate area, and label the lengths of the sides that you know.

   **b.** How much fence is left for the two sides you don't know the length of?

   *The sides we know cover 200 ft, so that leaves 240 ft for the remaining sides.*

**c.** What should the length of each side be? Justify your answer.

*120 feet; there are two sides and a length of 240 feet.*

**4.** *Check your answer.* Is your answer physically reasonable? Does it match the conditions of the problem? Does it answer the question? Discuss.

*The length we found is physically reasonable because it's positive and less than 440 feet. It matches the conditions of the problem, because it makes the total amount of fence 100 + 100 + 120 + 120, which is 440 feet. It answers the question because we were asked to find the length.*

## Did You Get It

Try this problem to see if you understand the concepts we just studied. The answer can be found at the bottom of the portfolio page.

3. A poster is being designed to advertise an upcoming art show. It will be rectangular, and the printer requires a 1-inch margin on all four sides. To keep from paying an oversize fee, the promoter of the show wants the overall height of the poster to be 24 inches. The designer feels like the printed area needs to have a perimeter of about 75 inches. How wide should the poster be to make it as big as possible and meet these conditions?

Many applied problems involve making a choice between two or more options. In that case, you could flip a coin, but it doesn't seem likely you'll get very far in life using that approach. A better idea would be to use reasoning skills to make an informed decision. In some cases, that requires solving math problems, like the next one.

**Problem 4:** So you've graduated from college and you're ready for that first real job. In fact, you have two offers. Dude! Sweet. One pays an hourly wage of $20.75 per hour, with a 40-hour work week. You work for 50 weeks and get 2 weeks' paid vacation. The second offer is a salaried position, offering $41,000 per year, with an opportunity for a $5,000 performance bonus. Which job will pay more? Which sounds like the better opportunity financially?

**5.** *Understand the problem.* Write down the important information provided in the text of the problem, and write a sentence clearly identifying what you're being asked to accomplish.

*Job 1: $20.75 per hour    40 hours per week    52 paid weeks per year*

*Job 2: $41,000 annual salary; chance for $5,000 bonus*

*We're asked to find which job will pay more, then analyze which sounds like a better opportunity.*

6. *Devise a plan to solve the problem.* What would you need to know about the first job in order to compare the amount of money you'd make to the second one? How can you find that out?

   *You'd need to know the amount of money you'd earn in one year. This can be found by multiplying the hourly rate by the number of hours worked, then multiplying that result by the number of weeks in a year.*

7. *Carry out the plan.*
   **a.** How much would the hourly job pay for each 40-hour week? Show your work.

   $40 \cdot \$20.75 = \$830$

   **b.** How much does the hourly job pay per year?

   $\$830 \cdot 52 = \$43,160$

   **c.** Which job pays more, hourly or salaried? Which is the better opportunity? Explain.

   *The hourly one, unless you get the $5,000 bonus. Which is the better opportunity is an opinion question.*

8. *Check your answer.* Here's a clever approach: Do the opposite of the calculations you did in Question 7 to find what the hourly rate would be for the salaried job. Does this confirm you answer?

   *$41,000 divided by 52 weeks is $788.46 per week. Divide that by 40 to get $19.71 per hour, which shows that the hourly job pays more.*

---

## Did You Get It

Try this problem to see if you understand the concepts we just studied. The answer can be found at the bottom of the portfolio page.

   4. One investment requires an initial deposit of $8,000, and generates interest at the rate of $1.35 per day. The other requires an initial investment of $12,000 and generates interest at the rate of $10.40 per week. Which will earn more interest in a year? Which is the more attractive investment?

Our last problem is intentionally left more open-ended. Rather than providing the specific steps, we're going to ask you to discuss among your group members to develop and execute a strategy. Show all work, and it's probably a good idea to write some sentences describing your approach as well. Make sure that you LIST each step in the four-step method, then follow that up with what you did to use that step.

**Problem 5:** The grade in Marlene's history class will be determined completely by three tests, each worth 100 points. She scored 78 and 84 on the first two tests, but still hopes to get an A, which would require an average of 92. What's the minimum score she can get on the third test?

There are different ways this problem can be attacked. Some will choose trial and error, some will try to set up and solve an equation. And some may surprise you! For what it's worth, here's the algebraic approach:

$$\frac{78 + 84 + x}{3} = 92$$
$$162 + x = 276$$
$$x = 114$$

Uh oh . . . looks like Marlene is out of luck. She can't get 114 out of 100 on the last test, so an A is out of reach.

> Use this result as an opportunity to talk about the fact that not all problems have a solution!

To close our lesson (and unit) on problem solving, we've compiled a list of strategies that can come in handy in ANY class, or any situation, where you need to solve a problem.

### Strategies for Understanding Problems

One reason that problem solving is challenging is that every problem can be a little different, so you can't just memorize a procedure and mimic it over and over. You actually have to think on your own! But here are some suggestions for helping to understand a problem and devise a strategy for solving it.

- If the problem describes something that can be diagrammed, a drawing almost always helps.
- If you find that you read through a problem and feel like you have no idea where to start, you should consider NOT reading the entire problem at first. This can sometimes lead to feeling overwhelmed or intimidated. Instead . . .
- Write down all the numeric information in the problem as you read it. This often helps to organize your thoughts. But maybe more importantly, it's a guaranteed way to get a START on every problem, so you avoid that moment of panic when you feel like you have no clue what to do.
- Sometimes making a chart to organize information is helpful, especially when you're trying to use trial and error.
- Don't expect that you'll know exactly how to solve a problem after reading it once! Most often you'll need to read through a problem several times, and even then you may need to just try some approaches before finding one that works. Don't be afraid to try! Nobody ever became a good problem solver by being afraid to make a mistake.

## 1-3 | Portfolio

Name _____

Check each box when you've completed the task. Remember that your instructor will want you to turn in the portfolio pages you create.

### Technology

1. ☐ One downside of solving problems using trial and error is that you often have to do many repeated calculations. If only there were a tool that we could use to quickly do repeated calculations . . . see where this is headed? A little bit of spreadsheet setup time can really pay off. In Question 3 of the Class portion of this lesson, you created a table while solving a problem using trial and error. Recreate that table using a spreadsheet. A template to help you get started can be found in the online resources for this lesson. Then on a separate worksheet (which you can add by clicking the plus sign near the bottom left corner) use what you learned to set up a spreadsheet to help you solve the question in Did You Get It 1.

### Online Practice

1. ☐ Include any written work from the online assignment along with any notes or questions about this lesson's content.

### Applications

1. ☐ Complete the applications problems.

### Reflections

Type a short answer to each question.

1. ☐ Do you feel better about your ability to solve word problems after learning and practicing Polya's procedure? Be specific: Provide a specific example of why you do or do not feel better about your ability.
2. ☐ Of the problem-solving strategies we studied, which do you feel like you're likely to use most often in your life?
3. ☐ Take another look at your answer to Question 0 at the beginning of this lesson. Would you change your answer now that you've completed the lesson? How would you summarize the topic of this lesson now?
4. ☐ What questions do you have about this lesson?

### Looking Ahead

1. ☐ Complete the Lesson 2-1 Prep Skills and read the opening paragraph in Lesson 2-1 carefully, then answer Question 0 in preparation for that lesson.

### Answers to "Did You Get It?"

1. Four bags of candy and seven packages of cupcakes works out to be exactly $120.
2. 160 tiles (did you forget the corners?)   **3.** The width should be 17.5 inches.
4. First investment: $492.75; second investment: $540.80. Which is better depends on how you feel about the larger initial investment.

## 1-3   Applications

Name _____

1. A physical therapy facility is building a new pool that is 60 feet long and 5 feet deep. They have ordered enough tile for a 220-foot-long border around the edge. How wide should the pool be to ensure that all tiles are used?

   *Sample solutions will be shown for each problem, with limited detail. We trust you.*

   *Two sides at 60 feet each gives us 120 feet, leaving 100 feet for the remaining two sides. So the width should be 50 feet.*

   > Note that we didn't provide instructions insisting that students list Polya's steps, or do anything other than solve the problem. Feel free to add further instructions if you wish. Our goal was to provide students with a framework, then let them work out preferred methods on their own.

2. A physical education teacher plans to divide the seventh graders at Wilson Middle School into teams of equal size for a year-ending mock Olympic event. He wants each team to have between 5 and 9 students, and has a strong preference to have the same number of students on each team. The seventh grade at Wilson consists of three classes; one with 24 students, one with 26, and one with 21. How many students should be on each team?

   *With 71 students total, there's no way to divide them up with the same number of students on each team.*
   *• With five on each team, there would be 14 teams, and one student left over to form a team with six students.*
   *• With six on each team, there would be 11 teams, with five students left over. So there's two possibilities. 11 teams with 6 students and 1 with 5, or 6 teams with 6 students and 5 teams with 7 students.*
   *• With seven on each, there would be 10 teams, and one student left over. So you get 9 teams with 7 students and 1 with 8 students.*
   *• With eight on each, there would be 8 teams with seven students left over. That makes 8 teams with 8 students and 1 with 7, or 1 team with 8 students and 7 with 9 students.*
   *• With nine on each, there would be 7 teams with eight students left over. That makes 1 team with 8 students and 7 with 9 students. How many he should choose depends on how large he wants the teams to be.*

## 1-3 Applications

Name _____

3. A condo on the water in Myrtle Beach can be rented for $295 per day, with a nonrefundable application fee of $50, and a daily parking fee of $11. Another one down the beach can be rented for $2,100 per week, plus a $600 refundable security deposit and a $4 per day Internet fee. Which condo costs less for a week's stay?

Daily rental: $50 + $295 · 7 + 7 · $11 = $2,192

Weekly rental: $2,100 + 7 · $4 = $2,128

The weekly rental is a little cheaper, provided that you don't destroy the place and get the entire security deposit back.

4. Bart is taking a pass-fail math class, and needs to average 70% to get a passing grade. The grade is determined by five 50-point tests, and Bart's doing really well: on the first four tests, he scored 48, 45, 45, and 47. The week of the final test, Bart has a really important chemistry test that he wants to focus on, but he doesn't want to risk failing math. Find the range of scores Bart can get on test five that will result in failing the class.

$$\frac{48 + 45 + 45 + 47 + x}{5} = 0.7 \cdot 50$$

$$185 + x = 175$$

$$x = -10$$

Great news for Bart: he doesn't even need to show up. As long as his score is greater than −10 he'll pass.

# Unit 2
# Managing Your Money

© Image Source RF

**Outline**

Lesson 1:  Giving 110 Percent (Review of Percents)
Lesson 2:  Building It Is the Easy Part . . . (Budgeting)
Lesson 3:  A Topic of Interest (Simple Interest)
Lesson 4:  Like a Snowball Rolling Downhill (Compound Interest)
Lesson 5:  Buying Stuff Without Money (Installment Buying)
Lesson 6:  Investing in Yourself (Education and Home Loans)
Lesson 7:  A Walk on Wall Street (Stocks and Bonds)
Lesson 8:  A Taxing Situation (Income Taxes)

# Math In    Paying for an Education

"If you think education is expensive, try the cost of ignorance." This famous quote comes from Dr. Derek Bok, the former president of Harvard University. (I like it so much that it's the only quote used twice in this book.) There are many nuanced interpretations of exactly what Dr. Bok was trying to say, but if you think of it strictly in terms of financial costs, it says that your earning power increases dramatically as you attain more education. This isn't a cliché or a myth, and it's not an opinion to be debated on cable news channels. The table below is based on cold, hard facts.

| Education level | Median salary in 2014 |
|---|---|
| Less than high school diploma | $25,376 |
| High school diploma | $34,736 |
| Some college | $38,532 |
| Associate degree | $41,184 |
| Bachelor's degree | $57,252 |
| Master's degree | $68,952 |
| Professional or doctorate degree | $83,980 |

*Source: Bureau of Labor Statistics*

The downside, of course, is that college is expensive, and costs continue to rise at a rate far greater than inflation. According to *Money* magazine, between 1985 and 2005, the price of average consumer goods in the U.S. went up by 108%. Ouch. But during the same period, college costs went up by 439%! The truth is that a small percentage of families have the means to pay all of the costs associated with college, meaning that student loans are a reality for an increasing segment of the population. Even the most optimistic students worry about whether or not they'll be able to afford college, and how much debt they'll run up while earning a degree.

This might lead you to a larger realization: long ago, survival depended on overcoming physical challenges that modern humans can only imagine, but today, survival is more about navigating the waters of the modern financial system. There are over 300 million people in the United States, and at any given time, it seems like half of them are trying to figure out a way to separate you from your hard-earned money. That's why this chapter is all about different aspects of our financial system that are particularly important to the average adult. Success in this chapter will help you to become a more well-informed consumer, which makes it less likely that those 150 million people will succeed in getting your cash.

One of the topics we'll study in this unit is student loans, and a goal will be to decide if a college education really pays off in the long run. Recently, the College Board reported that a typical college budget for an in-state public four-year college for the 2015–2016 academic year averaged $24,061. (This takes into account tuition, fees, room and board, and other living expenses.) Let's study the ramifications of this intimidating statistic.

1. How much would it cost to earn a four-year degree with this budget?
2. If you are able to obtain grants and scholarships to pay for 25% of these costs, and can also pay $5,000 per year out of pocket, how much money would you have to borrow to cover the rest?
3. If you obtain a federal student loan with an interest rate of 6.8% and a term of 10 years for the amount in question 2, what will your monthly payment be upon graduation if you pay interest on the loan while still in school? How much total will you pay in interest?
4. Repeat question 3 if you capitalize the interest on your loan.
5. Based on the median salaries in the table, how long would you have to work after obtaining a bachelor's degree to make back the total amount spent on student loan payments and the amount paid out of pocket? (Use the loan with interest capitalized, and don't forget to factor in how much you would have been able to make without going to college at all!)

## Lesson 2-1   Prep Skills

This is a short review of skills that will come in handy in the next lesson. In each case, answer the question, then rate your confidence level by checking one of the boxes. If you feel like you're struggling with these skills, consult the online resources provided by your instructor for extra practice.

### SKILL 1: REDUCING FRACTIONS

1. Reduce each fraction to lowest terms.
$$\frac{6}{10} \qquad \frac{24}{30} \qquad \frac{51}{21} \qquad \frac{11}{24}$$

2. Reduce each fraction to lowest terms.
$$\frac{60}{100} \qquad \frac{24}{100} \qquad \frac{98}{100} \qquad \frac{33}{100}$$

### SKILL 2: WRITE FRACTIONS IN DECIMAL FORM

3. Write the decimal form of each fraction.
$$\frac{12}{100} \qquad \frac{9}{30} \qquad \frac{11}{8} \qquad \frac{11}{3}$$

### SKILL 3: SOLVE EQUATIONS USING DIVISION

4. Solve: $12x = 84$

5. Solve: $0.3y = 210$

6. Solve: $0.125x = 47.99$

# Lesson 2-1 **Giving 110 Percent** (Review of Percents)

**LEARNING OBJECTIVES**

☐ 1. Perform conversions and calculations involving percents.

☐ 2. Find percent increase or decrease.

☐ 3. Solve problems using percents.

☐ 4. Evaluate the legitimacy of claims based on percents.

*I think I'm a kind of a person who works hard at whatever I do, literally from being a waitress to being on television. I always try to give 110 percent to whatever it is I'm doing.*
—Teri Hatcher

Coaches are fond of insisting that their players give 110% effort. Players that are good at math will sometimes counter with the fact that it's impossible to give more than you have, which by the way sounds like a good idea if you want to run laps for about a week. Can you really have 110% of something? Since percents play an important role in many, many different areas where studying numbers is useful, everyone that wants to be successful in our society should be armed with a solid understanding of percents: what they mean, how to compute and use them, and how to interpret information that they're providing. In this lesson, we'll review a lot of useful information about percents, information that will come in handy throughout the rest of the course. Pay attention, or you'll be doing pushups until you drop.

© RubberBall
Productions RF

**0.** After reading the opening paragraph, what do you think the main topic of this lesson will be?

> If students in your course have covered percents as a prerequisite, this lesson can be skipped. But percents play such an important role in consumer math that a detailed review is generally a good idea.

## 2-1 | Class

Surely you're familiar with the word "percent" but have you ever thought about what it literally means? "Percent" can be translated literally as "per hundred." So 1% = 1/100. For example, the International Mass Retail Association reported that 20% of adults plan to buy Valentine's Day cards next year. Of those who plan to buy them, 36% of women and 26% of men plan to buy romantic cards. This tells us that 20 out of every 100 adults plan to buy a card. Also, 36 out of 100 women who buy a card will choose a romantic one, and 26 out of 100 men will do so.

## Percent Conversions

To work with percents in calculations, we will need to convert them to either decimal or fractional form. But to interpret the answers to calculations, we will want to convert them back into percents.

1. Using the fact that "percent" means "per hundred," write 84% and 9% as fractions with denominator 100.

$$84\% = \frac{84}{100} \quad 9\% = \frac{9}{100}$$

> This simple little question is a great opportunity to continue setting the tone for the course. Rather than just memorizing formulas and procedures, like working with percents, we're going to really understand what it all means.

Here's a simple rule that can be learned from Question 1:

## Converting a Percent to a Fraction

To convert a percent to a fraction, drop the percent sign and use the percent number as the numerator of a fraction whose denominator is 100.

If you noticed that the fraction in the first part of your answer to Question 1 could be reduced, good job! When we're working with percents in fraction form, many times it will be easier if the fraction is reduced to lowest terms.

2. Convert each percent to a fraction in lowest terms.
   **a.** 42%

   $$42\% = \frac{42}{100} = \frac{21}{50}$$

   **b.** $37\frac{1}{2}\%$ (Hint: After initially writing as a fraction, multiply by $\frac{2}{2}$ so that the numerator and denominator of your fraction are both whole numbers.)

   $$37\frac{1}{2}\% = \frac{37.5}{100} \cdot \frac{2}{2} = \frac{75}{200} = \frac{3}{8}$$

A lot of times it's especially useful to write a percent in decimal form when doing calculations, so let's see how that works, using what we already know about fractions.

3. We know that we can write 12% as a fraction in the form $\frac{12}{100}$, and 72% in the form $\frac{72}{100}$. Use a calculator to perform the division in each case, writing the original percent in decimal form.

   $12\% = 0.12$
   $72\% = 0.72$

**4.** Use the result of Question 3 to fill in the blanks in our next rule for converting percents:

## Converting a Percent to a Decimal

To convert a percent to a decimal, drop the percent sign and move the decimal point __2__ places to the __left__.

**5.** Write each percent in decimal form.

   **a.** 41%          **b.** 6.7%          **c.** 120%

    0.41            0.067         1.20

    Sometimes, interpreting the story told by a percentage will require a conversion in the other direction: starting in decimal form, and converting to percent form. Not surprisingly, we accomplish this by doing exactly the opposite of the steps we did for converting from percent to decimal form.

**6.** The opposite of moving the decimal two places to the left is moving the decimal __2 places to the right__. The opposite of dropping the percent sign is __inserting the % sign__.

**7.** Write a procedure for converting a decimal to percent form, then use it to convert 0.34, 0.07, and 1.658 into percent form.

Move the decimal point two places to the right, then insert a percent sign.

0.34 = 34%, 0.07 = 7%, 1.658 = 165.8%

> This is a key idea in the course: Letting students discover and write rules on their own (with some leading) rather than just telling them. Let it happen!

## Math Note

Part c of Question 5 shows that our conversion rules work just fine for percentages greater than 100. We'll study the meaning of such a percentage in the Group portion of this lesson.

## Did You Get It

Try this problem to see if you understand the concepts we just studied. The answer can be found at the bottom of the portfolio page.

1. Perform each conversion.
   a. 47.3% to decimal            b. 0.24 to percent            c. 80% to fraction in lowest terms

In the most common calculations involving percents, the goal is to find a percentage of some quantity. To understand how to do so, consider the following example. You probably know that 50% of 10 is 5. Let's rewrite that statement, then turn it into a calculation:

50% of 10 is 5

$0.5 \times 10 = 5$

When writing a percentage statement in symbols, the word "of" becomes multiplication, and the word "is" becomes an equal sign. Also, we need to change the percent into decimal or fractional form. Let's look at some sample calculations using this idea. A restaurant was running a fundraiser tonight for the local food bank in which 30% of every purchase was donated for food relief. If my wife and I spent $24.59 at the restaurant, how much was donated?

8. Fill in the blank to describe the calculation described above: ___30___ % of ___$24.59___ is what amount?

9. What was the amount donated?

   $0.30 \cdot \$24.59 = \$7.38$

The same idea can be used for other calculations involving percentages. Like this one: A closeout store is advertising leather jackets at 70% off the original price, which means the sale price is 30% of the original price. If one jacket has a sale price of $59, how much did it cost originally?

10. Fill in the blanks to describe the calculation described above: ___30___ % of what amount is ___$59___ ?

11. Based on your answer to Question 10, set up and solve an equation to find the original price of the jacket.

    $0.30 x = \$59 \Rightarrow x = \$59/0.30 = \$196.67$

Guess what? The same idea can be used to find a percentage, but it's more straightforward to use division. For example, of the 32 teams in the National Football League, 12 make the playoffs each year. What percentage of teams make the playoffs?

12. Divide the number of teams that make the playoffs by the total number of teams, and write your answer in decimal form.

$$\frac{12}{32} = 0.375$$

13. Based on your answer to Question 12, what percentage of teams make the playoffs?

*37.5%*

## Did You Get It?

Try this problem to see if you understand the concepts we just studied. The answer can be found at the bottom of the portfolio page.

2. Calculate each amount involving percents.
    a. Find 38% of 400.
    b. $17.49 is 20% of what amount?
    c. What percentage of 42 is 15?

## 2-1 Group

If it doesn't make you uncomfortable, exchange the following information with the classmates in your Unit 2 group. This will be your small group for the second unit. It would be a good idea to schedule a time for the group to meet to go over homework, ask/answer questions, or prepare for exams. You can use this table to help schedule a mutually agreeable time.

| Name | Phone Number | Email | Available Times |
|------|--------------|-------|-----------------|
|      |              |       |                 |
|      |              |       |                 |
|      |              |       |                 |
|      |              |       |                 |
|      |              |       |                 |

1. Let's look further into the idea of "giving 110% effort." First, explain why a lot of people feel like that saying doesn't really make sense.

   *110% is more than the total that you have to give. If giving 100% is giving all of the effort you possibly can, then giving 110% effort is impossible.*

2. Convert 110% into decimal form, then multiply the result by 200 to find what 110% of 200 is.

   *$1.10 \cdot 200 = 220$*

3. Suppose that in a normal half hour of practice, a tennis player expends 280 calories of energy. How many calories would she need to expend if she were to "give 110%" effort?

   *$1.10 \cdot 280 = 308$ calories*

## Did You Get It

Try this problem to see if you understand the concepts we just studied. The answer can be found at the bottom of the portfolio page.

3. A real estate developer is looking for investors to help fund a new condo complex. He promises a 145% return on investment in 4 years. If you're interested in investing $30,000 and the developer follows through on his promise, how much money will you get back in 4 years?

Now let's go shopping. If I had a dollar for every time someone has asked me to calculate a discount price for them when a sign advertises a certain percent off, I'd be able to buy us both a very handsome gift indeed. In fact, shopping is one of the most common ways that people running loose in society are likely to encounter percents.

My wife is an absolute wizard with Macy's coupons: As a high-volume shopper there (sigh) she gets quite a few coupons in the mail. On one recent mall outing, she found a lovely red strapless number with a selling price of $79. She had two coupons to choose from: one offers $15 off any purchase of $50 or more, the other offers 20% off any item. Which was the better choice?

Courtesy of David Sobecki

4. Find 20% of $79.

   $0.2 \cdot \$79 = \$15.80$

5. Keeping in mind that you just found the amount the price would be discounted, which coupon should Cat have used? Explain.

   *The 20% off would save an extra $0.80.*

6. The sales tax in our county is 6.5%. Find the amount of tax on the dress purchase (after applying the coupon that you chose), and the total cost including tax.

   *Sale price = $79 − $15.80 = $63.20*
   *Sales tax = 0.065 · $63.20 = $4.11*
   *Cost including tax = $63.20 + $4.11 = $67.31*

## Did You Get It

Try this problem to see if you understand the concepts we just studied. The answer can be found at the bottom of the portfolio page.

4. A refrigerator has a regular price of $1,149 at Home Depot, and $1,219 at Lowe's. Home Depot is offering 15% off, but Lowe's offers $200 off if you put the purchase on store credit. Which is the better option?

7. It's common for stores to advertise a certain percentage off, then say "discount is reflected in the marked price," leaving you to trust that you're getting the percent off that they claimed. Suppose that a refrigerator is listed as 30% off, with a sale price of $749. What would that make the original selling price? (Look back at Question 11 in the Class section if you need help.)

$0.70\, x = 749 \Rightarrow x = 749/0.70 = \$1,070$

8. A large latte at Shaky's Caffeine Shack usually sells for the low low price of just $3.50, but today, Shaky has gone goofy and is offering it for just $3.00. Wow! Why not just give them away? Is this a better offer than the 20% off the coffee shop across the street is offering?

$0.50/\$3.50 \approx 0.143 = 14.3\%$

Nope, the 20% off is better, if by "better" you mean "greater percent off." Students might say that you'd need to know the original price across the street, which would be great!

The percentage you found in Question 8 is called the **percent decrease.** It's the amount that some quantity is decreased as a percentage of the original amount. Similarly, **percent increase** is the amount of increase as a percentage of the original amount. That sounds like a good opportunity for a colored formula box.

## Computing Percent Increase and Decrease

When some quantity gets larger, we calculate the percent increase using the formula

$$\text{Percent Increase} = \frac{\text{Amount of increase}}{\text{Original amount}} = \frac{\text{New amount} - \text{Original amount}}{\text{Original amount}}$$

If the quantity gets smaller, we calculate the percent decrease using the formula

$$\text{Percent Decrease} = \frac{\text{Amount of decrease}}{\text{Original amount}} = \frac{\text{New amount} - \text{Original amount}}{\text{Original amount}}$$

In each case, the result is a percentage in decimal form.

9. On July 24, 2009, the federal minimum wage was raised from $6.55 to $7.25. Find the percent increase.

$$\frac{7.25 - 6.55}{6.55} \approx 0.107 = 10.7\%$$

### Did You Get It

Try this problem to see if you understand the concepts we just studied. The answer can be found at the bottom of the portfolio page.

5. In an effort to show solidarity with his workers, a CEO offers to take a $300,000 per year pay cut. Last year, his salary was $11 million dollars. Find the percent decrease in pay.

10. On January 15, 2016, shares of stock in the Walt Disney Company were trading at $93.90, while shares of Carnival Corporation were trading at $49.83. Analysts predicted that Disney stock would be selling for $116.77 one year later, and that Carnival stock would reach a price of $60.47 in one year. Compare the expected increase in the two stocks, as well as the expected percent increase. Which sounds like a better investment to you? Explain.

Increase in Disney: $116.77 − $93.90 = $22.87

Increase in Carnival: $60.47 − $49.83 = $10.64

Percent increase in Disney: $\dfrac{\$22.87}{\$93.90} \approx 0.244 = 24.4\%$

Percent increase in Carnival: $\dfrac{\$10.64}{\$49.83} \approx 0.214 = 21.4\%$

Which sounds better is an opinion, but the higher percentage increase should be the choice.

Courtesy of David Sobecki

We would never, ever accuse any advertisers of being deceptive (wink wink), but let's just say that it's not uncommon for percents to be used incorrectly in marketing materials. Let's look at one such case to close our review of percents.

11. A department store advertised that certain merchandise was reduced 25%. Also, an additional 10% discount card would be given to the first 200 people who entered the store on a specific day. The advertisement then stated that this amounted to a 35% reduction in the price of an item. Explain why the store marketing manager is either a liar, or bad at math. Show calculations to back up your explanation.

*The additional 10% would be taken off the discounted price, not the original price. So it would not be an additional 10% off.*

12. In promotional materials, a company that increased their work force from 1,000 to 1,500 workers claimed that they hired 50% more workers. A rival of theirs bragged about decreasing emissions from 1,500 to 1,000 cubic feet per day, claiming a 33% reduction. Which company is lying? Explain.

*Neither. Let's calculate the percent change for each:*

$$\frac{1{,}500 - 1{,}000}{1{,}000} = 0.5 = 50\% \qquad \frac{1{,}000 - 1{,}500}{1{,}500} \approx -0.33 = -33.3\%$$

> Talk about how numbers can sometimes be spun to tell a certain story depending on the context.

**2-1**  ██ **Portfolio** ████████████████████████████

Name _____

Check each box when you've completed the task. Remember that your instructor will want you to turn in the portfolio pages you create.

### Technology

1. ☐ Build a spreadsheet that calculates percent increase or decrease, like the one shown below. Don't just enter numbers and compute the percent change on your own: you should use formulas with cell references to complete the calculations for amount of change and percent change. A template to help you get started is included in the online resources for this lesson.

| D3 | ▲▼ | ✕ ✓ | *fx* | =C3/A3 | |
|---|---|---|---|---|---|
| | A | B | C | D | E |
| 1 | Orig. Amt. | New Amt. | Change | % Change (Decimal) | % Change (%) |
| 2 | 3.5 | 3 | -0.5 | -0.142857143 | -14.3% |
| 3 | 6.55 | 7.25 | 0.7 | 0.106870229 | 10.7% |

### Online Practice

1. ☐ Include any written work from the online assignment along with any notes or questions about this lesson's content.

### Applications

1. ☐ Complete the applications problems.

### Reflections

Type a short answer to each question.
1. ☐ What is the literal translation of the word "percent"?
2. ☐ How can an understanding of percents be valuable to you as a shopper?
3. ☐ Do you think you can give 110% effort to doing well in this class? Explain.
4. ☐ Take another look at your answer to Question 0 at the beginning of this lesson. Would you change your answer now that you've completed the lesson? How would you summarize the topic of this lesson now?
5. ☐ What questions do you have about this lesson?

### Looking Ahead

1. ☐ Complete the Lesson 2-2 Prep Skills and read the opening paragraph in Lesson 2-2 carefully, then answer Question 0 in preparation for that lesson.

### Answers to "Did You Get It?"

1. **a.** 0.473  **b.** 24%  **c.** $\frac{4}{5}$  2. **a.** 152  **b.** $87.45  **c.** 35.7%  3. $43,500
4. $976.65 at Home Depot vs. $1,019 at Lowe's  5. 2.7%

## 2-1 | Applications

Name _____

Many people probably think that those who are good at math always do exact calculations, but we know better: estimation is actually a really useful tool, especially when it comes to things like percent discount. Suppose that you're shopping on a rack that offers 40% off the lowest ticketed price, and you're interested in a sweater with a ticket price of $47.99.

© PhotoLink/Getty Images RF

1. Given that 40% is being subtracted from the ticket price, explain why that makes the sale price 60% of the ticket price.

   *If you subtract 40% from 100%, what's left over is 60%.*

2. The ticket price can be rounded easily to $50, so you can estimate the sale price by multiplying 50 by 0.6. The easy way to do this is to multiply 50 by 6, which you can do in your head, then move the decimal one place to the left. Use this idea to estimate the sale price. (For what it's worth, I used this procedure about eight times yesterday while clothes shopping.)

   *50 · 6 = 300; sale price is $30.*

3. Now use the procedures we reviewed in this lesson to find the exact discount price.

   *0.6 · $47.99 = $28.79*

4. Would your estimate from Question 2 have been good enough for you to decide whether or not you wanted to buy the item? Discuss.

   *Answers will vary.*

## 2-1 Applications

Name _____

5. After a round of layoffs, a company that used to have 1,200 employees now has 900. They then issue a press release saying "In spite of trying economic times, we were able to limit job cuts to just 25% of our job force." A couple of years later, they raise the number of employees back to 1,200. This time, they claim "We were able to increase our job force by more than 33%!" In which press release were they lying? Explain.

*Check both percent changes:*

$$\frac{900 - 1,200}{1,200} = \frac{-300}{1,200} = -0.25 = -25\% \qquad \frac{1,200 - 900}{900} = \frac{300}{900} \approx 0.33 = 33\%$$

*They were telling the truth on both.*

6. An employer offers a retirement program in which 9.8% of a worker's salary is deducted from their pay and deposited into an investment fund. The company then adds an addition 12% of the worker's salary to the fund. How much would an employee have deposited into their fund in the first year if their starting salary is $43,000?

*The total is 21.8% of their salary: $0.218 \cdot \$43,000 = \$9,374$*

7. While shopping at Nordstrom, you pick out two pairs of jeans at $49 each and a pair of shoes on sale for $39. Then you splurge on a $95 sweater. You have two coupons but can only use one. The first offers 40% off any single item. The second offers 15% off your entire purchase. Which is the better choice?

*40% off of the sweater: $0.60 \cdot \$95 = \$57$. Total price: $\$49 + \$49 + \$39 + \$57 = \$194$*

*15% off total purchase: $0.85 \cdot (\$49 + \$49 + \$39 + \$95) = \$197.20$*

*40% off the most expensive item is the better choice.*

# Lesson 2-2   **Prep Skills**

This is a short review of skills that will come in handy in the next lesson. In each case, answer the question, then rate your confidence level by checking one of the boxes. If you feel like you're struggling with these skills, consult the online resources provided by your instructor for extra practice.

### SKILL 1: COMPUTE A PERCENTAGE

1. What percent of 100 is 40?

2. What percent of 520 is 100?

3. What percent of 12 is 15?

### SKILL 2: COMPUTE A PERCENTAGE OF A GIVEN AMOUNT

4. What is 30% of 100?

5. What is 85% of 1,200?

6. What is 3.1% of $1,118.13?

### SKILL 3: FIND AN AMOUNT INCREASED BY A CERTAIN PERCENTAGE.

7. If an amount of $500 increases by 15%, what is the new amount?

8. If an amount of $12,000 increases by 3.4%, what is the new amount?

# Lesson 2-2   Building It Is the Easy Part . . . (Budgeting)

### LEARNING OBJECTIVES

☐ 1. Calculate take-home pay and monthly expenses.

☐ 2. Identify necessary expenses and luxuries.

☐ 3. Prepare a monthly budget.

☐ 4. Prorate long-term expenses to save in advance for them.

© Glow Images RF

*A budget tells us what we can't afford, but it doesn't keep us from buying it.*

— William Feather

How much money did you spend last month? If you're like most folks, you probably can't answer that question exactly, and if you're like a lot of folks, it would take you a while to even come up with a ballpark guess. By some estimates, American consumers have a combined debt of over 11 trillion dollars. Trillion! That's an almost unimaginable amount of money. Imagine spending a million dollars a day, every day. That would be pretty much impossible, wouldn't it? But if you could, it would still take you over 2,700 YEARS to spend a trillion dollars. This debt problem happened because people spend more money than they make. And that happens because so few people put forth the effort to track exactly what they make and spend. Budgeting is the process of deciding how much money you can spend on various expenses based on your income: that is, the amount of money you're earning. Learning how to budget your money is a good first step in avoiding massive debt; the hard part is sticking to that budget!

**0.** After reading the opening paragraph, what do you think the main topic of this lesson will be?

## 2-2   Class

**1.** Marlene works full-time as an executive assistant, and she has a check for $1,023.07 direct-deposited into her checking account every other Friday. How much money does Marlene make per year? There are different approaches to calculating this amount, so make sure that you describe how you arrived at your answer.

*The tricky part is scaling biweekly pay up to a year. One approach is to estimate a year at 52 weeks, then multiply $1,023.07 by 26 to get $26,599.82. A more accurate approach would be to divide $1,023.07 by 14 to get a daily average, then multiply that by 365 days to get $26,672.90.*

Most people can tell you their hourly wage or salary, but because of deductions for taxes, insurance, and retirement, a lot of people don't know how much money is actually left for them to spend. This amount is known as **take-home pay,** while the amount earned before deductions is called **gross pay.** Since many common expenses occur on monthly cycles, it's useful to know exactly how much money you bring home per month.

2. Refer to Question 1. What is Marlene's monthly take-home pay? Again, you should describe how you got your answer.

*The answer depends on how the yearly amount was calculated in Question 1. In either case, divide that amount by 12. The results are either $2,216.65 or $2,222.74 for the two methods shown.*

### Did You Get It?

Try this problem to see if you understand the concepts we just studied. The answer can be found at the bottom of the portfolio page.

1. Eddie works 25 hours a week at a campus bookstore. He gets a weekly paycheck in the amount of $195.30. What is his monthly take-home pay?

By far the biggest difference between money earned and take home pay for most people is taxes. The percentage of your pay that is withheld for taxes depends on a large variety of factors including income level, where you live, and family status. Nationally, it's hard to pin down an exact average, but standard estimates are that the average person takes home about 70–75% of his or her pay.

3. If a worker is paid a salary of $47,400 per year and is in a tax bracket that results in 27% deductions, what is her monthly take-home pay?

*The annual take-home would be 73% of the salary, which is 0.73 · $47,400 = $34,602. Dividing by 12, we get a monthly take-home of $2,883.50.*

4. The main topic of this lesson is personal budgeting, but organizations—from small charities to the federal government—must also prepare a budget every year. For example, for fiscal year 2015, the president submitted a budget to Congress requesting $3.90 trillion dollars to be spent by the government. Of that amount, $229 billion went toward paying interest on the national debt. What percentage of the budget went to that one expense? (A trillion is a thousand billion, by the way.)

*$3.9 trillion is $3,900 billion, so we get 229/3,900 ≈ 0.059, so about 5.9%.*

Knowing how much money you bring home is half of budgeting: the other half is tracking your expenses, which is the amount of money you spend. Most people don't realize that expenses that seem minor can really add up.

5.  My friend Charles noticed that one of his students came to class every day with two cups of coffee from a well-known coffee chain that isn't exactly famous for their low prices. He asked her if she'd ever thought about how much she spent on that coffee over the course of a year; not surprisingly, she had not. If she paid $3.25 per cup for that coffee every day, how much would she spend on coffee in a year? First, make a guess without doing any calculations. Then calculate the actual amount and describe your reaction.

© McGraw Hill Education/John Flournoy, photographer

$2 \cdot \$3.25 = \$6.50 \, per \, day$

$\$6.50 \cdot 365 = \$2,372.50$

*Reactions vary, but it certainly surprised me. And I'm a mathematician!*

6.  How much would our coffee-drinking friend save over the course of a year if she settled for convenience store coffee at 79 cents per cup?

$2 \cdot \$0.79 = \$1.58 \, per \, day$

$\$1.58 \cdot 365 = \$576.70$

$\$2,372.50 - \$576.70 = \$1,795.80$

## Did You Get It?

Try this problem to see if you understand the concepts we just studied. The answer can be found at the bottom of the portfolio page.

2.  The average price of a pack of cigarettes in the U.S. in 2015 was about $6.25. How much money would a pack-a-day smoker set fire to in a year?

We'll call expenses like daily gourmet coffee **luxuries,** which are things you can live without. Everyone wants to be able to spend money on luxuries, but you won't know how much you can comfortably spend until you calculate your **necessary expenses.** These are the basic things you have to pay for: food, shelter, insurance, transportation, clothing, utilities, student loan payments. Some of those expenses are **fixed:** the amount you spend each month is consistent. Housing, insurance, utilities, loans, and transportation usually fall into this category. Other necessary expenses are **variable,** meaning they can change from month to month, like food and clothing.

The key to maintaining a sensible budget is to add up your necessary expenses and subtract them from your income. The result will let you know how much you have to spend on variable expenses, entertainment and luxuries. It will also let you know if you're able to save any money (which should be one of your goals every month).

7. Tremaine brings home $2,746.79 per month, and has fixed expenses shown in the table. How much can he afford to spend on food, clothing, and luxuries?

| Expense | Amount |
| --- | --- |
| Rent | $675 |
| Car Payment | $299.23 |
| Cell Phone | $79.50 |
| Gas | $110 |

| Expense | Amount |
| --- | --- |
| Insurance | $97.50 |
| Utilities | $175 |
| Student Loan | $211.53 |
| | |

Sum of expenses: $1,647.76

$2,746.79 − $1,647.76 = $1,099.03

8. Tremaine goes out for happy hour drinks and dinner with friends every Friday, and usually spends about $50. On average, what percentage of his budget after fixed expenses is eaten up by these happy hours?

An average month has four Fridays, so he's spending about $200 a month.

$200/$1,099.03 ≈ 0.182

Tremaine spends about 18.2% of his budget on happy hour.

9. In Question 8, you found a percentage. What expenses would you be willing to spend that percentage of your income on? Discuss with your group and make a list.

Answers vary.

10. Good news: Tremaine just got a 4% raise. (Looks like he may be spending more than the usual $50 this Friday.) How much more money does that leave him for variable expenses per month?

0.04 · $2,746.79 = $109.87

The raise doesn't affect his fixed expenses, so this entire extra amount can be spent on variable expenses.

## Did You Get It?

Try these problems to see if you understand the concepts we just studied. The answers can be found at the bottom of the portfolio page.

3. Leslie shares an apartment with two friends, and the rent and utilities are split equally by all three tenants. Find the amount left for variable expenses and luxuries if her monthly income is $1,556.27 and fixed expenses are shown below.

| | | | |
|---|---|---|---|
| Total rent: | $1,100 | Total utilities: | $327 |
| Public transportation: | $88 | Cell phone: | $91.50 |
| Insurance: | $48.20 | Gym membership: | $38.95 |

4. Leslie treats her roommates to salads and pizzas from Papa Antonio's every Monday and Thursday, at a cost of $29, including delivery and tip. What percentage of her budget after fixed expenses goes toward these semiweekly gatherings on average?

## 2-2   Group

The Group portion of this lesson is all about putting together a monthly budget. You can choose one of the three individuals whose financial parameters are provided below.

### Choice 1: Ellen

Ellen has a Bachelor's degree in sociology and works for her state's department of human services. Her salary is $38,200 per year, and her payroll deductions amount to 26% of her salary. She earns an additional $125 per week tutoring at-risk students at a community center, with 10% of that amount withheld for taxes. Ellen owns a small home and pays $260 per month in property taxes and insurance.

### Choice 2: Martin

Martin is a first-year college student taking 12 hours of classes, and working 25 hours per week at a coffee shop. He makes $9.75 per hour, and payroll deductions eat up 18% of his pay. Martin lives rent-free at his parents' house, but pays a share of the utility bill each month. His tuition and books are paid for by a combination of gifts from his parents and student loans. He makes payments on an 8-year-old used car, and pays for auto insurance as well.

### Choice 3: Maribel and Mark

Maribel and Mark are a young married couple with two children. Maribel makes $46,400 per year as an assistant bank manager, and has 29% of her pay deducted each month. Mark is a substitute teacher, and earns $22,166, with 21% deducted. The family rents a two-bedroom apartment, and must pay for day care for the kids five days a week. They have two car payments.

1. My group will be making up a budget for _____.

2. Find the monthly take-home pay for your choice.

Ellen: $38,200/12 = $3,183.33 per month; 74% of that is $2,355.66. Add to that 90% of $125, which is $112.50, to get $2,468.16.

Martin: 25 · $9.75 = $243.75 per week, or $12,675 per year. Divide by 12 to get $1,056.25 per month. 82% of that is $866.13.

Maribel and Mark: 71% of $46,400 plus 79% of $22,166 is $32,944 + $17,511.14 = $50,455.14 per year. Divide by 12 to get $4,204.60.

3. The most important part of building a budget is probably listing expenses. Think carefully about the person you're budgeting for, and make a list of expenses that your group agrees are reasonable for a person in that financial situation. You might consider doing a little bit of Internet research to come up with typical expenses, or you can ask your instructor or other groups for input. Wouldn't this be a GREAT place to use what you've learned about spreadsheets?

| Expense | Amount |
|---------|--------|
|         |        |
|         |        |
|         |        |
|         |        |
|         |        |
|         |        |
|         |        |
|         |        |
|         |        |
|         |        |
|         |        |
|         |        |
|         |        |

| Expense | Amount |
|---------|--------|
|         |        |
|         |        |
|         |        |
|         |        |
|         |        |
|         |        |
|         |        |
|         |        |
|         |        |
|         |        |
|         |        |
|         |        |
|         |        |

Total Necessary Expenses:

_____

*Answers vary for Questions 3–6.*

4. How much money is left in your budget for luxuries and savings?

> We felt it was important to leave this portion of the lesson open-ended. The intent is for students to give some serious thought to the types of expenses that people in different life situations are likely to have.

5. If the total expenses are greater than total income, what are some options they would have? Discuss.

**6.** If your person's car breaks down, resulting in a $597.43 repair, how does this affect the monthly budget? What do you think some options would be in that case? Discuss.

*Answers vary. Some possibilities to consider are a short-term loan, putting the amount on a credit card, picking up some extra work, cutting down on other expenses, or robbing a liquor store. (That last one was a joke. Please don't send mean emails.)*

So far, we've focused on monthly expenses. But some regular expenses occur on an annual or semiannual basis: car insurance, tuition payments, and property taxes are three examples that come to mind. If you manage your money by spending every penny you have each month, when those occasional large expenses pop up, it can be very hard to find the money to pay for them. The result is usually mounting debt that can take years to overcome.

One way to avoid the negative effects of these long-term expenses is to budget money every month in advance of the due dates, maybe putting it into a separate savings account. Then when the big expense is due, the money is there waiting.

**7.** Jin pays $337.24 every six months for car insurance. He also pays $2,623 for tuition at the beginning of both fall and spring semesters, and budgets $650 for books and supplies for each semester. If he wants to plan ahead, how much money should he put into savings every month? Explain how you decided on that amount.

*Each of the expenses listed is paid every six months, so the total amount will need to be saved in a six-month period. The sum of the expenses is $337.24 + $2,623 + $650 = $3,610.24. Dividing by 6 we get $601.71. Jin should put aside $601.71 per month.*

## Did You Get It?

Try this problem to see if you understand the concepts we just studied. The answer can be found at the bottom of the portfolio page.

5. Dharma and Greg have a combined monthly income of $5,280.94. They want to save ahead for semiannual property taxes ($1,146), semiannual car insurance ($493.21), and annual homeowners insurance ($893.20). What percentage of their income should be saved each month? (Semiannual means twice a year, by the way.)

8. Suppose that instead of starting a savings account with the money he sets aside monthly, Jin decides to just hide that amount of cash each month in his sock drawer. List as many reasons you can think of for why that's a bad decision.

   *Answers vary. Certainly interest and security should be among them.*

Hopefully, you know that when you save money with a financial institution, they pay you for access to your money. So the amount that you save grows. Good deal. The amount that they pay you is almost always described in terms of percents: more specifically, a percentage of the amount that you've invested. We'll study how this works in depth in the next two lessons.

9. The amount of money that Jin set aside in the very first month will be in his savings account for five months, and during that time will have 1.7% of the amount added to it by the bank. How much extra will Jin make on that initial deposit? (Note that this isn't the way a bank would describe savings: we'll learn everything you might want to know about that later.)

   $0.017 \cdot \$601.71 = \$10.23$

10. Before we close the lesson, take a look back at our friend Tremaine from Questions 7–10 in the Class portion. Suppose that disaster strikes: Tremaine's company goes out of business, and his income disappears just like that. Any financial planner worth a nickel advises clients to have a reserve of saved money, often called a **cushion** or **safety net,** in case of such an emergency. Based on his expenses, how much of a cushion would Tremaine need to get through three months while searching for a new job?

    *Tremaine's necessary expenses added up to $1,647.76, and this doesn't include food. So you'd have to figure he'd need at least $1,800 per month, for a safety net of $5,400.*

**Math Note**

Most financial experts advise having at least 3–6 months worth of expenses in your cushion fund.

# 2-2 Portfolio

Name _____

Check each box when you've completed the task. Remember that your instructor will want you to turn in the portfolio pages you create.

### Technology

1. ☐ When working out a personal budget, it's useful to list out your known expenses and make estimates of income and other expenses for a month. But it's a LOT better to actually keep track of those expenses for a month, and that's what you'll do here. That makes this an unusually long, but incredibly useful assignment. There's a template in the online resources for this lesson that you can use to get started. After you're done tracking your expenses, create a pie chart that will show you at a glance where your money goes.

### Online Practice

1. ☐ Include any written work from the online assignment along with any notes or questions about this lesson's content.

### Applications

1. ☐ Complete the applications problems.

### Reflections

Type a short answer to each question.

1. ☐ Why is it valuable to put together a monthly budget?
2. ☐ What is the difference between fixed and variable expenses?
3. ☐ How well do you feel you've done in the past at not spending more money than you bring in? Would a budget have helped you in the past?
4. ☐ What changes could you make now that would have a positive impact on your financial situation?
5. ☐ Take another look at your answer to Question 0 at the beginning of this lesson. Would you change your answer now that you've completed the lesson? How would you summarize the topic of this lesson now?
6. ☐ What questions do you have about this lesson?

### Looking Ahead

1. ☐ Complete the Lesson 2-3 Prep Skills and read the opening paragraph in Lesson 2-3 carefully, then answer Question 0 in preparation for that lesson.

### Answers to "Did You Get It?"

1. Somewhere around $846.30, depending on how you calculate it.

2. $2,281.25   3. $813.95   4. 28.5%   5. 6.6%

## 2-2 Applications

Name _____

1. If you drink two cans of Diet Coke (90 cents each) every day, how much do you spend on Diet Coke in a year?

   *$1.80 per day times 365 days is $657.*

2. Which costs more over the course of a year: a medium three-item pizza, which costs $7.25, four times a week, or going out to a fine dining restaurant ($85) twice a month?

   *4 · $7.25 · 52 = $1,508*

   *24 · $85 = $2,040*

   *The twice-monthly fine dining experience costs almost $500 more.*

3. After graduating with a degree in hospitality management, Edwin is hired to manage the front desk personnel at a resort hotel. His gross monthly pay is $4,142.86, and 29% is deducted for taxes and health insurance. His pay is divided into two checks per month. What is Edwin's monthly take-home pay, and how much is each paycheck worth?

   *71% of $4,142.86 is $2,941.43. That's his monthly take-home pay. Dividing by two, we find that each check is worth $1,470.72.*

4. Edwin's fixed expenses are shown below. How much money will he have left over every month after paying these fixed expenses?

   | Expense | Amount | | Expense | Amount |
   |---------|--------|---|---------|--------|
   | Rent | $845.00 | | Insurance | $112.17 |
   | Car Payment | $224.61 | | Utilities | $93.00 |
   | Cell Phone | $69.80 | | Student Loan | $256.25 |
   | Gas | $40.00 | | Gym | $39.00 |

   *The sum of fixed expenses is $1,679.83. Subtracting from the take-home pay of $2,941.43, we get $1,261.60 left.*

## 2-2  Applications

Name _____

5. What are some of the things that the amount of money you found in Question 4 would likely be used for?

   *Food, beverage, clothing, entertainment, and saving for the future would be good answers.*

6. Edwin enjoys visiting the casino at the resort where he works. But like most visitors, he tends to walk in with more money than he leaves with. In fact, on average he loses $85 every weekend. What percentage of his budget after expenses is he losing?

   *$85 times 52 divided by 12 is $368.33 a month on average.*

   *$368.33/$1,261.60 ≈ 0.292; he's losing 29.2% of his income after fixed expenses. That's bad.*

7. In many cases, property taxes when you own a home are paid every six months, homeowner's insurance is paid once per year, and car insurance is paid every six months. One homeowner pays $1,450 in property taxes twice a year, $946 in homeowner's insurance annually, and makes car insurance payments of $294.32 and $335.40 every six months. If this homeowner wants to spread these expenses out by putting some money each month into a savings account, how much should she put aside per month?

   *Let's figure out the annual expense: 2 · $1,450 + $946 + 2($294.32 + $335.40) = $5,105.44. Dividing by 12, we get an amount of $425.45 per month.*

8. In the last lesson of this unit, we'll study tax brackets. The short version is that if you make more money, you pay a higher percentage of your income in taxes. That's why the percentage of deductions varied for each individual we've studied in this lesson. If you have a job making $36,750, this puts you in the 15% federal tax bracket, and combining state and local taxes, you might end up having 20% deducted. You then get a raise to $38,200, which moves you up a bracket, and now 24% gets deducted. How much of that $1,450 raise do you actually get to keep?

   *80% of $36,750 is $29,400. 76% of $38,200 is $29,032. Not only do you not get to keep any of that money, you end up with $368 LESS!*

## Lesson 2-3   Prep Skills

This is a short review of skills that will come in handy in the next lesson. In each case, answer the question, then rate your confidence level by checking one of the boxes. If you feel like you're struggling with these skills, consult the online resources provided by your instructor for extra practice.

### SKILL 1: CONVERT A PERCENT TO DECIMAL FORM

1. Convert each percent to its decimal equivalent.

   12%     4%     2.99%

### SKILL 2: COMPUTE A PERCENTAGE OF A GIVEN AMOUNT

2. Find each requested percentage.

   12.3% of 100      3.1% of $1,118.13

### SKILL 3: EVALUATE ALGEBRAIC EXPRESSIONS

3. Find $A$ in $A = PQR$ if $P = 5$, $Q = 120$, and $R = 0.03$.

### SKILL 4: ENTER FRACTIONAL EXPRESSIONS INTO A CALCULATOR

4. Use a calculator to complete each computation:

   $$\frac{50 + 40}{120}$$        $$1{,}000\left(1 + \frac{0.06}{5}\right)$$

### SKILL 5: SOLVE LINEAR EQUATIONS

5. Solve the equation: $5 = \frac{x}{0.2}$

6. Solve the equation: $4.36 = 58.20(r)(3)$

# Lesson 2-3  **A Topic of Interest**  (Simple Interest)

**LEARNING OBJECTIVES**

☐ 1. Define interest and understand related terminology.

☐ 2. Develop simple interest formulas.

☐ 3. Use simple interest formulas to analyze financial issues.

*An investment in knowledge pays the best interest.*
              —Benjamin Franklin

© Photodisc/Getty Images RF

The topic of the next two lessons is of interest to anyone who plans to buy a house or a car, have a credit card, invest money, have a savings account—in short, pretty much everyone. This interesting topic is *interest*—a description of how fees are calculated when money is borrowed, and how your money grows when you save. If you prefer not to be separated from your hard-earned money, this is a topic you should be eager to understand well. The key to understanding isn't to just focus on a bunch of formulas: it's about understanding what interest is about and how it's calculated. This will give you the best chance to make sound financial decisions throughout your lifetime. So unless you can grow money, this should indeed be a topic of interest.

   **0.** After reading the opening paragraph, what do you think the main topic of this lesson will be?

## 2-3  Group

**Interest** is a fee paid for the use of money. For example, if you borrow money from a bank to buy a car, you must not only pay back the amount of money that you borrowed, but also an additional amount, called the interest, for the use of the bank's money. On the other hand, if you deposit money in a savings account, the bank will pay you interest for saving money since it will be using your money to provide loans, mortgages, etc. to people who are borrowing money. The stated rate of interest is generally given as a yearly percentage of the amount borrowed or deposited.

   There are two kinds of interest. *Simple interest* is paid strictly as a percentage of the original amount of money. *Compound interest* is a percentage of an original amount, as well as a percentage of the new amount including previously calculated interest. We will study simple interest in this lesson, and compound interest in the next.

   **1.** Let's say that you get a $600 tax refund, and you wisely decide to put it into a long-term investment that pays 5% in simple interest each year. How much money would that add to the account each year? (Remember, with simple interest a certain percentage of an original amount is added to the account.)

   *5% of $600 is $30, so $30 would be added to the account each year.*

2. Write out the multiplication you did to get your answer to Question 1. The next goal is to write a general formula for computing the amount of interest earned. Substitute the letter *P* for the original amount invested ($600) and the letter *r* for the percentage you multiplied by (written in decimal form, of course).

$$\$600 \times 0.05 = \$30$$
$$P \times r = \text{Interest}$$

A lot of people think that simple interest isn't used in "real" financial transactions, but that is absolutely not the case, as we'll see working through this lesson. You might do a search for "simple interest" for the class to find examples.

### Did You Get It

Try this problem to see if you understand the concepts we just studied. The answer can be found at the bottom of the portfolio page.

1. Suppose that you take out a loan to buy new furniture, borrowing $1,700. If the interest charge will be 7.9% of the borrowed amount per year, how much interest will you pay each year?

3. Fill in the following table, which shows the growth of the account over several years, as well as the total amount of interest earned. You'll need a correct answer to Question 1, and remember that this is simple interest, so the interest earned each year is always calculated on the original value of the investment.

| Time | Total Interest Earned | Value of Account |
|---|---|---|
| Start | – | $600 |
| After 1 year | $30 | $630 |
| After 2 years | $60 | $660 |
| After 3 years | $90 | $690 |
| After 4 years | $120 | $720 |
| After 5 years | $150 | $750 |
| After 10 years | $300 | $900 |

4. Look carefully at the first and second columns of your table. What is the relationship between the number of years that have passed and the total interest earned? Describe it verbally.

*The total amount of interest earned is the product of the amount earned in one year and the number of years that have passed.*

## 2-3 | Class

In the Group portion of this lesson, you actually developed formulas for computing simple interest—whether you realized it or not! Now let's formalize what we discovered.

In order to compute simple interest, we need exactly three pieces of information: the *principal,* the *rate,* and the *time.* The box below describes the terminology we'll use, as well as the letters we'll use to represent the key data.

**Interest** (*I*) is a fee charged for the use of money.

**Principal** (*P*) is the amount of money borrowed or placed into a savings account.

**Rate** (*r*) is the percent of the principal paid for having money loaned, or earned for investing money. Unless indicated otherwise, rates are given as a percent for a term of 1 year.

**Time** (*t*) or term is the length of time that the money is being borrowed or invested. When the rate is given as a percent per year, time has to be written in years.

**Future value** (*A*) is the amount of the loan or investment plus the interest paid or earned.

In the work we did in the Group portion, the principal was $P = \$600$; the rate was 5% written as a decimal, which is $r = 0.05$. The amount of time varied when filling out the table of interest and future value.

1. In Question 2, you should have discovered that the formula for computing the interest in 1 year is $P \times r$. Use this, and your answer to Question 4, to write a formula for finding the amount of interest *I* that accumulates in *t* years:

$$I = \underline{P \times r \times t}$$

2. The total value of the account after *t* years, which we're calling future value and representing with the letter *A*, is calculated by adding the total amount of interest to the principal amount. Use your answer to Question 1 above to write a formula for future value in terms of *P, r,* and *t*.

$$A = \underline{P + P \times r \times t}$$

3. Use your formula from Question 2 to find the future value of your original $600 investment at 5% interest in 30 years.

$$A = 600 + 600(0.05)(30) = \$1,500$$

### Did You Get It

Try this problem to see if you understand the concepts we just studied. The answer can be found at the bottom of the portfolio page.

2. Find the future value of a loan if $3,600 is borrowed for 3 years at a simple interest rate of 8% per year.

4. The right side of your answer to Question 2 should be a sum, meaning that it has two terms. Use some algebra to rewrite the formula so that it has just one term. The result should look like the principal amount times some quantity.

$A = P + Prt = P(1 + rt)$

Most groups will need a little nudge on the algebra here.

Here's a summary of the formulas we've built to describe simple interest:

### Formulas for Computing Simple Interest and Future Value

**1.** Interest = principal × rate × time:

$$I = Prt$$

**2.** Future value = principal + interest:

$$A = P + I \quad \text{or} \quad A = P(1 + rt)$$

5. To meet payroll during a down period, United Ceramics Inc. needed to borrow $2,000 at 4% simple interest for 3 months. Without doing any calculations, make an educated guess as to how much interest you think would be due.

Answers vary.

6. Now use formulas to find the interest they paid, and the future value at the end of three months. (Hint: How many years does three months correspond to?)

$I = \$2,000(0.04)(1/4) = \$20$
Future value: $2,020

## Did You Get It

Try this problem to see if you understand the concepts we just studied. The answer can be found at the bottom of the portfolio page.

3. Marta needs some quick cash for books at the beginning of spring semester, so she borrows $600 at 11% simple interest for 2 months. How much interest will she pay, and what is the future value of the loan?

It's very common for simple interest loans to be paid off in monthly installments. This is how many loans for things like furniture and electronics work. Let's look at finding the monthly payment for a simple-interest loan.

A biotech startup borrowed $68,000 to buy lab equipment at 9% simple interest for 1½ years.

7. Find the future value of the loan.

$A = \$68,000(1 + 0.09(1.5)) = \$77,180$

8. Divide the future value by the number of months to find the monthly payment.

$$\frac{\$77,180}{18} = \$4,287.78$$

## Did You Get It

Try this problem to see if you understand the concepts we just studied. The answer can be found at the bottom of the portfolio page.

4. The Lookout Restaurant took out a loan for $5,000. The simple interest rate was 6.5%, and the term of the loan was 3 years. Find the interest, future value, and monthly payment.

## 2-3   Group (Again)

Notice that the simple interest formula contains four variable quantities: interest, principal, rate, and time. Because we know how to solve equations from algebra, if we know three of those four quantities for a given account, we can solve to find the one we don't know.

**The Problem:** Phillips Health and Beauty Spa is replacing one of its workstations. The interest on a loan secured by the spa was $93.50. The money was borrowed at 5.5 % simple interest for 2 years. What was the amount that they borrowed?

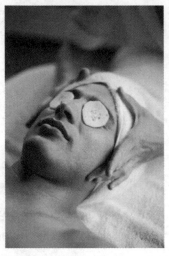

© Royalty-Free/Corbis

1. What information is provided in the problem? Write out each piece of information as an equation. For example, if the loan had been taken out for 8 years, you would write $t = 8$.

   $I = \$93.50$
   $t = 2$
   $r = 0.055$

2. What is it you're being asked to find? Answer in a complete sentence, please.

   *We are asked to find the principal of the loan.*

3. Use the simple interest formula to set up and solve an equation to solve the problem. Show all work!

   $I = Prt \quad \Rightarrow \quad \$93.50 = P(0.055)(2)$

   $0.11P = 93.50$

   $P = \dfrac{93.50}{0.11} = \$850$

Questions 1–3 illustrate a really useful framework for solving this type of problem. When you're using an algebraic formula, it's ALWAYS a good idea to clearly identify the information that you're given, as well as what it is you're being asked to find. Then you can plug that information into the known formula and solve the resulting equation.

4. After receiving an inheritance, a newly married couple invested $15,250 for 10 years and received $9,150 in simple interest. What was the rate that the investment paid? Use the framework from Questions 1–3, and show all of your work. Write your answer in the form of a sentence.

$P = \$15{,}250, t = 10, I = \$9{,}150$

$I = Prt \quad \Rightarrow \quad \$9{,}150 = \$15{,}250r(10)$

$\$152{,}500r = \$9{,}150 \quad \Rightarrow \quad r = 0.06$

The investment paid 6% interest.

> Point out to students that they'll be using a lot of formulas in this unit, and in most cases the difference between failure and success is clearly identifying all of the information needed to substitute into a formula.

5. If that couple had been able to find an investment that paid 9% interest, how much more quickly would they have made that $9,150 in simple interest? Use the framework from Questions 1–3, and show all of your work. Write your answer in the form of the sentence.

$P = \$15{,}250, r = 0.09, I = \$9{,}150$

$I = Prt \quad \Rightarrow \quad \$9{,}150 = \$15{,}250(0.09)t$

$\$1{,}372.50t = \$9{,}150 \quad \Rightarrow \quad t = 6\frac{2}{3}$

They would have made the amount in 3 years and 4 months less time.

## Did You Get It

Try this problem to see if you understand the concepts we just studied. The answer can be found at the bottom of the portfolio page.

5. If you invest $8,000 for 30 months and receive $1,000 in simple interest, what was the rate?

6. A pawn shop offers to finance a guitar costing $750 at 4% simple interest. The total interest charged will be $150. What is the term of the loan and the monthly payment?

If you look at it a certain way, simple interest in a savings account doesn't seem terribly fair. Remember, interest is a fee charged for using someone's money. So when you put money into a bank account, the bank is essentially paying you to borrow your money, because they can use it to increase their business in other areas. So far, so good.

But when you keep that money in the account for a long time, things start to go bad. Let's say that you invest $1,000 into a simple-interest account at 3% interest per year. Then according to the simple interest formula, after 1 year you would have earned $I = (\$1,000)(0.03)(1)$, or $30. Don't spend it all in once place! In any case, at the end of that first year, you now have $1,030 in your account, not $1,000. Yet when interest is simple, the amount of interest paid per year remains constant over the life of the investment. Why is this bad for you? Let's see.

6. Forget about the original amount, and just think of the $1,030 in your account at the end of year 1 as a new investment. If you get $30 in interest over the next year, what percentage did you actually get? Show work, please.

$I = Prt \implies \$30 = \$1,030\, r(1)$

$r = \dfrac{30}{1,030} = 0.02913$

> This closing material presents an important introduction to the idea of compound interest.

*You actually got about 2.9%, not 3%.*

7. If you'd actually been paid the full 3% on your $1,030 in the second year, how much more interest would you have earned? Again, show work!

*3% of $1,030 = 0.03 × $1,030 = $30.90; you'd earn 90 cents more.*

8. Following up on Question 7: How much interest would you earn in the third year if you get 3% on the new amount again?

*New amount after year 2 is $1,060.90.*

*3% of $1,060.90 = 0.03 × $1,060.90 = $31.83*

We'll take up this discussion in the next lesson. For now, refer back to these questions when answering the first question in the Looking Ahead section of the Portfolio.

## 2-3 Portfolio

Name _____

Check each box when you've completed the task. Remember that your instructor will want you to turn in the portfolio pages you create.

### Technology

1. ☐ A quick glance at the table you filled out in Question 3 at the beginning of this lesson should be enough to convince you that spreadsheets are particularly well-suited to interest calculations. First, recreate that table using a spreadsheet. Of course, the point is to use formulas to do the calculations, not just key in the results. Then use the "copy down" feature to calculate the future value of the account and the total interest earned for years 11 through 30. A template to help you get started is included in the online resources for this lesson.

   Next, suppose that your goal was for the future value of the investment to be $1,000 after 10 years. Use trial and error, changing the amounts in cells A2 and B2, to find (1) how much more you'd need to invest up front, and (2) what interest rate you'd need to earn to achieve that goal if you keep the original investment at $600.

### Online Practice

1. ☐ Include any written work from the online assignment along with any notes or questions about this lesson's content.

### Applications

1. ☐ Complete the applications problems.

### Reflections

Type a short answer to each question.
1. ☐ Why is it reasonable that a bank would pay interest on savings, or charge interest on a loan?
2. ☐ What is the key feature of simple interest?
3. ☐ Why is it important to understand the concept of interest?
4. ☐ Take another look at your answer to Question 0 at the beginning of this lesson. Would you change your answer now that you've completed the lesson? How would you summarize the topic of this lesson now?
5. ☐ What questions do you have about this lesson?

### Looking Ahead

1. ☐ Look back at Page 90. Write a brief description of why simple interest is somewhat unfair when applied to a savings account.
2. ☐ Complete the Lesson 2-4 Prep Skills and read the opening paragraph in Lesson 2-4 carefully, then answer Question 0 in preparation for that lesson.

### Answers to "Did You Get It?"

1. $134.30  2. $4,464  3. $11, $611  4. $975, $5,975, $165.97  5. 5%
6. 5 years; $15

## 2-3  Applications

Name _____

Some of the most common (and most dangerous) examples of simple interest are short-term payday loans, which some lenders also call "cash advances." (This is not to be confused with a cash advance on a credit card.) Let's say that you're going to get paid in 10 days, and you need some cash for a car repair now. A payday lender might lend you $350 now, and you'll be asked to pay them back when your paycheck comes. Of course, you'll have to pay interest. The median fee charged by these types of lenders is $15 per every $100 borrowed.

1.  How much would you have to pay back in 10 days?

    Fee:  $15 + $15 + $15 + $7.50 = $52.50

    Amount paid back: $402.50

2.  What is the percent interest you're charged?

    $\dfrac{\$52.50}{350} = 0.15$:  15% interest

    > It will be interesting here to see how many students recognize that they can simply do 15/100 to get the percentage interest. Not many would be my guess. But the really clever ones will.

3.  What portion of a year is the 10-day period for this loan? Write your answer as both a fraction, and a decimal.

    $\dfrac{10}{365} \approx 0.027397$ year

4.  As you know, one month is 1/12 of a year. If you paid 2% simple interest in one month on a loan, what percentage would you pay in a full year?

    24%, which of course is 2% times 12.

5.  In order to find the annual interest rate, you'll need to find the rate as a percent per year. Use your answers from Questions 2 and 3 to find the annual interest rate for this loan. Discuss how good or bad of a deal you're getting as the borrower. You can use your calculation from Question 4 as a guide.

    $\dfrac{15\%}{0.027397 \text{ year}} = 547.5\%$ per year

    This is a TERRIBLE deal for the borrower—about as bad as it gets without risking having your thumbs broken by a loan shark.

## 2-3 Applications

Name _____

Another example of simple interest is a certificate of deposit, or CD as they're more commonly known. This is an investment where you agree to leave your deposit untouched for a fixed amount of time, and in exchange you are guaranteed a certain percentage interest. Below are some CD rates listed in December of 2015 on Bankrate.com for CDs with a 1-year term.

6. For a $2,000 investment, how much more would you earn if you chose Synchrony over CIT?

Synchrony: $I = \$2,000(0.0125)(1) = \$25$

CIT: $I = \$2,000(0.0122)(1) = \$24.40$

Synchrony pays a big 60 cents more.

| 1 yr CD | | | |
|---|---|---|---|
| **Institution** | **APY** | **Rate** | **Min Deposit** |
| SYNCHRONY Bank   MEMBER FDIC | 1.25% Wed Dec 9 | 1.24% | $2,000 |
| ★★★★★ | | | |
| Great Rates + Safety = Peace of Mind | | | |
| CIT Bank   Member FDIC | 1.22% Wed Dec 9 | 1.21% | $1,000 |
| ★★★★★ | | | |
| Great rates, low minimum deposits, Member FDIC. | | | |
| My e-BAnC   BAC Florida Bank Member FDIC | 1.25% Wed Dec 9 | 1.24% | $1,500 |
| ★★★★★ | | | |
| Make sure to check our Jumbo Rates | | | |

7. If your goal was to earn $40 in interest on that $2,000 investment, what interest rate would you need to find?

$I = Prt \Rightarrow \$40 = \$2,000\, r(1)$

$r = \dfrac{40}{2,000} = 0.02$: 2% interest would be required.

8. If you got the same rate that Synchrony is offering for a longer length of time, how long would you need to invest to get that $40 interest you were shooting for?

$I = Prt \Rightarrow \$40 = \$2,000(0.0125)t$

$t = \dfrac{40}{2,000(0.0125)} = 1.6$: 1.6 years would be required, or a little more than a year and seven months.

9. As you can see, CDs don't return a ton of interest. What they DO offer is a guaranteed return. Suppose that you also had the opportunity to invest that $2,000 in a business venture that promised a 12.5% return in 1 year, unless the company failed to turn a profit, in which case you would get nothing at all back. Calculate the amount of interest you'd get, and discuss whether you'd prefer the risky investment over the CD.

$I = \$2,000(0.125)(1) = \$250$

Answer to risk vs. reward question, of course, will vary.

# Lesson 2-4　Prep Skills

This is a short review of skills that will come in handy in the next lesson. In each case, answer the question, then rate your confidence level by checking one of the boxes. If you feel like you're struggling with these skills, consult the online resources provided by your instructor for extra practice.

### SKILL 1: WRITE PERCENTAGES IN DECIMAL FORM

1. Write each percent in decimal form.

   47%

   9.4%

### SKILL 2: COMPUTE SIMPLE INTEREST

2. If you borrow $1,200 for furniture at 11% simple interest for two years, how much will you pay in interest?

### SKILL 3: INTERPRETING EXPONENTS AS REPEATED MULTIPLICATION

3. Write the expression below in a shorter form using an exponent:

   $500(1 + 0.03)(1 + 0.03)(1 + 0.03)(1 + 0.03)$

### SKILL 4: PERFORM CALCULATIONS INVOLVING ORDER OF OPERATIONS

4. Perform each calculation:

   $12[8 + 4(13)]$

   $$400\left(1 + \frac{0.05}{12}\right)^{60}$$

### SKILL 5: SUBSTITUTE INTO AN EXPRESSION

5. For the expression $a(1 + b)^c$, find the value when $a = 20$, $b = 0.09$, and $c = 6$.

# Lesson 2-4    **Like a Snowball Rolling Downhill**    (Compound Interest)

**LEARNING OBJECTIVES**

☐ 1. Describe how compound interest differs from simple interest.

☐ 2. Develop compound interest formulas.

☐ 3. Use compound interest formulas to analyze financial issues.

*My wealth has come from a combination of living in America, some lucky genes, and compound interest.*
                    —Warren Buffett

© McGraw-Hill Education

If you've ever made a snowman, you're familiar with how it starts. You make a little snowball in your hands, then plop it down and start rolling it through the snow. As you do, it picks up more snow on all sides (if you roll it well) and gets bigger. At first, not that much snow is picked up because the original ball is little. But as it gets bigger, it has more surface area to pick up more snow, and it starts to grow very quickly—to the point that before you know it, you need help pushing it to gather more snow. Push that baby down a steep hill, and you could end up with one massive snowball (and maybe a spanking or a lawsuit if something valuable gets in the way). At the very end of the last lesson, we looked into interest being calculated not just on the principal amount, but on interest that had previously been paid as well. As we'll see in this lesson, given enough time this can become the financial equivalent of a snowball rolling downhill, leading to a wonderful place we call "financial independence."

**0.** After reading the opening paragraph, what do you think the main topic of this lesson will be?

## 2-4    Group

We've already studied how an investment can grow when simple interest is calculated; the table below is borrowed from Lesson 2-3. (Borrowed … stolen … whatever.) In this case, a principal amount of $600 was invested at 5% interest.

Our first goal in this lesson is to recalculate the interest earned and value of the account, this time calculating the next year's interest on the entire value of the account (including previously earned interest), rather than just on the principal amount.

| Time | Total Simple Interest Earned | Value of Account |
|---|---|---|
| Start | – | $600 |
| After 1 year | $30 | $630 |
| After 2 years | $60 | $660 |
| After 3 years | $90 | $690 |
| After 4 years | $120 | $720 |

1. Compute the amount of interest earned during the second year if that amount is 5% of both the principal amount of $600 AND the $30 in interest that was already earned in the first year. Find the new ending value as well. Show work, please.

   5% of $630 is $31.50. The new amount is $630 + $31.50 = $661.50.

2. We know from Lesson 2-3 that we can compute the amount of interest earned in 1 year using the formula $I = Pr$. This is using $t = 1$ in the interest formula $I = Prt$. Use this formula with $P = \$630$ to show that you get the same answer you did in Question 1.

   $I = \$630(0.05) = \$31.50$. This matches the amount of interest found in Question 1.

3. Use your answer from Question 1 to fill in the row of the table corresponding to "After 1 year." Then repeat your calculations to fill in the remainder of the table, keeping in mind that in each case interest should be calculated on the *new amount at the beginning of the year.*

| Time | Total Interest Earned | Value of Account |
|---|---|---|
| Start | – | $600 |
| After 1 year | $30 | $630 |
| After 2 years | $61.50 | $661.50 |
| After 3 years | $94.58 | $694.58 |
| After 4 years | $129.30 | $729.30 |

If all went well, you should have found that at the end of 4 years, the account would have $9.30 more when interest is calculated on the new yearly amount, rather than the original principal. This type of interest is called **compound interest,** and each time the new amount is calculated (in this case, at the end of each year), we say that interest has been **compounded** at that time. Since interest is being compounded once per year in this example, we say that it is interest **compounded annually.**

You're probably not overly impressed by that extra nine bucks, but when we develop some formulas for efficiently computing compound interest, we'll be able to see that something VERY interesting happens in the long run. So let's get to work on developing a formula by looking for a pattern.

Value after 1 year $= 600(1 + 0.05)$

Value after 2 years $=$ Value after 1 year$(1 + 0.05) = \underbrace{[600(1 + 0.05)]}_{\text{Value after 1 year}}(1 + 0.05) = 600(1 + 0.05)^2$

4. Now fill in the boxes in the computation to find the value after 3 years:

Value after 3 years $=$ Value after 2 years$(1 + 0.05) = \underbrace{\boxed{600(1 + 0.05)^2}}_{\text{Value after 2 years}}(1 + 0.05) = 600(1 + 0.05)^{\boxed{3}}$

Now here comes the key observation of this lesson, so fasten your seat belts. So far, we know the following:

Value after 1 year $= 600(1 + 0.05)$

Value after 2 years $= 600(1 + 0.05)^2$

Value after 3 years $= 600(1 + 0.05)^3$

5. Make a conjecture as to the value after 4 years and 5 years, and write the type of reasoning you're using here.

Value after 4 years $= \underline{600(1 + 0.05)^4}$    *This is classic inductive reasoning.*

Value after 5 years $= \underline{600(1 + 0.05)^5}$

6. Make a conjecture as to the value after $t$ years, where $t$ represents any number of years:

Value after $t$ years $= \underline{600(1 + 0.05)^t}$

Congratulations! Your conjecture (you did get it, right?) can be formalized into our first important formula for compound interest.

## Formula for Compound Interest Compounded Annually

$$A = P(1 + r)^t$$

where

      $A$ is the future value.

      $P$ is the principal amount.

      $r$ is the interest rate in decimal form.

      $t$ is the term of the investment in years.

7. Use the formula for interest compounded annually to find the future value of the original $600 investment at 5% interest after 10, 20, 30, and 50 years. Then use the simple interest formula from Lesson 2-3 to find the future value if the interest is simple.

| Time | Future Value, Compounded Annually | Future Value, Simple Interest |
|------|-----------------------------------|-------------------------------|
| After 10 years | $977.34 | $900 |
| After 20 years | $1,591.98 | $1,200 |
| After 30 years | $2,593.17 | $1,500 |
| After 40 years | $4,223.99 | $1,800 |

8. Use the table to draw a graph of the future value for both accounts, then write a verbal description of what you learned from the table and the graph. Make sure you choose an appropriate scale for each axis, and of course label that scale on your graph. Do something to distinguish the two graphs: use different colors, or make one dashed or thicker. What kind of growth does each account illustrate?

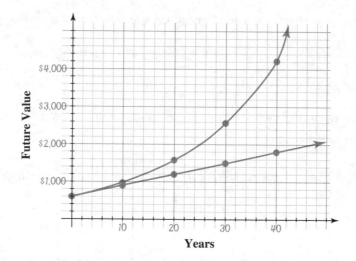

With simple interest, the graph is a line, meaning the growth is linear. With compound interest, the graph starts off growing gradually, but then starts to curve dramatically upward. This is typical of exponential growth.

If students haven't studied linear and exponential growth in a prerequisite course, they'll need some help here. We'll study these types of growth in Unit 5.

### Did You Get It

Try this problem to see if you understand the concepts we just studied. The answer can be found at the bottom of the portfolio page.

1. For an investment of $100,000 at 6% interest for 4 years, find (a) the simple interest, and (b) the compound interest if interest is calculated once per year.

## 2-4  Class

Based on what we've learned so far, if you're the one getting paid interest, compound interest is a MUCH better deal for you than simple interest. But what if you plan to invest your money for less than a year? You'd end up getting a whole lot of nothing, since the interest is compounded for the first time at the end of the first year. This would provide a competitive disadvantage for a banker, as wise investors would prefer more flexibility. At some point, bankers decided that compounding interest more often would make them more attractive to potential customers.

So let's say that interest is being compounded four times per year (or **quarterly**). Going back to our investment of $600 at 5% interest, the banker would not add 5% to the account 4 times per year—this would correspond to a far higher rate than the 5% they promised. Instead, they'd divide that rate by 4, and pay 1.25% every 3 months. The first calculation, after 3 months, would look like this:

$$A = 600\left(1 + \frac{0.05}{4}\right)$$

1. After 6 months, write a calculation that describes the future value, using the same idea from the Group portion of the lesson. Remember that interest is being calculated four times per year.

$$A = 600\left(1 + \frac{0.05}{4}\right)^2$$

2. By the time the first year is up, the interest would have been calculated ___4___ times, so the total exponent on the parentheses in our future value calculation will be ___4___, which is the number of times per year that interest has been compounded times the number of years that have passed.

3. If interest is compounded monthly, after 5 years it would be compounded ___60___ times.

4. If interest is compounded $n$ times per year, after $t$ years it would be compounded ___$nt$___ times.

5. Now adapt your answer from Question 1 into a formula for calculating the future value of that $600 investment at 5% interest if interest is compounded $n$ times per year for $t$ years. Remember that the interest rate needs to be divided into $n$ equal portions.

$$A = 600\left(1 + \frac{0.05}{n}\right)^{nt}$$

And that, friends, is how you develop a formula for interest compounded a certain number of times per year. Nicely done.

 ### General Formula for Compound Interest

$$A = P\left(1 + \frac{r}{n}\right)^{nt}$$

where

 $A$ is the future value.
 $P$ is the principal amount.
 $r$ is the interest rate in decimal form.
 $t$ is the term of the investment in years.
 $n$ is the number of times that interest is compounded per year.

6. Use the compound interest formula to calculate the future value of our $600 invested at 5% interest compounded quarterly for 10 years, then compare to the future value you calculated in Question 6 of the Group portion using interest compounded annually. Which results in more interest?

$P = \$600, r = 0.05, n = 4, t = 10$

$$A = 600\left(1 + \frac{0.05}{4}\right)^{40} \approx \$986.17$$

*This is almost $9 more in interest than when interest was compounded annually.*

## Math Note

Important note: This general formula makes the earlier formula for interest compounded annually obsolete. (You can just use this formula with $n = 1$.) *Don't think of it as two formulas.*

7. Repeat Question 6, this time using interest **compounded monthly** (12 times per year) and interest **compounded daily** (365 times per year). In each case, find the amount of interest that was earned (not just the future value).

Monthly:  $P = \$600, r = 0.05, n = 12, t = 10$

$$A = 600 \left( 1 + \frac{0.05}{12} \right)^{120} \approx \$988.21 \quad \text{Interest: } \$388.21$$

Daily:  $P = \$600, r = 0.05, n = 365, t = 10$

$$A = 600 \left( 1 + \frac{0.05}{365} \right)^{3,650} \approx \$989.20 \quad \text{Interest: } \$389.20$$

> Help students with Question 8. Thinking about that one will really help foster an understanding of the magic of compound interest.

8. Draw a general conclusion about what happens to the amount of interest as the number of times compounding yearly goes up. Then (and this question really requires some thought) see if you can come up with a reason why this makes perfect sense. A true understanding of the difference between simple and compound interest will really help.

In general, as the number of times compounded goes up, so does the future value. This actually makes sense for the same reason that compound interest in general leads to more interest than simple interest: Every time that interest is compounded, it's getting a percentage of the interest that has been previously added to the account. So the more often that happens, the greater the amount of interest should be.

## Did You Get It

Try this problem to see if you understand the concepts we just studied. The answer can be found at the bottom of the portfolio page.

2. Find the interest on an investment of $75,000 that pays 4.5% compounded weekly for 8 years.

## Effective Interest Rate

We've now seen that the number of times interest is compounded per year has an effect on how much interest is actually earned. It's not a *huge* effect, mind you, but is at least worth studying. The bottom line is that when interest is compounded more than one time per year, the actual percentage earned is a bit higher than the stated interest rate. That's good if you're the lender, not so good if you're the borrower. In any case, there's a formula that can be used to measure this effect. First, the terminology.

The **effective rate** (also known as the **annual yield**) is the simple interest rate that would yield the same future value over 1 year as the given compound interest rate. The compound interest rate is sometimes known as the **nominal rate**.

Now, the formula.

### Formula for Effective Interest Rate

$$E = \left(1 + \frac{r}{n}\right)^n - 1$$

where

$E$ is the effective rate.
$n$ is the number of times that interest is compounded per year.
$r$ is the nominal interest rate.

9. A loan has a nominal interest rate of 4%, and the interest is compounded weekly. Without doing any calculations, would you expect the effective interest rate to be higher or lower than 4%? Explain.

   Higher. We know that compound interest leads to more interest than simple, so to get the same return with simple interest, which is what the effective interest rate measures, you'd need a higher rate.

10. Refer to Question 9. Calculate the effective interest rate.

$$E = \left(1 + \frac{0.04}{52}\right)^{52} - 1 = 0.04079477$$

The effective rate is 4.079477%.

11. Find the future value after 1 year for an investment of $10,000 at 4% compounded weekly.

$$A = \$10,000\left(1 + \frac{0.04}{52}\right)^{52(1)} = \$10,407.95$$

12. Divide your answer to Question 11 by 10,000. What do you notice?

$$\frac{\$10,407.95}{\$10,000} = 1.040795$$

*The decimal part of the result is the effective interest rate.*

13. Comparing investments is a very important part of any financial strategy. Which savings account is a better investment: 6.2% compounded daily or 6.25% compounded semiannually? There are different ways you could approach this, so make sure you show all work and explain how you made your decision.

*Students may want to pick a principal amount and calculate the actual return, which is fine. But the simplest thing to do is simply compute the effective interest rate for each. As we can see below, the 6.2% compounded daily has a higher effective interest rate.*

$$E = \left( 1 + \frac{0.062}{365} \right)^{365} - 1 \approx 0.06396$$

$$E = \left( 1 + \frac{0.0625}{2} \right)^{2} - 1 \approx 0.06348$$

### Did You Get It

Try this problem to see if you understand the concepts we just studied. The answer can be found at the bottom of the portfolio page.

3. Which is a better investment, 3% compounded monthly or 3.25% compounded semiannually?

The remainder of this lesson can be considered optional if you don't want to cover interest compounded continuously. If you do choose to cover it, students will need some help with the algebra on the next two pages. You can choose to sort of gloss over that part and just focus on what the compound interest formula becomes when *n* approaches infinity. In that case, you'll need to define *e* for the class.

## Interest Compounded Continuously

The goal of the remainder of this lesson is to see if we can figure out what happens to the compound interest formula when the number of times that interest is compounded per year gets really, really large. Large to the point that in essence, interest is being compounded every instant of every day. Wow.

As you know, the compound interest formula is $A = P\left(1 + \frac{r}{n}\right)^{nt}$, where $n$ is the number of times per year that interest is compounded.

14. To rewrite this formula in a form that makes it easier to decide what happens when $n$ gets really big, we're going to introduce a new variable $u$, which will be defined by $u = \frac{n}{r}$. First, solve this equation to find a new name for $n$.

    $n = ur$

15. Now replace $n$ in the compound interest formula with the new name for $n$ that you found in Question 14 and simplify to show that the formula becomes $A = P\left(1 + \frac{1}{u}\right)^{urt}$.

    $A = P\left(1 + \frac{r}{ur}\right)^{urt} = P\left(1 + \frac{1}{u}\right)^{urt}$

16. Explain why this can be rewritten as $A = P\left[\left(1 + \frac{1}{u}\right)^{u}\right]^{rt}$.

    This is just a standard property of exponents. It's easiest to see if you look at it backward. In the ending form, we are raising an expression with an exponent to a further power. To do this, you multiply the exponents, so you get a single exponent of u r t.

17. Remember that $u = \frac{n}{r}$. What happens to this fraction when $n$ gets really big? Remember that $r$ is the interest rate, and it can't change.

    Since n is in the numerator of the fraction, when n gets really big the entire fraction does as well. In fact, since the number we're dividing by (the interest rate in decimal form) is always less than 1, then u is always BIGGER than n. So as n gets bigger and bigger, u gets bigger still.

Here's a summary of what we learned on the last page: The compound interest formula can be rewritten in the form below, and as we make the number of times that interest is compounded per year get larger and larger, the variable $u$ in that expression gets larger and larger as well. So next we'll study what happens to the expression inside the brackets when $u$ gets larger and larger, and we'll find that we can find a MUCH simpler form for this formula.

$$A = P\left[\left(1 + \frac{1}{u}\right)^u\right]^{rt}$$

What happens to this expression when $u$ gets larger and larger?

18. Using a calculator, fill in the table below. Round to three decimal places. What can you conclude about what happens to the value of $\left(1 + \frac{1}{u}\right)^u$ as the number of compounding periods tends to infinity? ("Tends to infinity" is the phrase we use to describe a variable getting larger and larger without bound.)

| $u$ | 50 | 100 | 500 | 1,000 | 1,500 | 2,000 | 2,500 |
|---|---|---|---|---|---|---|---|
| $\left(1 + \frac{1}{u}\right)^u$ | 2.692 | 2.705 | 2.716 | 2.717 | 2.717 | 2.718 | 2.718 |

19. The number that you should have found in Question 18 is about 2.718, and is denoted $e$. (Actually, $e$ is irrational, so its decimal equivalent neither terminates nor repeats: $e \approx 2.718\ldots$) What is the result of the compound interest formula above when the number of times interest is compounded gets larger and larger? In this case, we say that interest is **compounded continuously.** You can think of this as the interest being compounded every instant of every day.

$A = P\left[e\right]^{rt}$ or, more simply $A = Pe^{rt}$

## Using Technology: Evaluating Expressions Containing e

To evaluate $e^3$:

Standard Graphing Calculator:  [2nd] [LN] [3] [ENTER]

Standard Scientific Calculator: [3] [2nd] [LN]

Spreadsheet: = EXP(3)

20. Use the formula you wrote in Question 19 to find the future value after 20 years of a $5,000 account that earns 4% interest compounded continuously, then compare that to the future value of the same account if interest is compounded annually.

$$A = Pe^{rt} = \$5,000 \, e^{0.04(20)} = \$11,127.70$$

$$A = P\left(1+\frac{r}{n}\right)^{nt} = \$5,000\left(1+\frac{0.04}{1}\right)^{20} = \$10,955.62$$

21. Finally, let's compare interest compounded continuously to simple interest. Suppose that $50,000 is invested in two accounts: one earns 6% simple interest, the other earns 6% compounded continuously. Fill in the table with the future value of each account after each term, rounded to the nearest dollar. Wouldn't this be a GREAT spot to use a spread-sheet, or at least the table feature on a graphing calculator?

| Years | 5 | 10 | 15 | 20 | 25 | 30 |
|---|---|---|---|---|---|---|
| 6% simple interest | $65,000 | $80,000 | $95,000 | $110,000 | $125,000 | $140,000 |
| 6% compounded continuously | $67,492 | $91,106 | $122,980 | $166,006 | $224,084 | $302,482 |

### Did You Get It

Try this problem to see if you understand the concepts we just studied. The answer can be found at the bottom of the portfolio page.

4. Find the future value of a $40,000 investment with 6.9% interest compounded continuously 25 years after it's started.

## 2-4 Portfolio

Name _____

Check each box when you've completed the task. Remember that your instructor will want you to turn in the portfolio pages you create.

### Technology

1. ☐ After completing this lesson, you should be aware of the fact that the formulas involved are a little complicated, so you have to be really careful when doing the computations. Wouldn't it be nice if there were some sort of machine for doing computations? Wait, what? That's what the word "computer" means? Cool. In any situation where repeated calculations may be done, programming a spreadsheet to do them is likely to be helpful. So your task is to build a compound interest calculator, setting it up like the sample below. Obviously, you should use a formula to calculate future value. Then choose an amount you'd like to invest, an interest rate, and a time period, then use your spreadsheet to find the future value for interest compounded annually, quarterly, monthly, weekly, daily, and hourly. A template to help you get started can be found in the online resources for this lesson.

|   | A | B | C | D | E |
|---|---|---|---|---|---|
| 1 | Principal | Interest rate | Number of times compounded per year | Term (Yrs) | Future Value |
| 2 | $600.00 | 0.04 | 1 | 10 | $888.15 |
| 3 | $600.00 | 0.04 | 12 | 10 | $894.50 |
| 4 | $600.00 | 0.04 | 52 | 10 | $894.96 |

### Online Practice

1. ☐ Include any written work from the online assignment along with any notes or questions about this lesson's content.

### Applications

1. ☐ Complete the applications problems.

### Reflections

Type a short answer to each question.

1. ☐ Explain the difference between simple and compound interest.
2. ☐ Why is compound interest a much better deal for you if you're the investor?
3. ☐ What does the term "compounding" refer to?
4. ☐ Take another look at your answer to Question 0 at the beginning of this lesson. Would you change your answer now that you've completed the lesson? How would you summarize the topic of this lesson now?
5. ☐ What questions do you have about this lesson?

### Looking Ahead

1. ☐ Complete the Lesson 2-5 Prep Skills and read the opening paragraph in Lesson 2-5 carefully, then answer Question 0 in preparation for that lesson.

### Answers to "Did You Get It?"

**1. a.** $24,000;   **b.** $26,247.70   **2.** $32,482.97   **3.** 3.25% semiannually   **4.** $224,500.84

## 2-4  Applications

Name _____

Over the last two lessons, we've studied many aspects of interest. The goal of this assignment will be to compare various investments and decide which would be most beneficial. Of course, the amount of money that anyone chooses to invest at any given time is very personal and depends on too many factors to consider in a few lines of text. So we'll pick an amount and go with it, but if you'd prefer to work this assignment with a different amount, check with your instructor to see if that's okay.

Example: An investor has $12,000 to invest and is willing to keep it invested for up to 5 years. Each of the options below is available. Find the future value of the investment and the effective rate in each case. When you've completed all of them, write a short essay explaining which you think would be the best choice for you. Consider as many factors as you can.

1. A 1-year certificate of deposit that pays 2.1% simple interest

   $A = P(1 + rt) = \$12,000(1 + 0.021) = \$12,252$

   With simple interest, the effective rate is the same as the nominal rate.

2. A 5-year certificate of deposit that pays 2.9% interest compounded annually

   $A = P\left(1 + \dfrac{r}{n}\right)^{nt} = \$12,000\left(1 + \dfrac{0.029}{1}\right)^{5} = \$13,843.89$

   $E = \left(1 + \dfrac{r}{n}\right)^{n} - 1 = \left(1 + \dfrac{0.029}{1}\right)^{1} - 1 = 0.029$

3. You lend the money to a friend who's starting a business, and she writes a contract guaranteeing you a 12% return on your investment, to be paid in full at the end of 4 years, with an option to reinvest if the company is successful.

   12% of $12,000 = 0.12 × \$12,000 = \$1,440$

   Future value = $13,440

   This is simple interest, so the effective rate is 3% per year.

4. A savings account offers 1.98% interest compounded continuously. You can remove the money any time you like, but plan to keep it in the investment for 5 years. (For interest compounded continuously, the effective rate formula is $E = e^{r} - 1$.)

   $A = Pe^{rt} = \$12,000 \, e^{0.0198(5)} = \$13,248.80$

   $E = e^{0.0198} - 1 \approx 0.019997$

## 2-4   Applications

Name _____

5. A savings account that offers 2.18% compounded monthly: you can remove the money any time you like, but plan to keep it in the investment for 5 years.

$$A = P\left(1 + \frac{r}{n}\right)^{nt} = \$12{,}000\left(1 + \frac{0.0218}{12}\right)^{12(5)} = \$13{,}380.62$$

$$E = \left(1 + \frac{0.0218}{12}\right)^{12} - 1 \approx 0.022$$

6. A rival bank to the one in Question 5 offers the same interest rate, but they compound hourly. The plan is also to keep the money invested for 5 years.

$$A = P\left(1 + \frac{r}{n}\right)^{nt} = \$12{,}000\left(1 + \frac{0.0218}{365 \cdot 24}\right)^{365 \cdot 24 \cdot 5} = \$13{,}381.95$$

$$E = \left(1 + \frac{0.0218}{365 \cdot 24}\right)^{365 \cdot 24} - 1 \approx 0.022$$

7. So how would you invest the money? Obviously, you have to discuss you reasoning. Think about the fact that when investing, there are other potential concerns than simply the total amount at the end of the investment.

*Hopefully, answers will vary!*

# Lesson 2-5    Prep Skills

This is a short review of skills that will come in handy in the next lesson. In each case, answer the question, then rate your confidence level by checking one of the boxes. If you feel like you're struggling with these skills, consult the online resources provided by your instructor for extra practice.

I KNOW IT    THINK SO    UNSURE    NO IDEA

### SKILL 1: WRITE PERCENTAGES IN DECIMAL FORM

1. Write each percent in decimal form.

   91%

   6.48%

### SKILL 2: CALCULATE A PERCENTAGE OF A WHOLE

2. What is 1.8% of $11,375?

### SKILL 3: COMPUTE SIMPLE INTEREST

3. Suppose you borrowed $450 to buy an iPhone. If the interest is 14.7% simple interest for 2 years, how much would you have to pay back?

### SKILL 4: USE INFORMATION FROM A TABLE

4. The table below shows the number of violent crimes committed per 100,000 citizens in various cities during 2014. Given the fact that there were about 438,500 people in Omaha in 2014, how many violent crimes were committed there?

| City | Violent crimes per 100,000 citizens |
|---|---|
| Detroit | 1,989 |
| Columbus | 549 |
| Miami | 1,060 |
| Omaha | 561 |
| San Francisco | 795 |

# Lesson 2-5 **Buying Stuff Without Money** (Installment Buying)

## LEARNING OBJECTIVES

☐ **1.** Compute payments and charges associated with installment loans.

☐ **2.** Identify the true cost of a loan by computing APR.

☐ **3.** Evaluate the costs of buying items on credit.

*Never assume that all is well when it comes to your savings or loans. Get a printout to ensure you know exactly what is happening.*
　　　　　　　　　—Tagene Brown-McBean

© SW Productions/Getty Images RF

A lot of people celebrate their college graduation by getting a new car. Unless you're very wealthy, you won't be plunking down a stack of crisp hundred dollar bills to make that happen—you'll need to get a loan. In this case, you'll be doing what is called **installment buying.** This is when an item is purchased and the buyer pays for it by making periodic partial payments, or installments.

There are natural advantages and disadvantages to installment buying. The most obvious advantage is that it allows you to buy an item that you don't have enough money to pay for, and use it while you're raising that money. The most obvious disadvantage is that you pay interest on the amount borrowed, so you end up paying more for the item—in some cases a lot more. When you buy a car, for example, you know the price of the car, and you're usually told how much the monthly payment will be. If you're buying a car for $12,260 with a $3,000 down payment and are told the payment will be $231.50 per month for 48 months, how much will you actually end up paying for that car? Work through this lesson, and soon you will know.

　**0.** After reading the opening paragraphs, what do you think the main topic of this lesson will be?

## 2-5 | Group

### Fixed Installment Loans

A **fixed installment loan** is a loan that is repaid in equal payments. Sometimes the buyer will pay part of the cost at the time of purchase. This is known as a **down payment.** Here are some other key terms used to describe installment loans.

---

The **amount financed** is the amount a borrower will pay interest on.

　Amount financed = Price of item − Down payment

The **total installment price** is the total amount of money the buyer will ultimately pay.

　Total installment price = Sum of all payments + Down payment

The **finance charge** is the interest charged for borrowing the amount financed.

　Finance charge = Total installment price − Price of item

Now let's take a look at the problem posed in this lesson's opening paragraph. The pertinent information is this:

**Cost of car:** $12,260
**Down payment:** $3,000
**Monthly payment:** $231.50
**Term of loan:** 48 months

> **Math Note**
>
> You're often given quite a bit of information in a problem about finances. Identifying and writing out that information in an organized way, like we did here, is ALWAYS a good idea.

1. What was the amount financed? Refer to the definitions on the previous page if you need to.

   *Cost of car − Down payment = $12,260 − $3,000 = $9,260*

2. What's the total amount of all monthly payments?

   *48 × $231.50 = $11,112*

3. What's the total installment price? (This is the answer to the question "How much money will you actually end up paying for the car?")

   *$11,112 + $3,000 = $14,112*

4. Find the finance charge, then describe what that amount really represents.

   *$14,112 − $12,260 = $1,852*

   *This is the amount of interest paid over the life of the loan.*

## Did You Get It

Try this problem to see if you understand the concepts we just studied. The answer can be found at the bottom of the portfolio page.

1. If you buy a used car for $8,200 with a down payment of $1,000 and 36 monthly payments of $270, find the amount financed, the total installment price, and the finance charge.

In some cases, it's a good idea to be able to calculate a monthly payment before making a purchase. Not only can this help you to decide whether or not you can afford an item, it gives you a way to make sure you're not getting cheated when you're quoted a monthly payment. So how can you find the monthly payment for a loan? Using a formula, of course. (Although to be fair, there are many loan calculators online.)

## Calculating Monthly Payments on a Fixed Installment Loan

A monthly payment M can be calculated using the formula

$$M = \frac{P \cdot \frac{r}{12}}{1 - \left(1 + \frac{r}{12}\right)^{-n}}$$

where

P is the principal value of the loan.
r is the annual percentage rate (APR) in decimal form.
n is the total number of payments.

Memorize this formula, and then eat it. Hold on, we're just kidding—obviously the formula is pretty complicated. You'll need to be especially careful when performing calculations involving this formula. An important note: if you do the calculation in stages, which we don't necessarily recommend, make sure that you don't round too much. That can change the calculation considerably. A reasonable rule of thumb is at least four decimal places.

In order to calculate the monthly payment on an auto loan, we need to know the annual percentage rate, or APR. As we'll see shortly, this isn't exactly the same as the quoted interest rate for a loan. If the APR isn't quoted to you immediately when you start to talk about buying a car, ask for it! Salesman are fond of steering the conversation toward monthly payments, but what determines how good (or bad) of a deal you're getting is the APR. You should always check local rates in advance of buying a car so you know what rate you should be getting.

5. Have you noticed that car makers never have sales? They're always "events." Weird. Anyhow, for the Ford 2015 holiday "event," they offered a 2015 Taurus with a special APR of 2.9% for 60 months. If one particular vehicle has a selling price of $27,295 and a buyer trades in an older car for a down payment of $4,500, calculate the monthly payment for this loan.

Principal value (P) = $27,295 − $4,500 = $22,795; r = 0.029, n = 60

$$M = \frac{\$22,795 \cdot \frac{0.029}{12}}{1 - \left(1 + \frac{0.029}{12}\right)^{-60}} = \$408.58$$

If students are using a graphing calculator that can handle the entire calculation, encourage them to do so to avoid rounding error. A demonstration of how much rounding can affect a stage-by-stage calculation can be helpful.

**6.** If the loan was based on simple interest, the future value would be $22,795(1 + 0.029 × 5). Calculate this amount, then divide by 60 to find the monthly payment. What do you think accounts for the fact that simple interest makes it HIGHER?

$22,795(1 + 0.029 · 5) = $26,100.28
$26,100.28/60 = $435.00

With the fixed installment loan, the interest being charged each month is only calculated on the remaining balance of the loan. The simple interest loan is calculating interest on the entire principal for all 5 years.

---

## Did You Get It

Try this problem to see if you understand the concepts we just studied. The answer can be found at the bottom of the portfolio page.

2. A graphic design pro buys a new iMac for $1,499 with a $200 down payment, and gets manufacture financing for 5 years at 12% APR. Find: (a) the amount financed; (b) the monthly payment; (c) the total installment price, and (d) the finance charge.

---

## Annual Percentage Rate

Many lenders add upfront fees to a loan and then spread them over the life of the loan. This has the effect of making the actual interest rate that a borrower pays higher than the quoted rate. Because this can get confusing, lenders are required by law to disclose an annual percentage rate, or APR, that reflects the true interest charged. This allows consumers to compare loans with different terms. The mathematical procedures for computing APR are extremely complicated, so tables have been compiled that help you to estimate APR for a loan. There is also a wide variety of APR calculators available online. A partial APR table is shown in the following table.

| Number of Payments | 6.0% | 6.5% | 7.0% | 7.5% | 8.0% | 8.5% | 9.0% | 9.5% | 10.0% | 10.5% | 11.0% | 11.5% | 12.0% |
|---|---|---|---|---|---|---|---|---|---|---|---|---|---|
| | (Finance charge per $100 of amount financed) | | | | | | | | | | | | |
| 6 | $1.76 | $1.90 | $2.05 | $2.20 | $2.35 | $2.49 | $2.64 | $2.79 | $2.94 | $3.08 | $3.23 | $3.38 | $3.53 |
| 12 | 3.28 | 3.56 | 3.83 | 4.11 | 4.39 | 4.66 | 4.94 | 5.22 | 5.50 | 5.78 | 6.06 | 6.34 | 6.62 |
| 18 | 4.82 | 5.22 | 5.63 | 6.04 | 6.45 | 6.86 | 7.28 | 7.69 | 8.10 | 8.52 | 8.93 | 9.35 | 9.77 |
| 24 | 6.37 | 6.91 | 7.45 | 8.00 | 8.54 | 9.09 | 9.64 | 10.19 | 10.75 | 11.30 | 11.86 | 12.42 | 12.98 |
| 30 | 7.94 | 8.61 | 9.30 | 9.98 | 10.66 | 11.35 | 12.04 | 12.74 | 13.43 | 14.13 | 14.83 | 15.54 | 16.24 |
| 36 | 9.52 | 10.34 | 11.16 | 11.98 | 12.81 | 13.64 | 14.48 | 15.32 | 16.16 | 17.01 | 17.86 | 18.71 | 19.57 |
| 48 | 12.73 | 13.83 | 14.94 | 16.06 | 17.18 | 18.31 | 19.45 | 20.59 | 21.74 | 22.90 | 24.06 | 25.23 | 26.40 |
| 60 | 16.00 | 17.40 | 18.81 | 20.23 | 21.66 | 23.10 | 24.55 | 26.01 | 27.48 | 28.96 | 30.45 | 31.96 | 33.47 |

**Annual Percentage Rate**

## Procedure For Computing APR

**Step 1.** Find the finance charge per $100 borrowed using the formula

$$\frac{\text{Finance charge}}{\text{Amount financed}} \times \$100$$

**Step 2.** Find the row in the table marked with the number of payments and move to the right until you find the amount closest to the number from step 1.

**Step 3.** The APR (to the nearest half percent) is at the top of the corresponding column.

7. Find the finance charge per $100 for the loan described in Questions 1 through 4 (step 1 in computing APR).

Finance charge = $1,852 (from Question 4), amount financed = $9,260

$$\frac{\$1,852}{\$9,260} \times \$100 = \$20$$

8. Look at the row in the table corresponding to 48 months, and find the two entries that are closest to your answer from Question 7. Then find the APR corresponding to each, and use the result to estimate the APR for that loan (steps 2 and 3 in computing APR). Describe how you got your estimate.

In the 48-month row, $20 is almost exactly halfway between the amount in the 9.0% column ($19.45) and the one in the 9.5% column ($20.59), so we can estimate that the APR is pretty close to halfway between 9.0% and 9.5%, which would be 9.25%.

> Discuss interpolating between values for situations where the exact amount isn't in the table.

One way to save money on a fixed installment loan is to pay it off early. This will allow a buyer to avoid paying the entire finance charge. The amount of the finance charge that is saved when a loan is paid off early is called **unearned interest.** One way to calculate unearned interest for a loan uses the APR table we've already been introduced to: this is called the **actuarial method.**

## The Actuarial Method For Computing Unearned Interest

Unearned interest can be calculated using the formula

$$u = \frac{kRh}{100 + h}$$

where

$u$ is the unearned interest.
$k$ is the number of payments remaining, excluding the current one.
$R$ is the monthly payment.
$h$ is the fnance charge per \$100 borrowed for a loan with the same APR and $k$ monthly payments.

As a reminder, here are the specifics of the loan we've been working with:

**Cost of car:** \$12,260
**Down payment:** \$3,000
**Monthly payment:** \$231.50
**Term of loan:** 48 months

9. When making your 36th payment, how many payments would remain?

*12 payments remain. Don't overthink it!*

10. If you decide to pay this loan off at thc time of the 36th payment, how much money would you save? (You'll need to do some work to find the value of $h$. Use the 12 Payments row of the APR table.)

*$k = 12$, $R = \$231.50$, $h = \$5.08$, which comes from the 12 payments row of the APR table; more specifically from splitting the difference between the amounts for 9.0% and 9.5%.*

$$u = \frac{12 \cdot 231.50 \cdot 5.08}{100 + 5.08} = \$134.30$$

**11.** In this situation, you would surely want to know how much it would cost to pay off the loan. The first step would be to find the total cost of all the remaining payments after the 36th. So do that.

12 × $231.50 = $2,778

**12.** Your answer to Question 11 is what the payoff would be if you weren't getting credit for unearned interest. But you are, so subtracting the unearned interest you found will give you the payoff amount.

$2,778 − $134.30 = $2,643.70

**13.** Discuss the pros and cons of paying off that particular loan early. If you were in that situation, do you think it would have been worthwhile for you to pay it off early?

Pros: No more monthly payment, save about $135 overall.
Cons: You have to cough up over $2,600 all at once, which for many people is worse than paying a little more over the course of a year.

## Did You Get It

Try this problem to see if you understand the concepts we just studied. The answer can be found at the bottom of the portfolio page.

3. A $16,500 truck loan is to be paid off in 48 monthly installments of $387.50. The borrower decides to pay off the loan on his 42nd payment. Find the amount of interest saved.

## 2-5    Class

So far, we've covered examples of closed-ended credit; this is credit with a fixed number of payments and a specific payoff date. We turn our attention now to **open-ended credit,** where there is no fixed number of payments or payoff date. By far the most common example of this is credit cards. Since more and more people use credit cards for convenience, an understanding of open-ended credit is more important than ever. One of the easiest ways to end up in a really bad place financially is to not understand how open-ended credit works.

### The Unpaid Balance Method

One way that banks calculate finance charges on a credit card is the unpaid balance method. In this case, interest is charged only on the balance left over from the previous month.

Suppose that you had an unpaid balance of $356.75 at the beginning of August and made purchases of $436.50. A payment of $200.00 was made during the month. The interest on the unpaid balance is 1.8% per month. Our goal will be to find the finance charge and the balance on September 1. (The billing cycle for credit cards and loans can begin and end on any day of the month; however, for the examples given in this lesson, we'll assume the cycle ends on the last day of the month.)

> **Math Note**
>
> As of July 2015, total credit card debt in the U.S. was over nine hundred BILLION dollars, or almost $7,500 for every household in the country.

1. Find the amount of interest that would be charged on the unpaid balance. Show your work!

   *1.8% of $356.75 = $6.42*

   > When studying credit cards, it's impossible to overstate how dangerous it can be to start carrying credit card balances.

2. Use your answer from Question 1 and the information about payments and purchases to find the new balance on the card. Show all work again!

   *Purchases + Interest = $436.50 + $6.42 = $442.92*
   *Payment = $200*
   *New balance = $356.75 + $442.92 − $200 = $599.67*

### Did You Get It

Try this problem to see if you understand the concepts we just studied. The answer can be found at the bottom of the portfolio page.

4. For the month of January, Christina has an unpaid balance of $846.50 from December. Purchases for the month were $532.86 and a payment of $350.00 was made during the month. If the interest on the unpaid balance is 2% per month, find the finance charge and the balance on February 1.

## The Average Daily Balance Method

Because a company that issues credit cards doesn't make as much money when users pay off the balance every month, they sometimes charge an annual fee for use of the card. Another way for them to make money from all users is to use the average daily balance method for computing the finance charge. In this method, the balance for each day of the month is used to compute an average daily balance, and interest is computed on that average. So in effect, consumers start paying interest on the day they make a purchase. Ouch!

Calculations using the average daily balance method can be done in a series of steps, as illustrated by the next set of questions. The credit card statement shown here displays more detail on the account we studied in Questions 1 and 2.

| | | |
|---|---|---|
| August 1 | Previous Balance | $356.75 |
| August 7 | Purchases | $59.95 |
| August 12 | Purchases | $223.75 |
| August 18 | Payment | $200.00 |
| August 24 | Purchases | $152.80 |

The goal is to find the average daily balance, the finance charge for the month, and the new balance on September 1. The interest rate is 1.8% per month on the average daily balance.

**Step 1: Find the balance on each day that a transaction occurred.**

3. Write the new balance next to each day listed below in the first blank. Ignore the second blank for now.

August 1    $356.75      6

August 7    $416.70      5

August 12    $640.45      6

August 18    $440.45      6

August 24    $593.25      8

**Step 2: Find the number of days for each balance.**

4. How many days was the balance $356.75? Using the same idea, fill in the second blank next to each balance above with the number of days that the balance was at that amount. (Make sure the total number of days adds up to 31 days, which is the number of days in August.)

**Step 3: Multiply each balance by the number of days, and add these products.**

5. Copy the first two columns in the table below from your answers on the previous page, then multiply to fill in the last column. Then add your results.

| Date | Balance | # of days | Balance × # of days |
|---|---|---|---|
| August 1 | $356.75 | 6 | $2,140.50 |
| August 7 | $416.70 | 5 | $2,083.50 |
| August 12 | $640.45 | 6 | $3,842.70 |
| August 18 | $440.45 | 6 | $2,642.70 |
| August 24 | $593.25 | 8 | $4,746.00 |
| | | Sum | $15,455.40 |

**Step 4: Divide by the total number of days to get the average daily balance for the month.**

6. Divide your sum from Question 5 by the number of days in August. This gives you the average daily balance for the account.

$15,455.40 / 31 = $498.56

**Step 5: Find the finance charge by calculating the amount of interest on the average daily balance.**

7. Recall that interest on this card is 1.8% per month. How much interest would be due on the average daily balance?

$498.56 × 0.018 = $8.97

**Step 6: Find the new ending balance by adding the finance charge to the last balance.**

8. Find the final balance that would appear on the next statement.

$8.97 + $593.25 = $602.22

## Did You Get It

Try this problem to see if you understand the concepts we just studied. The answer can be found at the bottom of the portfolio page.

5. A credit card statement for the month of November showed the following transactions:

| November 1 | Previous Balance | $937.25 |
|---|---|---|
| November 4 | Purchases | $531.62 |
| November 13 | Payment | $400.00 |
| November 20 | Purchases | $89.95 |
| November 28 | Payment | $100.00 |

a. Find the average daily balance.
b. Find the finance charge. The interest rate is 1.9% per month on the average daily balance.
c. Find the new balance on December 1.

Each month when you get a credit card statement, there's a minimum payment that must be paid. Before 2003, these minimum payments had shrunk to the point that they didn't even cover the interest for the month, so if a cardholder paid just the minimum payment, the balance would continue to rise. In response to a public outcry, the federal government set new regulations in 2003 requiring credit card companies to set the minimum payment high enough that it covers the interest for the month, as well as part of the principal balance. (The exact minimum payment formula varies some from company to company.)

This is not to say that making minimum payments only is a good idea. If at all possible, you should always pay off the full amount each month. This is the only foolproof way to make sure that you don't get in the habit of spending more money than you can afford. We'll close this lesson by examining the effects of making only minimum payments.

Suppose you have a $2,300 balance on a credit card with an interest rate of 1.25% per month, and the minimum payment for any month is the amount of interest plus 2% of the principal balance, or $5, whichever is higher. If you don't make any more purchases on that card and make the minimum payment for 6 months, how much will you pay down the balance? Let's find out. (By the way, the interest and minimum payment percentages in this problem reflect industry averages in 2015.)

9. This certainly sounds like we'll need to compute some interest. After all, we were told that the interest is 1.25% per month. But sometimes problems contain extraneous information. Read the problem carefully and explain why we don't need to worry about the amount of interest in calculating how much the balance decreases.

*It says that the minimum payment is 2% plus the amount of interest. So each month you'd pay the interest, then 2% of the balance that remains. So the balance is decreasing by 2% each month.*

**10.** In fact, what really matters is that the balance is going to decrease by 2% each month. Use this fact to find the new balance after 1 month.

*If the balance decreases by 2%, 98% of it remains. 98% of $2,300 is $2,254.*

**11.** Repeat your calculations from Question 10 five more times to find how much the balance would have decreased after six months.

*Two months: 98% of $2,254 is $2,208.92*
*Three months: 98% of $2,208.92 is $2,164.74*
*Four months: 98% of $2,164.74 is $2,121.45*
*Five months: 98% of $2,121.45 is $2,079.02*
*Six months: 98% of $2,079.02 is $2,037.44*

**12.** Just make a guess: How long do you think it would take to pay off the full balance at this rate? Discuss, then ask your instructor to give their thoughts on this question.

*Answers vary, of course. This is a GREAT opportunity for a class discussion on credit card debt. You might also point out that they'll discover an answer to this question in the technology portion of the homework.*

**Math Note**

In the Technology portion of the homework, we'll use Excel to calculate how long it would take to pay off this card if you make minimum payments.

## 2-5 | Portfolio

Name _____

Check each box when you've completed the task. Remember that your instructor will want you to turn in the portfolio pages you create.

### Technology

**1.** ☐  At the end of the Class portion of this lesson, we began to study the effects of making minimum payments on credit card debt. We can set up a spreadsheet to help calculate how long it would take to pay down the $2,300 debt. *The key is to recognize that if 2% of the debt is paid every month, then the new balance is 98% of the previous balance.* This allows you to set up a formula that calculates 98% of the previous balance. Also, the bank requires that the minimum payment each month is not less than $20, so once the balance gets below $1,000, the monthly payment will be $20 per month. At that point, change your formula so that it subtracts $20 from the previous balance. Use your spreadsheet to find how long it takes to pay off the balance, in months and in years. A template to help you get started can be found in the online resources for this lesson.

### Online Practice

**1.** ☐  Include any written work from the online assignment along with any notes or questions about this lesson's content.

### Applications

**1.** ☐  Complete the applications problems.

### Reflections

Type a short answer to each question.
**1.** ☐  Explain the difference between closed-ended and open-ended credit.
**2.** ☐  What did you learn in this lesson about keeping balances on credit cards?
**3.** ☐  If making a large purchase, what factors do you need to consider?
**4.** ☐  Take another look at your answer to Question 0 at the beginning of this lesson. Would you change your answer now that you've completed the lesson? How would you summarize the topic of this lesson now?
**5.** ☐  What questions do you have about this lesson?

### Looking Ahead

**1.** ☐  Complete the Lesson 2-6 Prep Skills and read the opening paragraph in Lesson 2-6 carefully, then answer Question 0 in preparation for that lesson.

### Answers to "Did You Get It?"

**1.** Amount financed, $7,200; total installment price, $10,720; finance charge, $2,520
**2. a.** $1,299  **b.** $28.90  **c.** $1,934  **d.** $435  **3.** $40.21
**4.** Finance charge = $16.93; balance on Feb. 1 = $1,046.29  **5. a.** $1,198.69
   **b.** $22.78  **c.** $1,081.60

## 2-5    Applications

Name _____

In this assignment, we'll study various options for making a large purchase, including saving money in advance and paying cash, obtaining a fixed installment loan, and using a credit card. The goal is not just to perform calculations, but to think about all aspects and decide which you think is the best choice. We'll use furniture as an example, as it's pretty common to finance furniture purchases when you need to fill a new place. Let's say that the goal is to buy $3,500 worth of furniture.

We'll start with a fixed-installment loan from the furniture store. They're offering 3-year financing with no money down at 11.99% annual interest.

1. Find the monthly payment.

$$M = \frac{\$3,500 \cdot \dfrac{0.1199}{12}}{1 - \left(1 + \dfrac{0.1199}{12}\right)^{-36}} = \$116.23$$

2. Find the total installment price and finance charge.

Total installment price = $36 \cdot \$116.23 = \$4,184.28$

Finance charge = $\$4,184.28 - \$3,500 = \$684.28$

The store also offers 18-month financing with no payments and no interest, but if the balance isn't paid in full at the end of 18 months, 17.99% interest will apply to the entire purchase amount, and will continue on any unpaid balance after 18 months.

3. Let's say you take this option and forget to pay off the final amount before the 18 months is up. And believe me, it's easy to do—they don't exactly go out of their way to remind you of the end date. If you'd paid $100 per month up until that point, how much would you still owe after the interest charge kicks in?

At $100 per month, in 18 months you'd have paid $1,800. At that point, you incur a deferred interest charge of 17.99% of $3,500, which is $629.65. So at that point you'd still owe $3,500 − $1,800 + $629.65 = $2,329.65.

**2-5**   **Applications**

Name _____

The next option is to put the entire purchase on a bank-issued Visa card with an annual interest rate of 12.49%. Let's say that you use this particular card strictly for this purchase.

4. In this case, would the amount of interest calculated vary depending on whether the bank used the unpaid balance or the average daily balance method? Explain.

   *It depends on when during the billing cycle your monthly payment posts. If it's the same as the beginning date of the billing cycle, and you don't make any purchases, then the average daily balance would be the same as the previous month's balance, so the two methods would lead to the same amount of interest. If your payment posts sometime during the month, you'd pay a little less with the average daily balance method since the remaining balance would go down at some point during the month.*

5. This particular card has a minimum monthly payment of 3% of the balance plus any interest accrued during the month. What would your first minimum payment be?

   *3% of $3,500 is $105.00. Add to that the interest on $3,500. Since the interest rate is 12.49% annually, one-twelfth of that applies in the first month, so interest is 0.1249/12 times $3,500, or $36.43. Total payment: $105 + $36.43 = $141.43.*

6. In this case, the equation $y = 3,500(0.97)^t$ would describe the remaining balance, where $t$ is months after purchase. Graph this equation and use the graph to estimate how long it would take to pay off the purchase making only minimum payments. You can assume that once the balance reaches $100, you'd go ahead and pay off the rest.

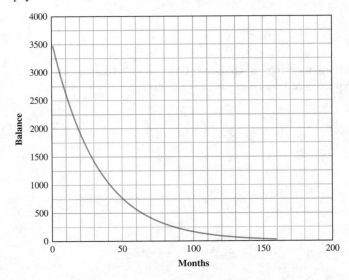

*Based on the visual of the graph, it would take about 120 months, or about 10 years. The actual time is about 117 months.*

## 2-5 Applications

Name _____

Suppose that you want to avoid paying interest and decide you'll only buy the furniture when you have the money to pay for it. An **annuity** is basically the opposite of a fixed-installment loan: you deposit a fixed amount each month and receive interest based on the total amount that's been saved. The future value formula is

$$A = \frac{12\,M\left[\left(1 + \frac{r}{12}\right)^{12t} - 1\right]}{r}$$

where $M$ is the regular monthly payment, $r$ is the annual interest rate in decimal form, and $t$ is the term of the annuity in years.

7. With a monthly payment of $120, what would the future value be if you chose an annuity with a term of 2 years at 4.8% interest?

$$A = \frac{12(120)\left[\left(1 + \frac{0.048}{12}\right)^{24} - 1\right]}{0.048} = \$3{,}016.45$$

8. Recalculate the amount if you're willing to raise your monthly payment by $20 per month.

$$A = \frac{12(140)\left[\left(1 + \frac{0.048}{12}\right)^{24} - 1\right]}{0.048} = \$3{,}519.19$$

9. Discuss the options you've seen for obtaining the furniture, focusing on which you think sounds like the best choice. You might consider combinations of these choices. Try to consider as many factors as you can.

*Answers really, really vary.*

# Lesson 2-6    Prep Skills

This is a short review of skills that will come in handy in the next lesson. In each case, answer the question, then rate your confidence level by checking one of the boxes. If you feel like you're struggling with these skills, consult the online resources provided by your instructor for extra practice.

### SKILL 1: COMPUTE SIMPLE INTEREST

1. Compute the simple interest on a $12,000 loan at 9% interest for 3 years.

2. Compute the future value of a $3,700 deposit that draws 4.95% simple interest for 18 months.

### SKILL 2: PERFORM COMPLEX CALCULATIONS

3. Use a calculator to perform each calculation:

$$8\left(1 - \frac{.09}{12}\right)^{-24}$$

$$\frac{17{,}000}{1 - (1 + 0.03)^{-120}}$$

### SKILL 3: EVALUATING FORMULAS

4. Find the value of the formula below if $k = -8.1$, $m = 0.0435$, and $W = 1{,}297.3$. Round your answer to six decimal places.

$$\frac{W\left(\frac{m}{k}\right)}{k - (1 + m)^k}$$

# Lesson 2-6 **Investing in Yourself** (Education and Home Loans)

## LEARNING OBJECTIVES

☐ 1. Understand different student loan options.

☐ 2. Compute interest and monthly payments on a student loan.

☐ 3. Evaluate the effects of capitalizing interest.

☐ 4. Analyze various aspects of a mortgage.

☐ 5. Compare two mortgages of different lengths.

☐ 6. Prepare an amortization schedule.

*If you think education is expensive, try ignorance.*
          —Derek Bok

© Digital Vision/SuperStock RF

Everyone knows that college is expensive. And some folks have opinions on whether or not it's really worth the investment. The numbers, however, say that it absolutely is, since your earning potential with a college degree increases to the point that you'll make back the cost long before retirement. When it comes to credit card debt, the best advice is often "Don't." But that's not a viable option for college costs, since the cost of NOT going to college is far more in the long run than the cost of attending. That makes student loans a necessary evil for most folks. And when you're finished with college and making a living, many of you will make the most expensive and rewarding purchase of your life: a home. If there's one common theme in this unit, it's that understanding the nuances of the financial transactions you're likely to deal with makes you far less likely to end up in a bad situation.

**0.** After reading the opening paragraph, what do you think the main topic of this lesson will be?

> You might consider beginning this lesson by seeing how many of your students are using student loans to pay college expenses. Discuss whether or not they really understand the details of their loans.

## 2-6 Group

### Student Loans

There are three basic types of loans that most undergraduates might consider: federal loans made by the government, federal loans made by banks or other lenders but guaranteed by the government, and private loans. Every student's first choice should be the federal loans due to stability: the interest rates are fixed for the life of the loan and are regulated by Congress, so you're unlikely to end up with a nasty surprise somewhere down the line. There are, however, limits on the amount that can be borrowed for one student through federal loan programs, and private loans might be the only alternative for an especially expensive education.

Other than the length of the loan, the big difference between student loans and other installment loans is that the payments are typically deferred until after graduation. This makes perfect sense, as in many cases students aren't working enough to make the money required to keep up with payments. So that's a pretty good deal. But it comes with a catch: in some cases, interest will accumulate on your loan while you're in school even though you're not making any payments. This can increase the principal balance considerably. The loan term can vary depending on the amount borrowed, but the standard term is 10 years, with payments deferred until 6 months after graduation.

Interest on student loans is simple interest: the interest accrues only on the principal balance, not on previously accrued interest. So while the student is still in school, the amount of interest that accrues each month remains constant. The interest is calculated using the simplified daily interest formula, which we can develop using things we know about simple interest.

1. If the principal balance of a loan is $6,500 and the interest rate is 6.8% annually, how much simple interest will accrue in 1 year?

   $I = Prt \Rightarrow I = \$6,500 \cdot 0.068 \cdot 1 = \$442$

2. Why does it make sense to use 365.25 days in a year for financial calculations?

   *Three out of every four years have 365 days, and every fourth (leap year) has 366. So, on average, the length of a year is 365.25 days. There's an expected value problem in there somewhere . . .*

3. Using Questions 1 and 2, find the daily amount of interest that accrues on that $6,500 loan. Make sure you explain how you got your answer.

   $\dfrac{\$442}{365.25} = \$1.21$

   *We found the amount of interest per year, so we just have to divide by the number of days in a year.*

4. How much interest accrues in a month? Be careful . . .

   *It depends on the month. For months with 31 days, it's 31 · $1.21 = $37.51. For months with 30 days, 30 · $1.21 = $36.30. For months with 29 days, $35.09, and for months with 28 days, $33.88.*

### The Simplified Daily Interest Formula

$$\text{Daily interest amount} = \frac{\text{Principal balance} \times \text{interest rate}}{365.25}$$

Monthly interest amount = Daily interest amount × days in month

**5.** For that $6,500 student loan we've been working with: If you start school in August, graduate in May (3 years and 9 months later), and payments begin 6 months after graduation, how much time will pass while interest is accruing?

_____4_____ Years and _____3_____ Months

**6.** Write out the months that come after the last full year ends, then the number of days in each of those months.

*September: 30 days. October: 31 days. November: 30 days.*

**7.** Find the amount of interest that accrues in the number of full years from your answer to Question 5.

*$442 per year times 4 years is $1,768.*

**8.** Write the amount of interest for each of the months listed in Question 6. Your answers to Question 4 will come in very handy.

*$36.30 + $37.51 + $36.30 = $110.11*

**9.** How much total interest accrues before payments begin?

*$1,768 + $110.11 = $1,878.11*

---

### Did You get It

Try this problem to see if you understand the concepts we just studied. The answer can be found at the bottom of the portfolio page.

1. Max borrows $11,500 for her last 2 years of college, acquiring a federal student loan at 6.2% interest.
   a. Find the monthly interest for 30- and 31-day months.
   b. Find the amount of interest that accrues if she acquires the loan in August, graduates 2 years later, and payments begin 3 months later.

When interest is covered by the government while the borrower is still in school, a student loan is called **subsidized.** If interest is added to the principal while the borrower is in school, the loan is called **unsubsidized.** For the loan in Questions 1–9, the student would have saved $1,878.11 by acquiring a subsidized loan.

When monthly payments begin on a student loan, they're based on the principal balance at that point in time. These payments can be computed using the following formula, which should look familiar: it's exactly the payment formula we studied in Lesson 2–5. We just thought we'd be nice and recopy it rather than making you page back. You should probably send us cash. Also, since most student loans have a 10-year term, we took the liberty of adapting the formula to that situation. Again, you should probably send us cash. Gift cards are appreciated, too.

## Monthly Payments on a Student Loan

For a 10-year student loan with principal $P$ and interest rate $r$ (written as a decimal), the monthly payment $M$ is given by

$$M = \frac{P \cdot \frac{r}{12}}{1 - \left(1 + \frac{r}{12}\right)^{-120}}$$

Reminder: Perform the calculation in one step if you can. If not, don't round too much. Always use at least four decimal places, and more than that won't kill you. I promise.

**10.** For the loan in Questions 1–9, what is the principal amount at the time payments begin? (This includes the original amount borrowed, plus the amount of interest that accrued until payments started.)

$6,500 + $1,878.11 = $8,378.11

**11.** Find the monthly payment on the loan.

$$M = \frac{\$8,378.11 \cdot \frac{0.068}{12}}{1 - \left(1 + \frac{0.068}{12}\right)^{-120}} \approx \$96.42$$

We've seen that with a student loan, you have the option of not making any payments until after graduation. When interest on an unsubsidized student loan is not paid during college, we say that the interest is **capitalized.** When interest is capitalized, it adds to the principal balance, which of course results in larger payments. When interest is not capitalized, payments have to be made during college, but only covering the amount of interest. This keeps the principal balance the same until full monthly payments start, which makes those payments smaller.

For the student loan we've been working with, the payment while still in school would simply be the amount of interest that's accruing, which you already calculated. For reference, in the space below write the amount you'd pay in an average 30-day month (see Question 4), as well as the total amount of interest you'd pay before regular monthly payments begin (Question 9).

30-day month: $36.30
Total interest: $1,878.11

12. With interest not capitalized, the principal balance of the loan will still be $6,500 when full payments start. Find what those payments will be.

$$M = \frac{\$6,500 \cdot \frac{0.068}{12}}{1 - \left(1 + \frac{0.068}{12}\right)^{-120}} \approx \$74.80$$

13. You'd make 120 payments on the loan (since you have 10 years to pay it back). Use your answer from Question 12 to find the total amount of money that you'd pay on the original $6,500 loan. (Hint: Don't forget the amount you would have already paid while in college!)

120 · $74.80 + $1,878.11 = $10,854.11

14. Now, the key question when studying whether or not to capitalize the interest: if interest is capitalized, after paying nothing while in school, you'll end up making 120 payments of the amount you found in Question 11. So how much money would you save by paying for the interest while still in school? More importantly, *discuss with your group whether or not you think the amount saved would make it worthwhile to scrape together those payments while in school, then write your thoughts.*

120 · $96.42 = $11,570.40
$11,570.40 − $10,854.11 = $716.29

Encourage students to really think about their response to this question. It's a very important part of understanding what they're getting into when acquiring student loans.

Answers vary on the value of each plan. For what it's worth, do I think it's worth making payments while in college to save an average of seventy bucks a year over ten years? Nope.

## Did You Get It

Try this problem to see if you understand the concepts we just studied. The answer can be found at the bottom of the portfolio page.

2. For the loan in Did You Get It 1:
   a. Find the monthly payment after graduation if interest is not capitalized. (Note that you found how much payments would be while in school in Did You Get It 1.)
   b. Find the full monthly payment after graduation if interest is capitalized.
   c. How much money would be saved by not capitalizing interest?

## Home Buying

© Brand X Pictures RF

For many people, the day they buy their first home is one of the proudest days of their life—and one of the scariest. There is nothing that compares to the feeling of looking at a house and knowing that it's all yours. But the buying process is tremendously intimidating. There are dozens of documents to sign, and the sheer numbers involved are enough to make almost everyone wonder if they're making a colossal mistake.

The most common home loans are paid over a 30-year span. That's a major commitment, and one that nobody should enter into without an understanding of the mathematics that go into the process. In the remainder of this lesson, we will study that math, hopefully helping you to become a well-informed home buyer. Maybe you're thinking, "Dude, I'm a college student. Buying a house is like a million years away." If so, you'll be surprised at how quickly that million years passes. I surely was.

A **mortgage** is a long-term loan where the lender has the right to seize the property purchased if the payments are not made. Homes are the most common items bought using mortgages. The most common mortgage term is 30 years, but they are widely available in terms from 10 to as many as 50 years.

There are several types of mortgages. With a **fixed-rate mortgage,** the rate of interest remains the same for the entire term of the loan. The payments (usually monthly) stay the same. With an **adjustable-rate mortgage,** the rate of interest may fluctuate (i.e., increase and decrease) during the period of the loan. If you opt for an adjustable-rate mortgage, it will start out with a lower interest rate than a fixed-rate loan of the same length.

**15.** Discuss the pros and cons of fixed and adjustable-rate loans.

*Answers vary of course. Some things we'd like to see discussed are the gamble of getting a lower interest rate in the short term vs. not knowing what it might go up to in the long term. This would be a GREAT opportunity to discuss how adjustable-rate mortgages were largely responsible for the number of people getting foreclosed on when the housing market collapsed in 2006–2007.*

**16.** Discuss the pros and cons of buying a house compared to renting a place to live.

*Answers vary widely. You might suggest that students think about things like maintenance, insurance, and property taxes, which they might not have thought about.*

One of the most useful (but frightening) things about home buying is calculating how much money you'll actually pay over the life of a loan. Let's see how that might work for one family.

The Petteys family plans to buy a home for $224,900, and has been offered a 30-year mortgage with a rate of 5.5% if they make a 20% down payment.

**17.** Calculate the down payment and the amount they'll have to borrow.

$0.20 \cdot \$224,900 = \$44,980$

$\$224,900 - \$44,980 = \$179,920$

> ### Math Note
>
> The word "mortgage" comes from a combination of Old French words "mort" (dead) and "gage" (pledge). It is believed the intent was that the debtor pledged the property to secure the loan, and if he or she failed to pay, the property was taken, and was therefore "dead" to the debtor.

**18.** The monthly payment on the loan will be $1,021.57. How much will the Petteys' actually pay for their $224,900 home? (Don't forget to add in the down payment.)

$\$44,980 + 30 \cdot 12 \cdot \$1,021.57 = \$412,745.20$

## Did You Get It

Try this problem to see if you understand the concepts we just studied. The answer can be found at the bottom of the portfolio page.

   3. The Trissel family agreed on a price of $229,500 for a home. Their company credit union offers a 5.0% 20-year loan with 15% down, resulting in a monthly payment of $1,287.50. Find the down payment amount, and the total amount they'll pay for the house.

## 2-6 | Class

When you apply for a home loan, the lender will tell you what your monthly payment will be. And if you're an incredibly trusting sort, that might be good enough for you. For most of us, though, a double-check of the quoted payment would be a big comfort. In addition, knowing how the payment is calculated makes it quite a bit easier to understand the factors that determine how much you'll pay. Better still, it will allow you to compare mortgages with different rates, down payments, and lengths. So let's have a look at computing monthly payments.

1. In the space below, recopy the formula that we used for computing monthly payments on a student loan with a term of 10 years. Then describe the significance of each part of the formula requested below:

$$M = \frac{P \cdot \frac{r}{12}}{1 - \left(1 + \frac{r}{12}\right)^{-120}}$$

*P:* The principal amount of the loan

*r:* The annual interest rate

12: The number of payments per year

2. Where do you think the 120 comes from in the formula? (Hint: Think of 120 as the product of two numbers.)

It's the number of payments per year multiplied by the term of the loan in years. In other words, it's the total number of payments.

Students may need some hints here. It's really important that they have a handle on this answer . . .

3. Using your answers to Questions 1 and 2, adapt the student loan monthly payment formula into a general formula for finding the periodic payment on a loan with principal value *P*, annual interest rate *r,* term *t* (in years), and *n* payments per year. *Check with your professor to make sure that you have the right formula before moving on to the remainder of the lesson!*

$$M = \frac{P \cdot \frac{r}{n}}{1 - \left(1 + \frac{r}{n}\right)^{-nt}}$$

. . . In order to be successful here. A correct answer here is crucial, so make sure that you check all groups to make sure they have the correct answer before moving on.

Earlier we studied a loan obtained by the Petteys family with these terms: purchase price $224,900, 20% down payment, 30-year mortgage with a rate of 5.5%. The monthly payment was $1,021.57.

4. How much higher would the monthly payment be if they'd put only 10% down? This would also raise the interest rate to 5.8%.

New principal $= 0.9 \cdot \$224,900 = \$202,410$

$$M = \frac{\$202,410 \cdot \frac{0.058}{12}}{1 - \left(1 + \frac{0.058}{12}\right)^{-360}} = \$1,187.65$$

The payment would be $166.08 more each month.

5. How much more would they end up paying over the life of the loan?

New amount $= 360 \cdot \$1,187.65 + \$22,490 = \$450,044$

Difference: $450,044 - $412,745.20 = $37,298.80

6. Now let's examine the term of the loan. If they choose a 15-year mortgage with 20% down at 5.5%, what would the monthly payment be?

$$M = \frac{\$179,920 \cdot \frac{0.055}{12}}{1 - \left(1 + \frac{0.055}{12}\right)^{-180}} = \$1,470.10$$

7. How would their total cost compare to the other two options we studied? Which mortgage do you think is the best choice? Discuss.

New amount $= 180 \cdot \$1,470.10 + \$44,980 = \$309,598$

Difference between this and the 30-year loan with 20% down:

$412,745.20 - $309,598 = $103,147.20

Difference between this and the 30-year loan with 10% down:

$450,044 - $309,598 = $140,446

Discussions vary.

## Math Note

A Google search for the phrase "mortgage calculator" results in over 60 million hits! There are thousands of pages available that can be used to quickly calculate monthly payments on a mortgage. But doing the calculations by hand will help you to become very familiar with the terms involved in mortgages.

## Did You Get It

Try this problem to see if you understand the concepts we just studied. The answer can be found at the bottom of the portfolio page.

4.  Find the monthly payment for the Trissels (Did You Get It 3) if they choose a 15-year loan instead of 20. How much money would they save overall?

## Computing an Amortization Schedule

After securing a mortgage, the lending institution will prepare an **amortization schedule.** This schedule shows what part of the monthly payment is paid on the principal and what part of the monthly payment is paid in interest. Here's the procedure for computing an amortization schedule:

### Computing an Amortization Schedule

**Step 1:** Find the interest for the first month. Use $I = Prt$, where $t = 1/12$. Enter this value in a column labeled Interest.

**Step 2:** Subtract the interest from the monthly payment to get the amount paid on the principal. Enter this amount in a column labeled Payment on Principal.

**Step 3:** Subtract the amount of the payment on principal found in step 2 from the principal to get the balance of the loan. Enter this in a column labeled Balance of Loan.

**Step 4:** Repeat the steps using the amount of the balance found in step 3 for the new principal.

In the next group of questions, we'll use these steps to compute the first three months of an amortization table for the Petteys loan: principal $179,920, rate 5.5%, monthly payment $1,021.57. A template for the table is on the next page: fill in the information as you find it.

8.  Calculate the interest for the first month on the loan, and put it into the interest column of the table.

$I = \$179{,}920 \cdot 0.055 \div 12 = \$824.63$

9.  Subtract the interest from the monthly payment to get the amount paid on the principal, then put that amount in the appropriate column in the table.

$\$1{,}021.57 - \$824.63 = \$196.94$

**10.** Calculate the new balance of the loan by subtracting the payment on principal from the original principal, then put that in the last column.

$179,920 - $196.94 = $179,723.06

**11.** Repeat the previous steps for the next 2 months. Do your calculation in this space, then put the results in the table.

$I = $179,723.06 \cdot 0.055 \div 12 = $823.73$

$1,021.57 - $823.73 = $197.84

$179,723.06 - $197.84 = $179,525.22

$I = $179,525.22 \cdot 0.055 \div 12 = $822.82$

$1,021.57 - $822.82 = $198.75

$179,525.22 - $198.75 = $179,326.47

| Payment Number | Interest | Payment on Principal | Balance of Loan |
|----------------|----------|----------------------|-----------------|
| 1 | $824.63 | $196.94 | $179,723.06 |
| 2 | $823.73 | $197.84 | $179,525.22 |
| 3 | $822.82 | $198.75 | $179,326.47 |

**12.** What does this table say about what the bulk of your payment goes to when you begin making payments on a mortgage? What about near the end of the term of your loan? Explain.

*With your earliest payments, most of what you pay is going toward interest, and doesn't do much to lower your balance. But by the time you get near the end of the term, the interest will be very low, and most of what you pay will go toward paying down the balance.*

## Did You Get It

Try this problem to see if you understand the concepts we just studied. The answer can be found at the bottom of the portfolio page.

5.  The Trissel loan from Did You Get It 3 has the following parameters: $195,075 principal, 5.0% interest rate, and monthly payment $1,287.50. Complete the first two months of an amortization schedule for this loan.

| Payment Number | Interest | Payment on Principal | Balance of Loan |
|:---:|:---:|:---:|:---:|
| 1 | | | |
| 2 | | | |

After learning about amortization schedules, most people think that mortgages sound like an awful deal: your early payments go almost completely to interest, so you're paying a LOT of money, and making almost no progress on paying down your loan. But here's the benefit to you: the interest paid on a home loan can be deducted from your income when computing the amount of income tax that you owe. So at least the way mortgages work gives you a bigger break on your income taxes during the early stages of the loan.

Financial advisors have coined two terms for borrowers: "good debt" and "bad debt." Good debt is when you borrow money to buy something that is going to increase in value. Student loans and home loans are pretty much the gold standard in good debt. Houses increase in value, and the amount that you pay for a college education is more than paid back by increased earning potential.

Bad debt, on the other hand, is borrowing to buy something that loses value immediately after purchase. An obvious example is car loans, although for most people this type of bad debt is unavoidable, so we'll coin a new term: "not-so-good debt." Car loans are manageable, but it's important to avoid really long-term loans. Dealers are now offering 60, 72, and even 84 month loans. You should think carefully before taking out a 60-month loan, and you should avoid longer loans than that at all costs. If you need to finance a car for that long, you can't afford that car.

The best example of bad debt (or worst example, I guess) is credit card debt. Keeping balances on credit cards is the easiest way to put yourself into a financial hole. Pretty much everything you might buy on credit is instantly worth less than what you paid, and the high interest rates attached to most credit cards makes them a financial disaster waiting to happen. The key to managing your financial life is to be an educated borrower and educated consumer. Hopefully these lessons have given you the means to make smart financial decisions when it comes to borrowing.

## 2-6 Portfolio

Name _____

Check each box when you've completed the task. Remember that your instructor will want you to turn in the portfolio pages you create.

### Technology

1. ☐ As you probably noticed in the Class portion of this lesson, making an amortization table is a bit time-intensive. There sure are a lot of repetitive calculations. Sounds like another job for technology! Your job here is to use a spreadsheet to make an amortization table for the Petteys loan we studied in the lesson. You already have the first three months filled in (Class Questions 8–11), so you can use that to double-check your spreadsheet results. A template to help you get started can be found in the online resources for this lesson.

2. ☐ In my humble opinion, the most valuable thing you can get out of this lesson is the ability to compare different loans. The second template in the class resources is built so that you can input the principal, percent down payment, interest rate, and term of a loan, then calculate the monthly payment, total amount of interest, and total cost over the life of the loan. Use this spreadsheet to explore different options for a home that you think you might pay for some day, and report on what you found.

### Online Practice

1. ☐ Include any written work from the online assignment along with any notes or questions about this lesson's content.

### Applications

1. ☐ Complete the applications problems.

### Reflections

Type a short answer to each question.

1. ☐ Describe some of the options you have in student loans.
2. ☐ What are the advantages and disadvantages of a mortgage with a shorter term?
3. ☐ Take another look at your answer to Question 0 at the beginning of this lesson. Would you change your answer now that you've completed the lesson? How would you summarize the topic of this lesson now?
4. ☐ What questions do you have about this lesson?

### Looking Ahead

1. ☐ Complete the Lesson 2-7 Prep Skills and read the opening paragraph in Lesson 2-7 carefully, then answer Question 0 in preparation for that lesson.

### Answers to "Did You Get It?"

**1. a.** 30 day: $58.50; 31 day: $60.45   **b.** $1,603.45   **2. a.** $128.83   **b.** $146.79   **c.** $551.75

**3.** Down payment: $34,425, total amount paid: $343,425   **4.** $1,542.64; $31,324.80

**5.** Payment 1: Interest = $812.81, Payment on Principal = $474.69, Balance = $194,600.31;
Payment 2: Interest = $810.83, Payment on Principal = $476.67, Balance = $194,123.64

## 2-6   Applications

Name _____

Many mortgage lenders offer a way to lower your interest rate by paying some of the interest up front. This prepaid interest is known in the industry as **points.** Each point corresponds to 1% of the amount borrowed. In short, you're paying a fee to lower your interest rate. The question is whether this is a good deal for you, or for the lender. Let's look into it.

1. A lender offers you a 30-year fixed mortgage of $130,000 at 4% interest with no points. Find the monthly payment.

$$M = \frac{\$130{,}000 \cdot \frac{0.04}{12}}{1 - \left(1 + \frac{0.04}{12}\right)^{-360}} = \$620.64$$

2. You can get the same 30-year mortgage of $130,000 at 3.6% interest by paying 2 points at closing. How much would you have to come up with to cover the 2 points?

   2% of $130,000 is $2,600.

3. Find the new monthly payment.

$$M = \frac{\$130{,}000 \cdot \frac{0.036}{12}}{1 - \left(1 + \frac{0.036}{12}\right)^{-360}} = \$591.04$$

4. How much are you saving each month with the new monthly payment?

   $620.64 − $591.04 = $29.60

5. How long will it take to recover the amount you had to come up with to pay the 2 points? What does this mean in terms of how long you should plan to stay in that home?

   $2,600/$29.60 per month = 87.8 months, or a little over seven years. If you don't stay in the home for more than seven years, then choosing the mortgage with points would have cost you money.

## 2-6 Applications

Name _____

**6.** If you were to stay in that home long enough to pay off the loan, how much would the mortgage with points save you?

$620.64 per month times 360 months is $223,430.40.
$591.04 per month times 360 months is $212,774.40; adding the points, the total cost is $215,374.40. You'd save $8,056.

**7.** Suppose that instead of paying the points, you instead invested that $2,600 into a long-term fund that paid 2.7% interest compounded monthly. How much would it be worth after 30 years?

$$A = P\left(1+\frac{r}{n}\right)^{nt} = \$2,600\left(1+\frac{.027}{12}\right)^{360} = \$5,839.25$$

**8.** Discuss which option seems the best to you. Justify your conclusions.

Answers vary.

**9.** If you acquire a $15,000 student loan at 4.3% interest and have to begin making payments 4 years later, how much would you save in interest if the loan is subsidized?

$$I = Prt = \$15,000(0.043)(4) = \$2,580$$

**10.** How would that subsidy affect your monthly payment?

Subsidized: $$M = \frac{\$15,000 \cdot \frac{0.043}{12}}{1-\left(1+\frac{0.043}{12}\right)^{-120}} \approx \$154.02$$

Unsubsidized: $$M = \frac{\$17,580 \cdot \frac{0.043}{12}}{1-\left(1+\frac{0.043}{12}\right)^{-120}} \approx \$180.51$$

The subsidy would shave $26.49 from the payment.

# Lesson 2-7  **Prep Skills**

This is a short review of skills that will come in handy in the next lesson. In each case, answer the question, then rate your confidence level by checking one of the boxes. If you feel like you're struggling with these skills, consult the online resources provided by your instructor for extra practice.

### SKILL 1: READING INFORMATION FROM A TABLE

1. Below is the nutrition information label for a certain brand of peanut butter.

Serving Size 32g

| Amount Per Serving | | |
|---|---|---|
| **Calories** 188 | Calories from Fat 135 | |
| | **% Daily Value*** | |
| **Total Fat** 16g | 25% | |
| Saturated Fat 3g | 17% | |
| Trans Fat 0g | | |
| **Cholesterol** 0mg | 0% | |
| **Sodium** 147mg | 6% | |
| **Total Carbohydrate** 6g | 2% | |
| Dietary Fiber 2g | 8% | |
| Sugars 3g | | |
| **Protein** 8g | | |

| | | | |
|---|---|---|---|
| Vitamin A | 0% | • Vitamin C | 0% |
| Calcium | 1% | • Iron | 3% |

  a. How many grams of fat are there in one serving?
  b. How much sodium is there in three servings?
  c. What percent of the daily recommendation of fiber is contained in one serving?

### SKILL 2: DO COMPUTATIONS INVOLVING PERCENTAGES

2. Based on the information in the table, what is the recommended daily value for total fat?

3. If you have 20g of this peanut butter, what percent of a full serving is that?

4. How many grams of protein would you get from that 20g of peanut butter?

### SKILL 3: SOLVE A FORMULA FOR ONE VARIABLE

5. Solve the equation $\dfrac{k}{M} = P$ for $M$.

# Lesson 2-7   **A Walk on Wall Street**   (Stocks and Bonds)

**LEARNING OBJECTIVES**

☐ 1. Read information from a stock listing.

☐ 2. Calculate costs of buying stock, and profit or loss from selling.

☐ 3. Study the price-to-earnings ratio, and use it to analyze the value of a stock.

☐ 4. Calculate profit from a bond sale.

*The real key to making money in stocks is not to get scared out of them.*
              —Peter Lynch

© Comstock Images RF

We have seen that the magic of compound interest allows your money to grow considerably over long periods of time. However, interest rates on basic savings accounts are usually quite low, so if you rely on savings alone to build a nest egg, you better hope that you live a very, very long life indeed. Most successful investors grow their money much more quickly using the stock market. In this lesson, we'll learn about the basics of stocks and bonds, and how to get information about the performance of stocks that you might be interested in. When a company files legal papers to become a corporation, it's able to issue **stock.** If you buy shares of stock, you literally become a part owner of the company; for example, if a company issues 1,000 shares of stock and you buy 250 shares, then you own one-quarter of the company. The market can be a very intimidating place, but education holds the key to overcoming that fear and getting a piece of the action.

**0.** After reading the opening paragraph, what do you think the main topic of this lesson will be?

## 2-7  Class

### Basic Definitions

As a shareholder in a company, you own part of that company. When the company makes money, it can choose to distribute part of the profit to its shareholders. This money is called a **dividend.** The stockholder receives a sum of money based on the number of shares of the stock that he or she owns. Sometimes if a company doesn't make a profit or its owners or managers decide to reinvest the money into the company, no dividends are paid. So when choosing whether to buy stock in a certain company, one consideration is whether or not that company typically pays a dividend.

**1.** If you own stock in a certain company, why are you entitled to a periodic dividend?

*Because you literally own part of the company. So if the company makes money, it's perfectly reasonable to expect that you would get a share of that profit.*

2. Describe any advantages or disadvantages of buying stock in a company that pays dividends.

   *The advantage is that you get periodic payments, and money is good. The disadvantage is that it might help the value of the company long-term if they invest that money back into growing the company rather than paying the stockholders.*

Besides issuing stock, a company can also issue **bonds.** Usually bonds are issued to raise money for the company for startup costs or special projects. A person who purchases a bond is really lending money to the company. The company, in turn, repays the owner of the bond its original value plus interest. As a general rule, bonds are a safer investment than stocks, but stocks have greater growth potential.

3. Describe the difference between stocks and bonds.

   *If you own stock in a company, you own a part of the company. If you buy bonds issued by a company, in essence you have lent money to that company. You're entitled to getting that money back with interest, but you're not entitled to any profit made by the company.*

Stocks can be bought and sold on a **stock exchange.** The price of a stock, which varies from day to day (even from minute to minute) depends completely on the amount that investors are willing to pay for it. This can be affected by the profitability of the company, the economy, scandals, even global political concerns. Investors buy or sell stock through a **stockbroker.** Traditionally, this was an individual working for a brokerage firm, but it has become common for people to use online brokers, in which the investor initiates the buying and selling of stocks online. In either case, the brokerage charges a fee, called a **commission,** for the service of having their representatives buy or sell the stock at an exchange. Bonds can also be bought and sold like stock.

4. How can an individual buy stock in a company?

   *By purchasing shares of stock through a stockbroker, either through a brokerage firm or an online trading site.*

5. What are some advantages of investing in the stock market?

   *There are two different ways that you can make money. If the company pays a dividend, you'll share in the company's profit. If the stock price increases, then you can sell your shares and make a profit.*

## Investing in Stocks

When all is said and done, there are two ways to earn money from stocks: buying a stock that pays a regular dividend, and selling shares for more than you paid for them. This means that investors are tremendously interested in the day-to-day price fluctuations of stocks, as well as indicators of how well the company is doing. A **stock table** is a listing of key information; stock tables can be found in newspapers and online financial sites.

The stock table shown below, generated at 10:37 A.M. on September 4, 2015, is for a company called Computer Programs & Systems Inc. Let's see if we can make sense of this mysterious mass of numbers.

### Computer Programs & Systems Inc. (CPSI) - NasdaqGS ⭐ Watchlist

**45.49** ↑ 0.05(0.11%) 10:37AM EDT - Nasdaq Real Time Price

| | | | |
|---|---|---|---|
| Prev Close: | 45.44 | Day's Range: | 45.02 - 45.60 |
| Open: | 45.02 | 52wk Range: | 43.24 - 64.86 |
| Bid: | 45.36 x 100 | Volume: | 5,119 |
| Ask: | 45.52 x 100 | Avg Vol (3m): | 96,911 |
| 1y Target Est: | 46.20 | Market Cap: | 514.16M |
| Beta: | 0.780949 | P/E (ttm): | 18.61 |
| Earnings Date: | Oct 28 - Nov 2 (Est.) | EPS (ttm): | 2.44 |
| | | Div & Yield: | 2.56 (5.64%) |

> Think of this material as an opportunity to run a more traditional-style class for a few minutes.

There's a whole lot of information here, and it's going to take some explanation. We suggest that you take notes as you read through the descriptions below, but you might try a quick read-through now, then refer back when you get to Questions 6–11.

At the top, we see the name of the company and the **ticker symbol** (CPSI in this case). This is a shorthand symbol assigned by the exchange that represents the stock. The "NasdaqGS" indicates that this particular stock is traded on the Nasdaq, one of the American stock exchanges. The big bold number at the top is the current price of the stock. The current price isn't like the price of milk at the grocery store: it reflects the most recent price at which the stock has been bought from someone trying to sell. This is followed by how much the price has changed during the current day's trading session.

If you can add and subtract, this makes the **Prev Close** price redundant: note that this stock has gone up by $0.05 in this session and is currently worth $45.49, so of course the closing price on the previous day was $45.44. **Open** refers to the price at the time today's session began. This is often different from the closing price because many factors can affect what people are willing to pay from day to day. **Bid** and **Ask** are a snapshot of what people have been bidding to buy the stock, and what price current shareholders have been asking for to sell. In this case, $45.36 × 100 indicates that an offer of $45.36 for up to 100 shares has been made. $45.52 × 100 means that someone has offered up to 100 shares for sale at $45.52.

**1y Target Est** is what analysts are predicting the stock price will be in 1 year. While this is at best an educated guess, it can at least give you some guidance as to whether the stock might be a good buy. **Beta** refers to the **volatility** of the stock, which is a measure of how much the price fluctuates. If the beta is close to 1, then the stock's stability is similar to the rest of the market. Lower numbers indicate that the price is more stable than average. The **Earnings Date** reflects the next time the company is expected to release data on how well the company is doing financially.

The ranges (**Day's Range** and **52wk Range**) indicate the highest and lowest price during the current session, as well as the last full year. The latter is particularly useful, as it gives you a quick snapshot of how the stock has fluctuated, and how its current price compares. **Volume** describes how many shares have been traded in the current session, while **Avg Vol (3m)** provides a 3-month average of shares traded. Lower-volume stocks can be more difficult to buy and sell due to availability.

**Market Cap** is the total value of the company: it's calculated by multiplying the number of shares that have been issued by the current price, so a little math allows you to calculate how many shares there are. This in turn makes the volume of sales more meaningful. **P/E (ttm)** refers to the P/E (price-to-earnings) ratio. This is a particularly important number, so we'll study that in detail a bit later. **EPS (ttm)** represents earnings per share, or the amount of money the company made for each share of stock that has been issued. Clearly, bigger is better here. **Div & Yield** is the dividend that the company pays for each share, and what percent of the current price that represents. If nothing else, this tells you whether or not the company pays a dividend on shares, but you can also use it for comparison purposes with other stocks.

Now let's put our new knowledge into practice by studying shares of Facebook, also on 9/4/15.

**Facebook, Inc. (FB)** - NasdaqGS ★ **Watchlist**

**87.27** ↓0.88(1.00%) 1:29PM EDT - Nasdaq Real Time Price

| | | | |
|---|---|---|---|
| Prev Close: | 88.15 | Day's Range: | 86.70 - 87.79 |
| Open: | 87.15 | 52wk Range: | 70.32 - 99.24 |
| Bid: | 87.06 x 400 | Volume: | 16,715,420 |
| Ask: | 87.07 x 300 | Avg Vol (3m): | 31,684,600 |
| 1y Target Est: | 111.75 | Market Cap: | 245.89B |
| Beta: | 0.89812 | P/E (ttm): | 88.69 |
| Earnings Date: | Oct 26 - Oct 30 (Est.) | EPS (ttm): | 0.98 |
| | | Div & Yield: | N/A (N/A) |

6. What is the current price of the stock? What are shareholders trying to sell it currently asking for?

   *The current price is $87.27 per share. Shareholders are asking for $87.07.*

7. What do analysts predict the price will be in 1 year?

   *The prediction is $111.75.*

8. Is this stock more or less volatile than the market as a whole? How do you know?

   *The beta is less than 1, so the stock has been more stable than the market in general.*

9. What's the highest stock price in the last 52 weeks?

   *$99.24*

10. Does Facebook pay a dividend to shareholders? If so, how much?

    *The N/A in the dividend row shows that they do not pay a dividend.*

**11.** Use the market cap to find how many shares the company issued.

*245.89 billion / 87.27 ≈ 2.82 billion*
*About 2.82 billion shares have been issued.*

As previously mentioned, there are two ways to make money from stocks: buy shares of a stock that pays dividends, or buy stock at a low price and sell it at a higher price. But of course, you can't just go buy stock at the corner store—you need to use a brokerage firm, placing an order that is then carried out by representatives at the stock exchange. In exchange for that service, the broker charges a commission, which varies among brokers. Brokers can also make recommendations concerning what stocks to buy and sell, which further justifies their commissions.

The amount that an investor receives from the sale of a stock is called the **proceeds.** The proceeds are equal to the amount of the sale minus the broker's commission. Next, we'll look at some examples of buying and selling stock.

Shares of Apple Computer (AAPL) closed at $12.89 on April 1, 2004. Suppose that an investor bought 600 shares at that price using a broker that charged a 2% commission.

**12.** Find the amount of commission that was paid.

*2% of $12.89 · 600 = $154.68*

**13.** Find the total cost of buying the stock.

*$154.68 + 600 · $12.89 = $7,888.68*

© McGraw-Hill Education/Jill Braaten, photographer

A **stock split** occurs when a company increases the number of outstanding shares. Most commonly, this is a **2-for-1 split,** in which the number of shares doubles. This can be done for a variety of reasons, but the simplest explanation is that when the price of one share gets particularly high, it tends to scare away smaller investors, and the split effectively halves the price of one share. In any case, the net result is that in an instant, the number of shares owned by shareholders doubles.

**14.** Apple did a 2-for-1 split on February 8, 2005, then a 7-for-1 split on June 9, 2014. How many shares would our investor have owned after the second split?

*600 · 14 = 8,400*

15. Our clever friend the Apple investor could have sold her shares for $130.28 on June 1, 2015. If she had done so, using a brokerage with a 1.5% commission, what would her profit have been? Remember profit is the difference between cost and final proceeds from the sale, which would be selling price minus commission. Needless to say, you should show your work.

$8,400 \cdot \$130.28 = \$1,094,352.00$
$0.015 \cdot \$1,094,352 = \$16,415.28$
$\$1,094,352 - \$16,415.28 = \$1,077,936.72$ *(Final proceeds)*
$\$1,077,936.72 - \$7,888.68 = \$1,070,048.04$ *(Profit)*

16. How much money would our investor have saved by using an online trading site with a flat commission of $19.95 per trade (for both the original purchase and the sale)?

*Commission on purchase:* $154.68

*Commission on sale:* $16,415.28

$\$154.68 + \$16,415.28 - 2 \cdot \$19.95 = \$16,530.06$ *saved*

> Good teaching moment here: Learning about investing to the point where you don't need a commissioned broker can save you a lot of money.

## Did You Get It?

Try this problem to see if you understand the concepts we just studied. The answer can be found at the bottom of the portfolio page.

1. a. When Facebook stock was first offered for public sale in May 2012, the share price was $38. If you'd bought 500 shares at that price, using a brokerage with a 1% commission, what would your total cost have been?
   b. If you'd then sold them at the opening price on 9/4/15 (see Questions 6–11), using an online brokerage with a $9.95 flat fee, would you have made or lost money? How much?

## 2-7 Group

### The Price-to-Earnings Ratio For a Stock

The price-to-earnings ratio, commonly known as P/E ratio, is a key indicator of how reasonable the current price of a stock is. It compares the selling price of the stock to the annual amount of money the company has earned per share. If the P/E ratio for a certain stock is 20, that means that the current selling price is 20 times as high as the earnings per share. This tells us that for every dollar you invest in the company, that company will earn $0.05.

P/E ratio can be a little tricky to interpret. On the one hand, a lower P/E ratio indicates that a stock is priced reasonably, as you need to invest less for the company to make a certain amount of profit. But if investors believe in the growth potential of a company, they may be willing to pay a premium for the stock, which would result in a higher P/E ratio.

To help get some perspective on P/E ratio, it's useful to do some calculations. First, a formal definition:

### The P/E Ratio

$$\text{P/E Ratio} = \frac{\text{Current market price}}{\text{Annual earnings per share}}$$

1. For the Facebook stock table from earlier in the lesson, calculate the P/E ratio using the current price and earnings per share. Compare to the P/E ratio listed in the table. Why do you think they're not identical?

$$\frac{\textit{Current market price}}{\textit{Annual earnings per share}} = \frac{\$87.27}{0.98} \approx 89.05$$

P/E ratio listed is 88.69. The discrepancy could be due to rounding in the earnings per share, as well as a recent change in market price not yet reflected in the P/E ratio.

Not every stock table you will encounter has quite the wealth of information that the ones at the beginning of this lesson have. A more abbreviated table might have the P/E ratio but not earnings per share listed, in which case you can rearrange the above formula to calculate earnings per share.

2. On September 8, 2015, Google stock closed at $600.70, and the P/E ratio was listed as 28.31. What was Google's earnings per share for the previous year? How does it compare to Facebook's? Which do you think was the better investment at that point?

Since P/E ratio is market price divided by earnings per share, earnings per share is market price divided by P/E ratio. $600.70/28.31 ≈ $21.22. The earnings per share are WAY higher than Facebook. Which is the better investment is an opinion, but based on P/E ratio Google seems like a much better bet. But the high price obviously means that you could buy far fewer shares of Google.

## Did You Get It

Try this problem to see if you understand the concepts we just studied. The answer can be found at the bottom of the portfolio page.

2. a. Use information in the stock table for CPSI earlier in the lesson to calculate the P/E ratio by hand, and compare to the P/E ratio in the table. If your result is different, discuss why you think that may be the case.
   b. If a competitor of CPSI has a P/E ratio of 21.4 and a market price of $38.74, calculate the earning per share.

The table below summarizes some basic rules of thumb when it comes to interpreting the P/E ratio for a stock. Remember that the best approach is to compare a stock's P/E ratio to other companies in the same industry, as current market conditions can have a pretty profound effect on P/E ratio.

| P/E Ratio | Common Interpretations |
|---|---|
| N/A | Company has no earnings; it's also standard for a company with negative earnings (that is, a loss) to have an undefined P/E ratio, even though mathematically a negative P/E ratio does make sense. |
| 0–10 | The stock may be undervalued, making it a good buy; alternatively investors might feel like the earnings are likely to decline. The company may have shown short-term profit from selling assets that will hurt earnings in the long term. |
| 10–17 | P/E ratios in this range are historically considered to represent stocks being sold at fair market value. |
| 17–25 | The stock may be overvalued, so shop carefully. On the other hand, earnings may have increased since the last official earnings report was released. The company might be up and coming, with earnings expected to increase dramatically at some point. |
| >25 | The stock might be very overpriced at the moment, or the company may be expected to have a big jump in earnings coming up. It could also be the case that the company's most recent earnings are unusually low for that company, with an expectation of recovery. |

3. Come up with some ideas why the Facebook P/E ratio might have been sky-high in September of 2015. You might want to look up the history of Facebook stock on the Internet.

*Answers vary. Prevailing wisdom is that this was not too long after Facebook was taken public, meaning that stock in the company was made available for the first time. Because Facebook is so ubiquitous, many investors assumed that it would be a very strong investment, leading to it being overvalued.*

## Investing in Bonds

When an investor buys bonds, the investor is actually loaning money to the company or government entity that issues the bonds. In exchange for lending that money, the investor will receive a fixed return on his or her investment for a given period of time. The ending value of the bond is called the **face value;** this is typically $1,000, but can vary. Bonds also have a **maturity date,** which is the date that the face value is returned to the investor, as well as interest. In some cases, no interest is paid until the maturity date, at which time the full amount of interest is paid. **Coupon bonds,** on the other hand, pay an annual or semi-annual interest payment, known as a **coupon.**

You can think of it this way: if someone offers to sell you a $20 bill for $15, that's a pretty darn good deal. But the catch is that you don't get the $20 until some predetermined time later down the road. That's what a bond is; it's actually pretty simple.

But here's where it can get more interesting. Suppose that you get tired of waiting for the time when you get that $20 bill, and you sell the bond to your neighbor for $18. You've made $3 on your investment and you're done. Your neighbor now waits until the maturity date, cashes in the bond, and makes the other $2 of the original $5 in profit. This is how bonds are bought and sold on the open market. Of course, your neighbor wouldn't pay more than $20 for a bond with a maturity value of $20. But if you were desperate for cash, you might be compelled to unload the bond for less than the $15 you originally paid. You've taken a loss, but at least you got some money out at the time you needed it.

Investors buy bonds for two main reasons. First, they're much safer investments than stocks, even though they have much less opportunity for a big profit. The interest is guaranteed, as long as the company that issued the bond stays in business and has the money to pay its debts. This makes bonds a safe, but not guaranteed, investment. Second, bonds are used to offset losses on stocks when the economy is in a down cycle, because the value of bonds tends to go up when the value of stocks goes down.

Here's a short version of why that makes sense: in our earlier hypothetical example where you're making a $5 profit for waiting to cash in your bond, if the economy is booming in the meantime, prices in general will tend to go up, so the $5 you're getting at some point in the future has less buying power than the $5 you were expecting when you made the investment. This makes the bond in effect worth less. The opposite is also true: if the economy fizzles after you buy that bond, the $5 you eventually get will in effect be worth more than the $5 you thought you were getting, so the bond is worth more. Stocks tend to rise when the economy is doing well and fall when it's not, so the value of bonds usually goes in the opposite direction of the stock market.

Suppose that you buy a bond with face value $1,000 that was originally issued 18 months ago. The maturity date is 4 years from the time it was issued, and the interest rate is 4% simple interest per year. If you pay $820 for the bond and keep it until the maturity date, what is your profit? What percent return would you get per year? Let's do some calculating.

4. Find the amount of interest that will be paid on the bond at maturity, and the total amount of money you'll get from the issuer at that point. You'll want to reach back into the archives and use the simple interest formula.

$$I = Prt \Rightarrow I = \$1,000 \cdot 0.04 \cdot 4 = \$160 \text{ in interest}$$

Total amount received: $1,160.

5. Find the profit you'd make on this transaction.

   *Total amount received — Amount paid = $1,160 — $820 = $340*

6. What percent of your investment is the profit made?

   *$340/$820 ≈ 41.5%*

7. If you divide your total percent return from Question 6 by the amount of time in years that you hold the bond, you'll get your percent return per year, or **annual** return, which is a key indicator of how well an investment performs. A long-standing rule of thumb on long-term investments in the stock market is that you can expect annual returns in the 6–7% range. How would this bond investment compare?

   *41.5%/2.5 years = 16.6% per year. By comparison, this is a very good investment.*

---

### Did You Get It

Try this problem to see if you understand the concepts we just studied. The answer can be found at the bottom of the portfolio page.

3. Rashard bought four bonds with face values of $1,000 each, simple interest rate of 5.8% per year, and a maturity date 10 years after they were issued. He paid $4,725 3 years after the bonds were issued. If he keeps the bonds until maturity, find his total profit, and his percent return per year.

## 2-7 Portfolio

Name _____

Check each box when you've completed the task. Remember that your instructor will want you to turn in the portfolio pages you create.

### Technology

1. ☐ This assignment will last longer than most. The plan is for you to pick three stocks to buy with a hypothetical investment of $5,000. Find a financial website that lists current stock prices, find three stocks you're interested in, and calculate how many shares you can buy with your $5,000. Keep in mind that you have to buy three different stocks, and assume a fixed commission of $9.95 for each purchase. Then track the closing price of that stock each day for the time period chosen by your professor, and input the closing price into a spreadsheet. Finally use formulas to calculate the amount of gain or loss on your investment. A template to help you set up the calculations can be found in the online resources for this lesson.

### Online Practice

1. ☐ Include any written work from the online assignment along with any notes or questions about this lesson's content.

### Applications

1. ☐ Complete the applications problems.

### Reflections

Type a short answer to each question.
1. ☐ Describe the difference between stocks and bonds.
2. ☐ What are some things you should consider when deciding whether or not to buy stock in a particular company?
3. ☐ What is the advantage of having stock in a company that pays dividends?
4. ☐ Take another look at your answer to Question 0 at the beginning of this lesson. Would you change your answer now that you've completed the lesson? How would you summarize the topic of this lesson now?
5. ☐ What questions do you have about this lesson?

### Looking Ahead

1. ☐ Complete the Lesson 2-8 Prep Skills and read the opening paragraph in Lesson 2-8 carefully, then answer Question 0 in preparation for that lesson.

### Answers to "Did You Get It?"

1. **a.** $19,190   **b.** You would have made $24,375.05
2. **a.** 18.64; answers vary on reasoning   **b.** $1.81   **3.** $1,595; 4.8% per year

## 2-7 Applications

Name _____

Use the stock listing for Wal-Mart to answer Questions 1–10.

**Wal-Mart Stores Inc. (WMT)** - NYSE

**60.75** ↓0.08(0.13%) 4:01PM EST

After Hours : **60.75** 0.00 (0.00%) 4:12PM EST

| | | | |
|---|---|---|---|
| Prev Close: | **60.83** | Day's Range: | **60.50 - 60.97** |
| Open: | **60.58** | 52wk Range: | **56.30 - 90.97** |
| Bid: | **60.73 x 4300** | Volume: | **5,296,196** |
| Ask: | **60.74 x 2900** | Avg Vol (3m): | **12,578,300** |
| 1y Target Est: | **63.63** | Market Cap: | **194.51B** |
| Beta: | **0.444396** | P/E (ttm): | **13.01** |
| Next Earnings Date: | **N/A** | EPS (ttm): | **4.67** |
| | | Div & Yield: | **1.96 (3.24%)** |

1. What is the ticker symbol you'd use to look up stock quotes for Wal-Mart?

   WMT

2. What was the highest and lowest price that the stock sold for during the last 52 weeks?

   $90.97 and $56.30

3. What was the amount of the dividend per share that the company paid last year?

   $1.96

4. If you own 682 shares, how much in dividends did you make last year?

   682 times $1.96 is $1,336.72.

5. How many shares were traded yesterday?

   5,296,196

6. What was the closing price of the stock yesterday?

   $60.83

## 2-7 | Applications

Name _____

**7.** Find the annual earnings per share.

*$4.67*

**8.** If you purchase 842 shares of Wal-Mart stock at $60.67 per share and the broker's commission is 2%, find the total cost of the purchase.

*842 · $60.67 = $51,084.14*
*1.02 · $51,084.14 = $52,105.82*

**9.** Using information in the table, do a calculation to confirm that the P/E ratio is correct as listed.

*Current price is $60.75, and earning per share are $4.67. $60.75/$4.67 = 13.01*

**10.** Based on the information in the table below, do you think Home Depot stock was a better buy than Wal-Mart at that point? Justify your response.

*This is an opinion question, but Home Depot had higher earnings per share and a much higher P/E ratio at that point.*

**The Home Depot, Inc. (HD)** - NYSE

**132.68** ↓0.22(0.17%) 4:00PM EST

After Hours : **132.43** ↓0.25 (0.19%) 5:19PM EST

| | | | |
|---|---|---|---|
| Prev Close: | **132.90** | Day's Range: | **131.89 - 132.90** |
| Open: | **132.25** | 52wk Range: | **92.17 - 135.47** |
| Bid: | **132.40 x 300** | Volume: | **2,607,226** |
| Ask: | **132.88 x 100** | Avg Vol (3m): | **5,027,970** |
| 1y Target Est: | **141.00** | Market Cap: | **168.22B** |
| Beta: | **0.965301** | P/E (ttm): | **24.89** |
| Next Earnings Date: | **N/A** | EPS (ttm): | **5.33** |
| | | Div & Yield: | **2.36 (1.79%)** |

## 2-7   Applications

Name _____

**11.** Compare the two investments below and decide which would have been the better choice, and why.

Investment 1: $10,000 was invested in a 24-month CD that earned 5.1% annual interest compounded monthly.

Investment 2: 1,400 shares of stock in the Lybarger Aviation Company were bought at $7.11 per share using a brokerage with a 0.75% commission rate on both buying and selling stock. Over the 2 years the stock was held, it paid a dividend of $0.48 per share in the first year and $0.36 per share in the second year. The stock was sold through the same brokerage for $7.95 per share.

Investment 1: $A = \$10,000 \left(1 + \dfrac{.051}{12}\right)^{24} = \$11,071.44$; Profit = $\$1,071.44$

Investment 2: Cost = $1,400 \cdot \$7.11 = \$9,954$; commission = $0.0075 \cdot \$9,954 = \$74.66$

Total investment: $\$9,954 + \$74.66 = \$10,028.66$

Dividends: $1,400 \cdot \$0.48 + 1,400 \cdot \$0.36 = \$1,176$

Proceeds from sale: $1,400 \cdot \$7.95 = \$11,130$; commission = $0.0075 \cdot \$11,130 = \$83.48$

Profit = $\$11,130 + \$1,176 - \$83.48 - \$10,028.66 = \$2,193.86$

Investment 2 made more than twice as much profit.

# 2-7 Applications

Name _____

12. A bond with face value $10,000, simple interest 6.45%, and term 12 years is originally bought by Larry. After 33 months, he sells it to Curly for $11,400. Curly then holds on to it for 7 years, eventually selling it to Moe for $14,950. Moe keeps the bond until it matures and cashes it in.
   a. Which investor made the greatest profit?
   b. Which got the greatest percent return on his investment?
   c. Which got the greatest percent return per year?

Larry's profit: $1,400

Curly's profit: $3,550

Final value of bond: $10,000(1 + 0.0645 \cdot 12) = \$17,740$

Moe's profit: $17,740 - \$14,950 = \$2,790$

Greatest profit was made by Curly.

Larry's percent profit: $\dfrac{\$1,400}{\$10,000} = 0.14$, or 14%, which is $\dfrac{14\%}{33 \div 12 \text{ yrs}} = 5.09\%$ per year.

Curly's percent profit: $\dfrac{\$3,550}{\$11,400} \approx 0.311$, or 31.1%, which is $\dfrac{31.1\%}{7 \text{ yrs}} = 4.44\%$ per year.

Moe's percent profit: $\dfrac{\$2,790}{\$14,950} \approx 0.187$, or 18.7%, which is $\dfrac{18.7\%}{27 \div 12 \text{ yrs}} = 8.31\%$ per year.

Greatest percent return was Curly, but greatest percent per year return was Moe.

# Lesson 2-8   Prep Skills

This is a short review of skills that will come in handy in the next lesson. In each case, answer the question, then rate your confidence level by checking one of the boxes. If you feel like you're struggling with these skills, consult the online resources provided by your instructor for extra practice.

### SKILL 1: CONVERT DECIMALS TO PERCENT FORM

1. Write each decimal in percent form.

   0.23

   0.794

   0.035

### SKILL 2: COMPUTE PERCENTAGES OF AN AMOUNT

2. What is 10% of $8,603?

3. What is 15% of $23,462.12?

### SKILL 3: COMPUTE PERCENTAGE OF A DIFFERENCE

4. Find 20% of the difference between $83,402 and $36,901.

# Lesson 2-8   **A Taxing Situation**   (Income Taxes)

**LEARNING OBJECTIVES**

☐ 1. Understand why we pay taxes.

☐ 2. Explain the basic process of paying taxes.

☐ 3. Determine the amount of tax due based on taxable income.

☐ 4. Complete a 1040EZ form.

© Photodisc/Punchstock RF

*In this world nothing can be said to be certain, except death and taxes.*
—Benjamin Franklin

"I really enjoy paying taxes," said no one. Ever. Of course, if we didn't have to pay taxes, we'd be missing out on some pretty cool stuff, like roads, police, trash pickup, fire fighters, schools, parks . . . Okay, so maybe taxes aren't THAT bad after all. And as our friend Mr. Franklin pointed out, it's not like you get a choice. Taxes are necessary to fund governments at three levels: local, state, and federal. Property taxes, local sales tax, and local income taxes are kept locally to fund services within your community. State income taxes, which are used to fund state governments, vary from state to state depending on revenue a state can generate from other sources, like tourism, oil, or sales tax. Some states have no income tax at all, and are funded entirely through other sources. Federal income tax is something that everyone who earns income has to pay. Based on your income and **deductions** (which are characteristics of your financial situation that allow you to subtract from the tax you have to pay), the percentage of your income that you pay can vary considerably. In this lesson we'll study some common aspects of taxation. These are things that every American *should* be aware of, but far too few actually are.

  **0.** After reading the opening paragraph, what do you think the main topic of this lesson will be?

## 2-8 Class

### How Does the Tax Process Work?

If you earn a paycheck, through a process called **withholding**, taxes are automatically taken from the amount you've earned. The amount of tax that is withheld is based on two main factors: how much you earn, and paperwork you fill out through your employer describing how many other people depend on you financially. The intent is to estimate the amount of tax that you'll owe at the end of the year and pay some of it during each pay period so that you don't end up with a big bill that you can't afford to pay at the end of the year. When it's time to file a tax return, you'll find out if you paid too much, which entitles you to a refund, or too little, which means you need to pay more.

    Our tax system is designed so that people that make more money pay a higher percentage of their income in taxes than do those who make less money. The range in which your income falls is known as a **tax bracket**, and the bracket you're in will determine how much of your income you will owe. It's essentially impossible to understand taxes without understanding tax brackets, so that's where we'll begin.

There are four different filing statuses: single, which is self explanatory; married filing jointly, which is when a married couple files a single return for both; married filing separately, which is when married individuals decide to file separate returns; and head of household, which is for unmarried individuals that financially support others. There are different income levels that qualify you for certain brackets depending on which filing status applies to you. The following is a table of tax brackets for 2014.

| Tax Rate | Single | Married Filing Jointly and Widow(er) | Married Filing Separately | Head of Household |
|----------|--------|--------------------------------------|---------------------------|-------------------|
| 10% | $1–$9,075 | $1–$18,150 | $1–$9,075 | $1–$12,950 |
| 15% | $9,076–$36,900 | $18,151–$73,800 | $9,076–$36,900 | $12,951–$49,400 |
| 25% | $36,901–$89,350 | $73,801–$148,850 | $36,901–$74,425 | $49,401–$127,550 |
| 28% | $89,351–$186,350 | $148,851–$226,850 | $74,426–$113,425 | $127,551–$206,600 |
| 33% | $186,351–$405,100 | $226,851–$405,100 | $113,426–$202,550 | $206,601–$405,100 |
| 35% | $405,101–$406,750 | $405,101–$457,600 | $202,551–$228,800 | $405,101–$432,200 |
| 39.6% | over $406,750 | over $457,600 | over $228,800 | over $432,200 |

For each filing status, the range of incomes listed in that column determines which tax bracket an individual falls into. For example, notice that in the second row of the Married Filing Separately column, the range is $9,076–$36,900, and that row has 15% in the Tax Rate column. This tells us that a married taxpayer filing separately with taxable income between $9,076 and $36,900 is in the 15% tax bracket. (In a while we'll study exactly what that tells us about the amount of tax he or she would pay.)

1. If a person filing as single has taxable income of $42,000, what tax bracket is she in? What about a married person filing jointly?

   *Single: 25% bracket*

   *Married filing jointly: 15%*

Now for the big question: How much would that single person pay in taxes? If you said 25% of $42,000, that's a fine guess. An incorrect one, mind you, but a fine guess nonetheless. So what's the deal? What does the 25% tax bracket mean?

In short, all taxpayers that are single pay 10% on the first $9,075. They then pay 15% on the next $27,825, which is the amount that falls into the range $9,076–$36,900. Finally, they pay 25% of the amount over $36,900.

**2.** Using the information just provided, calculate the amount of tax that our single person would pay on income of $42,000.

10% of $9,075 = $907.50

15% of ($36,900 − $9,075) = $4,173.75

25% of ($42,000 − $36,900) = $1,275

Total tax = $907.50 + $4,173.75 + $1,275 = $6,356.25

> **Math Note**
>
> The taxes here are federal only: the amount of tax due at the state and local level vary widely depending on where you live.

**3.** How much would she have overpaid had she simply paid 25% of her taxable income?

25% of $42,000 = $10,500

$10,500 − $6,356.25 = $4,143.75

She would have overpaid by $4,143.75.

Since many Americans are, shall we say, somewhat math-challenged, the Internal Revenue Service (IRS), the government agency responsible for collecting taxes, publishes tables that let filers look up the amount of tax that they should pay. Their documentation even includes an example with the instructions, in this case for form 1040EZ, which we'll study in a bit.

| 2014 Tax Table | | |
|---|---|---|

**Example.** Mr. Brown is single. His **taxable income** on line 6 of Form 1040EZ is $26,250. He follows two easy steps to figure his tax: **1.** He finds the $26,250-26,300 taxable income line. **2.** He finds the Single filing status column and reads down the column. The **tax** amount shown where the taxable income line and the filing status line meet is $3,488. He enters this amount on line 10 of Form 1040EZ.

| At least | But less than | Single | Married filing jointly |
|---|---|---|---|
| | | Your tax is— | |
| 26,200 | 26,250 | 3,480 | 3,026 |
| 26,250 | 26,300 | 3,488 | 3,034 |
| 26,300 | 26,350 | 3,495 | 3,041 |
| 26,350 | 26,400 | 3,503 | 3,049 |

**4.** Using the tax bracket info on the previous page, if Mr. Brown believes the tax table, will he pay too much or too little? By how much?

Mr. Brown's income puts him in the 15% bracket, so his tax computation is:

10% of $9,075 + 15% of ($26,250 − $9,075) = $907.50 + (0.15)($17,175) = $3,483.75

The amount shown in the table is $3,488, so Mr. Brown will pay $4.25 too much.

> Interesting fact to share with your class: if every filer paid $4.25 too much, in an average year the government would take in a little over a BILLION dollars extra.

**5.** What would happen to you if you fail to pay your taxes? Discuss, and if you're able, maybe do a little bit of Internet research.

*First, you'll get fined and owe more. Other consequences range from your credit rating taking a hit, to liens placed on your belongings, your wages being garnished, and in some extreme cases even prison time.*

## Where Do Your Tax Dollars Go?

While paying taxes really stings, it can help at least some to know exactly what those dollars are accomplishing. The government maintains a website (the link is listed under the graphic below) that illustrates where federal tax dollars go. And for people that stink at percents, which of course does not include you, it's possible to just enter a taxable income and see how that money gets divided up. But we don't need that . . . we can just use the percents.

### Your 2014 Taxpayer Receipt

Understand how and where your tax dollars are being spent. Enter your 2014 income tax info to get started.

| Income Tax | Calculate |

**Programs & Services**

| Program | Percent |
|---|---|
| Health Care | 27.49% |
| National Defense | 23.91% |
| Job and Family Security | 18.17% |
| Net Interest | 9.07% |
| Veterans Benefits | 5.93% |
| Education and Job Training | 3.59% |
| Immigration, Law Enforcement, and Administration of Justice | 2.00% |
| International Affairs | 1.85% |
| Natural Resources, Energy, and Environment | 1.64% |
| Science, Space, and Technology Programs | 1.13% |
| Agriculture | 0.97% |
| Community, Area, and Regional Development | 0.43% |
| Response to Natural Disasters | 0.39% |
| Additional Government Programs | 3.42% |

Source: https://www.whitehouse.gov/2014-taxreceipt

**6.** If you paid $6,500 in federal taxes in 2014, how much of your money went to education and job training?

$3.59% of $6,500 is $233.35.

**7.** In 2014, the president paid $93,362 in federal taxes. How much of his money went to national defense?

23.91% of $93,362 is $22,322.85.

## Did You Get It

Try these problems to see if you understand the concepts we just studied. The answer can be found at the bottom of the portfolio page.

1. Find the tax bracket for a person with status married filing jointly if she has a taxable income of $97,800.
2. Calculate the amount of federal tax that person would owe. What percentage of her taxable income would that be?

## 2-8 Group

### Tax Forms: A Lesson in Following Directions

Many people are intimidated into submission by filling out tax forms. To be fair, you don't want to be making mistakes on forms this important, but with a bit of education and a solid ability to follow written instructions, completing basic tax forms is very doable. In this case, we're going to study federal form 1040EZ, which is a short form that can be filled out by taxpayers that meet the following qualifications:

- Filing status is Single or Married Filing Jointly.
- Taxpayer (and spouse if filing jointly) were under age 65 and not blind at the end of the tax year.
- Taxpayer does not claim any dependents.
- Taxable income is less than $100,000.
- Income came from only wages, salaries, tips, taxable scholarship or fellowship grants, or unemployment compensation, or Alaska Permanent Fund dividends, and taxable interest was not over $1,500.

(There are a couple of other technical provisions, but these are the main qualifications.)

The next page is a copy of the 1040EZ form for 2014, and we'll practice filling out the form. But first, we should discuss how you get information about your income. For many folks, this will come from two sources: a W-2 form, which reports your wages, and a 1099-INT, which reports interest income.

| a Employee's social security number XXX–XX–XXXX | OMB No. 1545-0008 | Safe, accurate, FAST! Use  IRS e-file | Visit the IRS website at www.irs.gov/efile |
|---|---|---|---|

| b Employer identification number (EIN) | 1 Wages, tips, other compensation **58,584.78** | 2 Federal income tax withheld **8,941.46** |
|---|---|---|

| c Employer's name, address, and ZIP code<br><br>Kramerica Industries<br>129 West 81st Street, Apartment 5B<br>New York, NY 10029 | 3 Social security wages **66,482.21** | 4 Social security tax withheld **2,132.11** |
|---|---|---|
| | 5 Medicare wages and tips **66,482.21** | 6 Medicare tax withheld **963.99** |
| | 7 Social security tips | 8 Allocated tips |

| d Control number | 9 | 10 Dependent care benefits |
|---|---|---|

| e Employee's first name and initial   Last name   Suff.<br><br>Darin Roberts<br>18 Newman Ave, Apt. 4B<br>New York, NY 10012 | 11 Nonqualified plans | 12a See instructions for box 12 |
|---|---|---|
| | 13 Statutory employee [X]  Retirement plan [ ]  Third-party sick pay [ ] | 12b |
| | 14 Other | 12c |
| | | 12d |

| f Employee's address and ZIP code | | |
|---|---|---|

| 15 State | Employer's state ID number | 16 State wages, tips, etc. | 17 State income tax | 18 Local wages, tips, etc. | 19 Local income tax | 20 Locality name |
|---|---|---|---|---|---|---|
| NY | 47-325941 | 58,584.78 | 1,762.12 | 66,482.21 | 1,329.66 | NYC |

Form **W-2** Wage and Tax Statement

Department of the Treasury—Internal Revenue Service

**Copy B—To Be Filed With Employee's FEDERAL Tax Return.**
This information is being furnished to the Internal Revenue Service.

---

[ ] VOID   [ ] CORRECTED

| PAYER'S name, street address, city or town, state or province, country, ZIP or foreign postal code, and telephone no.<br><br>Great Eastern Savings and Loan<br>400 West 79th Street<br>New York, NY 10029 | Payer's RTN (optional) | OMB No. 1545-0112 | **Interest Income** |
|---|---|---|---|
| | 1 Interest income<br>$ 749.36 | Form **1099-INT** | |
| | 2 Early withdrawal penalty<br>$ | | Copy 1 |
| PAYER'S federal identification number | RECIPIENT'S identification number XXX–XX–XXXX | $ | |
| | 3 Interest on U.S. Savings Bonds and Treas. obligations<br>$ | | For State Tax Department |
| RECIPIENT'S name<br>Darin Roberts | 4 Federal income tax withheld<br>$ | 5 Investment expenses<br>$ | |
| Street address (including apt. no.)<br>18 Newman Ave, Apt. 4B | 6 Foreign tax paid<br>$ | 7 Foreign country or U.S. possession | |
| City or town, state or province, country, and ZIP or foreign postal code<br>New York, NY 10012 | 8 Tax-exempt interest<br>$ | 9 Specified private activity bond interest<br>$ | |
| | 10 Market discount<br>$ | 11 Bond premium<br>$ | |
| FATCA filing requirement [ ] | 12<br>$ | 13 Bond premium on tax-exempt bond<br>$ | |
| Account number (see instructions) | 14 Tax-exempt and tax credit bond CUSIP no. | 15 State | 16 State identification no. | 17 State tax withheld<br>$<br>$ |

Form **1099-INT**        www.irs.gov/form1099int        Department of the Treasury - Internal Revenue Service

Department of the Treasury—Internal Revenue Service

Form **1040EZ**

## Income Tax Return for Single and Joint Filers With No Dependents (99)   **2014**

OMB No. 1545-0074

| Your first name and initial | A = Archibald<br>D = Darin | Last name | | **Your social security number** |
|---|---|---|---|---|

| If a joint return, spouse's first name and initial | Last name | | **Spouse's social security number** |
|---|---|---|---|

| Home address (number and street). If you have a P.O. box, see instructions. | Apt. no. | ▲ Make sure the SSN(s) above are correct. |
|---|---|---|

| City, town or post office, state, and ZIP code. If you have a foreign address, also complete spaces below (see instructions). | **Presidential Election Campaign** |
|---|---|

Check here if you, or your spouse if filing jointly, want $3 to go to this fund. Checking a box below will not change your tax or refund. ☐ **You**  ☐ **Spouse**

| Foreign country name | Foreign province/state/county | Foreign postal code |
|---|---|---|

### Income

**Attach Form(s) W-2 here.**

Enclose, but do not attach, any payment.

*These lines don't apply to Darin or Archibald.*

| | | |
|---|---|---|
| **1** | Wages, salaries, and tips. This should be shown in box 1 of your Form(s) W-2. Attach your Form(s) W-2. | **1** A: 26,667<br>D: 58,584.78 |
| **2** | Taxable interest. If the total is over $1,500, you cannot use Form 1040EZ. | **2** A: 0<br>D: 749.36 |
| **3** | Unemployment compensation and Alaska Permanent Fund dividends (see instructions). | **3** |
| **4** | Add lines 1, 2, and 3. This is your **adjusted gross income**. | **4** A: 26,667<br>D: 59,334.14 |
| **5** | If someone can claim you (or your spouse if a joint return) as a dependent, check the applicable box(es) below and enter the amount from the worksheet on back.<br>☐ **You**  ☐ **Spouse**<br>If no one can claim you (or your spouse if a joint return), enter $10,150 if **single**; $20,300 if **married filing jointly**. See back for explanation. | **5** A: 10,150<br>D: 10,150 |
| **6** | Subtract line 5 from line 4. If line 5 is larger than line 4, enter -0-. This is your **taxable income**. ▶ | **6** A: 16,517<br>D: 49,184.14 |

### Payments, Credits, and Tax

Both Darin and Archibald have health insurance, so check this box.

| | | |
|---|---|---|
| **7** | Federal income tax withheld from Form(s) W-2 and 1099.   A: 3,518 | **7** D: 8,941.46 |
| **8a** | **Earned income credit (EIC)** (see instructions) | **8a** |
| **b** | Nontaxable combat pay election.   8b | |
| **9** | Add lines 7 and 8a. These are your **total payments and credits**. ▶ | **9** A: 3,518<br>D: 8,941.46 |
| **10** | **Tax.** Use the amount on **line 6 above** to find your tax in the tax table in the instructions. Then, enter the tax from the table on this line. | **10** A: 2,023.80<br>D: 8,152.29 |
| **11** | Health care: individual responsibility (see instructions)   Full-year coverage ☐ | **11** |
| **12** | Add lines 10 and 11. This is your **total tax**.   A: 2,023.80 | **12** D: 8,152.29 |

### Refund

Have it directly deposited! See instructions and fill in 13b, 13c, and 13d, or Form 8888.

| | | |
|---|---|---|
| **13a** | If line 9 is larger than line 12, subtract line 12 from line 9. This is your **refund.** If Form 8888 is attached, check here ▶ ☐ | **13a** A: 1,494.20<br>D: 789.17 |
| ▶ **b** | Routing number ☐☐☐☐☐☐☐☐☐  ▶ **c** Type: ☐ Checking ☐ Savings | |
| ▶ **d** | Account number ☐☐☐☐☐☐☐☐☐☐☐☐☐☐☐☐☐ | |

### Amount You Owe

| | | |
|---|---|---|
| **14** | If line 12 is larger than line 9, subtract line 9 from line 12. This is the **amount you owe**. For details on how to pay, see instructions. ▶ | **14** |

### Third Party Designee

Do you want to allow another person to discuss this return with the IRS (see instructions)? ☐ **Yes.** Complete below.   ☐ **No**

| Designee's name ▶ | Phone no. ▶ | Personal identification number (PIN) ▶ ☐☐☐☐☐ |
|---|---|---|

### Sign Here

Joint return? See instructions.

Keep a copy for your records.

Under penalties of perjury, I declare that I have examined this return and, to the best of my knowledge and belief, it is true, correct, and accurately lists all amounts and sources of income I received during the tax year. Declaration of preparer (other than the taxpayer) is based on all information of which the preparer has any knowledge.

| Your signature | Date | Your occupation | Daytime phone number |
|---|---|---|---|
| Spouse's signature. If a joint return, **both** must sign. | Date | Spouse's occupation | If the IRS sent you an Identity Protection PIN, enter it here (see inst.) ☐☐☐☐☐☐ |

### Paid Preparer Use Only

| Print/Type preparer's name | Preparer's signature | Date | Check ☐ if self-employed | PTIN |
|---|---|---|---|---|
| Firm's name ▶ | | | Firm's EIN ▶ | |
| Firm's address ▶ | | | Phone no. | |

**For Disclosure, Privacy Act, and Paperwork Reduction Act Notice, see instructions.**   Cat. No. 11329W   Form **1040EZ** (2014)

The goal of the group activity is to fill in the 1040EZ form on the previous page for one of two individuals: Darin, whose W-2 and 1099-INT were displayed earlier, and Archibald, whose W-2 is below. Each is single and has no dependents. Archibald works part time while still in college, and received $3,000 in scholarship money. Because he's not currently in a Bachelor's degree program or higher, that scholarship money is considered taxable income.

Choose which individual you want to help with their 1040EZ form. After filling it out, have another group perform an audit to check your work. In each case, you'll need to use the tax bracket information from earlier to calculate the amount of tax that should be paid.

| a Employee's social security number  xxx–xx–xxxx | | |
| --- | --- | --- |

OMB No. 1545-0008    **Safe, accurate, FAST! Use**    IRS e-file    Visit the IRS website at www.irs.gov/efile

| b Employer identification number (EIN) | 1 Wages, tips, other compensation  23,667 | 2 Federal income tax withheld  3,518 |
| --- | --- | --- |
| c Employer's name, address, and ZIP code  **Heisman Marketing  1975 Lane Ave.  Columbus, OH 43018** | 3 Social security wages  23,667 | 4 Social security tax withheld  943.12 |
| | 5 Medicare wages and tips  23,667 | 6 Medicare tax withheld  247.01 |
| | 7 Social security tips | 8 Allocated tips |
| d Control number | 9 | 10 Dependent care benefits |
| e Employee's first name and initial    Last name    Suff.  **Archibald Griffen  45 Buckeye Way  Columbus, OH 43085** | 11 Nonqualified plans | 12a See instructions for box 12 |
| | 13 Statutory employee [X]  Retirement plan [ ]  Third-party sick pay [ ] | 12b |
| | 14 Other | 12c |
| | | 12d |
| f Employee's address and ZIP code | | |

| 15 State  OH | Employer's state ID number  11-004141 | 16 State wages, tips, etc.  23,667 | 17 State income tax  852.19 | 18 Local wages, tips, etc.  23,667 | 19 Local income tax  356.97 | 20 Locality name  Colum |
| --- | --- | --- | --- | --- | --- | --- |

Form **W-2**   **Wage and Tax Statement**                    Department of the Treasury—Internal Revenue Service

**Copy B—To Be Filed With Employee's FEDERAL Tax Return.**
This information is being furnished to the Internal Revenue Service.

## Did You Get It

Try this problem to see if you understand the concepts we just studied. The answer can be found at the bottom of the portfolio page.

3. A taxpayer with status married filing jointly has no dependents other than her spouse. Her federal wages are $81,112, and she also had $1,462.12 in interest income. What would you write in the following lines on her 1040EZ form?
   a. 4      b. 5      c. 6      d. 10

If you want students to have access to detailed form 1040 EZ instructions provided by the IRS, you can find them in the online resources for this lesson.

**2-8** | **Portfolio**

Name _____

Check each box when you've completed the task. Remember that your instructor will want you to turn in the portfolio pages you create.

### Technology

1. ☐ There are TONS of free online tools to help you with tax forms and calculations. Find one you like and use it to calculate the amount of tax that Darin Roberts (tax forms displayed within this lesson) owes in federal taxes. Then decide if he would be due a refund or have to pay more, and describe how you decided. Make sure that you include a reference to the online tool you used. If you could include a screen shot of your work, your professor would be most appreciative.

### Online Practice

1. ☐ Include any written work from the online assignment along with any notes or questions about this lesson's content.

### Applications

1. ☐ Complete the applications problems.

### Reflections

Type a short answer to each question.

1. ☐ Why do we have to pay taxes?
2. ☐ What is a tax bracket? What is the point of tax brackets?
3. ☐ What is a 1040 form used for?
4. ☐ Take another look at your answer to Question 0 at the beginning of this lesson. Would you change your answer now that you've completed the lesson? How would you summarize the topic of this lesson now?
5. ☐ What questions do you have about this lesson?

### Looking Ahead

1. ☐ Complete the Lesson 3-1 Prep Skills and read the opening paragraph in Lesson 3-1 carefully, then answer Question 0 in preparation for that lesson.

### Answers to "Did You Get It?"

1. 25%     2. $16,162.50; 16.5%     3. Line 4: $82,574.12; Line 5: $20,300; Line 6: $62,274.12; Line 10: $8,433.62

# 2-8 Applications

Name _____

Everyone fears the tax auditor—that's a government employee who checks over tax returns for accuracy. This is your chance to play auditor. Check the 1040-EZ filed by the deputy sheriff whose W-2 and 1099 forms are below. The completed 1040 is on page 173. Rick is filing jointly for himself and his wife.

| **a** Employee's social security number XXX–XX–XXXX | OMB No. 1545-0008 | Safe, accurate, FAST! Use | IRS e-file | Visit the IRS website at www.irs.gov/efile |
|---|---|---|---|---|

| **b** Employer identification number (EIN) | **1** Wages, tips, other compensation 92,513 | **2** Federal income tax withheld 14,319 |
|---|---|---|

| **c** Employer's name, address, and ZIP code  King County Sherriff  411 W. Main Ave  Cynthiana, KY 41031 | **3** Social security wages 96,303 | **4** Social security tax withheld 3,601.11 |
|---|---|---|
| | **5** Medicare wages and tips 96,303 | **6** Medicare tax withheld 952.00 |
| | **7** Social security tips | **8** Allocated tips |

| **d** Control number | **9** | **10** Dependent care benefits |
|---|---|---|

| **e** Employee's first name and initial   Last name   Suff.  Richard Grimes  11 Apocalypse Circle  Cynthiana, KY 41031 | **11** Nonqualified plans | **12a** See instructions for box 12 |
|---|---|---|
| | **13** Statutory employee [X]  Retirement plan [ ]  Third-party sick pay [ ] | **12b** |
| | **14** Other | **12c** |
| | | **12d** |

| **f** Employee's address and ZIP code |
|---|

| **15** State KY | Employer's state ID number 21-006390 | **16** State wages, tips, etc. 96,303 | **17** State income tax 3,774 | **18** Local wages, tips, etc. 96,303 | **19** Local income tax 917 | **20** Locality name Cynthi |
|---|---|---|---|---|---|---|

**Form W-2** **Wage and Tax Statement**

Department of the Treasury—Internal Revenue Service

**Copy B—To Be Filed With Employee's FEDERAL Tax Return.**
This information is being furnished to the Internal Revenue Service.

---

☐ VOID    ☐ CORRECTED

| PAYER'S name, street address, city or town, state or province, country, ZIP or foreign postal code, and telephone no.  Kentucky State Employee Credit Union  142 Poplar St  Cynthiana, KY 41031 | Payer's RTN (optional) | OMB No. 1545-0112 | **Interest Income** |
|---|---|---|---|
| | **1** Interest income  $ 1,104.61 | Form **1099-INT** | |
| PAYER'S federal identification number | RECIPIENT'S identification number  XXX–XX–XXXX | **2** Early withdrawal penalty $ | Copy 1 |
| | | **3** Interest on U.S. Savings Bonds and Treas. obligations $ | For State Tax Department |
| RECIPIENT'S name  Richard Grimes | | **4** Federal income tax withheld $ | **5** Investment expenses $ |
| Street address (including apt. no.)  11 Apocalypse Circle | | **6** Foreign tax paid $ | **7** Foreign country or U.S. possession |
| City or town, state or province, country, and ZIP or foreign postal code  Cynthiana, KY 41031 | | **8** Tax-exempt interest $ | **9** Specified private activity bond interest $ |
| | | **10** Market discount $ | **11** Bond premium $ |
| | FATCA filing requirement ☐ | **12** | **13** Bond premium on tax-exempt bond $ |
| Account number (see instructions) | | **14** Tax-exempt and tax credit bond CUSIP no. | **15** State | **16** State identification no. | **17** State tax withheld $ $ |

Form **1099-INT**    www.irs.gov/form1099int    Department of the Treasury - Internal Revenue Service

## 2-8 Applications

Name _____

1. Using the table on page 162, calculate the tax due on the taxable income shown on Rick's 1040. Then compare to the amount shown in the IRS tax table to the right. Is Rick better off using his amount, or the IRS amount?

$0.10(\$18,150) + 0.15(\$73,800 - \$18,150) +$
$0.25(\$76,003 - \$73,800) = \$10,713.25$

*The table shows $10,719, so Rick is $5.75 ahead if he calculates the tax himself.*

| If line 43 (taxable income) is— | | And you are— | | | |
|---|---|---|---|---|---|
| At least | But less than | Single | Married filing jointly * | Married filing separately | Head of a house-hold |
| | | | Your tax is— | | |
| **76,000** | | | | | |
| 76,000 | 76,050 | 14,863 | 10,719 | 14,911 | 13,419 |
| 76,050 | 76,100 | 14,875 | 10,731 | 14,925 | 13,431 |
| 76,100 | 76,150 | 14,888 | 10,744 | 14,939 | 13,444 |
| 76,150 | 76,200 | 14,900 | 10,756 | 14,953 | 13,456 |
| 76,200 | 76,250 | 14,913 | 10,769 | 14,967 | 13,469 |

2. List any mistakes you found on the 1040, and write how they should be corrected. If you need extra space for calculations, use the blank space on the next page.

*1. He used the wrong income on line 1: the federal income is in box 1 of his W2: $92,513.*

*2. He failed to report $1,104.61 in interest income on line 2.*

*3. This makes his corrected taxable income $92,513 + $1,104.61 − $20,300 = $73,317.61. This should go on line 6.*

*4. He put the amount of state tax he paid on line 7, rather than the federal amount, which is $14,319. This goes on lines 7 and 9.*

*5. He calculated the tax correctly, but since it was on the wrong amount, that needs to be redone. The correct tax is 0.10($18,150) + 0.15($73,317.61 − $18,150) = $10,090.14, which goes on lines 10 and 12.*

*6. The amount of tax paid and owed are both wrong, so where he calculated what he owed, he was way off. See Question 3.*

3. Would our friend Rick have paid too much or too little in taxes without your corrections? By how much?

*WAY too much. He is actually due a refund of $14,319 − $10,090.14 = $4,228.86. So he cheated himself out of $7,112.14 + $4,228.86, which is $11,341.*

**2-8**  **Applications**

Name _____

**4.** Using the corrected tax that Rick paid after you finished your audit, how much of Rick's taxes will go to paying interest on the national debt?

*The amount he pays in taxes is $10,090.14. The bar graph on page 164 shows that 9.07% goes to interest, so Rick is paying 0.0907 · $10,090.14 = $915.18 toward interest on the national debt. Ugh.*

**2-8**  **Applications**

Name _____

| | |
|---|---|
| Form **1040EZ** | Department of the Treasury—Internal Revenue Service |

**Income Tax Return for Single and Joint Filers With No Dependents** (99)   **2014**

OMB No. 1545-0074

Your first name and initial: **Richard**   Last name: **Grimes**

Your social security number: XXX | XX | XXXX

If a joint return, spouse's first name and initial: **Lori**   Last name: **Grimes**

Spouse's social security number: XXX | XX | XXXX

Home address (number and street). If you have a P.O. box, see instructions.
**11 Apocalypse Circle**   Apt. no.

▲ Make sure the SSN(s) above are correct.

City, town or post office, state, and ZIP code. If you have a foreign address, also complete spaces below (see instructions).
**Cynthiana, KY 41031**

Foreign country name | Foreign province/state/county | Foreign postal code

**Presidential Election Campaign**
Check here if you, or your spouse if filing jointly, want $3 to go to this fund. Checking a box below will not change your tax or refund.   ☐ You   ☐ Spouse

**Income**

Attach Form(s) W-2 here.

Enclose, but do not attach, any payment.

| | | | |
|---|---|---|---|
| 1 | Wages, salaries, and tips. This should be shown in box 1 of your Form(s) W-2. Attach your Form(s) W-2. | 1 | 96.303 |
| 2 | Taxable interest. If the total is over $1,500, you cannot use Form 1040EZ. | 2 | |
| 3 | Unemployment compensation and Alaska Permanent Fund dividends (see instructions). | 3 | |
| 4 | Add lines 1, 2, and 3. This is your **adjusted gross income.** | 4 | 96,303 |
| 5 | If someone can claim you (or your spouse if a joint return) as a dependent, check the applicable box(es) below and enter the amount from the worksheet on back. ☐ You  ☐ Spouse  If no one can claim you (or your spouse if a joint return), enter $10,150 if **single;** $20,300 if **married filing jointly.** See back for explanation. | 5 | 20,300 |
| 6 | Subtract line 5 from line 4. If line 5 is larger than line 4, enter -0-. This is your **taxable income.** ▶ | 6 | 76,003 |

**Payments, Credits, and Tax**

| | | | |
|---|---|---|---|
| 7 | Federal income tax withheld from Form(s) W-2 and 1099. | 7 | 3,601.11 |
| 8a | **Earned income credit (EIC)** (see instructions) | 8a | |
| b | Nontaxable combat pay election.   8b | | |
| 9 | Add lines 7 and 8a. These are your **total payments and credits.** ▶ | 9 | 3,601.11 |
| 10 | **Tax.** Use the amount on **line 6 above** to find your tax in the tax table in the instructions. Then, enter the tax from the table on this line. | 10 | 10,713.25 |
| 11 | Health care: individual responsibility (see instructions)   Full-year coverage ☐ | 11 | |
| 12 | Add lines 10 and 11. This is your **total tax.** | 12 | 10,713.25 |

**Refund**

Have it directly deposited! See instructions and fill in 13b, 13c, and 13d, or Form 8888.

| | | | |
|---|---|---|---|
| 13a | If line 9 is larger than line 12, subtract line 12 from line 9. This is your **refund.** If Form 8888 is attached, check here ▶ ☐ | 13a | |
| ▶ b | Routing number | ▶c Type: ☐ Checking ☐ Savings | |
| ▶ d | Account number | | |

**Amount You Owe**

| | | | |
|---|---|---|---|
| 14 | If line 12 is larger than line 9, subtract line 9 from line 12. This is the **amount you owe.** For details on how to pay, see instructions. ▶ | 14 | 7,112.14 |

**Third Party Designee**

Do you want to allow another person to discuss this return with the IRS (see instructions)?   ☐ **Yes.** Complete below.   ☐ **No**

Designee's name ▶          Phone no. ▶          Personal identification number (PIN) ▶

**Sign Here**

Under penalties of perjury, I declare that I have examined this return and, to the best of my knowledge and belief, it is true, correct, and accurately lists all amounts and sources of income I received during the tax year. Declaration of preparer (other than the taxpayer) is based on all information of which the preparer has any knowledge.

Joint return? See instructions.

Keep a copy for your records.

Your signature   Date   Your occupation   Daytime phone number

Spouse's signature. If a joint return, **both** must sign.   Date   Spouse's occupation

If the IRS sent you an Identity Protection PIN, enter it here (see inst.)

**Paid Preparer Use Only**

Print/Type preparer's name   Preparer's signature   Date   Check ☐ if self-employed   PTIN

Firm's name ▶          Firm's EIN ▶

Firm's address ▶          Phone no.

For Disclosure, Privacy Act, and Paperwork Reduction Act Notice, see instructions.   Cat. No. 11329W   Form **1040EZ** (2014)

# Unit 3
# Place Your Bets

© View Stock/agefotostock RF

## Outline

# Math In Gambling

The fact that you're reading this sentence means that you're probably taking a math class right now. But maybe not . . . you could be an instructor evaluating the book, or maybe an editor looking for mistakes (unsuccessfully, no doubt). Still, I would be willing to bet that you're taking a math class. The word "probably" indicates a certain likelihood of something happening, and that basic idea is the topic of this unit. We call the study of the likelihood of events occurring *probability*.

Probability is one of the most useful concepts in math because being able to anticipate the likelihood of events can be useful in so many different areas. Games of chance, business and investing, sports, and weather forecasting are just a few samples from an essentially limitless list of applications. What are the chances of your team winning the championship? Should you take an umbrella to the golf course today? Will stock in a company you're keeping an eye on go up or down? Is that new job offer a good opportunity, or a disaster waiting to happen? Every day you make decisions regarding possible events that are governed at least in part by chance. The more you know about the likelihood of events, the more informed your decisions are likely to be.

We titled this chapter Place Your Bets not because everything we deal with will involve traditional gambling games, but to encourage you to think about the fact that almost everything we do is a gamble to some extent. And in that regard, almost everything we do relates to probability in some way. Have you ever gone outside during a thunderstorm? Not worn a seatbelt? Texted while driving? Smoked? Eaten a fatty diet? Ridden a motorcycle? Flown on a plane? Sped up to beat a red light?

In each of those instances, you were gambling, and not with something silly like casino chips. You were literally gambling with your life as the stakes. To be fair, the odds were DRAMATICALLY in your favor, and the fact that you're not currently deceased proves that you're on a heck of a winning streak. But the more you learn about probability, the more likely you'll be to give some deeper thought to the consequences of actions. And that's what we in academia call "getting an education."

So let's talk about gambling, both traditional and otherwise. You can think about these questions now, make some educated guesses, and maybe discuss them with your group. Eventually, you can come back and answer all of them, and see how accurate your guesses were.

1. Just last week the Powerball lottery reached a jackpot of $1.5 billion dollars. Billion. With a "b." If you bought ten tickets, were you more likely to win the jackpot or get struck by lightning? Make a guess, then look up the odds of winning the jackpot, and your probability of getting struck by lightning, on the Internet. Which is more likely?

2. What does texting while driving do to the probability that you'll be in a fatal accident? Again, make an educated guess, then do some research to see how you did.

3. A handful of gambling scenarios is provided below. In each case, find the expected value (that is, the average amount a person would win or lose) if placing the bet 100 times. Then rank the scenarios from best to worst in terms of your likelihood of winning or losing money. It's a GREAT idea to rank them before you do the calculations. You may be surprised at the results.

   - At a church fair, you bet $1 and roll two dice. If the sum is 2, 3, 11, or 12, you get back your dollar plus four more. On any other roll, you lose.
   - In a casino, you bet $1 on 33 at a roulette table. There are 38 possible numbers that can come up. If you win, you get your dollar back, plus 35 more.
   - You buy a one dollar ticket to a multistate lottery. If you match all six numbers, including the Mega Ball, you win the $20 million dollar jackpot. If not, you lose. There are 175,711,536 possible combinations, and only one of them will be a winner.
   - You bet $1 on flipping a coin with your roommate. Heads, you win, tails, your roommate wins.

# Lesson 3-1   Prep Skills

This is a short review of skills that will come in handy in the next lesson. In each case, answer the question, then rate your confidence level by checking one of the boxes. If you feel like you're struggling with these skills, consult the online resources provided by your instructor for extra practice.

### SKILL 1: REDUCING FRACTIONS

1. Write each fraction in lowest terms.

$$\frac{12}{16} \qquad \frac{65}{80}$$

### SKILL 2: CONVERTING BETWEEN FRACTIONS, DECIMALS, AND PERCENTS

2. Write each percent in decimal form.

60%

12.5%

3. Write each fraction in percent form.

$$\frac{3}{5}$$

$$\frac{12}{16}$$

4. Write each decimal in percent form.

0.13

0.058

### SKILL 3: INTERPRETING "AT MOST" AND "AT LEAST"

5. Write the whole numbers between 1 and 20 that are at least 15, and those that are at most 8.

# Lesson 3-1   So You're Saying There's a Chance . . .    (Basic Probability)

### LEARNING OBJECTIVES

☐ 1. Understand key terminology in the study of probability.

☐ 2. Compute and interpret theoretical and empirical probabilities.

☐ 3. Compare theoretical and empirical probability.

© Brand X Pictures RF

*A scientist worthy of a lab coat should be able to make original discoveries while wearing a clown suit, or give a lecture in a high squeaky voice from inhaling helium. It is written nowhere in the math of probability theory that one may have no fun.*

—Eliezer Yudkowsky

Walking into a casino without knowing anything about probability is kind of like going to a stick fight without a stick—you're likely to take a beating. Casinos aren't in the business of losing money, and the games are designed so that most people lose more than they win. But an understanding of what is likely to happen in a given situation can give you an advantage over other players, giving you a better chance of walking out the door with some cash in your pockets. (Although if you learn enough about probability, you might decide that staying away from casinos is your best approach.)

The study of probability originated in an effort to understand games of chance, like those that use coins, dice, and playing cards. Generally speaking, probability is simply a number that describes how likely an event is to occur. We will use games of chance to illustrate the ideas, but will eventually see that probability has many applications beyond simple games.

**0.**  After reading the opening paragraphs, what do you think the main topic of this lesson will be?

## 3-1   Class

In this lesson, we'll examine the basic concepts involved in studying **probability.** In short, the probability of something occurring is a number that represents how likely it is to occur. You can think of it as the percent chance of something happening. The major difference between percent chance and probability is that we write probability as a number between zero and one. So in that regard, it's like percent chance with the percentage written in decimal or fractional form.

**1.**  A forecaster says that there's a 70% chance of rain today. What is the probability of rain?

*The probability is 0.7, or 7/10.*

## Sample Spaces

Processes such as flipping a coin, rolling a die, or drawing a card from a deck are called probability experiments.

> A **probability experiment** is a process that leads to well-defined results called **outcomes**. An outcome is the result of a single trial of a probability experiment.

Some examples of a trial are flipping a coin once, rolling a single die, and drawing one card from a deck.

2. When a coin is tossed, there are __2__ possible outcomes. List them.

   *heads, tails*

3. When rolling a single die, there are __6__ possible outcomes. List them.

   *1, 2, 3, 4, 5, 6*

In a probability experiment, we can predict what outcomes are possible, but we can't predict with certainty which one will occur. We say that the outcomes occur at **random.** In any experiment, the set of all possible outcomes is called the **sample space.** What you did in Questions 2 and 3 was find the sample space for two different probability experiments.

4. For each experiment described below, write the sample space. The first is filled in for you as a reminder that a sample space is a SET, and we write sets inside braces with commas separating the elements.

| Experiment | Sample Space |
|---|---|
| Flip one coin | {head, tail} |
| Roll one die | *(1, 2, 3, 4, 5, 6)* |
| Answer a true-false question | *(Right, wrong) OR (True, False)* |
| Flip two coins | *(Tails tails, tails heads, heads heads, tails tails)* |

In finding probabilities, it's sometimes necessary to consider several outcomes of a probability experiment.

5. For example, when a die is rolled, we may want to consider obtaining an odd number; there are __3__ outcomes that satisfy this criterion. List them.

   *1, 3, 5*

Getting an odd number when rolling a die is an example of an *event*.

> An **event** is any subset of the sample space for a probability experiment. This means that an event could be a single outcome, or a set of several outcomes.

There's a subtle distinction between an outcome and an event: an outcome is a single occurrence, while an event can contain a number of outcomes. So rolling 2 with a single die is an outcome, but can also be considered an event. Rolling an odd number, on the other hand, is an event made up of three outcomes, but is not itself an outcome.

Let's look at that distinction more closely. You already listed out the sample space for flipping two coins. Look back at the table on the previous page, and make sure that you have FOUR outcomes in your sample space.

6. How many results match getting heads on the first flip and tails on the second?

   *Just one*

That's an outcome.

7. How many results match getting one head and one tail?

   *Two*

© Photodisc Collection/
Getty Images RF

Experiment: draw a card.
Sample space: 52 cards.
Outcome: draw the ace
of spades. Event: draw
an ace.

That's an event.

Identify each scenario in Questions 8–10 as an event, an outcome, or both.

8. When rolling two dice, getting 3 on the first die and 5 on the second.

   *This is an outcome. It's a specific single occurrence. That makes it an event as well.*

9. When rolling two dice, getting a total of 10.

   *This is an event. There are several different ways to get a total of 10.*

10. When flipping a coin ten times consecutively, getting tails eight times.

    *This is an event. You could get tails on the first eight trials, or the last eight, or . . . well, you get the picture.*

Some students may be unfamiliar with a standard deck of cards. Not surprisingly we'll be using cards quite a bit in the next few lessons, so you might want to bring in and describe a deck to be on the safe side.

### Did You Get It

Try this problem to see if you understand the concepts we just studied. The answer can be found at the bottom of the portfolio page.

1. A baseball team has 12 pitchers on the roster, and the manager, who evidently is intent on losing his job, decides to pick the starting pitcher for tonight's game randomly. What is the sample space? Write an example of an outcome, and an example of an event.

## Theoretical Probability

Now we're ready to specifically define what is meant by probability. The first type we'll study is called **theoretical probability.** The goal is to determine all of the possible outcomes in a sample space and determine the probability, or likelihood, of an event occurring without actually performing experiments. There is one key assumption we make in theoretical probability: that every outcome in a sample space is equally likely. For example, when a single die is rolled, we assume that each number is equally likely to come up. When a card is chosen from a deck of 52 cards, we assume that each card has the same probability of being drawn.

11. You'd have to be awfully bored to flip a coin 100 times, but if you did, about how many times do you think it would land tails side up?

    *Answers can vary, but a reasonable answer would have to be something close to 50.*

12. What percentage of the time would you expect the coin to land tails up?

    *50%*

13. Write a fraction with the number of flips in the denominator and the number of times you're expecting it to land tails up in the numerator. What does this have to do with your answer to Question 12?

    *50/100–This provides the percentage from Question 12.*

Congratulations: You've just computed your first theoretical probability. You didn't actually flip a coin 100 times: you just used reasoning ability to decide what the likelihood of getting tails is. That's what makes it a theoretical probability. You developed a theory by thinking, as opposed to gathering data experimentally. (We'll get to the experimental part in a bit.)

### Calculating a Theoretical Probability

The probability of an event $E$ in a sample space $S$ occurring is given by

$$P(E) = \frac{\text{The number of outcomes in } E}{\text{The number of outcomes in } S} = \frac{n(E)}{n(S)}$$

Take a minute to describe how students really used this formula mentally when they answered Question 12.

For Questions 14–16, a single six-sided die is rolled. Find the probability of each event. If you need to, look back at your sample space on page 180 for reference.

14. Rolling a 2.

    *1/6*

**15.** Rolling a number less than 5.

*4/6, or 2/3*

**16.** Rolling an odd number.

*3/6, or 1/2*

**17.** If THREE coins are flipped, write the sample space. Remember that Tails, Heads, Heads is a different outcome than Heads, Heads, Tails even though both result in one tail and two heads (which, by the way, sounds like a bunny rabbit from a horror story).

*(TTT, TTH, THH, THT, HTT, HTH, HHT, HHH)*

Now is a good time to point out that we often use abbreviations when listing sample spaces, like T and H for tails and heads.

© Brandon Laufenberg/Getty Images RF

For Questions 18–20, three coins are flipped. Find the probability of each event.

**18.** Two tails

*3/8*

**19.** At least one tail

*7/8*

**20.** At most one tail

*1/2*

### Did You Get It

Try these problems to see if you understand the concepts we just studied. The answers can be found at the bottom of the portfolio page.

2. There are 75 balls in a bingo hopper. The ones numbered 1–15 are labeled with B, the ones from 16–30 with I, from 31–45 N, from 46–60 G, and from 61–75 O. Find the probability of these events:
   a. Drawing N42
   b. Drawing N11
   c. Drawing a number less than 50
   d. Drawing an odd number

3. In the game of rock, paper, scissors, two people play, and it's equally likely that you will win, lose, or tie. Find the probability of
   a. Losing twice in a row.
   b. Winning at least once in two tries.
   c. Having the same outcome twice in a row.

Now that we know a little bit about probability, we can make a series of simple but important observations.

## Observation 1: Probability is never negative.

21. Explain why a probability can't be negative.

    *Because the formula divides two numbers, both of which are the number of ways something can occur. You can't have a negative number of possibilities.*

## Observation 2: Probability is never greater than one.

22. Explain why probabilities are never greater than one.

    *The denominator of the fraction is the total number of possible ways that something can occur. The numerator consists of some specific possibilities from that set, so it can't be more than the number in the denominator. To be greater than one, the numerator would have to be bigger.*

## Observation 3: When an event can't possibly occur, its probability is zero. When an event is certain to occur, its probability is one.

23. Explain why impossible events have probability zero and certain events have probability one.

    *If an event is impossible, the number of ways it can happen is zero. The only way we can consider an event to be "certain" is if it contains every possible outcome. In that case, it's obvious that the number of outcomes in the event is the same as the number of total outcomes, so the fraction has value one.*

**Observation 4: If you add the probabilities for every outcome in the sample space, the result is always one.**

24. Explain why the probabilities of all outcomes have to add up to one. Thinking of rolling a die might be helpful.

*If you add the fractions for all possible outcomes, they'll all have the same denominator. So the sum would come from adding all the numerators. But the numerators will consist of all possible outcomes, which gets us back to a fraction with the same numerator and denominator again.*

## 3-1 Group

If it doesn't make you uncomfortable, exchange the following information with the classmates in your Unit 3 group. This will be your small group for the third unit. It would be a good idea to schedule a time for the group to meet to go over homework, ask/answer questions, or prepare for exams. You can use this table to help schedule a mutually agreeable time.

| Name | Phone Number | Email | Available times |
|------|--------------|-------|-----------------|
|      |              |       |                 |
|      |              |       |                 |
|      |              |       |                 |
|      |              |       |                 |
|      |              |       |                 |

Probabilities are usually expressed as fractions or decimals between (and including) zero and one. But occasionally we'll express probabilities as percents. For example, when the probability of an event is 1/2, there's a 50% chance that it'll occur. If an event has probability close to zero, it's very unlikely to occur, and if the probability is close to one, it's very likely to occur.

© Stockbyte/Alamy RF

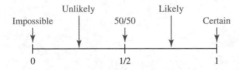

1. Describe exactly what you think it means when a weather forecaster says that there's a 10% chance of rain today.

*Answers vary.*

A lot of people think that a 10% chance of rain means that it will rain for 10% of the day, but that's not correct. The forecaster is expressing a probability—how likely he or she thinks it is that there will be SOME measurable precipitation in that area today. So in essence, it means that if you keep track of 10 days with a 10% chance of rain, you would expect rain on one of those 10 days.

In Questions 2–5, estimate the probability of each event. You don't have to do any calculations: the idea is just to think about the size of a probability compared to how likely something is to occur.

**2.** Passing this course

*Answers vary for each of these.*

**3.** Living past the age of 100

**4.** Winning a million-dollar lottery

**5.** Doing tonight's homework

Sometimes it's useful to find the probability that a given event will NOT occur. Here's an example.

**6.** What's the probability of rolling a 2 with one die?

*1/6*

**7.** How many outcomes are in the event of NOT rolling a 2?

*Five*

**8.** Use your answer to Question 7 to find the probability of NOT rolling a 2.

*5/6*

When you roll one die, you will either get 2, or you will not. If we call the event of rolling a 2 *E*, then we call the event of not rolling a 2 *E'*, and read it as "*E* complement" or "the complement of *E*."

---

For an event *E* in a sample space, the set of all outcomes that are not in *E* is called the **complement** of *E*.

**9.** Describe the complement of each event in detail. Don't just put "not" in front. Think hard! The full answer may not be the obvious one.

**a.** Passing this course

*Sample answer: failing the course, dropping the course, or taking an incomplete in the course.*

**b.** Winning $1,000,000 when you buy a lotto ticket

*Sample answer: winning nothing, winning some amount less than a million dollars, or winning some amount more than a million dollars.*

Given the fact that all probabilities for an experiment have to add up to 1, it makes perfect sense that the probability of rolling 2 plus the probability of not rolling 2 is 1. This line of reasoning gives us a general rule:

## The Probability of a Complement

For any event *E*, if *E'* is the event "*E* does not occur," then

$$P(E') = 1 - P(E)$$

**10.** Of the next 32 trials on the docket in a county court, 5 are homicides, 12 are drug offenses, 6 are assaults, and 9 are property crimes. If jurors are assigned to trials randomly, what's the probability that a given juror won't get a homicide case? Describe two different ways you could calculate this probability.

*Brute force method: $12 + 6 + 9 = 27$ are not homicides, so the probability of not getting a homicide is $27/32$.*

*Clever way: The probability of getting a homicide is $5/32$, so the probability of not getting a homicide is $1 - (5/32)$, which is $27/32$.*

## Did You Get It

Try this problem to see if you understand the concepts we just studied. The answer can be found at the bottom of the portfolio page.

4. For the docket in Question 10, what's the probability that a juror gets assigned to a case that isn't a drug offense?

## Empirical Probability

The second approach to probability we will study is computed using experimental data, rather than counting equally likely outcomes. For example, suppose that out of the last 100 days, you've gone to the gym 60 times. It would be reasonable to guess that the probability of you going to the gym on any given day is about 60/100, or 0.6.

This type of probability is called **empirical probability,** and is based on *observed frequencies*—that is, the number of times a particular event has occurred out of a certain number of trials. In this case, the observed frequency of days going to the gym is 60, the observed frequency of not going is 40, and the total number of trials is $60 + 40 = 100$.

11. On any given day, there are exactly two possibilities: you can go to the gym, or not go to the gym. Why would this fact and theoretical probability not be useful in deciding the probability that you'll go to the gym?

    *Because whether or not you go to the gym isn't a random occurrence. Although there are two outcomes, there's no reason to believe that they're equally likely.*

> This is probably THE key idea in understanding empirical vs. theoretical probability. Have students present their answers to this question and compare.

When calculating theoretical probabilities, we assumed that all outcomes were equally likely. But there are plenty of situations where that assumption would be faulty. In that case, we often perform an experiment to estimate probabilities.

12. If you flip a paper or plastic cup, it can land on its top, its bottom, or its side. Are these outcomes equally likely? Explain.

    *They are not. The cup is by far most likely to land on its side.*

13. Estimate the probability of each outcome.

    *It would be nice if students point out that it depends on the cup. Weight, shape, width of the base play a role. Make sure that their probabilities add up to one!*

The way that we estimated the probability that you go to the gym on any given day is a good model for how to compute empirical probabilities in general:

### Calculating an Empirical Probability

The empirical probability of an event *E* is given by

$$P(E) = \frac{\text{Observed frequency of the event}}{\text{The number of trials}} = \frac{f}{n}$$

14. Describe how you could design an experiment to develop empirical probabilities for flipping a cup.

    *You could flip the cup a bunch of times, keeping track of how many times it lands on its side, top, and bottom. Then divide each frequency by the total number of trials.*

15. Now let's perform that experiment. Your professor will supply your group with a cup. Flip it from about waist level and record how it lands in the table below. Complete as many trials as you feel like you need in order to get accurate empirical probabilities, and then compute those probabilities.

| Position | Put a mark for each occurrence | Add the marks |
|---|---|---|
| Land on top | | |
| Land on bottom | | |
| Land on side | | |

*Answers vary.*

> If possible, choose cups that are at least reasonably likely to land on their top or bottom. The experiment isn't particularly interesting if the cup always ends up on its side. Avoid glass. : )

The table you used to organize the results of your experiment is an example of a **frequency distribution.** This is a table that list categories that we call **classes** (in this case the outcomes of our experiment) and frequencies for each class.

Earlier, we talked about the number of times you might go to the gym in 100 days.

**16.** Complete a frequency distribution for going to the gym based on the data provided earlier.

| Result (Class) | Observed Frequency |
| --- | --- |
| Gym | 60 |
| No gym | 40 |
| Total | 100 |

**Math Note**

We'll study frequency distributions in much more depth a bit later in this course.

**17.** In a random sample of 500 people, 210 had type O blood, 223 had type A, 51 had type B, and 16 had type AB. Set up a frequency distribution for the data.

| Result (Class) | Observed Frequency |
| --- | --- |
| O | 210 |
| A | 223 |
| B | 51 |
| AB | 16 |

For Questions 18–21, use your frequency distribution to find the probability that a randomly selected person from the population has the given blood type.

**18.** Type O

210/500 = 0.42

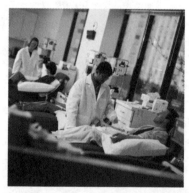

© Keith Brofsky/Getty Images RF

**19.** Type A or B

(223 + 51)/500 = 0.548

**20.** Neither type A nor type O

$(51 + 16)/500 = 0.134$

**21.** A blood type other than AB

$(210 + 223 + 51)/500 = 0.968$

OR

$1 - (16/500) = 0.968$

---

## Did You Get It

Try this problem to see if you understand the concepts we just studied. The answer can be found at the bottom of the portfolio page.

5. A 2-lb bag of Hershey's miniatures contains 33 milk chocolate bars, 27 Krackel bars, 26 Mr. Goodbars, and 19 Special Dark bars. Set up a frequency distribution and find the probability that a bar chosen from a randomly selected bag is
   a. A Mr. Goodbar.
   b. A Krackel or Special Dark.
   c. Not a milk chocolate bar.

---

We'll close the lesson with a comparison between the two types of probability we've studied, theoretical and empirical. The key thing to remember is that in theoretical probability, we use a sample space with a definite number of outcomes, and assume that all of them are equally likely. This makes theoretical probability a bad option for something like the probability of a team winning a given game, because in most cases it would be silly to assume that who wins a game is random.

Empirical probability, on the other hand, uses observed frequencies and a total number of trials to compute a probability. A perfectly reasonable question is, "How many trials are needed to get an accurate probability?" The answer, of course, is seven. Just kidding. There IS no answer to that question. All we can say is that the more trials you do in an experiment, the more likely it is that the probabilities you calculate are true representatives of the situation.

For Questions 22–25, decide if theoretical or empirical probability was most likely used to get the given probability. Justify your answer, of course.

**22.** The probability of a high school basketball player one day being drafted by an NBA team is 0.000408.

*Empirical. This would be based on gathering data about the number of high school players compared to the number of players that get drafted.*

**23.** The probability of being dealt one pair in five-card poker is 0.422569.

*Theoretical. Every hand is equally likely, so you can count the number of possible outcomes and the number that result in one pair.*

> ### Math Note
>
> Each of these probabilities was found by doing a Google search for the string "The probability of."

**24.** The probability of being in a fatal accident if you make two car trips a day for one year is $\frac{1}{13,750}$.

*Empirical. This is based on the number of fatal accidents and the total number of driving trips.*

**25.** The probability of winning some prize when buying one New York State Lottery scratch-off ticket is 0.216.

*Theoretical. The games are designed to have a certain number of winning tickets out of the total number that are sold.*

## 3-1  Portfolio

Name _____

Check each box when you've completed the task. Remember that your instructor will want you to turn in the portfolio pages you create.

### Technology

1. ☐ Have you ever seen a fifteen-sided die? I know I haven't. But you can roll one virtually in a spreadsheet. Actually, you can pick as many sides as you want using the **randbetween** command. Entering "=randbetween(1,15)" will generate a randomly selected number between 1 and 15, which of course is exactly the same thing as rolling a 15-sided die. In the tech template for this lesson (see online resources), we've set up a die rolling experiment. You can enter the number of sides you want, then copy down the formula in cell B2 as many times as you want. Each represents a single roll of the die. You decide on a number of trials, then compute empirical probabilities for each outcome. Finally, double the number of trials and repeat, comparing the second result to the theoretical probability of each number.

### Online Practice

1. ☐ Include any written work from the online assignment along with any notes or questions about this lesson's content.

### Applications

1. ☐ Complete the applications problems.

### Reflections

Type a short answer to each question.

1. ☐ Describe the connection between the probability of an event occurring and percent chance that it will occur.
2. ☐ Explain how theoretical probability differs from empirical probability.
3. ☐ When would you be likely to use empirical methods to calculate a probability rather than theoretical methods?
4. ☐ Take another look at your answer to Question 0 at the beginning of this lesson. Would you change your answer now that you've finished the lesson? How would you summarize the topic of this lesson now?
5. ☐ What questions do you have about this lesson?

### Looking Ahead

1. ☐ Complete the Lesson 3-2 Prep Skills and read the opening paragraph in Lesson 3-2 carefully, then answer Question 0 in preparation for that lesson.

### Answers to "Did You Get It?"

1. Sample space: all 12 pitchers. An outcome would be choosing one specific pitcher. An event would be something like choosing a left-handed pitcher.

2. **a.** $\frac{1}{75}$  **b.** 0  **c.** $\frac{49}{75}$  **d.** $\frac{38}{75}$  **3. a.** $\frac{1}{9}$  **b.** $\frac{5}{9}$  **c.** $\frac{1}{3}$

4. $\frac{5}{8}$  **5. a.** 0.248  **b.** 0.438  **c.** 0.686

# 3-1  Applications

Name _____

1. On *The Price Is Right* game show, to get into the showcase at the end, contestants spin a wheel with 20 equally sized spaces, numbered 5 cents, 10 cents, 15 cents, and so on, up to $1.00. If the contestant spins once, find the probability of each event below.

    **a.** $1.00

    *1/20*

    **b.** An amount less than 50 cents

    *9/20*

    **c.** An amount greater than 75 cents

    *1/4*

    **d.** An amount that is divisible by five

    *1*

© Valerie Macon/Getty Images

    **e.** Which type of probability (empirical or theoretical) are you using to answer these questions? Explain.

    *Theoretical. We know for sure how many total outcomes there are, and we count up how many outcomes satisfy the given event. Plus, each amount is equally likely.*

2. If there are only 50 lottery tickets for the Big Game, one of which is a winning ticket, and you buy 7 of those tickets at random, what is the probability that you'll win the super jackpot? Which type of probability (empirical or theoretical) did you use to answer these questions? Explain.

    *7/50. This is also theoretical, since we know the total number of outcomes, and the number that satisfy the event.*

# 3-1 Applications

Name _____

3. A recent survey reported that 67% of Americans approve of human embryonic stem cell research. If an American is selected at random, find the probability that he or she will disapprove or have no opinion on the issue. Which type of probability (empirical or theoretical) did you use to answer this question? Explain.

*If 67% approve, then 33% either disapprove or have no opinion. This corresponds to a probability of 0.33. This is empirical probability, since we're basing our calculation on numbers that were experimentally determined.*

4. There were 7,690 single-bias hate crime offenses reported in the United States in 2010. These crimes were divided into categories, with the following breakdown: 3,725 were based on racial bias, 1,409 on religious bias, 1,470 on sexual orientation bias, 1,040 on ethnic bias, and 46 on bias against those with disabilities.

   **a.** Make a frequency distribution for this data.

| Class | Frequency |
|---|---|
| Racial | 3,725 |
| Religious | 1,409 |
| Sexual Orientation | 1,470 |
| Ethnic | 1,040 |
| Disabilities | 46 |

Now use your frequency distribution to find the probability of each event in parts b–d.

   **b.** Crime was motivated by sexual orientation bias.

   *1,470/7,690 ≈ 0.19*

   **c.** Crime was motivated by bias against race or ethnicity.

   *(3,725 + 1,040)/7,690 ≈ 0.62*

   **d.** Crime was not motivated by bias against religion or those with disabilities.

   *1 − (1,409 + 46)/7,690 ≈ 0.81*

   **e.** Which type of probability (empirical or theoretical) are you using to answer these questions? Explain.

   *Empirical. All are based on actual gathered data. Also, there's no assumption about outcomes being equally likely.*

## 3-1  Applications

Name _____

5. In December 2008, 500 men and 500 women were surveyed by Omnitel about their opinion on whether federal government bailout money should be used to help homeowners in default. The number giving each response is shown below.

| Response | Men | Women |
|----------|-----|-------|
| Yes | 195 | 235 |
| No | 290 | 220 |
| Not sure | 15 | 45 |

**a.** If a person who participated in the survey is selected at random, what is the probability that he or she answered no?

$(290 + 220)/1{,}000 = 0.51$

**b.** What is the probability that the person selected is a man who answered either yes or no?

$(195 + 290)/1{,}000 = 0.485$

**c.** Based on the data from the survey, if you had stopped a random woman on the street in December 2008 and asked her opinion, what is the probability that she would have said that bailout money should not be used to help homeowners in default?

$220/500 = 0.44$

**d.** Which type of probability (empirical or theoretical) are you using to answer these questions? Explain.

Empirical. All are based on actual gathered data. Also, there's no assumption about outcomes being equally likely.

# Lesson 3-2    Prep Skills

This is a short review of skills that will come in handy in the next lesson. In each case, answer the question, then rate your confidence level by checking one of the boxes. If you feel like you're struggling with these skills, consult the online resources provided by your instructor for extra practice.

### SKILL 1: MULTIPLY STRINGS OF INTEGERS

1. Perform each multiplication without a calculator.

   $3 \cdot 2 \cdot 5$

   $4 \cdot 3 \cdot 5 \cdot 2$

### SKILL 2: COMPUTE PROBABILITIES

2. The math department at my school offers a total of 27 different classes, 3 of which are calculus classes. If someone is goofy enough to pick a math class randomly, what's the probability that they'll end up in a calculus class?

3. If you flip a coin twice, what is the probability of it landing heads up both times?

4. What's the probability of rolling a 5 with one die?

5. What's the probability of rolling a number less than 5 with one die?

# Lesson 3-2   **Make It Count**   (Sample Spaces and Counting Techniques)

## LEARNING OBJECTIVES

☐ 1. Describe how counting techniques are useful in probability theory.

☐ 2. Use tree diagrams and tables to determine sample spaces and compute probabilities.

☐ 3. Develop and use the fundamental counting principle.

© MedioImages RF

*Why does my brain insist on counting the steps every time I walk up a flight of stairs? I just can't help myself. There's something about my mind that always wants to keep counting.*
                    —Rachel Nichols

For centuries, people have tried a wide variety of techniques, some of them pretty bizarre, to try and influence the gender of their children. (Look it up sometime—it's pretty fascinating.) The truth is, without the aid of cutting-edge science, you don't get to choose. But that doesn't stop many young couples from planning the type of family they hope to have. Suppose that one couple would like to have three children, but they definitely want to have at least one boy and one girl. What is the probability that they'll get their wish without having to go beyond three kids?

Believe it or not, the subject of this lesson is counting. Seriously. When working with theoretical probabilities, we know that we need to decide on the sample space for an event, and then find how many individual outcomes are in that event. When situations start to get complicated, it might not always be apparent how to do so. That's where developing counting techniques will be a big help.

**0.** After reading the opening paragraphs, what do you think the main topic of this lesson will be?

## 3-2  Class

Alright, let's start counting. One, two, three, four . . . just kidding. That's not the kind of counting we're talking about. The first technique we will study involves diagramming all of the possible outcomes for probability experiments, like the one referenced in the opening paragraph above. The specific type of diagram we'll study is called a *tree diagram*.

> A **tree diagram** is a diagram where we use branches, similar to a flow chart, to list the outcomes of two or more probability experiments that are done in sequence.

While it's not the most sensitive thing we can do, we can regard the birth of each child for the couple above as a probability experiment: each child is either a boy or a girl. When you start to look at three such experiments in succession, it's helpful to diagram out the possible outcomes.

To draw a tree diagram, we start with branches emanating, or starting from, a single point to show the possible outcomes for the first experiment. Next, we show the outcomes for the second experiment using branches emanating from the end of each branch that was used for the first experiment, and so on.

1. Complete the tree to find the sample space for the genders of three children in a family. Use B to indicate the outcome of having a boy and G to indicate the outcome of having a girl. One outcome is completed for you.

| First Child | Second Child | Third Child | Overall Outcomes |
|---|---|---|---|
| | | B | BBB |
| | B | | |
| | | G | BBG |
| B | | B | BGB |
| | G | | |
| | | G | BGG |
| | | B | GBB |
| | B | | |
| | | G | GBG |
| G | | B | GGB |
| | G | | |
| | | G | GGG |

Two parents have a child

2. Now that a tree diagram is drawn, you can find the outcomes by tracing through all of the branches. List the sample space.

(BBB, BBG, BGB, BGG, GBB, GBG, GGB, GGG)

> Make sure that the students have eight outcomes in their sample space. They may try to list the genders of individual children rather than the genders of all three.

3. Find the probability that a family with three children will have exactly two boys.

3/8

## Math Note

Computing probability here requires assuming that there's a 50–50 chance of getting a boy every time. That's not exactly true, but it's pretty close.

**4.** Find the probability that a family with three children will have at least two girls.

*4/8 or 1/2*

**5.** Look back at the opening paragraph. What is the percent chance that the couple will get their wish?

*6/8 = 75%*

**6.** Describe how being able to count different possibilities helps us in computing probability.

*Answers vary. Look for references to the formula for probability, in which we need to know the total number of outcomes in a sample space, and the number that make up a given event.*

## Did You Get It

Try these problems to see if you understand the concepts we just studied. The answers can be found at the bottom of the portfolio page.

1. A soda machine dispenses both Coke and Pepsi products, in both 12-ounce cans and 20-ounce bottles. For each brand, it has a regular cola, diet cola, and lemon-lime drink. Use a tree diagram to find the sample space for the experiment of choosing one drink at random from this machine.
2. Suppose the soda machine goes berserk and starts dispensing drinks randomly. If you want a diet cola, what is the probability that you'll get one?

In order to collect information for a student survey, a researcher classifies students according to eye color (blue, brown, green), gender (male, female), and class rank (freshman, sophomore). A folder for each classification is then made up (e.g., freshman/female/green eyes).

**7.** How many different outcomes do you think make up the sample space here? Discuss and see if you can come up with an answer without using a tree diagram.

*We kind of want answers to vary here, although if they guess the fundamental counting principle before we develop it that would be pretty cool. For what it's worth, the answer is 12.*

8. Find the sample space for the folders using a tree diagram.

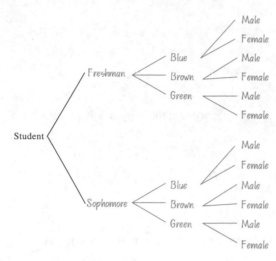

Write sample space here

Freshman, Blue, Male
Freshman, Blue, Female
Freshman, Brown, Male
Freshman, Brown, Female
Freshman, Green, Male
Freshman, Green, Female
Sophomore, Blue, Male
Sophomore, Blue, Female
Sophomore, Brown, Male
Sophomore, Brown, Female
Sophomore, Green, Male
Sophomore, Green, Female

9. If a folder is selected at random, find the probability that it includes students with blue eyes.

   4/12 or 1/3

10. If a folder is selected at random, find the probability that it includes students who are female and don't have brown eyes.

   4/12 or 1/3

11. If a folder is selected at random, find the probability that it includes students who are male freshmen.

   3/12 or 1/4

## Did You Get It

Try this problem to see if you understand the concepts we just studied. The answer can be found at the bottom of the portfolio page.

3. A coin is flipped, and then a die is rolled. Use a tree diagram to find the probability of getting heads on the coin and an even number on the die.

## Tables

Another way of determining a sample space is by making a table. Consider the sample space of selecting a card from a standard deck of 52 cards. (The cards are assumed to be shuffled to make sure that the selection occurs at random.) There are four suits—hearts, diamonds, spades, and clubs, and 13 cards of each suit consisting of the denominations ace (A), 2, 3, 4, 5, 6, 7, 8, 9, 10, and 3 picture or face cards—jack (J), queen (Q), and king (K). The sample space is shown in the table below.

|   | A | 2 | 3 | 4 | 5 | 6 | 7 | 8 | 9 | 10 | J | Q | K |
|---|---|---|---|---|---|---|---|---|---|----|---|---|---|
| ♥ | A♥ | 2♥ | 3♥ | 4♥ | 5♥ | 6♥ | 7♥ | 8♥ | 9♥ | 10♥ | J♥ | Q♥ | K♥ |
| ♦ | A♦ | 2♦ | 3♦ | 4♦ | 5♦ | 6♦ | 7♦ | 8♦ | 9♦ | 10♦ | J♦ | Q♦ | K♦ |
| ♠ | A♠ | 2♠ | 3♠ | 4♠ | 5♠ | 6♠ | 7♠ | 8♠ | 9♠ | 10♠ | J♠ | Q♠ | K♠ |
| ♣ | A♣ | 2♣ | 3♣ | 4♣ | 5♣ | 6♣ | 7♣ | 8♣ | 9♣ | 10♣ | J♣ | Q♣ | K♣ |

A card is drawn from an ordinary deck. In Questions 12–14, use the sample space shown above to find the probabilities of getting

**12.** A jack.

$4/52 = 1/13$

**13.** A black card with a number between 2 and 7.

$8/52 = 2/13$

**14.** A 3 or a diamond.

$16/52 = 4/13$

**15.** Describe why having the sample space listed out in table form is so useful for probability questions like this one.

*You don't really have to think that much—you just have to count up the outcomes that match the given event.*

## 3-2 Group

Let's continue our study of using tables to help us with probability by looking at an example where we need to construct our own table. When two dice are rolled, how many outcomes are in the sample space?

To get a handle on this question, let's pretend that one die is red and the other is green, and let's say that we roll the red die first, then the green one. If we get 1 on the red die, there are six possible overall outcomes: 1 on red and 1 on green, 1 on red and 2 on green, 1 on red and 3 on green, and so on. If we represent each possible outcome with an ordered pair, like (1, 3), then we can systematically list the possibilities in table form.

1. Complete the sample space table below for rolling a red die followed by a green one. The first few outcomes have been done for you because that's the way we roll.

Green Die

|   | 1 | 2 | 3 | 4 | 5 | 6 |
|---|---|---|---|---|---|---|
| **1** | (1, 1) | (1, 2) | (1, 3) | (1, 4) | (1, 5) | (1, 6) |
| **2** | (2, 1) | (2, 2) | (2, 3) | (2, 4) | (2, 5) | (2, 6) |
| **3** | (3, 1) | (3, 2) | (3, 3) | (3, 4) | (3, 5) | (3, 6) |
| **4** | (4, 1) | (4, 2) | (4, 3) | (4, 4) | (4, 5) | (4, 6) |
| **5** | (5, 1) | (5, 2) | (5, 3) | (5, 4) | (5, 5) | (5, 6) |
| **6** | (6, 1) | (6, 2) | (6, 3) | (6, 4) | (6, 5) | (6, 6) |

Red Die

Now that we have our sample space, we can calculate tons of probabilities. Notice, by the way, that the sum of the two dice gives us the total for the roll, so the outcome (1, 3) would be called "rolling a 4." Find each probability for a roll of two dice:

2. Rolling an 8.

5/36

3. Rolling doubles (the same number on each die).

6/36 = 1/6

4. Rolling less than 5.

6/36 = 1/6

## Did You Get It

Try this problem to see if you understand the concepts we just studied. The answer can be found at the bottom of the portfolio page.

4. Two dice are rolled. Use your sample space from Question 1 to find the probability of
   a. Rolling a 9.
   b. Rolling an even number.
   c. Rolling a number greater than 6.

After getting a cool new job, you naturally want a new apartment, and furniture to go along with it. The hip furniture boutique around the corner has the couch you want in either leather or micro suede, and each comes in your choice of four colors: tan, gray, red, and black.

5. Create a tree diagram for this situation to determine how many different couch options you have to choose from.

© Castle Rock Entertainment/
Everett Collection

> Note that the bottom layer of the answer here is requested in Question 9 on page 206, not this question.

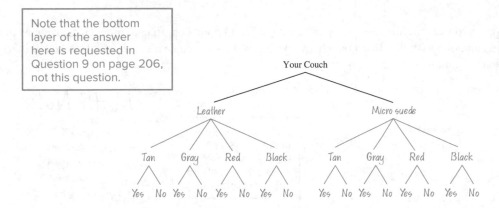

6. How many choices of couch are there? USING YOUR TREE DIAGRAM, explain why it makes perfect sense that the number of total choices is the product of the number of fabric choices and the number of color choices.

*There are two branches on the tree for choice of material, then each of those branches has four branches coming off of it for color choice. So there are 2 · 4 choices total.*

7. Here's a way to connect the first two topics of this lesson. The table below can be used to list all of the couch choices. Explain why this also justifies that the total number of choices is the product of the number of fabric choices and the number of color choices.

|  |  | Color | | | |
|---|---|---|---|---|---|
|  |  | **Tan (T)** | **Gray (G)** | **Red (R)** | **Black (B)** |
| **Fabric** | **Leather (L)** | LT | LG | LR | LB |
|  | **Micro Suede (M)** | MT | MG | MR | MB |

*The table has two rows and four columns, so it has 8 cells total.*

8. More choices is better, right? Suppose the furniture salesperson calls you and points out that your couch also comes in a version with an end recliner, and one without. Based on what we've learned so far, make a conjecture as to how this will change the number of options. Explain.

*Two more choices at the end will multiply the total number of choices by 2, making it 16.*

> If you have a few minutes to spare, do this search in class and talk about some of the results.

**Math Note**

Are more choices *really* better? There's some interesting research that says maybe not. Do a Google search for "choice paralysis" if you're interested.

9. Add this extra layer of choices to your tree diagram on the previous page. Does this confirm your answer to Question 8? Explain.

*It does. Adding an extra two choices under each of the 8 outcomes doubled that number to 16.*

We've now discovered an idea so important in counting that it's literally called "The Fundamental Counting Principle."

### The Fundamental Counting Principle

In a sequence of $n$ procedures, if the first can occur in $k_1$ ways, the second in $k_2$ ways, the third in $k_3$ ways, and so on, the total number of ways the sequence of procedures can occur is

$$k_1 \cdot k_2 \cdot k_3 \cdot \cdots \cdot k_n$$

The basic blood types are represented by letters: A, B, AB, and O. There is also an Rh factor represented by either positive or negative. If a local blood bank labels donations according to type, Rh factor, and biological gender of the donor, it would be useful to look at how many different ways a blood sample can be labeled, as this would have a significant impact on preparing for the labeling.

10. How many different blood types are listed?

    *Four*

© Dynamic Graphics/
JupiterImages RF

11. How many different Rh factors are possible?

    *Two*

12. How many different biological genders are likely to be listed?

    *Two*

13. Based on these answers and the fundamental counting principle, how many different ways can the blood sample be labeled?

    *4 · 2 · 2 = 16*

14. If you choose one of the labels randomly, what is the probability that it corresponds to male and AB-negative?

    *1/16*

15. In reality, the probability of a randomly selected person in the U.S. population being a male with AB-negative blood is about 0.0035. What does that fact and your answer to Question 14 tell you about blood type?

    *That blood types are not all equally likely. Since AB-negative males are far fewer than you'd expect based on theoretical probability, it must be the case that AB-negative blood is less common than other types, at least among males.*

**IMPORTANT NOTE:** The fundamental counting principle can only be used when the occurrence of the first event in no way affects the occurrence of the second event, which in turn does not affect the occurrence of the third event, and so on.

16. A company with 412 employees is designing new ID badges for its employees. Each badge will be coded with a four-letter sequence chosen from the letters A, B, C, D, and E. Will there be enough badges so that everyone gets a different code? Use the fundamental counting principle to decide. Note that letters can be used more than once.

    *There are five choices at each stage (stages corresponding to the letters in the ID), so using the fundamental counting principle, we get $5 \cdot 5 \cdot 5 \cdot 5 \cdot 5 = 3,125$. There are plenty of IDs to go around.*

17. Will there be enough badges to go around if no letter can appear more than once in the code? (Hint: Think about the number of choices at each stage.)

    *This time, there are five choices at the first stage, four at the second (since we can't reuse the first letter), three at the third stage, two at the fourth stage, and only one at the last. Using the fundamental counting principle, we get $5 \cdot 4 \cdot 3 \cdot 2 \cdot 1 = 120$. Now there aren't nearly enough badges.*

18. You could absolutely use a tree diagram to list out the possible codes. Explain why that's a tremendously bad idea.

    *You'd need an awful big piece of paper to list out that many different choices. And a lot of ink, and even more patience.*

## Did You Get It

Try these problems to see if you understand the concepts we just studied. The answers can be found at the bottom of the portfolio page.

5. A discount paint manufacturer plans to make several different paints. The categories include

   Color: Red, blue, white, black, green, brown, yellow
   Type: Latex, oil
   Texture: Flat, semigloss, high-gloss
   Use: Outdoor, indoor
   How many different kinds of paint can be made?

6. The lock on a storage facility is controlled by a keypad containing digits 1 through 5.

   How many three-digit codes are possible if digits can be repeated?
   How many three-digit codes are possible if digits cannot be repeated?

## 3-2 Portfolio

Name _____

Check each box when you've completed the task. Remember that your instructor will want you to turn in the portfolio pages you create.

### Technology

1. ☐ There's a feature in Excel that can be used to build tree diagrams. On the Insert menu, click Smart Art, then Hierarchy, and choose one of the displayed options. It will give you a starting diagram. You'll find further instructions on the technology template for this lesson, which illustrates the tree diagram you drew on page 205. Your job is to build a new tree diagram for possible results of a four-question quiz that has two true-false questions, and two multiple choice questions with four choices each. Then use your tree diagram to answer the probability questions on the tech template.

### Online Practice

1. ☐ Include any written work from the online assignment along with any notes or questions about this lesson's content.

### Applications

1. ☐ Complete the applications problems.

### Reflections

Type a short answer to each question.

1. ☐ What is meant by the term "counting" in this lesson?
2. ☐ Explain how counting techniques are important to the study of probability.
3. ☐ Why is the fundamental counting principle more widely applicable than tree diagrams?
4. ☐ Is the fundamental counting principle useful for empirical or theoretical probabilities? Why?
5. ☐ Take another look at your answer to Question 0 at the beginning of this lesson. Would you change your answer now that you've finished the lesson? How would you summarize the topic of this lesson now?
6. ☐ What questions do you have about this lesson?

### Looking Ahead

1. ☐ Complete the Lesson 3-3 Prep Skills and read the opening paragraph in Lesson 3-3 carefully, then answer Question 0 in preparation for that lesson.

### Answers to "Did You Get It?"

1. Sample space: {Coke, can, cola; Coke, can, diet cola; Coke, can, lemon-lime; Coke, bottle, cola; Coke, bottle, diet cola; Coke, bottle, lemon-lime; Pepsi, can, cola; Pepsi, can, diet cola; Pepsi, can, lemon-lime; Pepsi, bottle, cola; Pepsi, bottle, diet cola; Pepsi, bottle, lemon-lime}

2. $\frac{1}{3}$    3. $\frac{1}{4}$    4. a. $\frac{1}{9}$    b. $\frac{1}{2}$    c. $\frac{7}{12}$    5. 84

6. 125 repeated, 60 not repeated

## 3-2    Applications

Name _____

1. Use the sample space for a standard deck of cards (refer back to page 203 if necessary) to answer each question.

   **a.** We know that there are 52 cards in a standard deck. Explain how you can use the fundamental counting principle to arrive at this same number.

   Four suits, 13 cards in each suit: $4 \cdot 13 = 52$.

   **b.** Before the cards are dealt for a game of poker, what's the probability that the 31st card in the deck is a spade?

   1/4

   **c.** After 5 cards have been dealt to each of six players, with eight spades among those dealt, what's the probability that the 31st card in the deck is a spade?

   22 cards remain, and 5 spades remain, so the probability is 5/22.

2. Akira wants to buy his first new car and can select one option from each category:

   | Model | Engine Type | Color |
   |---|---|---|
   | Ford Focus | Hybrid | Burnt Copper |
   | Honda Civic | E-85 | Cobalt blue |
   | Toyota Corolla | | Metallic green |

   **a.** Using the fundamental counting principle, how many outcomes should there be in the sample space?

   $3 \cdot 2 \cdot 3 = 18$

## 3-2 Applications

Name _____

b. Draw a tree diagram and find the sample space for all possible choices.

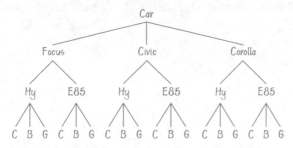

Sample space: (Focus hybrid copper, Focus hybrid blue, Focus hybrid green, Focus E-85 copper, Focus E-85 blue, Focus E-85 green, Civic hybrid copper, Civic hybrid blue, Civic hybrid green, Civic E-85 copper, Civic E-85 blue, Civic E-85 green, Corolla hybrid copper, Corolla hybrid blue, Corolla hybrid green, Corolla E-85 copper, Corolla E-85 blue, Corolla E-85 green)

In parts c–g, find the probability that the car, if chosen at random,

**c.** Has an E-85 engine.

1/2

**d.** Is a burnt copper Ford Focus.

2/18 = 1/9

**e.** Is a metallic green hybrid Honda Civic.

1/18

**f.** Is cobalt blue.

1/3

**g.** Is either a metallic green or cobalt blue Toyota Corolla.

4/18 = 2/9

**3-2** **Applications**

Name _____

3. In between classes, Jade plays a game of online Monopoly on her laptop. Using the sample space for rolling two dice that you created in the Group portion of this lesson, find the probability that when Jade rolls the two dice, she gets a

   **a.** Sum of 5.

   *1/9*

   **b.** Sum of 7 or 11.

   *2/9*

   **c.** Sum greater than 9.

   *1/6*

   **d.** Sum less than or equal to 5.

   *5/18*

   **e.** Three on one die or on both dice.

   *11/36*

   **f.** Sum that is odd.

   *1/2*

   **g.** Prime number on one or both dice.

   *3/4*

   **h.** Sum greater than 1.

   *1*

Name _____

While making up his schedule for spring semester, Tom complains that he doesn't have very many choices of schedule because of the general education requirements he has to meet. His advisor tells Tom that he has to take one course from each of English (three choices), history (five choices), math/stats (five choices), computer science (four choices), and general science (six choices). Does Tom have a legitimate gripe? Let's examine this in Questions 4–7.

4. If every possible course is available at the time he's registering, how many possible schedules can he choose from (disregarding when the classes meet)?

   $3 \cdot 5 \cdot 5 \cdot 4 \cdot 6 = 1,800$

5. If Tom hasn't met the prerequisites for two of the math/stat courses and three of the general science courses, by how much does this reduce his number of possible schedules?

   $3 \cdot 5 \cdot 3 \cdot 4 \cdot 4 = 720$; he has 1,080 less choices now.

6. Good news! The prerequisite issue was a mistake on his transcript, so all courses are back in play. But when trying to schedule, Tom finds that all but one of the English courses is closed, as are two history courses and one general science course. How many schedules does he have to choose from now?

   $1 \cdot 3 \cdot 5 \cdot 4 \cdot 5 = 300$

7. In an unprecedented effort to make the general education requirements more accessible, the dean of Tom's college decides to double the number of acceptable courses in each of those five areas. What effect does this have on the number of possible schedules?

   $6 \cdot 10 \cdot 10 \cdot 8 \cdot 12 = 57,600$; it sends it into the stratosphere! (Mathematically, it multiplies the number by $2^5$, or 32.)

# Lesson 3-3  **Prep Skills**

This is a short review of skills that will come in handy in the next lesson. In each case, answer the question, then rate your confidence level by checking one of the boxes. If you feel like you're struggling with these skills, consult the online resources provided by your instructor for extra practice.

### SKILL 1: USE THE FUNDAMENTAL COUNTING PRINCIPLE

1. How many possible outcomes are there if you flip a coin then roll one six-sided die?

2. When eating at his campus cafeteria, Deshaun can choose from six sand-wiches, four sides, and six drinks. If he wants a different combination every day, how many days can he eat without repeating a meal?

### SKILL 2: COMPUTE THEORETICAL PROBABILITIES

3. There are 38 spaces on a roulette wheel, and 18 of them are colored red. What's the probability of getting red on one spin?

4. There are also 18 black spaces on a roulette wheel. If you repeatedly bet on a space that is neither red nor black, what percent of the time will you be likely to win?

### SKILL 3: DIVIDE OUT COMMON FACTORS

5. Write each fraction in lowest terms:

$$\frac{7 \cdot 6 \cdot 5 \cdot 4 \cdot 3 \cdot 2 \cdot 1}{3 \cdot 2 \cdot 1}$$

$$\frac{10 \cdot 9 \cdot 8 \cdot 7 \cdot 6 \cdot 5 \cdot 4 \cdot 3 \cdot 2 \cdot 1}{8 \cdot 7 \cdot 6 \cdot 5 \cdot 4 \cdot 3 \cdot 2 \cdot 1}$$

# Lesson 3-3  Combining Forces  (Combinatorics)

**LEARNING OBJECTIVES**

☐ 1. Understand how combinatorics are useful in probability theory.

☐ 2. Distinguish between permutations and combinations.

☐ 3. Find the number of permutations and combinations of *n* objects.

☐ 4. Find the number of permutations and combinations of *n* objects chosen *r* at a time.

*Most discoveries even today are a combination of serendipity and of searching.*
              —Siddhartha Mukherjee

© Design Pics/Darren Greenwood RF

Ah, the high school locker: providing students the thrill of fumbling with a combination lock for over 100 years. The combination to my locker was 3-24-32. If I had absentmindedly tried 24-3-32—a reasonably common occurrence given that school started at 7:30 and I am NOT a morning person—would that have opened the locker? Of course not. The point of a combination lock is that you need an exact string of numbers in the exact correct order. Anything other than that, and you're spinning that wheel at least twice to the right and trying again. In the last lesson, we learned that being able to count up possibilities is a really important part of computing probabilities. Now it's time to expand our counting repertoire. The key idea of this lesson is deciding whether or not order matters when counting the number of outcomes in an event or a sample space. And we'll eventually find out that combination locks are completely misnamed.

**0.** After reading the opening paragraph, what do you think the main topic of this lesson will be?

## 3-3  Class

Two couples go out to dinner, and as you might expect are given a table for four.

**1.** How many different people could choose to sit in the first seat?

*Four*

**2.** Once that person is seated, how many different people could sit in the second seat?

*Three*

**3.** Then how many in the third seat?

*Two*

**4.** And the fourth?

*One*

5. Now use the fundamental counting principle to calculate the number of ways that Cat, Dave, Nikki, and Brian can sit at that table.

   $4 \cdot 3 \cdot 2 \cdot 1 = 24$

6. Using Question 5 as a model, how many different ways could a group of 18 friends sit at a table with 18 chairs? Write out the calculation, but you don't need to perform it.

   $18 \cdot 17 \cdot 16 \cdot 15 \cdot 14 \cdot 13 \cdot 12 \cdot 11 \cdot 10 \cdot 9 \cdot 8 \cdot 7 \cdot 6 \cdot 5 \cdot 4 \cdot 3 \cdot 2 \cdot 1$

Courtesy of David Sobecki

Kind of annoying to write, wasn't it? (You can be honest.) Fortunately, there's a notation that will allow us to write calculations of this sort concisely: it's called *factorial notation,* and it plays a really important role in the next few counting methods we'll study.

## Factorial Notation

The symbol we'll use to represent the computation you did in Question 5 is 4!, which we read "Four factorial." To find *n!,* you simply multiply all of the whole numbers from *n* down to 1.

7. Fill in the blanks, using the first two lines for reference if you need to.

   $1! = 1 = 1$

   $2! = 2 \cdot 1 = 2$

   $3! = \underline{3} \cdot \underline{2} \cdot \underline{1} = \underline{6}$

   $4! = \underline{4} \cdot \underline{3} \cdot \underline{2} \cdot \underline{1} = \underline{24}$

   $5! = \underline{5} \cdot \underline{4} \cdot \underline{3} \cdot \underline{2} \cdot \underline{1} = \underline{120}$

> **Math Note**
>
> The reason we advised against performing the calculation in Question 6? Eighteen factorial is 6,402,373,705,728,000.

### Using Technology: Computing Factorials

The factorial command is on the MATH-PRB menu on a TI-84. To compute 5! easily:

5 **MATH**; then use arrow keys to select PRB and press

In Excel, enter =FACT(5)

**8.** Look back at your answers to Questions 5 and 6. Using factorial notation, fill in the blanks:

The number of ways to arrange 4 people around a table is ___*4!*___ .

The number of ways to arrange 18 people around a table is ___*18!*___ .

---

An arrangement of *n* distinct objects in a specific order is called a **permutation** of the objects.

**9.** In the case of our diners, each different way they could be seated is called a permutation, and we would say that the number of permutations of four objects (people) in this case is ___*4!*___ . (See Question 8.)

**10.** Now you should be able to fill in the blank in the colored box below, which provides our first counting formula in this lesson.

## Permutations of *n* Objects

The number of permutations of *n* distinct objects using all of the objects is ___*n!*___ .

**11.** There are seven horses in a race and a large jackpot for anyone who can pick the finishing order of all seven exactly right. Find the number of possible orders in which the horses can finish.

$7! = 7 \cdot 6 \cdot 5 \cdot 4 \cdot 3 \cdot 2 \cdot 1 = 5{,}040$

**12.** What is the probability of picking the exact correct finishing order?

*1/5,040, or about 0.0002*

---

## Did You Get It

Try this problem to see if you understand the concepts we just studied. The answer can be found at the bottom of the portfolio page.

1. A hospital floor nursing supervisor needs to assign her five nurses to five different rotations. How many different ways can she assign them?

So far, in calculating permutations, we've used all of the available objects. But what if only some of them are selected?

13. Most horse tracks offer a trifecta bet, in which the goal is to predict the exact order of the first three finishers. For the seven-horse race in Questions 9 and 10:

   **a.** How many different horses could finish first?

   7

   **b.** Once you know which horse finished first, how many could finish second?

   6

   **c.** So we know who finished first and second. How many horses could finish third?

   5

   **d.** Use the fundamental counting principle to find the number of possible ways to pick the trifecta in a seven-horse race.

   $7 \cdot 6 \cdot 5 = 210$

Now let's go back to our original two couples enjoying a night out. Suppose that the only available table when they arrive has six chairs. Here's how we calculate the number of possible seating arrangements:

| 6 | · | 5 | · | 4 | · | 3 |
|---|---|---|---|---|---|---|
| Chairs the 1st person can choose | | Chairs the 2nd person can choose | | Chairs the 3rd person can choose | | Chairs the 4th person can choose |

This is not a factorial because we didn't continue down to one, but it kind of looks like one. If we're clever, we can figure out how to write this calculation in terms of factorials. First, we're going to multiply by one, because of course we can without changing the value.

$$6 \cdot 5 \cdot 4 \cdot 3 \cdot \frac{2 \cdot 1}{2 \cdot 1}$$

Okay, so we multiplied by one in a strange way, but the fraction is still a perfectly good way to say one. Now we'll do some very basic rewriting:

$$\frac{6 \cdot 5 \cdot 4 \cdot 3}{1} \cdot \frac{2 \cdot 1}{2 \cdot 1} = \frac{6 \cdot 5 \cdot 4 \cdot 3 \cdot 2 \cdot 1}{2 \cdot 1}$$

14. Presto! Each of the numerator and denominator is now a factorial. Write this expression as a single fraction with a factorial in the numerator, and one in the denominator.

   $$\frac{6!}{2!}$$

Now the key observation: The point of that calculation was to find the number of ways we can arrange 4 objects chosen from a set of 6. Notice that in the numerator you have 6!, and in the denominator, you have $(6 - 4)!$. You've just discovered our next important counting formula.

## Permutations of $n$ Objects Taken $r$ at a Time

The arrangement of $n$ objects in a specific order using $r$ of those objects without replacement is called a **permutation** of $n$ objects taken $r$ at a time. It is written as $_nP_r$, and is calculated using the formula

$$_nP_r = \frac{n!}{(n - r)!}$$

15. An iPhone running OS 9 or above allows users to choose either a four- or six-digit lock code. How many four-digit codes are possible if you decide you don't want any number repeated?

    *This is a permutation problem because we're picking 4 numbers from 10 possible digits with no repetition, and the order is important. So we use the permutation formula with $n = 10$ and $r = 4$.*

    $$_{10}P_4 = \frac{10!}{(10 - 4)!} = \frac{10!}{6!} = 5{,}040$$

    > We've left it to your discretion to decide if you want to teach the shortcut of writing 10!/6! as $10 \cdot 9 \cdot 8 \cdot 7$.

16. How many more choices do you have if you DO allow numbers to be repeated? (Hint: Think fundamental counting principle.)

    $10 \cdot 10 \cdot 10 \cdot 10 = 10{,}000$

    *Allowing repeats gives you 4,960 more possible lock codes.*

What if we're interested in a permutation of $n$ objects taken $n$ at a time, like the original question about four diners picking four chairs? Ideally, the above formula should still work, but we already know that for a permutation of $n$ objects, the number of possibilities is $n!$. Let's see what happens if we try our new formula:

$$_nP_n = \frac{n!}{(n - n)!} = \frac{n!}{0!}$$

This presents us with a problem: What exactly does 0! even mean? In terms of how we defined factorials, it doesn't make sense. So . . .

17. In order to make the above formula provide the answer that we already know is correct ($n!$), what should we define 0! to be?

    *0! is defined to be one. You might point out that there are other reasons that defining 0! this way is a good idea.*

## Using Technology: Computing Permutations

The permutation command is on the MATH-PRB menu on a TI-84. To compute $_{10}P_4$:

10 **MATH** ; then use arrow keys to select PRB and press 2 4 ENTER

In Excel, enter =PERMUT(10,4)

## Did You Get It

Try this problem to see if you understand the concepts we just studied. The answer can be found at the bottom of the portfolio page.

2.  In a lottery game, 30 numbered ping-pong balls are put in a bin, and 5 are randomly chosen. To win the jackpot, you need to match all 5 numbers in the order in which they were drawn. How many different winning orders are there?

## Summary of Permutations

These are the key elements that distinguish when we need to use a permutation formula:

*   Finding the number of ways to arrange a certain number of objects.
*   Order matters.
*   Once an object is used, it can't be used again.

# 3-3   Group

Suppose that after waiting in line overnight, you manage to snag the last three tickets to a big concert. Sweet! The bad news is that you can only take two of your four housemates. How many different ways can you choose the two friends that get to go?

This sounds a little bit like a permutation problem, but there's a key difference: the order in which you choose two friends doesn't make any difference. They either get to go or they don't. So choosing Ruth and Ama is exactly the same as choosing Ama and Ruth.

When order matters in a selection, we call it a permutation, but when order is not important, we call the selection a *combination*.

© Robert Kohlhuber/Getty Images RF

A selection of *n* distinct objects without regard to order is called a **combination** of the objects.

To clarify, let's study the difference between permutations and combinations.

1. Given four housemates, Ruth, Elaine, Ama, and Jasmine, list all the ways you can choose two of them to attend the concert with you. Is this a permutation or a combination? (Use R, E, A, and J to represent housemates.)

R and E    R and A    R and J    E and A    E and J    A and J
This is a combination because the order doesn't matter.

2. What if seating is assigned, and you're not only choosing who gets to attend, but also which of two seats each will sit in? List all the ways you can choose now. Is this a permutation or combination?

R and E    R and A    R and J    E and A    E and J    A and J
E and R    A and R    J and R    A and E    J and E    J and A
This is a permutation because the order does matter.

3. There are ___12___ permutations, but only ___6___ combinations.

If all went well, the number of combinations you found was half the number of permutations. Here's why this makes perfect sense: after you picked your two guests, there were exactly two ways to arrange them. So by ignoring order, you essentially cut the number of possibilities in half. This provides an important fact:

> *The number of combinations of a certain number of objects is the number of permutations divided by the number of orders you can arrange those objects in.*

4. How many different ways can you order $r$ objects?

$r!$

Now we have a formula for finding a number of combinations.

## Combinations of $n$ Objects Taken $r$ at a Time

The arrangement of $n$ objects in any order using $r$ of those objects without replacement is called a **combination** of $n$ objects taken $r$ at a time. It is written as $_nC_r$, and is calculated using the formula

$$_nC_r = \frac{_nP_r}{r!} = \frac{n!}{(n-r)!r!}$$

Notice that there are two ways to think of this formula: as the number of permutations divided by the number of orders, or "from scratch," as $n$ factorial divided by the product of $(n - r)$ factorial and $r$ factorial.

**5.** Use the combination formula to find the number of ways you can choose two of four housemates to go to the concert with you. Does it agree with your earlier conclusion?

$$_4C_2 = \frac{4!}{(4-2)!2!} = \frac{24}{4} = 6$$

*This matches what we got when we wrote out the combinations.*

## Using Technology: Computing Combinations

The combination command is on the MATH-PRB menu on a TI-84. To compute $_4C_2$:

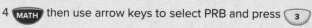

4 MATH then use arrow keys to select PRB and press ( 3 ) ( 2 ) (ENTER)

In Excel, enter =COMBIN(4,2)

## Did You Get It

Try this problem to see if you understand the concepts we just studied. The answer can be found at the bottom of the portfolio page.

3. How many combinations of eight objects are there taken five at a time?

**6.** While studying abroad one semester, Tran is required to visit 10 different cities. He plans to visit 3 of the 10 over a long weekend. How many different ways can he choose the 3 to visit? Assume that distance isn't a factor.

*There's no indication that order matters here, so it's a combination problem.*

$$_{10}C_3 = \frac{10!}{(10-3)!3!} = \frac{10!}{7!3!} = 120$$

### Math Note

Some people use the terminology "10 choose 3" to describe the combination $_{10}C_3$, and it's also represented by $\binom{10}{3}$.

## Did You Get It

Try this problem to see if you understand the concepts we just studied. The answer can be found at the bottom of the portfolio page.

4. An instructor posts a list of 12 group projects to her website. Every group is required to do four projects at some point during the semester. How many different ways can a group choose the four projects they want to do?

In some cases, it's useful to use the combination rule in conjunction with the fundamental counting principle. The next two problems illustrate some specific situations.

**Problem 1:** At one school, the student government consists of seven women and five men. How many different committees can be chosen that consist of three women and two men?

7. How many ways can the three women be chosen?

$$_7C_3 = \frac{7!}{(7-3)!3!} = 35$$

8. How many ways can the two men be chosen?

$$_5C_2 = \frac{5!}{(5-2)!2!} = 10$$

9. Why does the fundamental counting principle apply to this situation?

*Because the two outcomes have no effect on each other. Which women get selected doesn't have any bearing on which men get selected.*

10. Find the number of different committees that can be formed.

$35 \cdot 10 = 350$

**Problem 2:** To raise money for a charity event, a sorority plans to sell a calendar featuring tasteful photos of some of the more attractive professors on campus. They will need to choose six models from a pool of finalists that includes nine women and six men. How many possible choices are there if they want to feature at least four women?

11. How many different choices could they make if they decide on exactly four women? Note that this question is very similar to Problem 1 on the previous page.

$$_9C_4 \cdot _6C_2 = \frac{9!}{(9-4)!4!} \cdot \frac{6!}{(6-2)!2!} = 126 \cdot 15 = 1{,}890$$

12. So four women and two men is one possible composition of the calendar. There are two others: Find the number of different choices for each of those. Then decide what to do with your results to solve Problem 2, and solve it.

Five women and one man: $_9C_5 \cdot _6C_1 = \dfrac{9!}{(9-5)!5!} \cdot \dfrac{6!}{(6-1)!1!} = 126 \cdot 6 = 756$

Six women and no men: $_9C_6 \cdot _6C_0 = \dfrac{9!}{(9-6)!6!} \cdot \dfrac{6!}{(6-0)!0!} = 84 \cdot 1 = 84$

Total number of possibilities is the sum of the three we found: $1{,}890 + 756 + 84 = 2{,}730$

---

### Did You Get It

Try this problem to see if you understand the concepts we just studied. The answer can be found at the bottom of the portfolio page.

5. A four-person crew for the international space station is to be chosen from a candidate pool of 10 Americans and 12 Russians. How many different crews are possible if there must be at least two Russians?

---

This is a good time to talk about the significance of the words *and* and *or* when applying counting techniques. In Problem 1 on the previous page, we needed a committee with three women AND two men; this led us to conclude that we could think of it as a two-stage process and multiply using the fundamental counting principle. In Problem 2, we end up choosing between three possible options: four women OR five women OR six women. In this case, we found the number of possibilities for each and added them.

In using counting to continue our study of probability, of course it's important to know the formulas. But the formulas do no good unless you know *which* formula to use in a given situation. In the Applications, you'll be asked to identify whether a given problem matches the fundamental counting principle, the permutation formula, or the combination formula. In preparation for that, you should end this lesson by reviewing the work we've done. Make sure you're clear on exactly what each formula is used for.

13. Oh, one final question: Why did we say earlier that combination locks are misnamed?

Because the order matters! The "combination" in a combination lock is actually a permutation.

## 3-3   Portfolio

Name _____

Check each box when you've completed the task. Remember that your instructor will want you to turn in the portfolio pages you create.

### Technology

1. ☐   In this problem, you're going to compute the probability of winning a variety of different games of chance, using Excel. In each case, you need to decide whether to use the =PERM command, or the =COMBIN command, then use that command to find the number of possible outcomes. You'll then compute the probability of winning in another column. A template to help you get started can be found in the online resources for this lesson, along with descriptions of the outcomes you'll be counting.

### Online Practice

1. ☐   Include any written work from the online assignment along with any notes or questions about this lesson's content.

### Applications

1. ☐   Complete the applications problems.

### Reflections

Type a short answer to each question.

1. ☐   What is the difference between permutations and combinations?
2. ☐   Why are we studying these counting techniques in this unit?
3. ☐   Describe how to compute a factorial.
4. ☐   Take another look at your answer to Question 0 at the beginning of this lesson. Would you revise your answer now that you've completed the lesson? How would you summarize the topic of this lesson now?
5. ☐   What questions do you have about this lesson?

### Looking Ahead

1. ☐   Complete the Lesson 3-4 Prep Skills and read the opening paragraph in Lesson 3-4 carefully, then answer Question 0 in preparation for that lesson.

### Answers to "Did You Get It?"

   **1.** 120    **2.** 17,100,720    **3.** 56    **4.** 495    **5.** 5,665

## 3-3  Applications

Name _____

In preparation for this assignment, it would be a good idea for you to review the three major counting rules that we've studied.

| Rule | Description | Formula |
|---|---|---|
| Fundamental counting principle | The number of ways a sequence of $n$ events can occur. Each event is unaffected by the others. The first event can occur in $k_1$ ways, the second in $k_2$ ways, and so on. | $k_1 \cdot k_2 \cdot k_3 \dots k_n$ |
| Permutation rule | The number of ways we can choose $r$ objects from a set of $n$, with order important. | $_nP_r = \dfrac{n!}{(n-r)!}$ |
| Combination rule | The number of ways we can choose $r$ objects from a set of $n$, without regard to order. | $_nC_r = \dfrac{n!}{(n-r)!r!}$ |

For Questions 1–4, decide if each selection is a permutation or a combination, and briefly explain your choice.

1. From a class of 25 students, a group of 5 is chosen to give a presentation.

   *This is a combination because there are no distinct roles for the 5 group members, so order is not important.*

2. A starting pitcher and catcher are picked from a 12-person intramural softball team.

   *This is a permutation because each selected person has a distinct position, so order matters.*

3. A 5-digit passcode is chosen from the numbers 0 through 9.

   *This is a permutation because the order matters for the numbers entered for a passcode.*

4. A gardener picks 4 vegetable plants for his garden from 10 choices.

   *This is a combination because the order of the 4 chosen vegetables doesn't matter.*

## 3-3 | Applications

Name _____

For Questions 5–7, write the appropriate counting method to use, then answer the question.

5. A campus pizzeria offers regular crust, thin crust, or pan pizzas. You can get either white or red sauce. The owner is kind of eccentric, and only sells pizzas with one topping, chosen from pepperoni, sausage, ham, onions, and ground beef. Determine the number of possible choices of pizza.

   *Fundamental Counting Principle:* $3 \cdot 2 \cdot 5 = 30$

6. Suppose that a chef is choosing from 20 toppings to make a gourmet pizza, and he plans to choose 6 of them. How many different ways can he do so if you're keeping track of the order in which he adds them?

   *Permutation:* $_{20}P_6 = 27{,}907{,}200$

7. Let's be real, though . . . when you're putting toppings on a pizza, it doesn't really matter what order you choose. So how many different pizzas can the chef make?

   *Combination:* $_{20}C_6 = 38{,}760$

For the remaining questions, find the number requested and show your work.

8. A major league baseball team has 25 players on the active roster. How many choices does a manager have for batting order, listing the nine starters from 1 through 9?

   $_{25}P_9 = 25!/16! \approx 7.41 \times 10^{11}$

9. In 5-card poker, each player is dealt 5 cards (go figure) from a standard deck of 52 cards. How many different hands can be dealt?

   $_{52}C_5 = 2{,}598{,}960$

10. At the movies, Shana wants to get snacks for her friends. How many ways can she choose three types of candy and two types of soda from the eight types of candy and five types of soda available?

    $_8C_3 \cdot _5C_2 = 560$

## 3-3   Applications

Name _____

11. Steve wants to download new music into his iPod from iTunes. How many ways can Steve pick two rock songs, three alternative songs, and three hip hop songs from a list of eight rock songs, six alternative songs, and ten hip hop songs?

$_8C_2 \cdot {}_6C_3 \cdot {}_{10}C_3 = 67{,}200$

12. A college basketball team has 14 women on the roster. In how many ways can the coach choose a lineup featuring five different positions?

$_{14}P_5 = 240{,}240$

13. An inspector with the Nuclear Regulatory Commission is tasked to visit five nuclear plants this month, randomly chosen from three in Ohio, four in New York, and five in Pennsylvania. How many different ways can he choose the plants to visit if at least three will be in Pennsylvania?

$_5C_3 \cdot {}_7C_2 + {}_5C_4 \cdot {}_7C_1 + {}_5C_5 = 10 \cdot 21 + 5 \cdot 7 + 1 = 246$

14. For the new fall season, a network president has 11 shows in development, and six openings in the prime time schedule. In how many ways can she arrange new shows to fit into the schedule?

$_{11}P_6 = 332{,}640$

15. Think about the definitions of what $_nP_r$ and $_nC_r$ actually mean (NOT the formulas for computing them). Explain why both have to be zero when $r$ is greater than $n$.

In both cases, we're choosing r objects from a collection of n. If r is the bigger number, that can't be done! You can't choose 58 cards from a deck of 52, for example.

16. Now look at the formulas for $_nP_r$ and $_nC_r$. Can you use either of them if $r$ is bigger than $n$? Why or why not?

You can't. Each formula has an $(n - r)!$ in it, and if r is bigger, that would be a negative factorial. We have no idea what that even means.

# Lesson 3-4   Prep Skills

This is a short review of skills that will come in handy in the next lesson. In each case, answer the question, then rate your confidence level by checking one of the boxes. If you feel like you're struggling with these skills, consult the online resources provided by your instructor for extra practice.

### SKILL 1: COMPUTE COMBINATIONS

1. Find each combination.

   The number of combinations of 11 objects taken 4 at a time.

   $_9C_2$

### SKILL 2: COMPUTE PERMUTATIONS

2. In how many different orders can 5 distinct objects be arranged?

3. Find the number of permutations of 12 objects taken 9 at a time.

4. Compute $_7P_3$.

### SKILL 3: USE THE FUNDAMENTAL COUNTING PRINCIPLE

5. If you have 7 choices of entree, 5 choices of side, and 3 choices of dessert, how many different meals could you have?

### SKILL 4: COMPUTE THEORETICAL PROBABILITY

6. A tech company has 144 employees, 90 of whom have a Bachelor's degree. There are 32 with Master's degrees and 4 PhD's. What's the probability that a randomly selected employee has a Bachelor's?

7. What's the probability that a randomly selected employee has an Associate's or no college degree?

# Lesson 3-4   **Too Good to Be True?**   (Probability Using Counting Techniques)

## LEARNING OBJECTIVES

☐ 1. Recognize probability problems where permutations are useful, and where combinations are useful.

☐ 2. Use permutations to calculate probabilities.

☐ 3. Use combinations to calculate probabilities.

© Stockbyte/PunchStock RF

*If you're playing a poker game and you look around the table and can't tell who the sucker is, it's you.*

—Paul Newman

Sometimes a friendly game of poker can become less friendly when someone seems just a bit too lucky. Suppose one player in such a game gets dealt all four aces in one hand. Would you suspect that something fishy was going on? What is the probability of that happening?

Initially, we used tree diagrams and tables to find sample spaces and the number of outcomes in certain events. This was a pretty good strategy, but when the number of possibilities gets larger, diagrams can get out of hand. Fortunately, we know about counting techniques that are tailor-made for answering questions about probability. If our job is to find how many ways something can happen, the combination and permutation rules from Lesson 3-3 will be our best friends. Our general game plan will be to use these rules to find the number of outcomes that satisfy a certain event, as well as the total number of outcomes in the sample space. Then we can divide the first number by the second to obtain the probability of the event occurring.

**0.** After reading the opening paragraphs, what do you think the main topic of this lesson will be?

## 3-4   Class

Like most math classes, you probably got one choice of book in this course. Sorry. But in other areas, there's sometimes a book list, and students have to choose which ones they want to read. Let's say that a student named Stacy is taking a humanities class with a reading list that contains 10 biographies and five books on current events. She's required to read three books of her choice at some point during the semester. Being a fan of probability, Stacy decides to roll the dice and pick her three books randomly. What she doesn't realize is that her professor won't look very kindly on a student that totally avoids biographies. So how likely is it that Stacy will inadvertently hurt her grade?

**1.** What we're really interested in is whether or not Stacy gets three books on current events. Is this a permutation or combination problem?

*Combination, because the description doesn't say anything about reading order.*

2. Specifically, we want to know how many ways we can choose ___3___ books from ___5___ current events books.

3. Find the number of ways described in Question 2.

$_5C_3 = 10$

So now we've identified the number of outcomes in the event of choosing three current events books. Next, we need to find the total number of outcomes in the sample space.

4. Every student is choosing ___3___ books from ___15___ books on the list.

5. How many outcomes are in the sample space?

$_{15}C_3 = 455$

© BananaStock/Jupiterimages RF

6. Find the probability that Stacy will get three current events books, and describe how likely you think it is.

$\dfrac{10}{455} \approx 0.022$

This is barely more than a 2% chance, so it's not likely at all.

## Did You Get It    **?**

Try this problem to see if you understand the concepts we just studied. The answer can be found at the bottom of the portfolio page.

1. There are 12 women and 8 men in a seminar course. If the professor chooses five-person groups at random, what is the probability that the first group chosen will consist of all women?

Now back to that poker game . . . In Questions 7–13, our goal is to find the probability of getting 4 aces when drawing 5 cards from a standard deck of 52 cards.

7. First, we need to know how many five-card hands have four aces in them. The key observation is that there are only four aces in the deck, so we need to get them all. How many ways can this happen?

   *Just one! You could write it as $_4C_4$, but there's not a particularly good reason to do so.*

8. After we have all four aces, we still need one more card, right? How many ways can we choose a fifth card once we have all four aces?

   © Pixtal/SuperStock RF

   *There are 48 other cards in the deck.*

9. How many five-card hands have all four aces?

   *$1 \cdot 48 = 48$*

10. Will we be using permutations or combinations to find the total number of five-card hands? Why?

    *Combinations, because order is unimportant.*

11. The total number of five-card hands comes from choosing __5__ cards from __52__ possibilities.

12. Find the number of five-card hands.

    *$_{52}C_5 = 2{,}598{,}960$*

13. Find the probability of getting four aces when drawing five cards from a standard deck. Write your answer as a fraction.

    *$\dfrac{48}{2{,}598{,}960}$*

**14.** Now let's study the decimal equivalent of your answer to Question 13. If you round to three decimal places, what do you get? Why would this be a dreadful answer to the probability question we're working on?

*0.000. This is a terrible answer because there are 48 ways the event can happen, so we know the probability isn't zero.*

**15.** To avoid the issue you ran into in Question 14, we can use the idea of *significant digits*. When working with really small decimal numbers, the zeroes at the beginning are really just place holders: most of the information comes from the numbers after the initial string of zeroes. We call any digit (zero or nonzero) that comes after an initial string of zeroes **significant digits.** Write the decimal form of the probability you found, rounded to two significant digits.

*0.000018*

**16.** Now the key question: if your friend comes up with four aces, is she cheating? Discuss, using the probability you found as evidence.

*We don't KNOW that she's cheating, because it is possible to get dealt all four aces. On the other hand, it's INCREDIBLY unlikely, so it would be reasonable to at least suspect that something fishy is going on.*

### Did You Get It

Try this problem to see if you understand the concepts we just studied. The answer can be found at the bottom of the portfolio page.

2. Suppose the deck of cards in Questions 7–13 has all 32 cards with numbers less than 10 removed, so that only 10s, jacks, queens, kings, and aces remain. Now what is the probability of getting 4 aces when drawing 5 cards?

# 3-4 ▮ Group

For the next few probability questions, we're going to provide a little less guidance than we did on the last two. Fortunately, you have group mates to work with, so we're sure you'll be just fine.

© F Schussler/PhotoLink/
Getty Images RF

This lock has 40 numbers on it, from zero to 39. In Questions 1–4, our goal is to find the probability that if the combination to unlock it consists of 3 numbers, it will contain the numbers 1, 2, and 3 in some order. Assume that numbers can't be repeated in the combination.

1. Does the order matter? Do we want to use permutations or combinations?

   *The order definitely matters, so we want permutations.*

2. How many different combinations for the lock contain 1, 2, and 3?

   *$3! = 6$. This is simply the permutations of those three numbers.*

3. How many different combinations are there total?

   *$_{40}P_3 = 59,280$*

4. Write the probability that the combination contains 1, 2, and 3 in some order as a fraction, and as a decimal rounded to three significant digits.

   *$\dfrac{6}{59,280} \approx 0.000101$*

## Did You Get It

Try this problem to see if you understand the concepts we just studied. The answer can be found at the bottom of the portfolio page.

3. A different "permutation" lock has letters from A through L on it, and the combination consists of four letters with no repeats. What is the probability that the combination is I, J, K, and L in some order?

Ah, politics. It used to be that the easiest way to get in a fight with someone was to make fun of their mom. Now, all you have to do is disagree with someone on a political issue or candidate. We've become a frighteningly polarized society in that regard, and the makeup of committees among political bodies has become a very common issue.

5. In one town, the city council consists of seven Republicans and three Democrats. A committee of three is being selected by random draw to revise the town's election laws. Based on the overall composition of the council, what would be a reasonable makeup for the committee?

   *The only reasonable answer here is 2 Republicans and 1 Democrat. No Democrats wouldn't be fair as 30% of the council are Democrats, and only 1 Republican wouldn't make sense since they hold the majority.*

   > Make sure they have a good answer here, as it affects the calculation in the next several problems.

6. Are we dealing with permutations or combinations here? Why?

   *Combinations. The order is unimportant.*

7. How many different ways can the Republican(s) on the committee be chosen, based on the composition you chose?

   $_7C_2 = 21$

8. How many different ways can the Democrat(s) be chosen?

   $_3C_1 = 3$

9. Look back at your answer to Question 5. Does it contain the word "and" or "or"? Does that word indicate that you should multiply or add to find the number of committees that match the composition you specified?

   *And, which means the fundamental counting principle applies, and we should use multiplication.*

10. Find the number of ways a committee can be chosen that matches your composition.

    $21 \cdot 3 = 63$

11. Find the probability that the committee will work out the way you think it should.

    $\dfrac{63}{_{10}C_3} = \dfrac{63}{120} = 0.525$

**Did You Get It**

Try this problem to see if you understand the concepts we just studied. The answer can be found at the bottom of the portfolio page.

4. A store has six different fitness magazines and three different news magazines. Find the probability that a customer picking three magazines randomly gets at least two fitness magazines.

---

12. You're in a room with 29 other people and someone says "I'll bet you fifty bucks that two people in this room have the same birthday." Would you take the bet? Why or why not?

*Answers vary, but of course most people say they would, unless they just flat-out don't gamble.*

> We're going back to Class here because students will need a correct answer to at least the last question in order to do the tech assignment. Think of it as more group work with extra careful intervention.

## 3-4   Class (Again)

The goal of the remainder of this lesson, and of the tech assignment, is to study this question to see if you made a wise decision in either taking, or turning down, the bet. It's not a particularly simple question, so we'll start out with a case that's not so bad, and see if we can generalize.

1. It turns out it's easier to first find the probability that everyone in the room has a different birthday, so we'll begin there. If there are only three people in the room, how hard can it be? In that case, there are 365 choices for the first person's birthday (assuming it's not a leap year). If the second person has a different birthday, there are 364 choices, then 363 for the third. So the number of ways that all three can have different birthdays is

   $\underline{365 \cdot 364 \cdot 363}$ . (Write as a product, and don't multiply it out.)

2. The total number of possible birthdays for the three people, on the other hand, is

   $\underline{365 \cdot 365 \cdot 365}$ , or $\underline{365^3}$ .

3. Use your answers from the last two questions to find the probability that all three people have different birthdays. Find a decimal equivalent rounded to three significant digits.

   $$\frac{365 \cdot 364 \cdot 363}{365^3} \approx 0.992$$

4. What is the probability that at least two of the people have the SAME birthday? (Hint: This event is the complement of everyone having a different birthday.)

   $1 - 0.992 = 0.008$

5. Look carefully at the calculation of the number of ways that all three can have the same birthday (Question 1). If it doesn't look familiar, you probably need to review permutations. That was a hint. Write that calculation as a permutation in the form $_nP_r$.

$$_{365}P_3$$

6. Summary so far: with three people in the room, the probability that at least two have the same birthday can be written as: (Fill in the blanks.)

$$1 - \frac{_{365}P_3}{365^3}$$

7. Now here's the key to the entire problem: we can repeat all of the steps we've done for any other number of people in the room, and the only thing it changes is where the number of people appeared in your answer to Question 6. If there are 30 people in the room, you should now be able to find the probability that at least 2 have the same birthday. That's the question we started this activity with. Find the probability now.

$$1 - \frac{_{365}P_{30}}{365^{30}} \approx 0.706$$

8. Now would you take the bet? Why or why not?

*Answers vary, but you'd hope more would say no than the first time they were asked.*

9. In the technology portion of the homework, you'll use Excel to study the probability that at least two people in a room have the same birthday for many different room populations. In order to do so, you'll want to have a general formula for that probability when there are $k$ people in the room. Write that here, and save it for reference when you start the tech assignment.

$$1 - \frac{_{365}P_k}{365^k}$$

## 3-4 Portfolio

Name _____

Check each box when you've completed the task. Remember that your instructor will want you to turn in the portfolio pages you create.

### Technology

1. ☐ In the last part of this lesson, we learned the surprising fact that with just 30 people in a room, there's over a 70% chance that 2 of them will have the same birthday. This fact is so nonintuitive that a lot of people flat-out don't believe it even after computing it. It's true, I promise. Using the formula you developed in the last question of the lesson, you can set up a spreadsheet that will calculate the probability for any number of people in the room. There's a template in the online resources for this lesson to help you get started. If you need to, review the Excel command for computing permutations in the previous lesson. Make sure to answer the questions on the template as well.

### Online Practice

1. ☐ Include any written work from the online assignment along with any notes or questions about this lesson's content.

### Applications

1. ☐ Complete the applications problems.

### Reflections

Type a short answer to each question.

1. ☐ Now that we've completed this lesson, reflect back on why we spent so much time in the early parts of this unit learning to count. Write some of your thoughts.
2. ☐ What was the point of defining significant digits in this lesson? How did understanding the concept help us to study probability?
3. ☐ Discuss the birthday problem we closed the lesson with. What do you find surprising about it? Why?
4. ☐ Take another look at your answer to Question 0 at the beginning of this lesson. Would you revise your answer now that you've completed the lesson? How would you summarize the topic of this lesson now?
5. ☐ What questions do you have about this lesson?

### Looking Ahead

1. ☐ Complete the Lesson 3-5 Prep Skills and read the opening paragraph in Lesson 3-5 carefully, then answer Question 0 in preparation for that lesson.

### Answers to "Did You Get It?"

1. $\frac{33}{646} \approx 0.051$    2. $\frac{1}{969} \approx 0.00103$    3. $\frac{1}{495} \approx 0.002$    4. $\frac{65}{84} \approx 0.77$

## 3-4   Applications

Name _____

1. In a class of 18 students, there are 11 men and 7 women. Four students are randomly picked to present a demonstration on the use of graphing calculators. Find the probability that the group consists of

   **a.** All women.

   $$\frac{_7C_4}{_{18}C_4} = \frac{35}{3{,}060} \approx 0.011$$

   **b.** Two men and two women.

   $$\frac{_{11}C_2 \cdot _7C_2}{_{18}C_4} = \frac{1{,}155}{3{,}060} \approx 0.377$$

2. A chef is choosing from 12 different entrees for an important banquet, 3 of which contain spinach. The guests will have a choice of 4 entrees. If the chef chooses those 4 at random, find the probability that

   **a.** At least one has spinach. (Hint: Complements will help.)

   $$P(none\ have\ spinach) = \frac{_9C_4}{_{12}C_4} = \frac{126}{495} \approx 0.255$$

   $$P(at\ least\ one\ has\ spinach) \approx 1 - 0.255 = 0.745$$

   © Purestock/SuperStock RF

   **b.** Three have spinach.

   $$\frac{_3C_3 \cdot _9C_1}{_{12}C_4} = \frac{9}{495} \approx 0.018$$

   **c.** All four have spinach.

   Zero! Only three dishes have spinach.

## 3-4 Applications

Name _____

3. An engineering company has four openings and the applicant pool consists of six database administrators and eight network engineers. If the hiring is done without regard for the specific qualifications of the applicants, find the probability that the four hired will be
**a.** All network engineers.

$$\frac{_8C_4}{_{14}C_4} = \frac{70}{1{,}001} \approx 0.07$$

**b.** Three database administrators and one network engineer.

$$\frac{_6C_3 \cdot _8C_1}{_{14}C_4} = \frac{160}{1{,}001} \approx 0.16$$

In one lottery game, contestants pick five numbers from 1 through 40 and have to match all five for the big prize (in any order). Questions 4–6 refer to this game. Round your answers to two significant digits.

4. What's the probability you'll win if you buy one ticket? (Hint: Your chances are NOT good.)

$$\frac{1}{_{40}C_5} = \frac{1}{658{,}008} \approx 0.0000015$$

5. You'll get twice your money back if you match three of the five numbers. If you buy two tickets, what's the probability of matching three out of five numbers?

$$2 \cdot \frac{_5C_3 \cdot _{35}C_2}{_{40}C_5} = 2 \cdot \frac{5{,}950}{658{,}008} \approx 0.018$$

## 3-4    Applications

Name _____

6. To celebrate Fourth of July week, the lottery commission is offering a $1 million bonus if a winner of the big prize matches the numbers in the order in which they were drawn. What's the probability of this happening if you buy one ticket?

$$\frac{1}{_{40}P_5} = \frac{1}{78,960,960} \approx 0.000\,000\,013$$

Think you can guess your way into someone's garage by guessing the garage door code? Well let's just see about that.

7. What is the probability that you can guess my 4-digit garage code in 10 random guesses if repeat digits are not allowed? Give your answer as a fraction.

$$\frac{10}{_{10}P_4} = \frac{10}{5,040} = \frac{1}{504}$$

Courtesy David Sobecki

8. What is the probability that you can guess my 4-digit garage code in 10 random guesses if repeat digits are allowed? Write as a fraction.

$$\frac{10}{10^5} = \frac{10}{10,000} = \frac{1}{1,000}$$

9. If you don't have any repeated numbers in your 4-digit code, and someone suspects that, how much easier are you making it for them to guess the code?

It's pretty close to half as easy.

10. Let's go back to no repeats. What's the probability of guessing a 6-digit code in 10 tries? What does that suggest about security?

$$\frac{10}{_{10}P_6} = \frac{10}{151,200} = \frac{1}{15,120}$$

A 6-digit code is MUCH more secure.

# Lesson 3-5    **Prep Skills**

This is a short review of skills that will come in handy in the next lesson. In each case, answer the question, then rate your confidence level by checking one of the boxes. If you feel like you're struggling with these skills, consult the online resources provided by your instructor for extra practice.

I KNOW IT    THINK SO    UNSURE    NO IDEA

### SKILL 1: DIVIDE FRACTIONS AND REDUCE THE RESULT

1. Perform the division. Make sure your answer is in lowest terms.

$$\dfrac{\dfrac{1}{5}}{\dfrac{3}{5}}$$

$$\dfrac{\dfrac{8}{13}}{\dfrac{10}{13}}$$

### SKILL 2: COMPUTE THEORETICAL PROBABILITIES

2. What is the probability of rolling a total of 6 with two dice? What about a total greater than 6?

3. There are 2 seniors, 1 junior, 7 sophomores, and 11 freshmen in a math course. If one student is randomly picked for extra credit, what's the probability that it's either a freshman or senior?

### SKILL 3: CALCULATE A SUM OF PRODUCTS

4. Find the value of the expression below in both fractional and decimal form:

$$-10 \cdot \frac{4}{9} + 2 \cdot \frac{2}{9} + 4 \cdot \frac{2}{9} + 15 \cdot \frac{1}{9}$$

# Lesson 3-5 Odds and Ends (Odds and Expected Value)

## LEARNING OBJECTIVES

☐ 1. Distinguish between odds and probability.

☐ 2. Compute and interpret the odds in favor of and odds against an event.

☐ 3. Compute odds from probability and vice versa.

☐ 4. Develop a procedure for finding expected value.

☐ 5. Compute and interpret expected values.

*When something is important enough, you do it even if the odds are not in your favor.*

—Elon Musk

© Focus on Sport/Getty Images

The New England Patriots won the Super Bowl on February 1, 2015, and by the time the ink dried on newspapers reporting the victory, oddsmakers in Las Vegas had listed the odds against the Patriots winning it again in 2016 as 7 to 1. But what exactly does that mean? The term "odds" is used all the time in describing the likelihood of something happening, but a lot of people don't understand exactly what a given set of odds means. Odds are used by casinos, racetracks, and other gambling establishments to determine the payoffs when bets are made or lottery tickets are purchased. They're also used by insurance companies in determining the amount to charge for premiums. In a very real sense, odds are a way of stating what you expect will happen. So in this lesson, we'll study odds and expectations.

**0.** After reading the opening paragraph, what do you think the main topic of this lesson will be?

## 3-5 Class

The formulas for computing odds are similar to the formula we've been using for classical probability, and shortly we will see a strong connection between the two concepts.

If an event $E$ has $a$ favorable outcomes and $b$ unfavorable outcomes, then

- The **odds in favor** of event $E$ occurring are $\frac{a}{b}$ (also written as $a{:}b$).
- The **odds against** event $E$ occurring $\frac{b}{a}$ (also written as $b{:}a$).

Odds can be expressed as a fraction or a ratio.

1. Write the odds against New England repeating as Super Bowl champion as a fraction, and as a ratio.

   *7/1 and 7:1*

*Math Note*

In common usage, the phrase "the odds of" means the same thing as "the odds against." Odds are also commonly written with a hyphen rather than a colon: 7–1, for example.

2. Write the odds in favor of New England repeating as Super Bowl champion as a fraction, and as a ratio.

   *1/7 and 1:7*

3. By setting New England's odds at 7 to 1, the odds makers were predicting that if the season were played eight times, New England would win the Super Bowl ___*1*___ time, and not win it ___*7*___ times.

## Did You Get It

Try this problem to see if you understand the concepts we just studied. The answer can be found at the bottom of the portfolio page.

1. What are the odds in favor of rolling a prime number sum with a roll of two dice? What are the odds against? Look back at your answer to Question 1 in the Group portion of Lesson 3-2 for reference.

4. Based on the answer to Question 3, write the probability of New England winning the Super Bowl and the probability of New England not winning the Super Bowl in fraction form. Then compare your answers with the formula below.

   $P$(winning) = *1/8*

   $P$(not winning) = *7/8*

 ## Formula for Probability in Terms of Odds

If the odds in favor of an event $E$ are $a{:}b$, then the probability that the event will occur is

$$P(E) = \frac{a}{a + b}$$

5. Fill in the blanks to make this a true statement: $P(\text{winning}) = \underline{\quad 1 \quad} - P(\underline{\quad \text{not winning} \quad})$.

6. Explain why your answer to Question 5 makes perfect sense based on a fact about probability that we studied earlier in this unit.

   *Not winning the Super Bowl is the complement of winning the Super Bowl. The formula for probability of the complement of some event is 1 the probability of that event occurring.*

7. Compute and simplify $\dfrac{P(\text{winning})}{P(\text{not winning})}$. What does your answer represent in terms of odds?

   $$\frac{\frac{1}{8}}{\frac{7}{8}} = \frac{1}{8} \cdot \frac{8}{7} = \frac{1}{7}$$

   *This is the same as the odds in favor of winning.*

8. Compute $\dfrac{P(\text{not winning})}{P(\text{winning})}$. What does your answer represent in terms of odds?

   $$\frac{\frac{7}{8}}{\frac{1}{8}} = \frac{7}{8} \cdot \frac{8}{1} = \frac{7}{1}$$

   *This is the same as the odds against winning.*

   The results of Questions 7 and 8 can be summarized in this formulas:

## Formula for Odds in Terms of Probability

If the probability that an event $E$ will occur is $P(E)$, then

$$\text{Odds in favor of } E = \frac{P(E)}{1 - P(E)} \quad \text{and Odds against } E = \frac{1 - P(E)}{P(E)}$$

9. According to the National Safety Council, the odds in favor of dying due to injury at some point in your life are about 10:237. Find the probability of dying from injury.

$$P(Dying) = \frac{10}{10 + 237} = \frac{10}{247}$$

10. The probability of getting exactly one pair in a five-card poker hand is 0.423. Find the odds in favor of getting exactly one pair, and the odds against.

$$Odds\ in\ favor = \frac{P(getting\ one\ pair)}{1 - P(getting\ one\ pair)} = \frac{0.423}{1 - 0.423} = \frac{0.423}{0.577}\ or\ \frac{423}{577}$$

$$Odds\ against = \frac{577}{423}$$

> This is a good time to remind students that the odds in favor of an event and the odds against the same event are reciprocals. You should probably also help with converting the odds in favor to a form where both numerator and denominator are whole numbers.

## Did You Get It

Try these problems to see if you understand the concepts we just studied. The answers can be found at the bottom of the portfolio page.

2. According to the American Cancer Society, the probability of an American female developing some type of cancer at some point in her life is about 1/3. Find the odds in favor of and against an American woman developing cancer.

3. When two dice are rolled, the odds in favor of getting a sum of 9 are 1:8. Find the probability of not getting a sum of 9 when two dice are rolled.

11. On the morning of the 2015 Kentucky Derby, American Pharoah was listed as the favorite, with odds of 5:2. Write a sentence or two describing what this means.

*This says that in the opinion of the oddsmakers, if the race were run seven times, American Pharoah would win twice.*

12. If someone had bet $10 on American Pharoah to win (which he did), about how much money do you think they would have gotten back? Justify your answer.

*This is to some extent an opinion question. The odds, however, say that you would expect to get back about 2.5 times what you bet, so $25 is a reasonable answer.*

# 3-5 | Group

## Expected Value

If you play lottery games regularly (something we completely advise against, by the way), how much money do you expect to win? Obviously, this is not the same question as "How much money do you hope to win?" The concept of **expectation,** or **expected value**, is used to determine the result that would be expected over the long term in some sort of gamble. It's used not only for games of chance, but in areas like insurance, management, engineering, and others.

Here's the key thing to remember as we study expected value: *It only makes sense for events that have numerical outcomes.* For example, rolling a die has a numerical outcome (1 through 6), and expected value can be used to determine what the average long-run result is likely to be. But it doesn't make sense to ask what the long-term average of flipping a coin is. (There's nothing between heads or tails, while an average roll of 2.7 at least has some meaning.)

Now let's illustrate a procedure for computing the expected value of a game, and then we'll summarize that procedure for future reference.

Suppose you pay a dollar to roll two dice. If you roll 5 or 6, you get your dollar back plus two more just like it. If not, you get nothing and like it. The goal will be to find the amount of money you can expect to win or lose if you play this game 100 times. First, we'll find the probability of winning and losing. We know that there are 36 possible rolls of two dice. (Refer back at your answer to Question 1 in the Group portion of Lesson 3-2 if you need to.)

1. How many outcomes result in 5? List them.

   Four: (1, 4), (2, 3), (3, 2), and (4,1).

2. How many outcomes result in 6? List them.

   Five: (1, 5), (2, 4), (3, 3), (4, 2), and (5,1).

3. What's the probability of winning the game?

   9/36 or 1/4

4. What's the probability of losing the game?

   $1 - (1/4) = 3/4$

5. Based on Questions 3 and 4, on average, you can expect to win ___25%___ of the time.

6. So if you play the game 100 times, on average you'd expect to win ___25___ times and lose ___75___.

7. With each win, you make ___$2___, and with each loss, you lose ___$1___.

8. Multiply the number of times you expect to win by the amount you'd win each time.

   $25 \times \$2 = \$50$

9. Multiply the number of times you expect to lose by the amount you'd lose each time.

   $75 \times \$1 = \$75$

The next three questions are the key points in this part of the lesson.

10. After playing the game 100 times, find how much you would expect to win or lose total. Show how you got your answer.

    *You'd expect to lose $25, because the total expected winnings are $50 and the total expected loss is $75.*

11. Divide your answer to Question 10 by 100, and use your result to answer the next question.

    $-\$25/100 = -\$0.25$

12. You would expect to ___lose___ (win/lose) on average ___25 cents___ every time you play this game. This amount is the **expected value** of the game.

---

### Did You Get It

Try this problem to see if you understand the concepts we just studied. The answer can be found at the bottom of the portfolio page.

4. On a roulette wheel, there are 38 slots, 18 of which are colored red. If you bet $5 on red and win, you get $10 back. If red doesn't come up, you lose your $5. Find the expected value of playing the game 100 times. If you need help, follow Questions 3–12, which built the procedure for finding expected value.

Your answer to Question 12 might seem really puzzling if you think about it. How can you lose 25 cents on one trial of the game? The problem is that you can't: you either win $2 or lose $1. The expected value never tells you what will happen on any given outcome: it tells you what the average result will be in the long run. That's a key difference.

The procedure that we built for computing expected value was based on 100 trials of a probability experiment. If we apply that same procedure to just one trial, and extend to cases with more than two possible outcomes, we get a general formula for the expected value of a probability experiment.

### Formula for Expected Value

The expected value for the outcomes of a probability experiment is

$$E = X_1 \cdot P(X_1) + X_2 \cdot P(X_2) + \ldots X_n \cdot P(X_n)$$

where the $X$'s correspond to the numerical outcomes and the $P(X)$'s are the corresponding probabilities of the outcomes.

Verbally, the expected value formula tells us to multiply each outcome by its probability, then add the results.

13. When a single die is rolled, make a guess as to what the expected value of the roll will be.

*Answers vary.*

To describe all of the outcomes in a probability experiment, we can build a **probability distribution**. A probability distribution consists of a list of all outcomes and the corresponding probabilities for a probability experiment. A quantity that can vary randomly from one individual trial to another, like the number on a die, is called a **random variable**. Why? Because it's random, and it can vary. See, math DOES make sense!

14. To help us calculate the expected value, complete the probability distribution below, listing the possible outcomes and their probabilities:

| Number on die ($X$) | 1 | 2 | 3 | 4 | 5 | 6 |
|---|---|---|---|---|---|---|
| $P(X)$ | $\frac{1}{6}$ | $\frac{1}{6}$ | $\frac{1}{6}$ | $\frac{1}{6}$ | $\frac{1}{6}$ | $\frac{1}{6}$ |

15. Using information from your table and the formula in the box above, calculate the expected value of one roll.

$$E = 1 \cdot \frac{1}{6} + 2 \cdot \frac{1}{6} + 3 \cdot \frac{1}{6} + 4 \cdot \frac{1}{6} + 5 \cdot \frac{1}{6} + 6 \cdot \frac{1}{6} = \frac{21}{6} = 3.5$$

## Did You Get It ?

Try this problem to see if you understand the concepts we just studied. The answer can be found at the bottom of the portfolio page.

5.  If seven cards are numbered with integers from –2 to 4, then placed into a box and picked out at random, find the expected value.

In gambling games, the expected value equation amounts to multiplying net gain for each outcome by the corresponding probabilities and then finding the sum.

The prize in a raffle is a flat-screen TV valued at $350, and 1,000 tickets are sold for a dollar each. Let's find the expected value if you buy 1 ticket.

16.  For a win, the net gain is ___$349___, since you don't get the cost of the ticket ($1) back.

17.  For a loss, the net gain is represented by a negative number, in this case, ___–$1___.

18.  Fill in the probability distribution, and use the results to compute the expected value.

| Outcome | Probability |
|---------|-------------|
| $349    | 1/1,000     |
| –$1     | 999/1,000   |

$$E = -\$1 \cdot \frac{999}{1,000} + \$349 \cdot \frac{1}{1,000} = \frac{-\$650}{1,000}$$
$$= -\$0.65$$

19.  Can you lose 65 cents from buying one ticket?

*You sure can't. Nope.*

20.  If that 65 cents looks familiar, your result isn't incorrect. What does that result mean?

*Again, this doesn't mean that you'd lose 65 cents from buying a ticket, because you can only lose a dollar or win a $350 prize. It means that if you were to buy tickets to a similar raffle repeatedly, in the long run you'd average a 65 cent loss for each ticket bought.*

A favorite game for small children at fairs and carnivals is a game some folks call Pick-a-Duck. It's a simple game, which makes it ideal for little ones. A small pool is full of rubber ducks. Children get to pick one of the ducks and their prize is determined by the color of the dot on the bottom of the duck. Of course, the probability of winning a certain prize is based on how many ducks are in the pool, and how many have each color.

Courtesy Brian Mercer

In one such game, you pay $1 to select one of 50 ducks from the pool and prizes are determined by the following list:

| Number of ducks | Outcome |
|---|---|
| 20 ducks with red dots | Lose the money you paid to play* |
| 10 ducks with orange dots | Win a sticker valued at $0.05 |
| 10 ducks with green dots | Win a small toy valued at $0.10 |
| 6 ducks with blue dots | Get to play again |
| 4 ducks with purple dots | Win a stuffed animal valued at $4.00 |

*Then threaten to cry unless Mom lets you play again.

**21.** Fill in the probability distribution.

| Color of dot | Net gain X | Probability P(X) |
|---|---|---|
| Red | −$1 | 2/5 |
| Orange | −$0.95 | 1/5 |
| Green | −$0.90 | 1/5 |
| Blue | 0 | 3/25 |
| Purple | $3 | 2/25 |

**22.** Find the expected value of playing the game once.

$$E = -\$1 \cdot \frac{2}{5} + -\$0.95 \cdot \frac{1}{5} + -\$0.90 \cdot \frac{1}{5} + \$0 \cdot \frac{3}{25} + \$3 \cdot \frac{2}{25}$$

$$= \frac{-\$10 - \$4.75 - \$4.50 + \$6}{25} = \frac{-\$13.25}{25} = -\$0.53$$

**23.** Is the owner of the game making money? Explain.

*Yes they are. For every dollar that mom spends, on average the owner of the game is keeping 53 cents. We know this because on average the loss per game for players is 53 cents.*

---

### Did You Get It

Try this problem to see if you understand the concepts we just studied. The answer can be found at the bottom of the portfolio page.

6. The profit made by a small ski resort, not surprisingly, depends largely on the seasonal weather. In a season with more than 75 inches of snow, it makes an average of $250,000. If snowfall is between 40 and 75 inches, the average profit is $160,000, and if snowfall is less than 40 inches, it loses $70,000. The resort gets over 75 inches of snow 40% of years, between 40 and 75 inches 45% of years, and less than 40 inches 15% of years. Find the resort's expected yearly profit.

---

In gambling games, if the expected value of the gain is 0, the game is said to be fair. If the expected value of the gain of a game is positive, then the game is in favor of the player. That is, the player has a better-than-even chance of winning. If the expected value of the gain is negative, then the game is said to be in favor of the house. That is, in the long run, the players will lose money.

**24.** The expected value of different casino games varies, but the expected values of every game in every casino have one thing in common. What is it?

*They're all negative. Casinos don't run games that will lose them money in the long run.*

## Math Note

In American roulette, there are 22 different types of bets you can place, but it's interesting to note that all but 1 of them have the exact same expected value: −$0.053 on a $1 bet. (Betting on 0, 00, 1, 2, and 3, called a five-number bet, is worse, at −$0.079.)

A final note: The computation for expected value can be programmed into a spreadsheet. In fact, that's what you'll be doing in the technology assignment. There's also a command for computing expected value on a TI-84 graphing calculator. There's a document in the online resources for this lesson that walks you through that process.

# 3-5 Portfolio

Name _____

Check each box when you've completed the task. Remember that your instructor will want you to turn in the portfolio pages you create.

## Technology

1. ☐ In computing expected value, we set up a table, then did some calculations using the numbers in that table. That sure sounds an awful lot like what a spreadsheet is designed to do. Your job is to set up a spreadsheet that will calculate expected value when you input numerical outcomes in one column and the corresponding probabilities in the column next to it. Then you can use formulas to multiply each outcome by its probability, then add the results. First, do so for the experiment of rolling one die. Then repeat the process, this time for the experiment of rolling two die. The table from Question 1 in the Group portion of Lesson 3-2 will be a big help. A template to help you get started can be found in the online resources for this lesson.

## Online Practice

1. ☐ Include any written work from the online assignment along with any notes or questions about this lesson's content.

## Applications

1. ☐ Complete the applications problems.

## Reflections

Type a short answer to each question.

1. ☐ It's illegal to bet on political races in the United States, but overseas betting on American elections is common. At the time of this writing, Hillary Clinton is the favorite to win the presidency in 2016, with odds listed as 8/11. Explain what that means, including relating it to probability.
2. ☐ How is it possible for the expected value of a game to be losing 65 cents if the only outcomes are win $2 or lose $1?
3. ☐ Take another look at your answer to Question 0 at the beginning of this lesson. Would you revise your answer now that you've completed the lesson? How would you summarize the topic of this lesson now?
4. ☐ What questions do you have about this lesson?

## Looking Ahead

1. ☐ Complete the Lesson 3-6 Prep Skills and read the opening paragraph in Lesson 3-6 carefully, then answer Question 0 in preparation for that lesson.

## Answers to "Did You Get It?"

**1.** In favor 5:7; against 7:5    **2.** In favor 1:2, against 2:1    **3.** $\frac{8}{9}$    **4.** –$26.32
**5.** 1    **6.** $161,500

## 3-5 Applications

Name _____

1. A charity is running an auction. One thousand tickets are sold at $2 each for four prizes of $100, four of $50, four of $25, and four of $10. What are the odds in favor of winning $100?

   *There are 4 favorable outcomes and 996 unfavorable, so the odds in favor of winning $100 are 4:996 or 1:249.*

2. What are the odds against winning any prize at all?

   *There are 16 favorable outcomes and 984 unfavorable, so the odds against winning a prize are 984:16 or 123:2.*

3. What is the expected value if you buy one ticket? Fill in the probability distribution to help organize the needed information.

   $$E = -\$2 \cdot \frac{123}{125} + \$8 \cdot \frac{1}{250} + \$23 \cdot \frac{1}{250} + \$48 \cdot \frac{1}{250} + \$98 \cdot \frac{1}{250}$$

   $$= \frac{-\$246 + \$8 + \$23 + \$48 + \$98}{250} = -\$0.276$$

   | Outcome | Gain | Probability |
   |---------|------|-------------|
   | Lose | − $2 | 123/125 |
   | Win $10 | $8 | 1/250 |
   | Win $25 | $23 | 1/250 |
   | Win $50 | $48 | 1/250 |
   | Win $100 | $98 | 1/250 |

4. What does your answer to Question 3 mean?

   *If you bought tickets repeatedly, in the long run on average you'd lose almost 28 cents for each ticket purchased.*

# 3-5  Applications

Name _____

5. A stock you bought two years ago with high hopes is now selling for less than you paid, and things look grim for the company. Do you sell, or hold on and hope it will come back to the original price before you sell? A model economists use for such situations is a game no one wants to play. Suppose you have a choice: lose $100, or take a 50–50 chance between losing nothing and losing $300. Which do you choose? Find the expected value for each strategy.

*You can lose $100 with probability 1, or lose $300 with probability 0.5. If you take the first choice, your expected value is easy: it's just −$100. With the second choice, you get E = $0 · 0.5 + −$300 · 0.5 which is −$150. Ultimately you'd be better off sucking it up and losing the $100.*

There's an old joke among math and stats professors that lotteries are a tax on people who are bad at math. Let's take a look at one lottery game and use what we've learned about odds and expected value to study how good of an idea it would be to play the game. The image below is the back of a $5 scratch-off ticket from the Illinois Lottery.

- SEND WINNING TICKETS TO ILLINOIS LOTTERY, P.O. BOX 19080, SPRINGFIELD, IL, 62794-9080.
- Tickets, transactions and winners are subject to all Lottery procedures, rules, directives and state law. Official game rules are on file at the Illinois Lottery.
- Approximate overall odds of winning (including break-even prizes) are 1 in 4.05. Approximate Prize odds are: $5 - 1 in 12.00; $10 - 1 in 8.57; $15 - 1 in 120.00; $20 - 1 in 48.00; $25 - 1 in 150.00; $30 - 1 in 300.00; $50 - 1 in 300.00; $100 - 1 in 250.00; $200 - 1 in 3,000.00; $1,000 - 1 in 6,667; $2,000 - 1 in 60,000; $5,000 - 1 in 160,800; $10,000 - 1 in 268,000; $200,000 - 1 in 1,340,000.

Courtesy of Brian Mercer

6. Some of the data above are described as "odds." Are they really odds? Describe exactly what these numbers represent, using terminology from this lesson.

*They're actually probabilities. For the $5 prize, for example, "One in 12" means one out of twelve times you will win that prize. In odds terms, that means the odds against winning are 11:1 and the odds in favor of winning are 1:11.*

## 3-5   Applications

Name _____

7.  Fill in the probability distribution below by using the "odds" on the back of the ticket to calculate probabilities for each numerical outcome (from the perspective of a player, not the lottery commission). Remember, you have to pay $5 for the ticket. Round probabilities to three significant digits. We strongly suggest using a spreadsheet to do the calculations for this question and the next one.

| Outcome | Probability |
|---------|-------------|
| –$5 | 0.753 |
| $0 | 0.0833 |
| $5 | 0.117 |
| $10 | 0.00833 |
| $15 | 0.0208 |
| $20 | 0.00667 |
| $25 | 0.00333 |
| $45 | 0.00333 |

| Outcome | Probability |
|---------|-------------|
| $95 | 0.00400 |
| $195 | 0.000333 |
| $995 | 0.000150 |
| $1,995 | 0.000 0167 |
| $4,995 | 0.00 000 622 |
| $9,995 | 0.00 000 373 |
| $199,995 | 0.000 000 746 |

8.  Use your table to find the expected value of buying one ticket. Again, a spreadsheet would be a great idea.

| | | |
|---|---|---|
| –$5 | 0.753 | –$3.77 |
| $0 | 0.0833 | $0 |
| $5 | 0.117 | $0.59 |
| $10 | 0.00833 | $0.08 |
| $15 | 0.0208 | $0.31 |
| $20 | 0.00667 | $0.13 |
| $25 | 0.00333 | $0.08 |
| $45 | 0.00333 | $0.15 |
| | | –$2.42 |

| | | |
|---|---|---|
| $95 | 0.00400 | $0.38 |
| $195 | 0.000333 | $0.06 |
| $995 | 0.000150 | $0.15 |
| $1,995 | 0.0000167 | $0.03 |
| $4,995 | 0.00000622 | $0.03 |
| $9,995 | 0.00000373 | $0.04 |
| $199,995 | 0.000000746 | $0.15 |
| | | $0.85 |

$$E = -\$2.42 + \$0.85 = -\$1.57$$

## 3-5 Applications

Name _____

9. Carefully explain exactly what your answer to Question 8 represents. If you don't have an answer for Question 8, make an educated guess as to what you think the expected value would be and explain what it would mean.

*If you play this game a lot, in the long run you'll lose $1.57 every time you play.*

10. How much profit would the state expect to make if they sold 5,000,000 of these tickets?

*5,000,000 × $1.57 = $7,850,000*

11. Some people think that lotteries are a bad idea because they encourage gambling among people who can least afford to lose money. Others feel like the revenue that states make from lotteries is important to education and other social services. What are your thoughts?

*Answers will vary.*

# Lesson 3-6   **Prep Skills**

This is a short review of skills that will come in handy in the next lesson. In each case, answer the question, then rate your confidence level by checking one of the boxes. If you feel like you're struggling with these skills, consult the online resources provided by your instructor for extra practice.

### SKILL 1: COMPUTE THEORETICAL PROBABILITIES

1. After winning a drawing at a social club, one of the members gets to pick an envelope out of a bin. There are 40 envelopes in the bin: one has $1,000 in it, 2 have $50, 10 have $20, and the rest contain blank scraps of paper. What is the probability the she'll pick an envelope with some cash in it?

2. What's the probability that she'll win more than $20?

### SKILL 2: ADD FRACTIONS WITH THE SAME DENOMINATOR

3. Find the sum: $\dfrac{2}{11} + \dfrac{7}{11}$

4. Find the sum: $\dfrac{3}{16} + \dfrac{9}{16}$

5. Compute: $\dfrac{27}{80} + \dfrac{13}{80} - \dfrac{9}{80}$

### SKILL 3: SOLVE BASIC EQUATIONS

6. Solve: $0.36 = 0.28 + 0.39 - P$

# Lesson 3-6 **An Exclusive Club** (Addition Rules for Probability)

## LEARNING OBJECTIVES

☐ 1. Distinguish between events that are and are not mutually exclusive.

☐ 2. Develop addition rules for finding probabilities of "or" events that are and are not mutually exclusive.

☐ 3. Use the addition rules to calculate probabilities.

*When politicians start talking about large groups of their fellow Americans as "enemies," it's time for a quiet stir of alertness. Polarizing people is a good way to win an election, and also a good way to wreck a country.*
　　　　　　　—Molly Ivins

© tupungato/Getty Images RF

As you know if you pay any attention at all to the news, ours is a country that is becoming increasingly divided by political affiliation. As the animosity between the two major parties grows, our lawmakers become more predictable. On most issues, you can have a pretty good idea of which side a politician will take just by seeing if they have a D or an R after their title. Of course, other characteristics come into play as well, and some political reporters make a living trying to forecast how our leaders are going to react to the key issues of the day.

As you may know, every member of Congress declares a single party affiliation, either Democrat, Republican, or independent. Suppose that one commentator feels like a particular issue before Congress is most likely to be supported by women and Democrats. It would be useful to find the probability that any given representative is either female or a Democrat. At first thought, it seems reasonable to add up the number of women and the number of Democrats in Congress, then divide by the total number of representatives. But if you think about it, this won't work—those that are both female and Democrats will get counted twice. Developing rules for more complicated probability situations will allow us to analyze more problems in a complex world.

**0.** After reading the opening paragraphs, what do you think the main topic of this lesson will be?

## 3-6 Group

The situation described in the opening paragraphs would be a lot simpler if the commentator were interested in the probability of a representative being either a Republican or an independent. The key difference is that everyone has to be either one or the other. (Of course, that's not the case when the two categories are women and Democrats.) This distinction leads to our first important new term:

> Two events are called **mutually exclusive** if they can't both occur at the same time. Another way of saying this is that the two events have no outcomes in common.

1. The example of finding the probability of a congressperson being a woman or a Democrat illustrates events that are not mutually exclusive. Explain why. Extra props if your answer identifies specific outcomes.

   *Because there are congresspersons that are both women and Democrats. So that's the outcome that's in common, which violates the definition of mutually exclusive.*

For Questions 2–4, assume that a random member of Congress is being chosen and decide whether or not the given events are mutually exclusive. Please justify your answer.

2. The representative is not a Democrat, the representative is an independent.

   *Not mutually exclusive. The outcome of being an independent is in both events, because no independent is a Democrat.*

3. The representative is from a state west of the Mississippi River, the representative is a man.

   *Not mutually exclusive, assuming that there's at least one congresswoman from a state west of the Mississippi.*

4. The representative has been in Congress for more than ten years, the representative is serving their first two-year term in Congress.

   *Mutually exclusive. If you're in your first two-year term, you obviously haven't been in Congress for more than ten years.*

## Did You Get It

Try this problem to see if you understand the concepts we just studied. The answer can be found at the bottom of the portfolio page.

1. If student government picks students at random to win free books for a semester, determine whether or not the two events are mutually exclusive.
   a. The winner is a sophomore or a business major.      b. The winner is a junior or a senior.

A type of diagram used in set theory is often used to illustrate sample spaces in probability. **Venn diagrams** use circles to portray relationships between sets of objects, in this case people. Each circle represents a set, with the objects in the set, or the number of objects in the set, written inside. If two circles overlap, the region that's common to both circles represents objects that are in both sets. We'll study Venn diagrams in much greater depth in Unit 6.

In this lesson, we'll first use a Venn diagram to develop a rule for working with mutually exclusive events in probability. In 2015, there were 54 Republican senators, 44 Democratic, and 2 independents. The Venn diagram below illustrates this composition, with the orange circle representing Republicans and the blue circle representing independents. The 44 written outside of the circles represents the number of senators who are neither Republican nor independent (that is, the Democrats).

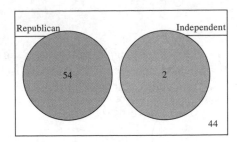

Since a senator can't be both Republican AND independent, notice that the two circles don't overlap at all. This indicates that the conditions of being a Republican senator and being an independent senator are mutually exclusive.

5. Find the probability of a senator being Republican.

   *54/100 or 0.54*

6. Find the probability of a senator being independent.

   *2/100 or 0.05*

7. How many senators are either Republican or independent? Use this to find the probability that a senator is either Republican or independent.

   *56, so the probability is 56/100, or 0.56.*

8. Describe the relationship between the probabilities found in Questions 5, 6, and 7, then use the Venn diagram to explain why that makes perfect sense when events are mutually exclusive.

   *The probability of a senator being Republican or independent is the sum of the probability of being Republican and the probability of being independent. This makes sense because to get the number of senators that are one or the other, you can just add the number of Republicans to the number of independents.*

---

 **Addition Rule for Probability (Mutually Exclusive Events)**

When two events A and B are mutually exclusive, the probability that A or B will occur is

$$P(A \text{ or } B) = P(A) + P(B)$$

9. In the House of Representatives, there are 435 total representatives. Eight are from Maryland, 13 are from North Carolina, 12 are from New Jersey, and 11 are from Virginia. Find the probability that a randomly chosen representative is from North Carolina or Virginia.

*13/435 + 11/435 = 24/435, or about 0.055*

10. In 2015, if you picked a random senator, you would have had a 0.13 probability of getting one who had been in the Senate since before 1995, and a 0.43 probability of getting one who took office sometime after 2010. What is the probability that you chose a senator who had been in office either since before 1995 or took office after 2010?

*0.13 + 0.43 = 0.56*

## Did You Get It

Try this problem to see if you understand the concepts we just studied. The answer can be found at the bottom of the portfolio page.

2. When the ace of spades is removed from a standard deck of cards, if one card is randomly drawn, the probability of getting a spade is $\frac{4}{17}$ and the probability of an ace is $\frac{1}{17}$. What is the probability of drawing an ace or a spade?

11. There's a key difference between Questions 9 and 10. You can answer Question 9 two different ways, while Question 10 requires our first addition rule. Describe the two ways you can find the probability in Question 9.

*You can use the addition rule for mutually exclusive events, or you can add the number of representatives from North Carolina and Virginia, then divide by 435. You don't have that option in Question 10 because we only know probabilities, not raw numbers.*

12. Can our addition rule be extended to more than two events? Suppose that you draw one card from a standard deck. Find three probabilities: the probability that the card is a club, the probability that it's a heart, and the probability that it's a diamond.

    $P(Club) = 1/4$, $P(Heart) = 1/4$, $P(Diamond) = 1/4$

13. Use the complement rule from back in Lesson 3-1 to find the probability that the card is not a spade.

    $P(Not\ a\ spade) = 1 - P(Spade) = 1 - (1/4) = 3/4$

    > Students are likely to need a little prodding here to think of this in terms of complement.

14. How does your answer to Question 13 relate to the three probabilities in Question 12? Explain why this makes sense, and what it indicates about the addition rule for more than two events. This should be a reasonably in-depth answer.

    The sum of the probabilities of the card being a club, a heart, or a diamond is the same as the probability that the card is not a spade. The condition of being a club, heart, or diamond is exactly the same thing as the condition of not being a spade. That tells us that if we add the three probabilities from Question 12, we in fact get the correct probability that the card is either a club, heart, or diamond. This tends to indicate that we can extend the addition rule for mutually exclusive events to cases where an event is made up of more than two mutually exclusive events.

    > Excellent teaching moment here. While this doesn't prove anything (hello inductive reasoning) a good way to test out a conjecture is to see if you can find another way to get an answer that you already know is correct, like the rule for complements in this case.

## 3-6 Class

You can probably guess what's next: what about events that are not mutually exclusive? We can turn to our friend the Venn diagram again to develop a rule for finding probabilities involving "or" when events can have outcomes in common.

This diagram illustrates the number of women and Democrats in the U.S. Senate in 2015.

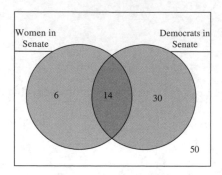

1. How many senators are women? (Pay attention to the entire left circle!)

   20

2. How many are Democrats?

   44

3. Write the probability of a senator being a woman, and the probability of a senator being a Democrat.

   Woman: 0.20. Democrat: 0.44

4. If we try to use our first addition rule, we'd conclude that the probability of a senator being a woman or a Democrat is 0.44 + 0.20 = 0.64. How can we be sure that this is incorrect?

   The outside of the circles shows that there are 50 senators, out of 100, that are neither women nor Democrats. So the probability of being female or Democratic can't be more than 0.5.

5. Explain why using our addition rule doesn't work here. Make sure your answer refers to the Venn diagram! I didn't draw that baby for nothing.

   *The senators that are both women and Democrats get counted twice.*

6. Fill in the blanks:

   The number of senators that are either female or Democrats = the number that are _____*female*_____

   PLUS the number that are _____*Democrats*_____ MINUS the number that are _____*both*_____.

7. Fill in numbers in this calculation, using your answer to Question 6 and the Venn diagram.

   $$P(\text{woman or Democrat}) = \frac{\text{Number that are women or Democrat}}{100} = \frac{20 + 44 - 14}{100}$$

8. Now we're going to use some algebra: split the fraction in the calculation above into three separate fractions with denominator 100, then describe why you're allowed to do that. It might help to look at it backward, starting with three separate fractions and going back to one fraction.

   $$P(\text{woman or Democrat}) = \frac{20 + 44 - 14}{100} = \frac{20}{100} + \frac{44}{100} - \frac{14}{100}$$

   *If you read it from right to left, it's just adding or subtracting fractions that have a common denominator. So this step is just the opposite of adding and subtracting fractions.*

9. Describe what the three fractions at the end of this calculation represent in terms of probability.

   *In order they are: the probability that a senator is a woman, the probability that a senator is a Democrat, and the probability that a senator is both.*

If all went well (and if it didn't you should ask for help!), you've just discovered our second addition rule for probability. You're pretty smart.

### Addition Rule for Probability (General)

When two events $A$ and $B$ are not mutually exclusive, the probability that $A$ or $B$ will occur is

$$P(A \text{ or } B) = P(A) + P(B) - P(A \text{ and } B)$$

10. In the House of Representatives, there are 84 women, 22 of whom are Republican. There are 435 total representatives, and 247 of those are Republican. If one representative is randomly chosen for a TV interview, what's the probability that the representative is either a woman or a Republican? Make sure you show your work!

$P(woman) + P(Republican) - P(both)$
$= 84/435 + 247/435 - 22/435 \approx 0.71$

Source: Architect of the Capitol

11. At Big Tony's Pizzas and Loans, 45% of customers order pizzas with either sausage or pepperoni. If 31% get pizzas with pepperoni and 26% with sausage, find the probability that the next person to call will order both sausage and pepperoni. (Hint: This will require the general addition rule and some ingenuity.)

$P(sausage \text{ or } pepperoni) = P(sausage) + P(pepperoni) - P(sausage \text{ and } pepperoni)$
$0.45 = 0.31 + 0.26 - P(sausage \text{ and } pepperoni)$
$P(sausage \text{ and } pepperoni) = 0.31 + 0.26 - 0.45 = 0.12$

### Did You Get It

Try this problem to see if you understand the concepts we just studied. The answer can be found at the bottom of the portfolio page.

3. When drawing a single card from a standard deck of cards, what's the probability that the card you draw is either a face card or a heart?

12. We now have two addition rules. Or do we? Look carefully at the general addition rule on page 268. Explain why it will also work when two events are mutually exclusive, and in that regard is the only addition rule you need to know.

    *If the events are mutually exclusive, then the probability of both occurring is zero. So the formula just reverts back to*
    *P(first event) + P(second event).*

    We've now studied two distinctly different situations involving two events: the key difference between them is the word that connects the descriptions of the two events: "and" or "or."

13. If we're trying to find the probability of one event AND another, what operation do we use on the individual probabilities?

    *Multiplication. That's the fundamental counting principle.*

14. If we're trying to find the probability of one event OR another, what operation do we use on the individual probabilities?

    *Mostly addition, with subtraction thrown in when we need to subtract off the probability of both.*

15. When a lot of information is provided verbally, it's often helpful to organize it when problem solving. In a hospital there are 86 nurses and 41 physicians. Seventy nurses and 14 physicians are females. If a staff person is selected, find the probability that the subject is a nurse or a male. Organizing the information in the table below should probably help.

| Staff | Male | Female | Total |
|-------|------|--------|-------|
| **Doctor** | 27 | 14 | 41 |
| **Nurse** | 16 | 70 | 86 |
| **Total** | 43 | 84 | 127 |

    *P(nurse) + P(male) − P(both)*
    *= 86/127 + 43/127 − 16/127 = 113/127 ≈ 0.89*

### Did You Get It

Try this problem to see if you understand the concepts we just studied. The answer can be found at the bottom of the portfolio page.

4. In one class, there are 15 freshmen and 10 sophomores. Six of the freshmen are education majors and four of the sophomores are education majors. If a student is selected at random, find the probability that the student is a sophomore or an education major.

16. Earlier, we thought about an addition rule for three mutually exclusive events. What about three events that are NOT mutually exclusive? That turns out to be quite a bit more complicated. It will require the three circle Venn diagram below. For three events, *A, B,* and *C,* see if you can make a conjecture on a formula for finding the probability of *A* or *B* or *C* occurring.

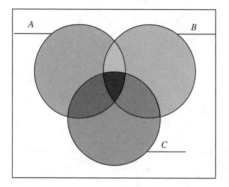

*You start with P(A) + P(B) + P(C). This counts all of the stuff in pink, gray, and orange twice, and the stuff in red three times. Next, subtract P(A and B), P(A and C) and P(B and C) to account for the pink, gray, and orange regions. In doing so, you've subtracted off the red portion three times, and it's gone. So you have to put one back, giving a final result of:*

P(A or B or C) = P(A) + P(B) + P(C) − P(A and B) − P(A and C) − P(B and C) + P(A and B and C)

I guess everything in this book is optional—it's your class, and you can cover whatever you want. But consider this question more optional than others. It's a really nice critical thinking exercise, but it's tricky and students can spend a LOT of time arguing over it.

# 3-6 Portfolio

Name _____

Check each box when you've completed the task. Remember that your instructor will want you to turn in the portfolio pages you create.

## Technology

1. ☐ In Question 16 of the Class portion of this lesson, you were asked to make a conjecture about what the addition rule would look like for three sets that are not mutually exclusive. Your job is to do some online research to find an addition rule for that scenario. If it matches the rule you came up with in Question 16, awesome work! If not, explain where you went wrong, and why the correct rule makes sense, based on the Venn diagram. Then use the rule to answer this question: If you draw one card from a standard deck, what's the probability that it's a black face card, a spade, or a king? Make sure you submit the general rule, as well as your answer to this particular question.

## Online Practice

1. ☐ Include any written work from the online assignment along with any notes or questions about this lesson's content.

## Applications

1. ☐ Complete the applications problems.

## Reflections

Type a short answer to each question.

1. ☐ How do you decide if two events are mutually exclusive?
2. ☐ Explain why deciding if events are mutually exclusive is important in probability. Make sure you describe the types of probability problems where this comes up.
3. ☐ Describe the two addition rules in your own words.
4. ☐ Take another look at your answer to Question 0 at the beginning of this lesson. Would you change your answer now that you've finished the lesson? How would you summarize the topic of this lesson now?
5. ☐ What questions do you have about this lesson?

## Looking Ahead

1. ☐ Complete the Lesson 3-7 Prep Skills and read the opening paragraph in Lesson 3-7 carefully, then answer Question 0 in preparation for that lesson.

## Answers to "Did You Get It?"

1. **a.** Not mutually exclusive   **b.** Mutually exclusive   2. $\frac{5}{17}$   3. $\frac{11}{26}$   4. $\frac{16}{25}$

## 3-6 Applications

Name _____

| Rank | Program | Network | 2 + (000) |
|------|---------|---------|-----------|
| 1 | NBC Sunday Night Football | NBC | 20,812 |
| 2 | The Big Bang Theory | CBS | 19,053 |
| 3 | NCIS | CBS | 18,257 |
| 4 | NCIS: New Orleans | CBS | 17,421 |
| 5 | Empire | FOX | 17,333 |
| 6 | CBS + NFLN Thursday Night Football | CBS | 17,087 |
| 7 | The Big Bang Theory - 2 | CBS | 15,842 |
| 8 | Sunday Night NFL Pre-Kickoff | NBC | 15,577 |
| 9 | Dancing With the Stars | ABC | 14,727 |
| 10 | Madam Secretary | CBS | 14,168 |
| 11 | Criminal Minds | CBS | 14,111 |
| 12 | The Voice | NBC | 13,802 |
| 13 | Blue Bloods | CBS | 13,778 |
| 14 | The Blacklist | NBC | 13,765 |
| 15 | Scorpion | CBS | 13,628 |
| 16 | The Voice - Tuesday | NBC | 13,450 |
| 17 | The OT | FOX | 12,928 |
| 18 | Scandal | ABC | 12,656 |
| 19 | 60 Minutes | CBS | 12,382 |
| 20 | Hawaii Five-O | CBS | 12,288 |

This table shows the top 20 highest-rated American TV shows for the 2014–2015 season. The last column is the average number of viewers in thousands. You'll be using this table throughout the Applications, so memorize it and then eat it. Or I guess you could just refer back to it. That probably makes more sense.

1. If one of the top 20 shows is chosen at random, what is the probability that it was on NBC or CBS?

   16/20, or 4/5

2. If you choose one top 20 show randomly, what is the probability that it was on CBS or had more than 14 million viewers on average?

   11/20 + 11/20 − 7/20 = 15/20 = 3/4

3. When choosing a random top 20 show, what's more likely: that it was on CBS, or that it was on ABC or NBC? Justify by calculating probabilities, please.

   CBS: 11/20
   ABC or NBC: 7/20
   More likely that it was on CBS.

## 3-6 Applications

Name _____

4. In the rankings of all shows for the season, the probabilities of a show being on Fox, NBC, or CBS were all 0.229. The probability of a show being on ABC was 0.202, and the probability of being on CW was 0.112. Find the probability that one randomly selected network show was not on NBC or CBS.

   Not on NBC or CBS is the same as being on Fox, ABC, or the CW. Because these are all mutually exclusive, the probability is 0.229 + 0.202 + 0.112 = 0.543.

5. Back to the information from the table. Write an example of an event involving "or" based on the table where two or more events ARE mutually exclusive. Write a sentence or two to justify your choice.

   Answers vary, but the easiest way to do this is to choose shows from different networks.

6. Write an example of an event involving "or" based on the table where two or more events ARE NOT mutually exclusive. Write a sentence or two to justify your choice.

   Sample answer: A show in the top 20 was on NBC or had more than 13 million viewers on average.

7. There were 188 total shows listed, and Fox, NBC, and CBS each had 43 shows listed in the rankings. Find the probability that a randomly selected show was on CBS or was ranked in the top 20.

   $P(CBS) + P(top\ 20) - P(CBS\ and\ top\ 20) = 43/188 + 20/188 - 11/188 = 52/188 \approx 0.277$

8. Find the probability that a randomly selected show was on CBS or had more than 13 million viewers.

   $P(CBS) + P(more\ than\ 13\ million) - P(CBS\ and\ more\ than\ 13\ million)$
   $= 43/188 + 16/188 - 9/188 = 50/188 = 25/94 \approx 0.266$

# Lesson 3-7  **Prep Skills**

This is a short review of skills that will come in handy in the next lesson. In each case, answer the question, then rate your confidence level by checking one of the boxes. If you feel like you're struggling with these skills, consult the online resources provided by your instructor for extra practice.

### SKILL 1: MULTIPLYING FRACTIONS

1. Perform each multiplication. Write your answer in lowest terms.

$$\frac{1}{3} \cdot \frac{6}{11} \qquad \frac{9}{10} \cdot \frac{3}{10} \qquad \frac{1}{5} \cdot \frac{2}{3} \cdot \frac{3}{5}$$

### SKILL 2: COMPUTING BASIC PROBABILITY

2. A fast-food restaurant has 11 meal choices on their value menu. If a friend runs to pick up some food and chooses your meal randomly, what's the probability that you'll get your favorite?

### SKILL 3: COMPUTING PROBABILITY FROM A DECK OF CARDS

3. When drawing a single card randomly from a deck, find the probability that the card is a 10.

4. Find the probability that the card is a heart.

5. Find the probability that the card is a red face card.

### SKILL 4: FIND PROBABILITY FROM DATA IN TABLE FORM

6. The table shows light conditions for November 4, 2015, in the Cincinnati area, as well as a month later. Find the probability that a randomly selected hour on one of those days had sunny conditions.

| Date | Hours sunny | Hours cloudy | Hours dark |
|------|-------------|--------------|------------|
| **Nov. 4** | 6.2 | 4.05 | 13.75 |
| **Dec. 4** | 1.7 | 7.8 | 14.5 |

# Lesson 3-7   **Independence Day**   (Multiplication Rules and Conditional Probability)

**LEARNING OBJECTIVES**

☐ 1. Distinguish between events that are and are not independent.

☐ 2. Develop multiplication rules for finding probabilities of "and" events that are and are not independent.

☐ 3. Use the multiplication rules to calculate probabilities.

☐ 4. Define, compute, and interpret conditional probabilities.

© Creatas/PictureQuest RF

*The five separate fingers are five independent units. Close them and the fist multiplies strength.*

— James Cash Penney

Even after learning about probability, a lot of people are tempted to play lottery games, looking for that one big score that will put them on easy street. Suppose that you play a daily game in which you try to match a randomly selected four-digit number. On Monday, the number is 2471. On Tuesday, the number is again 2471. Would you play 2471 on Wednesday? People are usually split on this question: some say "There's no way it's going to come up three days in a row!" while others say "That number's hot! Go with it!"

The logic in both of those arguments is faulty, however, assuming that the game isn't rigged and the numbers really are chosen at random. When Wednesday's numbers are being drawn, they have no idea what may have been drawn on Monday and Tuesday: that's all in the past and has no effect on Wednesday's draw. Let's recast the question this way: What's the probability that 2471 will come up three times in a row? In this lesson, we'll study rules for finding the probability of consecutive events occurring. In every case, we'll have to decide if any event affects the outcome of the ones that follow.

**0.** After reading the opening paragraphs, what do you think the main topic of this lesson will be?

## 3-7   Class

The key idea in the opening paragraphs is that when finding probabilities of consecutive events, it's important to decide whether any of the later events are in some way affected by the ones that already occurred. One of the terms we use to describe this condition is *independence*.

Two events *A* and *B* are **independent** if the fact that *A* occurs has no effect on the probability of *B* occurring.

**1.** Based on our description above, are the lottery numbers that are drawn on Tuesday and Wednesday independent events or not? Why?

*They're independent events because the numbers drawn on Tuesday can't jump into the future and affect what happens on Wednesday.*

On the other hand, when the occurrence of the first event changes the probability of the occurrence of the second event, the two events are said to be *dependent*. For example, suppose a card is drawn from a deck and not replaced, and then a second card is drawn. The probability for the second card is changed since the sample space contains only 51 cards when the first card isn't replaced.

---

Two events *A* and *B* are **dependent** if the outcome of *A* has some effect on the probability of *B* occurring.

---

Suppose each day a professor picks a student at random to work out a homework problem on the board.

2. If the student is selected regardless of who already went, the events are _____*independent*_____ .

3. If the student is selected from the pool of students who haven't gone yet, the events are _____*dependent*_____ .

© moodboard/age fotostock RF

In Questions 4–9, the goal is to decide if the two events described are independent or dependent.

4. Rolling a die and getting a 6, and then rolling a second die and getting a 3

   Independent

> How often do you have students do what's in this picture? Having groups present their work from time to time is a great way to keep them on a relatively similar pace. And there are many other benefits, of course.

5. Drawing a card from a deck, not replacing it, and then drawing a second card

   Dependent

6. Parking in a no-parking zone and getting a parking ticket

   Dependent

7. Drawing a card from a deck and getting a queen, replacing it, and drawing a second card and getting a queen

   Independent

8. Selecting a lottery ball from a tumbler, not replacing it, and then drawing a second ball

   Dependent

9. Flipping a coin and then flipping it again

   Independent

> Make sure students recognize that the events in Question 9 are independent. This is crucial in building our first multiplication rule.

10. Speaking of flipping a coin twice consecutively: What's the probability of getting tails on the first flip? What's the probability of getting tails on the second flip?

    *The probability is 1/2 on each flip.*

11. Complete the sample space for two flips of a coin: {HH, <u>TT</u>, <u>HT</u>, <u>TH</u>}.

12. What is the probability of getting tails twice?

    *The probability is 1/4.*

13. How do your answers to Question 10 relate to your answer to Question 12? Make a conjecture on a rule for finding the probability of two events occurring consecutively when those events are independent.

    *When you multiply the two probabilities from Question 10, the result is the answer to Question 12. This tends to indicate that the probability of two independent events occurring consecutively is the product of the probability of each event occurring separately.*

If you did well, your conjecture from Question 13 is our first multiplication rule for probability.

### The Multiplication Rule for Independent Events

When two events *A* and *B* are independent, the probability of both occurring is

$$P(A \text{ and } B) = P(A) \cdot P(B)$$

14. A coin is flipped and a die is rolled. Find the probability of getting heads on the coin and a 4 on the die. (Are you sure that the multiplication rule applies?)

    *First, the multiplication rule does apply because the events are independent.*

    $P(heads) = 1/2; P(4) = 1/6$

    $P(heads \text{ and } 4) = \dfrac{1}{2} \cdot \dfrac{1}{6} = \dfrac{1}{12}$

## Math Note

You could find the probability in Question 14 using standard sample space methods, but as outcomes get more complicated, it can be extremely difficult to list sample spaces. That's why multiplication rules are so helpful.

## Did You Get It

Try this problem to see if you understand the concepts we just studied. The answer can be found at the bottom of the portfolio page.

1. Talk about a bad day: If the probability of your alarm not going off is 1/20, and the probability of getting a ticket on your way to work is 1/200, find the probability that both will happen in the same morning.

As part of a psychology experiment on perception and memory, colored balls are picked from an urn. The urn contains three red balls, two green balls, and five white balls. A ball is picked and its color is noted, then it's replaced. A second ball is picked and its color is noted. Find the probability of each event in Questions 15–18.

15. Picking two green balls

   Note that since balls are replaced after being chosen, consecutive choices are independent and our multiplication rule applies.

   $P(green) = 1/5$, so $P(green\ and\ green) = \dfrac{1}{5} \cdot \dfrac{1}{5} = \dfrac{1}{25}$

16. Picking a green ball and then a white ball

   $P(green) = 1/5$, $P(white) = 1/2$, so $P(green\ and\ white) = \dfrac{1}{5} \cdot \dfrac{1}{2} = \dfrac{1}{10}$

17. Picking a red ball and then a green ball

   $P(red) = 3/10$, $P(green) = 1/5$, so $P(red\ and\ green) = \dfrac{3}{10} \cdot \dfrac{1}{5} = \dfrac{3}{50}$

18. Picking a white ball, then a red ball, and then a green ball

   $P(white) = 1/2$, $P(red) = 3/10$, $P(green) = 1/5$, so $P(white\ and\ red\ and\ green) = \dfrac{1}{2} \cdot \dfrac{3}{10} \cdot \dfrac{1}{5} = \dfrac{3}{100}$

   (assuming that the multiplication rule works for more than two events).

19. Did you make up a new rule in Question 18? Explain.

   We did. The multiplication rule has been stated only for two independent events, but we had to extend it to three events to answer Question 18.

> We wanted to give students a chance to think about extending the first multiplication rule to more than two events. Make sure you assure them that the rule does in fact work for any number of events provided that they're ALL independent.

## Did You Get It

Try these problems to see if you understand the concepts we just studied. The answers can be found at the bottom of the portfolio page.

2. As part of a card trick, a card is drawn from a deck and replaced; then a second card is drawn. Find the probability of getting a queen and then an ace.

3. Given that the probability of rain on any given day in March in Daytona Beach is 1/5, find the probability that

   a. It rains three straight days in March.
   b. It rains on March 10 and 12, but not March 11.

   Assume that weather on any day is independent of the others.

## 3-7 | Group

We know when a card is picked from a deck and not replaced, this changes the probabilities for what can happen when a second card is drawn. Let's explore exactly how the probabilities are affected.

**1.** Find the probability of drawing a queen from a standard deck of cards.

4/52, or about 0.077

**2.** Now assuming you actually drew a queen and didn't replace it, how many queens are left in the deck?

3

**3.** How many total cards are left in the deck?

51

**4.** Find the probability of drawing a second queen from the remaining cards.

3/51, or about 0.059

**5.** Find the relative change between the probability of drawing the first queen and the second queen. What does this mean?

$$\frac{0.059 - 0.077}{0.077} = -0.23$$

It means that if you've already drawn a queen and don't replace it, you're about 23% less likely to get a queen on the next draw.

> This is the key idea in understanding why independence of events matters: Emphasize the fact that the first occurrence had a very significant effect on the probability of the second one.

**6.** Now let's change the situation. Suppose instead of one deck, there were 1,000 standard decks, all mixed together. How many queens are in this gigantic deck? How many are left after drawing one?

*4,000, with 3,999 left after drawing one.*

> ## Math Note
>
> I just did a quick calculation and found that a stack of 1,000 decks of standard playing cards would be about 52 feet tall. Why would I do this? Because I can, and I wondered.

**7.** Do you think that not replacing the queen in this case will significantly affect the probability on the second draw? Explain.

*This is an opinion question. It's better if answers vary and students discuss among themselves.*

**8.** Well let's just see about that. Find the probability of drawing a first queen from 1,000 decks, and round to three significant digits.

*4,000/52,000, or about 0.0769*

**9.** Now find the probability of drawing a second queen assuming you don't replace the first one. What do you notice?

*3,999/51,999, or about 0.0769. These probabilities are identical out to the ten thousandths place. Wow.*

This illustrates a useful idea in computing probabilities in our world: If the sample space is really large, choosing a handful of objects without replacement technically makes the choices dependent, but the effect on probability is so small that we can pretend the choices are independent, making the calculations simpler. We'll use this idea in the next group of questions.

According to a study done by the *Princeton Review* in 2012, 86 percent of college-bound students indicated that financial aid would be "very necessary" for them to attend college. Our goal for Questions 10–13 is to find the probability that four randomly chosen college-bound students would rate financial aid as very necessary.

**10.** For any individual student, what is the probability that financial aid is very necessary?

*0.86, based on the described percentage*

**11.** Explain why the four choices are technically not independent events.

*After surveying the first student, it would be silly to survey the same one again. So in essence we're not "replacing" him or her.*

**12.** Explain why the four choices can be treated as independent events.

*Even though the four choices are not independent because students were not replaced after being chosen, in an average year over 2 million students start college, so having one or two fewer in the sample has a negligible effect on the probabilities.*

**13.** Treating the four choices as independent and using the multiplication rule for independent events, find the probability that all four described financial aid as very necessary.

*$0.86 \cdot 0.86 \cdot 0.86 \cdot 0.86 \approx 0.547$*

## Did You Get It

Try this problem to see if you understand the concepts we just studied. The answer can be found at the bottom of the portfolio page.

4. The *Princeton Review* also reported that just 29% of college-bound students reported that their stress level wasn't either high or very high. If three college-bound students are picked at random, find the probability that all three rate their stress as high or very high.

When we are interested in finding the probability of consecutive events that are dependent, we can still use the multiplication rule, but with a minor modification. For example, let's go back to drawing two cards at random from a standard deck. We know that the probability of drawing a queen on the first draw is 4/52, and on the second draw is 3/51.

**14.** What does multiplication provide as the probability of getting a queen on both the first and second draws?

*$\dfrac{4}{52} \cdot \dfrac{3}{51} = \dfrac{12}{2,652} \approx 0.0045$*

> If you want to dive into the realm of proving our second multiplication rule, you can point out that what we really did here is use the fundamental counting principle to calculate the number of ways to draw two queens and the number of total draws. We then used the rule for multiplying fractions and the definition of theoretical probability to get our answer.

The procedure we developed in Question 14 is a multiplication rule that can be used for any two events, whether they're independent or not.

### The Multiplication Rule for Any Two Events

For two events $A$ and $B$, the probability of both occurring is

$$P(A \text{ and } B) = P(A) \cdot P(B \text{ given that } A \text{ has already occurred})$$

15. An appliance store gets a shipment of 25 plasma TVs, and 3 of them are defective. If two of the TVs are chosen at random, find the probability that both are defective. (The first TV is not replaced after it's tested because that would be silly.)

$$P(\text{First TV defective}) = 3/25; \ P(\text{Second TV defective}) = 2/24$$

$$P(\text{Both}) = \frac{3}{25} \cdot \frac{2}{24} = \frac{6}{600} = \frac{1}{100}$$

## Math Note

Notice that if the two events are independent, then the probability of $B$ given that $A$ has already occurred is just the regular probability of $B$ occurring, and we get our first multiplication rule back. Good deal.

### Did You Get It

Try this problem to see if you understand the concepts we just studied. The answer can be found at the bottom of the portfolio page.

5. The 2015 NCAA men's basketball tournament field had (among 64 teams) 7 teams each from the Big Twelve and Big Ten conferences, 6 each from the ACC and Big East, and 5 from the Southeastern conference. If you were randomly assigned two teams in a dorm pool, find the probability that
   a. Both were from the Big Twelve.
   b. The first was from the Southeastern conference and the second was from the Big Ten.

## Conditional Probability

We know that to find the probability of two dependent events occurring, it's important to find the probability of the second event occurring given that the first has already occurred. We call this the **conditional probability** of event $B$ occurring given that event $A$ has occurred, and denote it $P(B|A)$.

Now that we have a symbol to represent the probability that an event $B$ has occurred given that an event $A$ already occurred, it makes sense to write a formula for calculating it.

16. Solve the general multiplication rule in the box above to find $P(B|A)$.

$$P(A \text{ and } B) = P(A) \cdot P(B|A) \ \Rightarrow \ P(B|A) = \frac{P(A \text{ and } B)}{P(A)}$$

## Computing Conditional Probability

The probability that a second event $B$ occurs given that a first event $A$ has occurred can be found by dividing the probability that both events occurred by the probability that the first event has occurred. The formula is

$$P(B|A) = \frac{P(A \text{ and } B)}{P(A)}$$

Hate crimes are defined to be crimes in which the victim is targeted because of one or more personal characteristics, such as race, religion, or sexual orientation. The table below lists the motivation for certain hate crimes as reported by the FBI for 2015.

| Motivation | Crimes against persons | Crimes against property | Crimes against society | Total |
|---|---|---|---|---|
| Race | 2,068 | 985 | 28 | 3,081 |
| Religion | 361 | 719 | 12 | 1,092 |
| Sexual Orientation | 876 | 298 | 4 | 1,178 |
| Total | 3,305 | 2,002 | 44 | 5,351 |

In Questions 17–19, write your answer as both an unreduced fraction and a decimal rounded to three significant digits.

**17.** Find the probability that a hate crime was a crime against persons. We'll call this $P(A)$.

$$P(A) = \frac{3,305}{5,351} \approx 0.618$$

**18.** Find the probability that a hate crime was racially motivated. We'll call this $P(B)$.

$$P(B) = \frac{3,081}{5,351} \approx 0.576$$

**19.** Find the probability that a hate crime was against persons and was racially motivated. Use an appropriate notation for this event in your answer.

$$P(A \text{ and } B) = \frac{2,068}{5,351} \approx 0.386$$

20. Use your unreduced fractional answers and the conditional probability formula to find the probability that a hate crime was racially motivated given that it was a crime against persons. Write your answer as a decimal rounded to three significant figures.

$$P(B|A) = \frac{P(A \text{ and } B)}{P(A)} = \frac{\dfrac{2{,}068}{5{,}351}}{\dfrac{3{,}305}{5{,}351}} = \frac{2{,}068}{3{,}305} \approx 0.626$$

21. Use your decimal approximations and the conditional probability formula to find the probability that a hate crime was racially motivated given that it was a crime against persons. How does your answer compare to Question 20?

$$P(B|A) = \frac{P(A \text{ and } B)}{P(A)} = \frac{0.386}{0.618} = \frac{2{,}068}{3{,}305} \approx 0.625$$

This is close, but not exactly correct due to rounding error being compounded.

22. Find the probability that a hate crime was against property given that it was motivated by the victim's sexual orientation. Don't use the conditional probability formula: just use information in the table.

This time we're given that the crime was motivated by sexual orientation, so we only need to look at that row. There were 1,178 such crimes total, and 298 were against property, so the probability is 298/1,178 ≈ 0.253.

## Did You Get It

Try this problem to see if you understand the concepts we just studied. The answer can be found at the bottom of the portfolio page.

6. Based on the data in the table on page 283, find the probability that
   a. A crime was motivated by either race or religion given that it was a crime against society.
   b. A crime was against persons given that it was motivated by religion or sexual orientation.

## 3-7 Portfolio

Name _____

Check each box when you've completed the task. Remember that your instructor will want you to turn in the portfolio pages you create.

### Technology

1. ☐ In Questions 1–9 of the Group portion, we studied the probability of drawing two consecutive queens, first from 1 deck of cards, and then from 1,000 decks. The point was that not replacing the card changes the probability that the second card will be a queen, but that effect becomes negligible when you use 1,000 decks. In that case, you can treat the two draws as independent. That got me to thinking: how many decks is *enough* (whatever that means) to justify treating the first and second draw as independent events? That's what we'll study in the tech assignment. The template for this lesson is a spreadsheet where we'll compute the probability of drawing two consecutive queens first the "correct" way (treating the draws as dependent, like in Questions 1–5), then treating the draws as independent and using our first multiplication rule. Your job is to try different numbers of decks and decide how many are necessary for the difference in probability to be negligible (whatever that means).

### Online Practice

1. ☐ Include any written work from the online assignment along with any notes or questions about this lesson's content.

### Applications

1. ☐ Complete the applications problems.

### Reflections

Type a short answer to each question.

1. ☐ Describe the difference between dependent and independent events, and give an example of each.
2. ☐ What is meant by the term conditional probability?
3. ☐ When can you treat dependent events as if they were independent? Why is it reasonable to do so?
4. ☐ Take another look at your answer to Question 0 at the beginning of this lesson. Would you revise your answer now that you've completed the lesson? How would you summarize the topic of this lesson now?
5. ☐ What questions do you have about this lesson?

### Looking Ahead

1. ☐ Complete the Lesson 3-8 Prep Skills and read the opening paragraph in Lesson 3-8 carefully, then answer Question 0 in preparation for that lesson.

### Answers to "Did You Get It?"

**1.** 1/4,000  **2.** 1/169  **3. a.** 1/125  **b.** 4/125  **4.** 0.358  **5. a.** 0.010  **b.** 0.009  **6. a.** 0.909  **b.** 0.545

## 3-7   Applications

Name _____

In Questions 1–4, decide whether the events are independent or dependent, and explain your answer.

1.  Flipping a coin and drawing a card from a deck

    *Independent: neither event can possibly affect the other in any way.*

2.  Getting a raise in salary and buying a new car

    *Dependent: most people would be more likely to get a new car if they get a raise.*

3.  Driving on ice and having an accident

    *Dependent: you're more likely to have an accident when driving on ice.*

4.  Having a large shoe size and having a high IQ

    *Independent: there's no reason to suspect that shoe size has anything to do with IQ. (Although I DO wear size 13 shoes. Just saying.)*

Use this information for Questions 5 and 6: A telecommunications company has six satellites, two of which are sending a weak signal. Assume two are picked at random without replacement.

5.  Find the probability that both are sending a weak signal.

    $P(\text{both weak}) = P(\text{one weak}) \cdot P(\text{the other weak}) = \dfrac{2}{6} \cdot \dfrac{1}{5} = \dfrac{2}{30} = \dfrac{1}{15}$

6.  Find the probability that one satellite sends a strong signal and the other sends a weak signal.

    $P(\text{one strong, one weak}) = P(\text{one strong}) \cdot P(\text{one weak}) = \dfrac{4}{6} \cdot \dfrac{2}{5} = \dfrac{8}{30} = \dfrac{4}{15}$

## 3-7 Applications

Name _____

In Questions 7–9, find each probability assuming three cards are drawn from an ordinary deck and not replaced.

7. Getting three jacks

$$P(3 \text{ jacks}) = \frac{4}{52} \cdot \frac{3}{51} \cdot \frac{2}{50} = \frac{24}{132,600} = \frac{1}{5,525} \approx 0.00018$$

8. Getting an ace, a king, and a queen in order

$$P(\text{ace, king, then queen}) = \frac{4}{52} \cdot \frac{4}{51} \cdot \frac{4}{50} = \frac{64}{132,600} = \frac{8}{16,575} \approx 0.00048$$

9. Getting a club, a spade, and a heart in order

$$P(\text{club, spade, then heart}) = \frac{13}{52} \cdot \frac{13}{51} \cdot \frac{13}{50} = \frac{2,197}{132,600} = \frac{169}{10,200} \approx 0.017$$

A survey of 200 college students shows the average number of text messages sent per month. Find each probability in Questions 10–13.

|  | Less than 1,000 | 1,000–1,999 | 2,000–2,999 | 3,000 or more |
|---|---|---|---|---|
| Men | 56 | 18 | 10 | 16 |
| Women | 61 | 18 | 13 | 8 |

10. The student sent less than 1,000 texts given that it was a woman.

$61/100 = 0.61$

## 3-7    Applications

Name _____

11. The student sent more than 3,000 texts given that it was a man.

$16/100 = 0.16$

12. The student was a woman given that they sent between 1,000 and 1,999 texts.

$18/36 = 1/2$

13. The student was a man given that they sent between 1,000 and 2,999 texts.

$28/59 \approx 0.47$

Use this information for Questions 14–16. On one large campus, 18% of students surveyed said that they spend less than an hour a night studying, 72% of students surveyed said they were in a math class, and 13% of students surveyed said that they spend less than an hour a night studying and that they're in a math class.

14. If three students are picked at random, what's the probability that all three spend less than an hour a night studying?

$P(all\ three) = P(first) \cdot P(second) \cdot P(third) = 0.18 \cdot 0.18 \cdot 0.18 \approx 0.0058$

15. What's the probability that the first two of the three students picked spend less than an hour a night studying?

$P(two\ less\ and\ one\ more) = P(first\ less) \cdot P(second\ less) \cdot P(third\ more) = 0.18 \cdot 0.18 \cdot 0.82 \approx 0.027$

16. Find the probability that a randomly selected student spends less than an hour a night studying given that the student is in a math class.

$P(less\ than\ an\ hour\ |\ in\ math\ class) = \dfrac{P(less\ than\ an\ hour\ and\ in\ math\ class)}{P(in\ math\ class)} = \dfrac{0.13}{0.72} \approx 0.18$

## 3-7   Applications

Name _____

17. Classify each statement as sensible or silly, and briefly explain your answer.

   **a.** I flipped a coin five times in a row and got heads, so I'm willing to bet $100 that it will be tails on the next flip.

*Silly, and probably the most common misconception in games of chance. Your coin has no memory. What happened on the previous five flips has no effect whatsoever on the next flip.*

   **b.** There's a 30% chance of rain tomorrow and there's a 50–50 chance of my only class getting canceled, so there's a 35% chance I'll be able to go golfing without missing class. (By the way, I'm not going to go golfing if it rains.)

*This equates to the probability of it not raining and class being canceled, which is $0.7 \cdot 0.5 = 0.35$. Sensible.*

   **c.** According to duilawblog.com, the probability of being convicted when charged with DUI in California is 0.794. If 50% of those convicted get at least 48 hours in jail, the probability of spending at least 48 hours in jail if charged with DUI in California is 1.294.

*Silly. It doesn't matter what the description is: a probability can't be more than 1, period.*

## Lesson 3-8      Prep Skills

This is a short review of skills that will come in handy in the next lesson. In each case, answer the question, then rate your confidence level by checking one of the boxes. If you feel like you're struggling with these skills, consult the online resources provided by your instructor for extra practice.

### SKILL 1: COMPUTE COMBINATIONS

1. Compute each combination.

   $_5C_5$         $_{12}C_8$

### SKILL 2: COMPUTE POWERS OF A FRACTION

2. Compute each power. Write your answer in fraction form, then in decimal form rounded to three significant digits.

   $\left(\frac{1}{2}\right)^3$         $\left(\frac{4}{5}\right)^9$

### SKILL 3: INTERPRET A TREE DIAGRAM

3. The tree diagram illustrates the outcomes for the experiment of flipping two coins then playing one game of rock, paper, scissors (where each of win, lose, or tie is equally likely). What's the probability of getting one head and one tail on the coins and not losing rock, paper, scissors?

# Lesson 3-8   **Either/Or**   (The Binomial Distribution)

### LEARNING OBJECTIVES

☐ 1. Identify binomial experiments.

☐ 2. Compute and interpret probabilities of outcomes in a binomial experiment.

☐ 3. Compute cumulative binomial probabilities.

© Veer RF

*When you wake up every day, you have two choices. You can either be positive or negative; an optimist or a pessimist. I choose to be an optimist. It's all a matter of perspective.*

—Harvey Mackay

Many years ago, I might have read the quote above and said "Bah! That's a bunch of psychobabble." Then one day I started to get tired of being crabby every morning, and wondered maybe if I *pretended* to be in a good mood, I might actually *feel* that way. And I'll be darned if it didn't work. It didn't change my life overnight, but I've become a believer in the notion that on most days, we have the power to choose whether to be in a good mood or a sour one. It's an either/or proposition, so why not choose the more pleasant outcome?

What does this have to do with a unit on probability? Many probability problems involve situations that have just two outcomes. When a baby is born, it will be either male or female. When a coin is flipped, it will land either heads or tails. When the New York Yankees play, they either win or they lose. That cute girl that sits behind you in class will either go out with you or she won't. Other situations can be reduced to two outcomes. For example, medical procedures can be classified as either successful or unsuccessful. An answer to a multiple choice exam question can be classified as right or wrong even though there may be four answer choices. Since either/or situations like this are common, it's worth a bit of our time and effort to study probability in this setting.

**0.**  After reading the opening paragraph, what do you think the main topic of this lesson will be?

## 3-8   Class

Situations like the ones mentioned above are called *binomial experiments*. This is the only type of probability question we'll study in this lesson, so we should begin by clearly defining exactly what types of questions qualify.

A **binomial experiment** is a probability experiment that satisfies the following requirements:

1. Each trial has only two outcomes, or outcomes that can be reduced to two outcomes. These outcomes can be considered as either a success or a failure.
2. The outcomes must be independent of each other.
3. There must be a fixed number of independent trials.
4. The probability of a success must remain the same for all trials of the experiment.

In Questions 1–4, decide whether or not each is a binomial experiment, and briefly explain your choice.

**1.** Drawing a card from a deck and seeing what suit it is

*No, because there are four outcomes: heart, diamond, spade, or club.*

**2.** Answering a question on a true-false test

*Yes. There are only two outcomes, true or false. And if the questions are randomly mixed, for any given person the probability of getting one right should be consistent.*

**3.** Asking 100 people whether or not they smoke

*Yes. There are exactly two outcomes, and if you choose your subjects randomly the probability that any individual smokes should be the same as any other.*

**4.** Drawing cards at random from a deck without replacement and deciding if they are red or black cards

*No. Even though there are two outcomes, since the cards aren't being replaced, the probability changes from one trial to another.*

## Did You Get It

Try this problem to see if you understand the concepts we just studied. The answer can be found at the bottom of the portfolio page.

1. Decide whether or not each experiment is a binomial experiment.

   a. Picking a colored ball with replacement from an urn containing three balls of different colors, and seeing if the chosen ball is orange
   b. Picking a number from a bingo machine
   c. Drawing a card at random from a deck with replacement and noting its color, red or black
   d. Rolling a die and getting a 3

Here's a more specific example of a binomial probability experiment. You're one of four finalists in a raffle, and each finalist is represented by a single colored ball thrown into a box. The colors are red, black, white, and green (you). A ball is picked from the box and its color is recorded, then it's mixed back into the box and a second ball is picked. If your green ball is picked twice, you win a 2-year lease on a Fiat convertible. As each ball is chosen, you don't care what color it is if it isn't green. All you're interested in is whether the chosen ball is green or not. The tree diagram for two trials of this experiment is shown below.

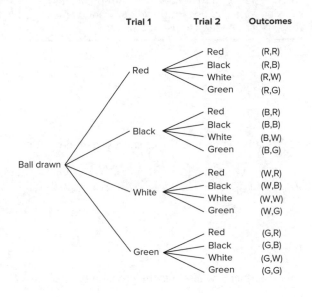

5. How many outcomes are in the sample space?

   *16*

6. How many outcomes result in no green balls being picked? List them.

   *9: (R, R), (R, B), (R, W), (B, R), (B, B), (B, B), (W, R), (W, B), (W, W)*

7. How many outcomes result in one green ball being picked? List them.

   *6: (R, G), (B, G), (W, G), (G, R), (G, B), (G, W)*

8. How many outcomes result in you driving away in a brand new Fiat? List them.

   *Just 1: (G, G)*

9. Use your answers from Questions 5–8 to fill in the probability distribution.

| Number of green balls picked | Probability |
|---|---|
| 0 | *9/16* |
| 1 | *6/16* |
| 2 | *1/16* |
| Sum of probabilities | *16/16, or 1* |

Let's understand how the experiment can be considered a binomial experiment. We'll make sure it meets the four conditions of a binomial experiment.

10. Even though four colors can be chosen in each trial, why are there only two outcomes that we're interested in? Explain.

   *Because if we don't win, we don't care who does. All we're interested in is whether the ball drawn is green, or not green.*

**11.** Are the outcomes independent of each other? Why?

*They are, because the first ball chosen is replaced. That means that the first draw doesn't affect the second.*

**12.** Is there a fixed number of trials? What is that fixed number?

*Yes. We're told that a ball will be drawn exactly twice.*

> Make sure you emphasize that everything in the world with two choices is not a binomial experiment. This can help you to review the wider point that knowing formulas doesnt do you any good unless youre clear on when to use them.

**13.** Explain how the probability of success remains the same for each trial. What is the probability of success and the probability of failure on each trial?

*Same answer as Question 11. By 'success,' we mean drawing a green ball, and that probability is 1/4. The probability of failure is 3/4.*

Now let's think about how we could get $x$ successes in $n$ trials of a binomial experiment, where $p$ is the probability of success on any trial and $q$ is the probability of failure.

**14.** If $n$ is the number of trials and there are $x$ successes, write an expression for the number of failures.

*$n - x$*

**15.** If the probability of each success is $p$, what's the probability of three successes? (We can use the multiplication rule for independent events.) Write your answer using an exponent.

*$p^3$*

**16.** Using your answer to Question 15, we can conclude that the multiplication rule for independent events tells us that ___*$p^x$*___ is the probability of $x$ successes and that ___*$q^{n-x}$*___ is the probability ___*$n - x$*___ failures.

**17.** If we multiply the probabilities from Question 16, we'll get the probability of getting $x$ successes and $n - x$ failures. The last thing we need is the number of different ways we can get $x$ successes in $n$ trials. This is a combination because we're interested in the total number of successes, not what order they came in. Write an expression for the combination we'd need.

*The number of ways to get $x$ successes in $n$ trials is $_nC_x$.*

Multiplying our results from Questions 16 and 17, we get a handy formula for finding the probability of a certain number of successes in a binomial experiment.

### The Binomial Probability Formula

When conducting a binomial probability experiment, the probability of getting $x$ successes in $n$ trials is

$$P(x) = {_nC_x} \cdot p^x \cdot q^{n-x}$$

where $p$ is the probability of a success on one trial, and $q$ is the probability of failure on one trial. Note that $q$ is $1 - p$.

Now let's get back to trying to win you that convertible. Remember, we were drawing a ball from a box with four balls, colored red, green, black, and white. The ball was then replaced and another was drawn.

**18.** Our goal is to find the probability of getting two green balls in two draws. In this case, $n =$ ___2___ , $x =$ ___2___ , $p =$ ___1/4___ , and $q =$ ___3/4___ .

**19.** Use the binomial probability formula to find the probability of the green ball being drawn twice.

$$_2C_2 \cdot \left(\frac{1}{4}\right)^2 \cdot \left(\frac{3}{4}\right)^{2-2} = 1 \cdot \frac{1}{16} = \frac{1}{16}$$

**20.** If your color is picked once, you at least get 100 bucks and a bag of muffins. What's the probability of that happening?

$$_2C_1 \cdot \left(\frac{1}{4}\right)^1 \cdot \left(\frac{3}{4}\right)^{2-1} = 2 \cdot \frac{1}{4} \cdot \frac{3}{4} = \frac{3}{8}$$

**21.** How do your answers to Questions 19 and 20 compare to the results you got from the tree diagram? Why is it worthwhile to compare them?

*Fortunately, they're the same. That's a pretty good sign, and it indicates that the formula we developed just might be correct.*

This is yet another good reminder that if you can test a new formula or procedure by solving an example problem using a method that you already know works, it's a good idea to do so.

22. Suppose that the morning after your birthday, you remember that you have a 20-question true or false quiz in your early class. Uh oh! Completely unprepared and a little woozy, you decide to guess on every question. Use the binomial probability formula to find the probability that you'll get 12 out of 20 right, and just barely pass. Begin by identifying values for all variables in the formula.

$$n = 20, x = 12, p = 1/2, q = 1/2$$

$$P(12) = {}_{20}C_{12} \cdot \left(\frac{1}{2}\right)^{12} \cdot \left(\frac{1}{2}\right)^{20-12} = 125{,}970 \cdot \frac{1}{4{,}096} \cdot \frac{1}{256} \approx 0.12$$

### Math Note

There are 20 trials in this experiment, so to say the very least it would be cumbersome to draw a tree diagram. To say the very most, it would be completely ridiculous. The last level of the tree would have over a million branches.

## Did You Get It

Try this problem to see if you understand the concepts we just studied. The answer can be found at the bottom of the portfolio page.

2. If you take a 10-question multiple choice quiz, with four choices for each question, and completely guess on every one, what's the probability of getting exactly 6 questions right? (Only one of the choices is the right answer.)

Not surprisingly, both graphing calculators and spreadsheets have commands for computing binomial probabilities.

## Using Technology: Computing Binomial Probabilities

**TI-84 Plus**

You could certainly calculate directly using the combination command we already know multiplied by $p^x$ and $q^{n-x}$. But graphing calculators have a built-in command for computing binomial probabilities directly. The **binompdf(n,p,x)** command can be found by pressing **2nd VARS,** which is the **DISTR** menu. Then scroll down to binompdf. (Don't confuse this with binomcdf, which we'll use later.) The screen shot shows how this works for finding the probability of guessing 12 out of 20 true/false questions correctly.

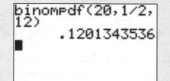

Notice that the inputs in parentheses correspond to the number of trials ($n$), then the probability of success ($p$), and finally the number of successes ($x$).

*See the Lesson 3-8-1 Using Tech video in class resources for further instruction.*

## Using Technology: Computing Binomial Probabilities

**Excel**

The Excel command is =BINOM.DIST. When you start typing =BINOM.DIST in Excel here's what appears, as a guide to help you:

= BINOM.DIST(number_s, trials, probability_s, cumulative), where

- number_s = number of successes (This is our $x$.)
- trials = number of trials ($n$)
- probability_s = the probability of success ($p$)
- cumulative = false; this tells Excel that you want the probability of EXACTLY $x$ successes.

The sample below also shows the calculation for guessing 12 of 20 true/false questions correctly.

| A1 | ▲▼ | ✕ ✓ | $fx$ | =BINOM.DIST(12,20,1/2,FALSE) |

|  | A | B | C | D |
|---|---|---|---|---|
| 1 | 0.1201344 | | | |

> Using technology in this lesson becomes a lot more important later, when we look at cumulative questions, like the one in the first paragraph of the Group portion below.

*See the Lesson 3-8-2 Using Tech video in class resources for further instruction.*

# 3-8 Group

We were able to compute the probability of getting exactly 12 questions right when guessing on a 20-question quiz. But wouldn't it be more reasonable to ask a question like "What's the probability of getting AT LEAST 12 questions right?" You'd be a whole lot more likely to wonder how likely you were to pass, rather than to get exactly 12 right. You'll answer that question in the homework. For now, we'll look at a similar, but simpler, question.

Of five physical therapists that work at a rehab center, three have master's degrees and two have doctorates. Each therapist is equally likely to be assigned to a patient on any given visit. Suppose Tom has five sessions scheduled in the next two weeks.

1. Find the probability that he gets a therapist with a doctorate twice.

   *This is a direct application of the binomial probability formula with $n = 5$, $x = 2$, $p = 2/5$, and $q = 3/5$.*

   $$_5C_2 \cdot \left(\frac{2}{5}\right)^2 \cdot \left(\frac{3}{5}\right)^{5-2} = 10 \cdot \frac{4}{25} \cdot \frac{27}{125} = 0.3456$$

In Questions 2–5, we'll work on finding the probability that he gets a therapist with a doctorate less than two times.

2. List the possible number of times he could get a therapist with a doctorate if it is less than two times.

   *Less than two times means either zero or one time.*

**3.** Are these outcomes mutually exclusive? Explain.

*Yes. You can't have both. You can't have a therapist with a doctorate zero times and have a therapist with a doctorate one time.*

**4.** In that case, what should we do with the probabilities?

*This is an 'or' question with mutually exclusive events, so we need to add the probabilities.*

**5.** Find the probability using the binomial probability formula and the operation you specified in Question 4.

$$P(1 \text{ doctorate}) = {_5}C_1 \cdot \left(\frac{2}{5}\right)^1 \cdot \left(\frac{3}{5}\right)^4 = 5 \cdot \frac{2}{5} \cdot \frac{81}{625} = 0.2592$$

$$P(0 \text{ doctorate}) = {_5}C_0 \cdot \left(\frac{2}{5}\right)^0 \cdot \left(\frac{3}{5}\right)^5 = 1 \cdot 1 \cdot \frac{243}{3,125} = 0.07776$$

$$P(0 \text{ or } 1 \text{ doctorate}) = 0.2592 + 0.07776 = 0.33696$$

## Did You Get It

Try this problem to see if you understand the concepts we just studied. The answer can be found at the bottom of the portfolio page.

3. If a different patient at the rehab center in Questions 1–5 has seven appointments scheduled, find the probability that she gets a therapist with a master's degree
   a. Every time.
   b. At least five times.

Questions 1–5 show that we can use the binomial probability formula and the addition rule for independent events to answer questions like "What's the probability of getting at least 12 questions right when guessing on a 20-question true/false quiz?" But doing so requires calculating several individual probabilities: the probability of getting exactly 12 right, then 13, 14, 15, 16, 17, 18, 19, and 20. Who has the time (or the patience) for that?

Fortunately, technology can save the day. Graphing calculators and spreadsheets have functions that are specifically designed to find the probability of *x* successes OR LESS in a binomial experiment. This is known as a **cumulative probability**.

## Using Technology: Computing Cumulative Binomial Probabilities

### TI-84 Plus
The **binomcdf(*n,p,x*)** command can be found by pressing **2nd VARS,** which is the **DISTR** menu. Then scroll down to binomcdf. This calculates the probability of getting *x* successes or less in *n* trials. The screen shot shows how this works for finding the probability of zero or one therapists with a doctorate (Questions 1–5).

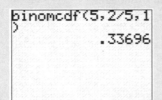

Notice that the inputs in parentheses correspond to the number of trials (5), then the probability of success (2/5), and finally the number of successes or less that we're interested in (1).

### Excel
To find a cumulative binomial probability, use the same command we already learned: =BINOM.DIST, followed by the number of successes, the number of trials, and the probability of success on each trial in parentheses. The only difference is that you finish the string in parentheses with true rather than false. This tells the formula to find the probability of *x* successes OR LESS.

| A1 | | $f_x$ | =BINOM.DIST(1,5,2/5,TRUE) | |
|---|---|---|---|---|
| | A | B | C | D |
| 1 | 0.33696 | | | |

*See the Lesson 3-8-3 Using Tech video in class resources for further instruction.*

We'll close the lesson with some practice on using technology to find binomial probabilities.

We can only use the binomial probability formula for a series of trials that are independent. As we saw in Lesson 3-7, when subjects are chosen from a sample and not replaced, the choices aren't independent, but if the sample is really large, the lack of replacement has a negligible effect on probability. So we can treat the choices as independent even though they technically aren't, which comes in handy when using the binomial probability formula.

According to the U.S. General Accountability Office, 20% of college undergrads don't have health insurance. Suppose that 10 undergrads are surveyed at random.

6. Find the probability that half of them will be uninsured. Why can we use our binomial probability formula?

   When 10 undergrads are chosen from a population of millions, we can assume there's no replacement, but the large sample size allows us to treat the choices as independent. There are two outcomes for each trial: the student either has health insurance or not. So this is a binomial probability problem with $n = 10$, $x = 5$, $p = 0.2$, and $q = 1 - 0.2 = 0.8$. Using binompdf(10, 0.2, 5), we get a probability of about 0.026.

**7.** Find the probability that less than seven will be uninsured.

*Note that less than 7 means up to and including 6. So we use binomcdf(10, 0.2, 6) ≈ 0.999.*

**8.** Find the probability that four or more will be uninsured. (This requires a little bit of thought.)

*Using binomcdf(10, 0.2, 3), we can find the probability that 3 or less will be uninsured. It works out to be about 0.879. This event is the complement of the event we're asked about, so the probability that four or more will be uninsured is about 1 — 0.879, or 0.121.*

---

### Did You Get It

Try this problem to see if you understand the concepts we just studied. The answer can be found at the bottom of the portfolio page.

4. In a large community, it was determined that 44% of the residents use the public library at least once a year. If 10 people are picked randomly, find the probability that
   a. Exactly 2 of them have used the library during the last year.
   b. At least 5 of them have used the library during the last year.

# 3-8 Portfolio

Name _____

Check each box when you've completed the task. Remember that your instructor will want you to turn in the portfolio pages you create.

## Technology

**1.** ☐ In this tech assignment, you'll complete a probability distribution, listing exact and cumulative probabilities, for the binomial experiment of flipping a coin and calling heads four consecutive times. Since we're calling heads, then the coin landing heads up is a success, and tails up is a failure (FAIL). There are further instructions in the template for this lesson (see online resources). You'll first find the probabilities using a list of all outcomes, then using Excel commands. Finally, you should check to make sure that you got the same results using both methods.

## Online Practice

**1.** ☐ Include any written work from the online assignment along with any notes or questions about this lesson's content.

## Applications

**1.** ☐ Complete the applications problems.

## Reflections

Type a short answer to each question.

**1.** ☐ How can we recognize when a probability experiment qualifies as a binomial experiment?
**2.** ☐ Give a brief description of how an experiment with several outcomes can be reduced to one with two outcomes.
**3.** ☐ In a binomial experiment, given the probability of any trial being a success, explain how to find the probability of a failure.
**4.** ☐ Take another look at your answer to Question 0 at the beginning of this lesson. Would you revise your answer now that you've completed the lesson? How would you summarize the topic of this lesson now?
**5.** ☐ What questions do you have about this lesson?

## Looking Ahead

**1.** ☐ Complete the Lesson 4-1 Prep Skills and read the opening paragraph in Lesson 4-1 carefully, then answer Question 0 in preparation for that lesson.

## Answers to "Did You Get It?"

**1. a.** Yes    **b.** No    **c.** Yes    **d.** Yes    **2.** About 0.016
**3. a.** About 0.028    **b.** About 0.420    **4. a.** About 0.084    **b.** About 0.470

## 3-8 Applications

Name _____

In Questions 1–6, decide if the experiment or question described is or is not a binomial experiment, then explain your reasoning. You don't need to find probabilities.

1. Keeping track of the number of customers in a week that get pepperoni on their pizza

   *It is. Every customer either gets pepperoni or does not, each pizza is independent of the others, and for a random batch of customers the probability of ordering pepperoni should be consistent.*

2. Recording the numerical results of rolling two dice 20 different times

   *It is not. There are six outcomes, not two.*

3. Playing 10 different people in golf and recording whether or not you win

   *It is not. While there are two outcomes, and you could make a case that the results are independent, the individual probabilities are not, because we're playing a different person in each match*

4. Drawing 12 different cards from a standard deck and recording whether or not each is a spade

   *It is not. It doesn't say that the cards are being replaced, which means the probability of any card being a spade is affected by which cards have already been picked.*

5. According to the U.S. Department of Health and Human Services, just 3.9% of men in America are taller than 6′2″. What is the probability that three out of five men chosen in your class are 6′3″ or taller?

   *It is. Even though there's no replacement, we can treat the outcomes as independent because we're choosing 3 men out of the entire male population of the U.S. So the probability is the same for each trial, and there are two outcomes for each person: 6′3″ or taller, or not.*

6. Playing 25 rounds of rock, paper, scissors against the same person and recording the result (If you're not familiar with the game, you can find the rules online very easily.)

   *It is not. Every trial has three possible outcomes: Win, lose, or tie.*

## 3-8 Applications

Name _____

7. Of all identity thefts, 27% are solved in 1 day or less. If 10 cases are studied, find the probability that exactly 5 are solved in 1 day or less.

$P(5) = {}_{10}C_5 \cdot (0.27)^5 \cdot (0.73)^5 \approx 0.075$

8. Of all people who do banking, 16% prefer to use ATMs. Of 20 people who are banking customers, find the probability that exactly 4 prefer to use the ATM.

$P(4) = {}_{20}C_4 \cdot (0.16)^4 \cdot (0.84)^{16} \approx 0.1951$

9. The Nielsen company reported that in 2011, 28% of smartphones in operation in the United States were iPhones. If this is still accurate, what's the probability that less than 4 of the next 10 smartphone users you see have iPhones?

Using binomcdf(10,0.28,3), we get right about 0.70.

10. A Telenav survey in August 2011 found that one in five people surveyed would rather go shoeless than cell phone-less for a week. Find the probability that if 25 people are surveyed, between 20% and 40% of them would be more willing to give up their shoes than their phones (include 20% and 40% of respondents).

Twenty and forty percent of 25 people, respectively, would be 5 and 10, so the goal is to find the probability that 5, 6, 7, 8, 9, or 10 people would give up their shoes. You can either calculate each individually, or find the probabilities of less than or equal to 10, and less than or equal to 4, and subtract. Using the latter approach: binomcdf(25, 0.2, 10) ≈ 0.994; binomcdf(25, 0.2, 4) ≈ 0.421. So the probability of the number being between 5 and 10 is 0.994 − 0.421 = 0.573.

## 3-8  Applications

Name _____

**11.** A survey done by Harris International QUICKQUERY found that 10% of women had a fear of flying. If 50 women are randomly selected, find the probability that less than 3 will have a fear of flying.

*Using binomcdf(50,0.10,2), we get about 0.112.*

**12.** In a recent survey, 2% of the people surveyed said that they would keep their current job if they won a multi-million-dollar lottery. If 20 people are chosen randomly, find the probability that 3, 4, or 5 of them would keep their job.

*In this case, it's probably simplest to find the probabilities separately and add.*

$$P(3, 4, \text{ or } 5) = {}_{20}C_3 \cdot (0.02)^3 \cdot (0.98)^{17} + {}_{20}C_4 \cdot (0.02)^4 \cdot (0.98)^{16} + {}_{20}C_5 \cdot (0.02)^5 \cdot (0.98)^{15}$$
$$\approx 0.00647 + 0.00056 + 0.00004 = 0.00707$$

*You can also use binomcdf(20,0.02,5) − binomcdf(20, 0.02,2).*

**13.** If you take a true-false quiz with 20 questions and totally guess on every one, find the probability that you pass (get at least 60% right).

*Using binomcdf(20,1/2,11), we find that the probability of getting 11 or less is about 0.748. This is the probability of failing, so the probability of passing is 1 − 0.748, or 0.252.*

**14.** After taking a 10-question multiple-choice quiz where there are four choices on each question (and only one is correct), a classmate who scored 9 out of 10 right says he didn't study, didn't even read the questions, and randomly guessed on all 10. Would you believe him? Use what we've learned in this lesson to back up your answer.

*I surely wouldn't. He'd have a one in four chance on any question, so the probability of getting exactly 9 right would be binompdf(10, 1/4, 9), which is about 0.0000286. Worse still, the probability of getting less than 9 right is binomcdf(10, 1/4, 8), or 0.99997. I'm not buying it. So why would he lie? Some people just need attention, I guess.*

# Unit 4
# Statistically Speaking

© James W. Hall

**Outline**

# Math In Sociology

Broadly defined, sociology is the study of human behavior within society. One important branch is criminology. This is not about investigating crimes, but rather studying patterns of criminal behavior and their effect on society. One of the main tools used by sociologists is statistics. This important area of math allows researchers to study patterns of behavior objectively, by analyzing information gathered from a mathematical perspective, not a subjective one.

It all begins with the gathering of data. Data are measurements or observations that are gathered for a study of some sort. Let's look at an example. There's an old adage in police work that violent crime increases with the temperature. A statement like "My cousin Jed is a cop, and he told me that there are more violent crimes during the summer" is not evidence, nor is it data. It's the subjective opinion of one guy. In order to study whether this phenomenon is legitimate, we would need to gather information about the number of violent crimes at different times during the year, as well as temperature information, and study those numbers objectively to see if there appears to be a connection. This is one of the most important topics in this chapter.

Data on its own isn't good for very much unless we develop methods for organizing, studying, and displaying that data. These are the methods that make up the bulk of this chapter. After discussing methods of gathering data, we'll learn effective methods for organizing and displaying data so that it can be presented in a meaningful, understandable way. We will then turn our attention to techniques of analyzing data that will help us to unlock the secrets of what sets of data may be trying to tell us.

As for math in sociology, the table shows the number of homicides committed in each month of 2011 in Chicago, along with the average high temperature for that month in degrees Fahrenheit. After finishing the chapter, you'll be able to analyze the data and answer the following questions. For now, discuss the table with your group and see if you can come to a consensus as to whether the claim about violent crime being connected to temperature seems to be legitimate.

| Month | Avg. high temp. | Homicides |
|-------|-----------------|-----------|
| 1 (Jan.) | 29 | 32 |
| 2 | 23 | 20 |
| 3 | 44 | 35 |
| 4 | 60 | 35 |
| 5 | 70 | 49 |
| 6 | 77 | 49 |
| 7 | 82 | 53 |
| 8 | 81 | 55 |
| 9 | 78 | 62 |
| 10 | 63 | 29 |
| 11 | 54 | 35 |
| 12 | 44 | 30 |

1. Draw a histogram (similar to a bar graph) for the homicide data using month on the horizontal axis. What patterns do you notice? Do the data appear to be normally distributed? Discuss.

2. There are four different numbers that might be considered an "average" for the number of homicides: mean, median, mode, and midrange. Find each for the data. Which do you think is most revealing? Explain.

3. Based on a graph of the data called a scatter plot, does there appear to be a relationship between temperature and homicide rate?

4. Can you conclude, using a measure called the correlation coefficient, with 95% certainty that there is in fact a relationship between the data sets? What about with 99% certainty?

5. Do the results indicate that warmer temperatures cause people to behave in a more violent manner? Discuss. A one-sentence answer here won't cut it: this is a really important question.

# Lesson 4-1   Prep Skills

This is a short review of skills that will come in handy in the next lesson. In each case, answer the question, then rate your confidence level by checking one of the boxes. If you feel like you're struggling with these skills, consult the online resources provided by your instructor for extra practice.

### SKILL 1: ORGANIZE INFORMATION FROM A TABLE

The cost in thousands of dollars of all houses sold in one town for the last week are below.

| 146 | 197 | 112 | 124 | 133 | 219 | 245 | 150 | 165 | 179 |
|-----|-----|-----|-----|-----|-----|-----|-----|-----|-----|
| 119 | 133 | 202 | 107 | 198 | 348 | 167 | 209 | 124 | 123 |

1. How many houses sold for less than $125,000?

2. What was the cost of the most expensive house that sold?

3. What was the cost of the least expensive house that sold?

4. How many houses sold last week?

5. How many houses had a sale price between $150,000 and $175,000?

# Lesson 4-1 Crunching the Numbers (Gathering and Organizing Data)

### LEARNING OBJECTIVES

☐ 1. Explain the difference between a population and a sample.

☐ 2. Compare and contrast different sampling methods.

☐ 3. Organize data with frequency distributions.

☐ 4. Analyze data with stem and leaf plots.

© Chad Baker/Getty Images RF

*Errors using inadequate data are much less than those using no data at all.*
        —Charles Babbage

One of the big issues being discussed over the last 10 years or so in higher education is grade inflation—the perception that college students in general are getting much higher grades than they used to. But perception and reality are often two different things, so how could we decide if this is actually taking place? And if so, what are some possible reasons? Are students just getting smarter? Are professors lowering their standards?

In order to examine questions like this, it would be very valuable to gather some **data,** which are measurements or observations that are gathered for an event under study. The term "data age" is coming into vogue to describe this era because of the vast amount of data that is available to anyone with Internet access and a web browser. But the expense of having access to so much data is that knowing how to gather data appropriately, and how to organize it into a useful form, is more important than it's ever been. So that's what we'll study in this lesson.

**0.** After reading the opening paragraph, what do you think the main topic of this lesson will be?

## 4-1 | Class

As we begin our study of statistics, it would seem reasonable to have a really good idea of what that actually means. **Statistics** is a branch of math that involves collecting, organizing, summarizing, and presenting data and drawing general conclusions from that data. If we're talking about grade inflation, then relevant data might be average grade point averages for students in several different years. The table below shows some GPA data from the website Gradeinflation.com.

| School Year | Average Undergraduate GPA |
|---|---|
| 1991–1992 | 2.93 |
| 1996–1997 | 2.99 |
| 2001–2002 | 3.07 |
| 2006–2007 | 3.11 |

**Math Note**

The data in this table caused so much negative publicity that many schools stopped sharing GPA data after they were published in 2009, making it harder to see if the trend continued.

In statistics, we *start* with a question we'd like to answer, like "Is grade inflation a real phenomenon?" *Then* we gather data, and try to interpret it in order to answer that question.

1. Write a verbal description of the information provided in the table. Do you think it supports the idea of grade inflation?

   *Average GPAs have been going up pretty steadily every five years. The increase in each five-year period was 0.06, 0.08, and 0.04. Certainly GPAs have gone up, but the numbers don't say anything about why that might be happening.*

2. How do you think these numbers were calculated? What students' GPAs were considered? Discuss.

   *Answers vary. It's good to have students discuss this before we study sampling vs. population, and sampling methods.*

© Scott Speakes/Corbis RF

The ideal way to gather GPA data would be to add the GPAs of every college student in America during each year, then divide by the number of students. Needless to say, that's not particularly realistic. Aside from legal ramifications, in any given year there are more than 20 million students enrolled in American colleges, and by the time all of that GPA data were gathered and recorded, many of them would be contemplating retirement. Instead, GPA data is obtained from a *sample* of college students.

A **population** consists of all subjects under study. A **sample** is a representative subgroup or subset of a population.

3. In the case of the GPA data we've been studying, the population is ___every college student___.

4. The sample is ___the group of students whose GPAs were included in the averages___.

In this case, GPA data from a sample of 70 different colleges were used to compute the average. The thing that makes the data compelling is that the sample is representative of the population as a whole. The schools chosen vary in size, cost, and geographic location. Some are public, some are private.

5. Discuss what exactly is meant by a representative sample, and why it's so important in answering questions using statistics.

   *Answers vary. Get students to focus on the fact that since you're not getting data from every individual in a population, you have to do everything you can to ensure that the individuals you sample provide data that's consistent with data you'd get if you were able to sample the entire population.*

   > This is probably the key point in understanding what sampling is all about, and is the main reason this portion of the lesson is listed as Class. Make sure that you discuss good answers to these questions.

## Sampling Methods

We will study four basic sampling methods that can be used to obtain a representative sample: random, systematic, stratified, and cluster.

In order to obtain a **random sample,** every subject of the population has to have an equal chance of being selected. The best way to obtain a random sample is to use a list of random numbers. These can be generated from a variety of Internet sources, or from a computer or calculator. Subjects in the population are numbered, and then the ones to be studied are picked by using the corresponding random numbers.

> **Math Note**
>
> The word "data" is plural, so we say "data are," not "data is." The singular version is "datum."

6. If you were going to do a survey with every student at your campus as the population, describe how you might obtain a random sample to survey. More specific is better.

   *Answers can vary for all of Questions 6–9. Some sample answers provided.*

   *Use student ID numbers, and have a computer choose random numbers from that list.*

A **systematic sample** is taken by numbering each member of the population and then selecting every $k$th member, where $k$ is some natural number. For example, the researcher from Gradeinflation.com might have numbered all of the colleges willing to release grade information and chosen every tenth one. In this case, $k = 10$. When using systematic sampling, it's important that the starting number is chosen randomly.

7. Let's get back to the campus survey mentioned in Question 6. Describe how you might develop a systematic sample.

   *Use student ID numbers in order, then choose every 10, or every 100, or something like that.*

When a population is divided into groups where the members of each group have similar characteristics (like large public schools, large private schools, small public schools, and small private schools) and a certain number of members from each group are chosen at random, the result is called a **stratified sample.** For example, the grade inflation researcher might have decided to choose five schools from each of those groups. Medical researchers often stratify samples by dividing subjects into gender groups, age groups, racial groups, or many other categories. They would then choose a similar number of subjects from each group to compose the stratified sample.

8. Describe how you'd put together a stratified sample for that campus survey we've been talking about.

   *One obvious choice would be to divide students up by class standing, then choose the same number from each class.*

When an existing group of subjects that represent the population is used for a sample, it is called a **cluster sample.** For example, an inspector might pick at random one carton of laptops from a large shipment and test each one to see how many are defective. The group in this carton represents a cluster. In this case, the researcher assumes that the laptops in the carton represent the population of all laptops manufactured by the company. In the case of the grade inflation survey, researchers might have looked for an existing organization that many colleges of different types already belong to, then used contact information from that organization to reach out to the schools.

9. Describe how you might develop a cluster sample for our campus survey.

   *Depending on what the survey was geared toward, you might be able to use students taking a particular course, in a certain major, or in a particular student organization.*

## Math Note

In the last lesson of this unit, we'll study some ways that samples can be poorly chosen, either intentionally or not, which can invalidate the conclusions of a study.

Think about four different sampling methods the researcher from Gradeinflation.com could have used. For Questions 10–13, write which of the sampling methods we've studied was used for each situation. Explain your choice.

10. The researcher randomly selected three states and then asked all colleges willing to release grade information from those states.

    *Cluster sample: the states are the clusters.*

11. The researcher numbered all of the colleges willing to release grade information and chose every tenth one.

    *Systematic sample, because every tenth school in an ordered list was chosen.*

12. The researcher numbered all of the colleges willing to release grade information and chose several of them using a random number generator.

    *Random sample. There was no order for the assigned numbers, just a random group chosen.*

13. The researcher grouped the schools by two-year state schools, four-year state schools, two-year private schools, and four-year private schools. The researcher then decided to choose five schools from each of those groups.

    *Stratified sample. The key is that a certain number of schools were chosen from each category.*

14. Rank the four sampling methods in Questions 10–13 from best to worst in terms of how representative you think the sample would be. Explain your rankings.

    *This is completely opinion.*

---

## Did You Get It?

Try this problem to see if you understand the concepts we just studied. The answer can be found at the bottom of the portfolio page.

1. To study the number of credit hours taken by a typical student, Shawna asks the registrar to provide email addresses for 10 freshmen, 10 sophomores, 10 juniors, and 10 seniors. From each group, she asks for one whose student ID ends in 0, one whose ends in 1, and so forth.
   a. What method of sampling did she use?
   b. Do you think the sample will be representative?

## 4-1   Group

If it doesn't make you uncomfortable, exchange the following information with the classmates in your Unit 4 group. This will be your small group for the fourth unit. It would be a good idea to schedule a time for the group to meet to go over homework, ask/answer questions, or prepare for exams. You can use this table to help schedule a mutually agreeable time.

| Name | Phone Number | Email | Available times |
|------|--------------|-------|-----------------|
|      |              |       |                 |
|      |              |       |                 |
|      |              |       |                 |
|      |              |       |                 |
|      |              |       |                 |

## Frequency Distributions

The data collected for a statistical study are called **raw data.** Raw data can be really difficult to interpret; in order to describe situations and draw conclusions, we need to organize the data in a meaningful way. Two methods that we will use are *frequency distributions* and *stem and leaf plots*. First, we'll study **categorical frequency distributions,** which are a way to organize data that are divided into distinct categories, like gender, your class standing in school, or conferences for college football teams.

A categorical frequency distribution is a table in which you list different categories, then count up how many individuals in a sample or population fall into each category and list those frequencies. In Questions 1 and 2, you'll create a categorical frequency distribution.

1. Twenty-five volunteers for a medical research study were given a blood test to obtain their blood types. The data are shown below. What would the categories for this data be? Why?

| | | | | |
|---|---|---|---|---|
| A | B | B | AB | O |
| O | O | B | AB | B |
| B | B | O | A | O |
| AB | A | O | B | A |
| A | O | O | O | AB |

*The blood types, because that's the thing in this scenario that can be divided into categories.*

**2.** Build a categorical frequency distribution by writing in your categories, then putting tally marks in the second column as you count the number of individuals in each category.

| Categories | Tally Marks | Frequency |
|---|---|---|
| A | ＴＨＬ | 5 |
| B | ＴＨＬ ΙΙ | 7 |
| AB | ΙΙΙΙ | 4 |
| 0 | ＴＨＬ ΙΙΙΙ | 9 |

**3.** Use your distribution to write some conclusions on blood types in the population. Do you think that there's enough data for your conclusions to be reliable?

*Based on these data, 0 is the most common blood type, occurring in more than twice as many individuals as the rarest, AB. But with only 25 individuals out of 7 billion on the planet, these results shouldn't be considered reliable.*

## Did You Get It?

Try this problem to see if you understand the concepts we just studied. The answer can be found at the bottom of the portfolio page.

2. A health-food store recorded the type of vitamin pills 35 customers purchased during a one-day sale. Construct a categorical frequency distribution for the data.

C C C A D E C E E A B D C E C E C C

C D A B B C C A A E E E E A B C B

Another type of frequency distribution that can be constructed uses numerical data and is called a **grouped frequency distribution.** In a grouped frequency distribution, the numerical data are divided into **classes.** For example, if you gathered data on the weights of people in your class, there's a decent chance that no two people have the exact same weight. In that case, everyone would be in a separate category, and each category would have one weight in it. This, of course would make the frequency distribution no more useful than the original list of raw data!

So it would be reasonable to group people into weight ranges, like 100–119 pounds, 120–139 pounds, and so forth. In the 100–119 pound class, we call 100 the **lower limit** and 119 the **upper limit.**

**4.** With these ranges, where would we put someone that weighs 119.8 pounds?

*Nowhere, which is a problem.*

As Question 4 illustrates, the way we choose classes is dependent on how the data values are rounded. The weight classes we chose earlier would be fine if all the weights are rounded to the nearest pound. But if weights were rounded to the tenth of a pound, we'd want to make the classes 100–119.9, 120–120.9, and so on.

## Constructing a Grouped Frequency Distribution

**Step 1:** Decide how many classes you want to divide the data into. Between 5 and 15 is acceptable, depending on the number of data values in the set.

**Step 2:** Determine the width of each class:

$$\text{Class width} = \frac{\text{largest data value} - \text{smallest data value}}{\text{number of classes}}$$

*Then round this value up to the next biggest whole number.*

**Step 3:** Use the lowest number in the data set or a "nice" number lower than that number for the lower limit of the first class.

**Step 4:** Add the class width to the first lower class limit to get the second lower class limit. Do this for all classes.

**Step 5:** Find the upper class limit for each class by subtracting one from each lower class limit.

**Step 6:** Tally up the number of data values in each class, then put the frequencies next to each class in a table.

We'll illustrate by organizing the following data, which are the record high temperatures for each of the 50 states in degrees Fahrenheit.

| State | Temp. | State | Temp. | State | Temp. | State | Temp |
|---|---|---|---|---|---|---|---|
| Alabama | 112 | Indiana | 116 | Nebraska | 118 | South Carolina | 113 |
| Alaska | 100 | Iowa | 118 | Nevada | 125 | South Dakota | 120 |
| Arizona | 128 | Kansas | 121 | New Hampshire | 106 | Tennessee | 113 |
| Arkansas | 120 | Kentucky | 114 | New Jersey | 110 | Texas | 120 |
| California | 134 | Louisiana | 114 | New Mexico | 122 | Utah | 117 |
| Colorado | 118 | Maine | 105 | New York | 108 | Vermont | 105 |
| Connecticut | 106 | Maryland | 109 | North Carolina | 110 | Virginia | 110 |
| Delaware | 110 | Massachusetts | 107 | North Dakota | 121 | Washington | 118 |
| Florida | 109 | Michigan | 112 | Ohio | 113 | West Virginia | 112 |
| Georgia | 112 | Minnesota | 114 | Oklahoma | 120 | Wisconsin | 114 |
| Hawaii | 100 | Mississippi | 115 | Oregon | 119 | Wyoming | 115 |
| Idaho | 118 | Missouri | 118 | Pennsylvania | 111 | | |
| Illinois | 117 | Montana | 117 | Rhode Island | 104 | | |

*Source: National Climactic Data Center*

5. Why would a categorical frequency distribution be a bad idea for this data? (Hint: What would the categories be?)

   *Individual temperatures would be the categories. Data values range from 100 to 134, so there would be 20 or more categories.*

**Step 1:** Decide how many classes we want.

6. How far apart are the largest and smallest values in the data set?

   *34 degrees*

7. How wide would this make each class if we went with 15 classes? Does this sound like a good idea? Explain.

   *34/15 is 2.27, and rounding up to the next whole number we'd get classes of width 3. In that case, 15 classes would cover a 45-degree range, but the total range is only 34 degrees. Bad idea.*

8. I think seven classes seems like a really good idea for this data. Why do you think I chose seven?

   *With a range of 34 degrees, seven classes would make each category cover 5 degrees, and that will make it easy to organize the data.*

**Step 2:** Find the class width.

9. Divide the range of values you found in Question 6 by the number of classes we chose, then round up to get the class width.

   *See previous question: 5.*

**Step 3:** Decide on a lower limit for the first class.

10. Why is the smallest value in the data set a very good choice for the lower limit of the first class in this case? (As opposed to some value less than it, that is.)

   *Our class width is 5, so starting with 100 will make all classes start with either zero or five. Nice and organized.*

**Step 4:** Find the lower limit for all the other classes.

11. Starting with the lower limit we chose in the last question, keep adding the class width you found in Question 9, recording each result, to make a list of the lower limit for each of the seven classes.

*100, 105, 110, 115, 120, 125, 130*

**Step 5:** Find upper limits for each class.

12. Subtract 1 from each lower class limit you found in Question 11 to get the upper class limit for the previous class. For example, if the first two classes in a grouped frequency distribution are 50 and 58, the upper limit for the first class would be 57. (Remember, if a data set contains numbers with decimal parts, we would adjust the upper limits to reflect that. For example, if values in the data set are rounded to two decimal places, and a class limit is 2, the upper class limit below it would be 1.99.)

*104, 109, 114, 119, 124, 129, 134*

**Step 6:** Set up a table and build the grouped frequency distribution.

13. Fill in the table below, using the class limits you decided on in Questions 11 and 12.

| Class | Tally Marks | Frequency |
|---|---|---|
| 100–104 | III | 3 |
| 105–109 | ₩ III | 8 |
| 110–114 | ₩ ₩ ₩ I | 16 |
| 115–119 | ₩ ₩ III | 13 |
| 120–124 | ₩ II | 7 |
| 125–129 | II | 2 |
| 130–134 | I | 1 |

14. Write down at least three observations you can make from analyzing your frequency distribution.

*Answers vary.*

## Did You Get It?

Try this problem to see if you understand the concepts we just studied. The answer can be found at the bottom of the portfolio page.

3. The online homework system I use in my calculus classes allows me to track how much time students spend working on homework. In my two Calc 2 sections last semester, here are the average number of hours spent per week for each student. Construct a grouped frequency distribution for the data.

| 1 | 2 | 6 | 7 | 12 | 13 | 2 | 6 | 9 | 5 |
|----|----|----|----|----|----|----|----|----|----|
| 18 | 7 | 3 | 15 | 15 | 4 | 17 | 1 | 14 | 5 |
| 4 | 16 | 4 | 5 | 8 | 6 | 5 | 18 | 5 | 2 |
| 9 | 11 | 12 | 1 | 9 | 2 | 10 | 11 | 4 | 10 |
| 9 | 18 | 8 | 8 | 4 | 14 | 7 | 3 | 2 | 6 |

## Stem and Leaf Plots

Another way to organize data is to use a stem and leaf plot (sometimes called a stem plot). Each data value or number is separated into two parts. For a two-digit number such as 53, the tens digit, 5, is called the **stem,** and the ones digit, 3, is called its **leaf.** For the number 72, the stem is 7, and the leaf is 2. For a three-digit number, say 138, the first two digits, 13, are used as the stem, and the third digit, 8, is used as the leaf. For values rounded to the tenths place, like 8.4, you can use the value to the left of the decimal place as stem and the tenths place as leaf, as in our next example. In any case, the very last digit is used as the leaf, and what comes before is the stem. Note that we'll include a key with our plot that clarifies what the stems and leaves represent.

The data below are the July 2015 unemployment rates for each state.

| State | Rate | State | Rate | State | Rate | State | Rate |
|-------|------|-------|------|-------|------|-------|------|
| Alabama | 6.2 | Indiana | 4.6 | Nebraska | 2.8 | South Carolina | 6.0 |
| Alaska | 6.6 | Iowa | 3.7 | Nevada | 6.8 | South Dakota | 3.7 |
| Arizona | 6.3 | Kansas | 4.6 | New Hampshire | 3.6 | Tennessee | 5.7 |
| Arkansas | 5.4 | Kentucky | 5.2 | New Jersey | 5.7 | Texas | 4.1 |
| California | 6.1 | Louisiana | 6.0 | New Mexico | 6.7 | Utah | 3.7 |
| Colorado | 4.2 | Maine | 4.5 | New York | 5.2 | Vermont | 3.6 |
| Connecticut | 5.3 | Maryland | 5.1 | North Carolina | 5.9 | Virginia | 4.5 |
| Delaware | 4.9 | Massachusetts | 4.7 | North Dakota | 2.9 | Washington | 5.3 |
| Florida | 5.3 | Michigan | 5.1 | Ohio | 4.7 | West Virginia | 7.6 |
| Georgia | 5.9 | Minnesota | 4.0 | Oklahoma | 4.6 | Wisconsin | 4.5 |
| Hawaii | 3.5 | Mississippi | 6.3 | Oregon | 6.1 | Wyoming | 4.0 |
| Idaho | 4.2 | Missouri | 5.6 | Pennsylvania | 5.4 | | |
| Illinois | 5.6 | Montana | 4.1 | Rhode Island | 5.6 | | |

*Source: U.S. Bureau of Labor Statistics*

15. If you were to build a grouped frequency distribution, what classes would you choose?

Answers vary. I'd choose 2–2.9, 3–3.9, 4–4.9, 5–5.9, 6–6.9, and 7–7.9.

16. What will you choose to be the stems for this data?

    *The first digits of the unemployment rates.*

17. What will you choose to be the leaves for this data?

    *The second digit, which is the tenths place.*

18. List all whole number parts that appear in the unemployment data; that is, the digits to the left of the decimal point. (You don't need to repeat them if they appear more than once.)

    *2, 3, 4, 5, 6, 7*

19. Write your answers from Question 18 in order under "Stems" in the table below. Write the lowest value first, then larger values as you work your way downward.

20. Go through the data values in the table, and one by one write the tenths digit in each value under "Leaves," next to the corresponding stem. For example, since the first data value is 6.2, you'd write a 2 in the leaves column next to 6 in the stems column. Separate leaves that correspond to the same stem with some space, but not with commas. Put in ALL tenths place digits, including repeats.

| Stems | Leaves |
|---|---|
| 2 | 8 9 |
| 3 | 5 7 6 7 7 6 |
| 4 | 2 9 2 6 6 5 7 0 1 7 6 1 5 5 0 |
| 5 | 4 3 3 9 6 2 1 1 6 7 2 9 4 6 7 3 |
| 6 | 2 6 3 1 0 3 8 7 1 0 |
| 7 | 6 |

Key: 6|2 means 6.2

> If you want to be adventurous, you can use this as a first introduction to data that may be normally distributed.

21. Write at least three observations about the unemployment data from looking at your stem and leaf plot.

*Answers vary.*

© Janis Christie/Getty Images RF

Deciding on stems and leaves for the unemployment data was fairly simple because there was a natural choice of stems (the whole number part of each rate) that gave us a reasonable number of them (6). That's not always the case: for the high-temperature data eariler in this lesson, the natural choice of stem would seem to be the first two digits. But here's what the stem and leaf plot would look like in that case.

| Stems | Leaves |
|---|---|
| 10 | 0 6 6 9 0 5 9 7 6 8 4 5 |
| 11 | 2 8 0 2 8 7 6 8 4 4 2 4 5 8 7 8 0 0 9 1 3 3 7 0 8 2 4 5 |
| 12 | 8 0 1 5 2 1 0 0 0 |
| 13 | 4 |

Key: 13|4 means 134

22. Explain why this stem and leaf plot isn't really very helpful in organizing the data.

*There aren't enough categories. Forty-nine of the fifty data values are in just three categories.*

In general, it's a good idea to choose stems so that there are between 5 and 15 categories. In the case of the high-temperature data, we'd get a better organization if we divided the categories in half, so that the first category covers 100 to 104, the second 105 to 109, and so on. To signify this, we can use the symbols $10^{(0)}$ to represent a stem of 10 with leaves that are digits from zero to four, and $10^{(5)}$ to represent a stem of 10 with leaves that are digits from five to nine. In that case, this is what the high-temperature stem and leaf plot would look like:

| Stems | Leaves |
|---|---|
| $10^{(0)}$ | 0 0 4 |
| $10^{(5)}$ | 6 6 9 5 9 7 6 8 5 |
| $11^{(0)}$ | 2 0 2 4 4 2 4 0 0 1 3 3 0 2 4 |
| $11^{(5)}$ | 8 8 7 6 8 5 8 7 8 9 7 8 5 |
| $12^{(0)}$ | 0 1 2 1 0 0 0 |
| $12^{(5)}$ | 8 5 |
| 13 | 4 |

Key: $10^{(0)}|4$ means 104; $10^{(5)}|6$ means 106

**23.** Describe why this stem and leaf plot makes it easier to analyze the organized data than the one above.

*With more categories, we can see that the largest number of states have a high in the 110–114 range, and that the 115–119 range is a close second. Just a sample answer, of course.*

---

### Did You Get It?

Try this problem to see if you understand the concepts we just studied. The answer can be found at the bottom of the portfolio page.

4. It's no secret that gas prices have fluctuated wildly in the last few years, but from 1980–1999, they were surprisingly stable. According to the Energy Information Administration, the data below represent the average price (in cents) per gallon of regular unleaded gas for those years. Draw a stem and leaf plot of the data.

| | | | | | | | | | |
|---|---|---|---|---|---|---|---|---|---|
| 119 | 131 | 122 | 113 | 112 | 86 | 90 | 90 | 100 | 115 |
| 114 | 113 | 111 | 111 | 115 | 123 | 123 | 123 | 106 | 117 |

---

**24.** Compare grouped frequency distributions and stem and leaf plots. How are they similar? Which do you think makes it easier to analyze a set of data?

*Answers vary.*

## 4-1 Portfolio

Name _____

Check each box when you've completed the task. Remember that your instructor will want you to turn in the portfolio pages you create.

### Technology

1. ☐ Excel can be used to do two tasks from this lesson that are both useful and tedious to do by hand: sorting data, and building a grouped frequency distribution. In the online resources for this lesson, there's a spreadsheet that has two of the data sets from this lesson entered: blood types and record high temperature by state. Your first job is to sort the data based on the instructions that appear on the spreadsheet. Note that there's a different worksheet for each data set, and you can change from one to another using the tabs along the bottom. After sorting, there will be further instructions on the template for building the frequency distribution. There are also two short videos in the class resources for this lesson that cover sorting and frequency distributions.

### Online Practice

1. ☐ Include any written work from the online assignment along with any notes or questions about this lesson's content.

### Applications

1. ☐ Complete the applications problems.

### Reflections

Type a short answer to each question.

1. ☐ What is the point of sampling in statistics? What's the difference between a sample and a population?
2. ☐ What makes cluster sampling different from stratified?
3. ☐ Why is it bad to have too few or too many categories in a grouped frequency distribution?
4. ☐ Take another look at your answer to Question 0 at the beginning of this lesson. Would you change your answer now that you've completed the lesson? How would you summarize the topic of this lesson now?
5. ☐ What questions do you have about this lesson?

### Looking Ahead

1. ☐ Complete the Lesson 4-2 Prep Skills and read the opening paragraph in Lesson 4-2 carefully, then answer Question 0 in preparation for that lesson.

### Answers to "Did You Get It?"

1. **a.** Stratified sample   **b.** The last digit of a student ID number is likely to be totally random, so this should lead to a representative sample.   **2–4 can be found at the end of the applications section.**

## 4-1  Applications

Name _____

1. Twenty-five fans of reality TV were asked to rate four shows, and the data below reflect which one each rated highest. (S = Survivor, D = Dancing with the Stars, B = Big Brother, A = The Amazing Race)

S   S   B   A   D   B   S   D   A   B   A   A   S
B   A   D   B   A   S   A   D   B   B   S   A

   **a.** Construct a frequency distribution for the data.

| Class | Frequency |
|-------|-----------|
| S | 6 |
| D | 4 |
| B | 7 |
| A | 8 |

   **b.** Which show did those 25 fans rate the highest?

   The Amazing Race

2. The data shown are the cigarette taxes per pack in cents imposed by each state as of Oct 1, 2015.

| 68 | 84 | 320 | 129 | 351 | 170 | 166 | 103 | 153 | 30 |
|----|----|-----|-----|-----|-----|-----|-----|-----|-----|
| 200 | 365 | 57 | 60 | 200 | 64 | 435 | 131 | 62 | 303 |
| 200 | 160 | 198 | 86 | 290 | 180 | 45 | 160 | 141 | 55 |
| 115 | 134 | 100 | 200 | 68 | 178 | 44 | 375 | 170 | 252 |
| 87 | 37 | 136 | 200 | 17 | 270 | 160 | 57 | 308 | 60 |

   *Source: tobaccofreekids.org*

   **a.** Construct a grouped frequency distribution for this data using seven classes with the first one being 0–69.

| Class | Frequency |
|-------|-----------|
| 0–69 | 14 |
| 70–139 | 10 |
| 140–209 | 16 |
| 210–279 | 2 |
| 280–349 | 4 |
| 350–419 | 3 |
| 420–489 | 1 |

   **b.** Which class contains the most number of values? Write a sentence explaining what this means using units on any numbers used.

   140–209. This means that the largest number of states impose a tax between $1.40 and $2.09.

## 4-1 Applications

Name _____

3. As an experiment in a botany class, plants are placed in a greenhouse, and their growth in centimeters after 25 days is recorded, with the results shown below in a stem and leaf plot.

| Stems | Leaves |
|-------|--------|
| 1 | 2 |
| 2 | 0 3 |
| 3 | 2 5 8 8 9 |
| 4 | 1 3 3 |
| 5 | 0 1 2 3 3 5 8 9 9 |

Key: 1|2 means 12

**a.** How many plants grew 203 cm?

*None*

**b.** How many plants grew 38 cm?

*Two*

**c.** How many plants had their growth measured and recorded?

*Twenty*

**d.** What was the largest growth recorded for any plant?

*59 cm*

4. The National Insurance Crime Bureau reported that these data represent the number of registered vehicles per car stolen for 35 selected cities in the United States. For example, in Miami, one automobile is stolen for every 38 registered vehicles in the city. (The data have been rounded to the nearest whole number.)

| | | | | | | |
|----|----|----|----|----|----|----|
| 38 | 53 | 53 | 56 | 69 | 89 | 94 |
| 41 | 58 | 68 | 66 | 69 | 89 | 52 |
| 50 | 70 | 83 | 81 | 80 | 90 | 74 |
| 50 | 70 | 83 | 59 | 75 | 78 | 73 |
| 92 | 84 | 87 | 84 | 85 | 84 | 89 |

**a.** Build a stem and leaf plot for the data.

| Stems | Leaves |
|-------|--------|
| 3 | 8 |
| 4 | 1 |
| 5 | 0 0 3 8 3 6 9 2 |
| 6 | 8 6 9 9 |
| 7 | 0 0 5 8 4 3 |
| 8 | 4 3 3 7 1 4 0 5 9 9 4 9 |
| 9 | 2 0 4 |

## 4-1   Applications

Name _____

**b.** Build a grouped frequency distribution for the data, where the classes correspond to the stems that you chose.

| Class | Frequency |
|-------|-----------|
| 30–39 | 1 |
| 40–49 | 1 |
| 50–59 | 8 |
| 60–69 | 4 |
| 70–79 | 6 |
| 80–89 | 12 |
| 90–99 | 3 |

**c.** A **histogram** is very much like a bar graph that represents the information in a frequency distribution. There are two main differences between a typical bar graph and a histogram. First, the width of the bars has meaning, and is representative of the class width. Second, the bars are drawn right next to each other with no space in between. Create a histogram from the grouped frequency distribution above.

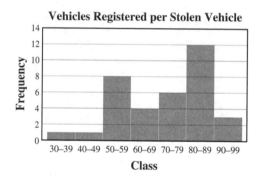

**Math Note**

We'll learn a bit more about histograms in the next lesson. They get really important later in this unit.

**d.** Which class contains the most values? Explain what this tells us.

*The 80–89 class has the most values. This means that the most common rates of stolen cars among these cities are between 1 in 80 and 1 in 89.*

**e.** Which class would you want to have your city listed in? Why?

*The 90–99 class, because I like my car. Higher is better, as 1 in 99 means that 1 out of every 99 cars will get stolen, while 30 is 1 in every 30 cars. That's bad.*

**4-1** | **Applications**

Name _____

**f.** Of the three methods you used to represent the data, which was the easiest to interpret in your opinion? Explain.

*This is completely an opinion, but very important for students to think about in terms of analyzing the different methods we've used.*

**Additional Answers to "Did You Get It?"**

**2.**

| Type | Tally Marks | Frequency |
|------|-------------|-----------|
| A | 卌 I | 6 |
| B | 卌 | 5 |
| C | 卌 卌 II | 12 |
| D | III | 3 |
| E | 卌 IIII | 9 |

**3.**

| Class | Tally Marks | Frequency |
|-------|-------------|-----------|
| 1–3 | 卌 卌 | 10 |
| 4–6 | 卌 卌 IIII | 14 |
| 7–9 | 卌 卌 | 10 |
| 10–12 | 卌 I | 6 |
| 13–15 | 卌 | 5 |
| 16–18 | 卌 | 5 |

**4.**

| Stems | Leaves |
|-------|--------|
| 8 | 6 |
| 9 | 0 0 |
| 10 | 0 6 |
| 11 | 9 3 2 5 4 3 1 1 5 7 |
| 12 | 2 3 3 3 |
| 13 | 1 |

Key: 13|1 means 131

# Lesson 4-2   **Prep Skills**

This is a short review of skills that will come in handy in the next lesson. In each case, answer the question, then rate your confidence level by checking one of the boxes. If you feel like you're struggling with these skills, consult the online resources provided by your instructor for extra practice.

### SKILL 1: COMPUTATIONS INVOLVING PERCENTS

1. What is 27% of 360?

2. There were 93 people in my high school graduating class. Sixty-two went on to college. What percent went on to college?

### SKILL 2: FINDING THE MIDPOINT OF TWO NUMBERS

3. What number is halfway between 8.5 and 16.5 on a number line?

### SKILL 3: ADDING AND SUBTRACTING A FIXED NUMBER

4. Starting with 0.75, add 0.5 repeatedly until doing so one more time would result in a number greater than 8. List all of your results.

5. Expand your list of numbers from Question 4 by also subtracting 0.5 from 0.75 one time.

### SKILL 4: PLOT POINTS

6. Plot each point on the axes. Make sure you indicate an appropriate scale on each axis!

   A. (−12, 100)
   B. (18, 0)
   C. (−6, −60)
   D. (4, −10)

# Lesson 4-2   **Picture This**   (Representing Data Graphically)

## LEARNING OBJECTIVES

☐ 1. Draw and interpret bar graphs from frequency distributions.

☐ 2. Draw and interpret pie charts from frequency distributions.

☐ 3. Draw and interpret histograms and frequency polygons from frequency distributions.

☐ 4. Draw and interpret time series graphs.

*The greatest moments are those when you see the result pop up in a graph or in your statistics analysis—that moment you realize you know something no one else does and you get the pleasure of thinking about how to tell them.*
        —Emily Oster

Now we've gathered some data, and we think maybe some of it has an interesting story to tell. How can we most effectively present that data? In Lesson 4-1, we displayed data in table form, using frequency distributions, and using stem and leaf plots. All are perfectly valid, but . . . they don't exactly pop. The graphic on this page, which appeared in a major newspaper, displays data related to identity theft complaints that could have been put in table form:

| Year | '01 | '02 | '03 | '04 | '05 | '06 | '07 | '08 | '09 | '10 | '11 | '12 | '13 |
|------|-----|-----|-----|-----|-----|-----|-----|-----|-----|-----|-----|-----|-----|
| Complaints (1,000s) | 86 | 162 | 215 | 247 | 256 | 246 | 258 | 295 | 264 | 251 | 279 | 370 | 290 |

The information is the same, but with the graph, just a quick glance is enough to see that identity theft rose sharply from 2001 to 2004, leveled off, and spiked in 2008 and 2012. Simply put, if you want your data to really catch someone's eye, you can't do much better than a nice graphical representation of the data. In Lesson 1-2, we studied interpreting information from graphs that had been supplied for us. But those graphs don't just appear out of thin air. In this lesson, we'll study several methods for turning data into graphical form.

**0.** After reading the opening paragraph, what do you think the main topic of this lesson will be?

## 4-2   Class

The first type of frequency distribution we studied in Lesson 4-1 was the categorical frequency distribution. When data are representative of certain categories, rather than numerical, we often use pie charts or bar graphs to illustrate the data. We'll start with a pie chart.

    Pie charts are most appropriate for data where every individual datum fits into just one category. Consider two different surveys about candidates for the presidency: If the question is "Which candidate is your favorite?" everyone will give exactly one response. So if we calculate the percentage of respondents that chose each candidate, those percentages will add to 100% and a pie chart would be a good choice for illustrating the survey results. But if the question is "What candidates do you find acceptable?" many respondents will list more than one candidate, and the percentages would add to more than 100%. That type of data is more appropriately illustrated with a bar graph.

1. When measured in degrees, a full circle measures 360°. If 50% of the respondents to our candidate survey chose one particular candidate, how many degrees would make up his or her slice of a pie chart? What about if they got 25% of the responses?

   50%:   180°

   25%:   90°

**Math Note**

We studied reading the types of graphs in this lesson back in Unit 1. Now we'll focus more on creating them to represent data that has been gathered.

2. Describe how you got the degree measures in Question 1.

   50% of 360° is half of 360°, then 25% is half again.

> Make sure that you discuss how this simple idea leads to the method for finding the number of degrees for each slice. Emphasize that this course is NOT about memorizing formulas!

## Drawing a Pie Chart

**Step** 1: Find the percentage and number of degrees corresponding to each slice. If *f* is the frequency for each class and *n* is the sum of all frequencies, then

$$\text{Percentage} = \frac{f}{n} \times 100 \quad \text{and} \quad \text{Degrees} = \text{Percentage} \times 360°$$

**Step** 2: Using a protractor or special graph paper, graph each section on the circle using the angles you calculated.

**Step** 3: Label the chart so that it's clear what each slice represents.

3. The marketing firm Deloitte Retail conducted a survey of 80 grocery shoppers. The frequency distribution below represents the responses to the survey question "Which grocery store is your favorite?" Complete the table below and use that information to create a pie chart to represent this data.

| Store | Frequency | Percent | Degrees |
|-------|-----------|---------|---------|
| Publix | 13 | 16 | 58 |
| Trader Joe's | 29 | 36 | 130 |
| Fareway | 23 | 29 | 104 |
| Aldi | 10 | 13 | 47 |
| Other | 5 | 6 | 22 |

Note that degrees add to 361 due to rounding error.

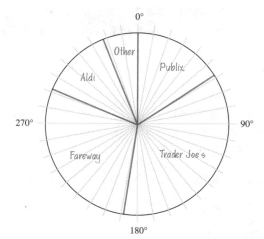

## Using Technology: Creating a Pie Chart

To create a pie chart in Excel:

1. Type the category names in one column (or row).
2. Type the category values in the next column (or row).
3. Use the mouse to drag and select all the data in those two columns (or rows).
4. With the appropriate cells selected, click the **Insert** tab, then choose **Chart** and Pie chart. There are a few different styles you can experiment with, but starting with the simplest is a good idea.

You can add titles, change colors and other formatting elements by right-clicking on certain elements, or using the options on the **Charts** menu. Try some options and see what you can learn!

*See the Lesson 4-2-1 Using Tech video in class resources for further Instruction.*

The purpose of a pie chart is to show the relationship of the parts to the whole by visually comparing the sizes of the sections.

4. What can you observe by looking at the pie chart for the grocery store survey?

*Answers vary. These are my thoughts.*

*Trader Joe's is most popular, followed by Fareway, and between the two of them, they dominate the results. Publix is a little more popular than Aldi, and the top four vote getters account for the vast majority of the votes.*

5. Let's revisit the marketing firm's survey of 80 grocery shoppers. Suppose the frequency distribution below represents the responses to the survey question "Which grocery stores have you shopped at in the last month?" Would a pie chart make sense for this data? Why or why not?

| Store | Frequency |
|---|---|
| Publix | 50 |
| Trader Joe's | 40 |
| Fareway | 28 |
| Aldi | 33 |
| Other | 65 |

*It would not. We know there were only 80 respondents total, so clearly a lot of the respondents shopped at more than one store. Pie charts are great for comparing parts of a whole, but that's not what's going on in this chart.*

While a pie chart is used to compare parts to a whole, a bar graph is used for comparing parts to other parts. That makes a bar graph an outstanding choice for the second grocery store survey.

## Drawing a Bar Graph

**Step 1:** Draw and label the axes. If you're drawing a vertical bar graph, the responses go on the horizontal axis and the frequencies on the vertical. For a horizontal bar graph, reverse that.

**Step 2:** Draw vertical bars with heights that correspond to the frequencies, or horizontal bars with lengths that correspond to the frequencies.

6. Draw a vertical bar graph illustrating the data from the survey about which grocery stores shoppers had visited in the last month.

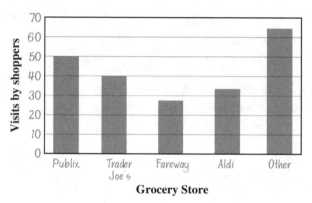

> # Math Note
>
> When drawing ANY graph on axes, labeling those axes is CRUCIAL. Without a scale on the vertical axis, this bar graph will be completely worthless.

7. What can you observe by looking at a bar graph for this data?

*Answers vary. Sample: The most visits went to stores not in the top four, with Fareway having the least. Aldi and Trader Joe's had similar numbers of visits, while Publix was the highest of the top four.*

## An Important Note on Drawing Bar Graphs

In drawing a vertical bar graph, it's very important that the scale on the vertical axis begins at zero and has consistent spacing. As you'll see in Lesson 4-9 (covering misuses of statistics), an improperly labeled axis can lead to a deceptive graph.

> If you want to include a look ahead to misuses of graphs, it's REALLY easy to find bar graphs online with a bad scale on the *y* axis.

## Using Technology: Creating a Bar Graph

To create a bar graph in Excel:

**Step 1:** Type the category names in one column (or row).

**Step 2:** Type the category values in the next column (or row).

**Step 3:** Use the mouse to drag and select all the data in those two columns (or rows).

**Step 4:** With the appropriate cells selected, click the **Insert** tab, then choose **Chart** and Column or Bar graph. ("Column" gives you vertical bars, "Bar" gives you horizontal.) Again, there are a few different styles you can experiment with, but starting with the simplest is a good idea.

You can add titles, change colors and other formatting elements by right-clicking on certain elements, or using the options on the **Charts** menu. Try some options and see what you can learn!

*See the Lesson 4-2-2 Using Tech video in class resources for further instruction.*

## Did You Get It

Try this problem to see if you understand the concepts we just studied. The answer can be found at the bottom of the portfolio page.

1. Two surveys of 100 people were done on calorie information at fast food restaurants. The first asked how much impact posted calorie information has on buying choices. The second asked which (if any) restaurants the subjects tend to avoid because they think the food is unhealthy. Results are below. Draw a pie chart for one set of data and a bar graph for another. Choose which data set is appropriate for each type of graph.

**Impact of Posted Calorie Information**

| Response | Frequency |
|---|---|
| Great impact | 40 |
| Some impact | 42 |
| Not much impact | 11 |
| None at all | 7 |

**Restaurants Avoided for Health Reasons**

| Response | Frequency |
|---|---|
| McDonalds | 46 |
| Burger King | 38 |
| Wendy's | 35 |
| Subway | 18 |

## 4-2 Group

### Histograms and Frequency Polygons

When data are organized into grouped frequency distributions, two types of graphs are commonly used to represent them: histograms and frequency polygons. A histogram is similar to a vertical bar graph in that the heights of the bars correspond to frequencies. The difference is that the boundaries of the classes are placed on the horizontal axis, rather than categories.

### Drawing a Histogram

**Step 1:** Write the scale for the frequencies on the vertical axis and the boundaries of the classes on the horizontal axis.

**Step 2:** Draw vertical bars with heights that correspond to the frequencies for each class.

*Note:* When drawing a histogram, make sure that there is no horizontal space between the bars (unlike a bar graph) unless two bars are separated by a class with frequency zero. Also make sure that all classes are included, even if the frequency is zero.

In Lesson 4-1, we analyzed and organized data representing the record high temperature in every state. It would therefore seem reasonable, if not expected, for us to illustrate that data graphically. So that's just what we'll do. Below is a grouped frequency distribution for the data. We'll use it to draw a histogram.

1. First, put a scale on the horizontal axis. You'll need to decide what number the scale should start at, but having tick marks at 100, 105, 110, etc. certainly seems like a good idea, as those are the class limits.

| Class | Frequency |
|---------|-----------|
| 100–104 | 2 |
| 105–109 | 8 |
| 110–114 | 18 |
| 115–119 | 13 |
| 120–124 | 7 |
| 125–129 | 1 |
| 130–134 | 1 |

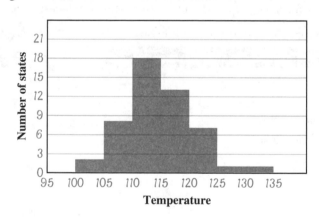

2. Now put a scale on the vertical axis. This time, you don't get a choice for starting value: the heights MUST start at zero, or the histogram will be deceiving. Choose a scale so that most of the space is filled, but that the highest bars don't go off the top of the chart.

3. Draw in bars corresponding to the frequencies, making sure that there is no horizontal space between the bars.

Note: Statisticians will sometimes label the horizontal axis of a histogram a bit differently to make it clearer which class a value right on a class limit falls into. For example, if you labeled 100, 105, 110, etc. on the *x* axis, it wouldn't be clear whether a temperature of 105 lives in the first bar or the second. If it's unclear at some point what values a given bar represents, refer to the frequency distribution for that data.

4. Write at least three things you can observe from the histogram. Then look back to see how these observations compare to the observations you wrote when building the grouped frequency distribution in Lesson 4-1. Write a brief description of similarities or differences.

*Answers vary, and of course depend on the answers from 4-1.*

A frequency polygon is similar to a histogram, but instead of bars, a series of line segments is drawn connecting the midpoints of the classes. The heights of those points match the heights of the bars in a histogram.

## Drawing a Frequency Polygon

**Step 1:** Find the midpoints for each class. This is accomplished by adding the upper and lower limits and dividing by 2.
**Step 2:** Write the scale for the frequencies on the vertical axis, and label a scale on the horizontal axis so that all midpoints will be included.
**Step 3:** Plot points at the midpoints with heights matching the frequencies for each class, then connect those points with straight lines.
**Step 4:** Finish the graph by drawing a line back to the horizontal axis at the beginning and end. The horizontal distance to the axis should equal the distance between the midpoints.

5. List the midpoints for each class in the high temperature frequency distribution. (Hint: Once you find the first midpoint, you can get all the others by just continually adding the width of the classes.)

*102, 107, 112, 117, 122, 127, 132*

6. Look at the scale you used on the horizontal axis for your histogram in Questions 1–3. Will that scale be appropriate for your frequency polygon? Why or why not?

*It depends on the scale. The point here is that there needs to be room to extend the frequency polygon back to 97 and ahead to 137. You might also think about altering the scale so that the midpoints correspond to tick marks, but that's not necessary.*

7. Subtract the length of the classes from the first midpoint, and add it to the last midpoint. This will tell you the values along the horizontal axis where you'll plot points at height zero to begin and end the frequency polygon.

   *97 and 137*

8. Now you should be ready to draw the frequency polygon. Plot all of the points from the frequency distribution, then plot points at height zero as described in Question 7. Finally, connect all points with straight line segments. If you have a straightedge handy, that would be brilliant.

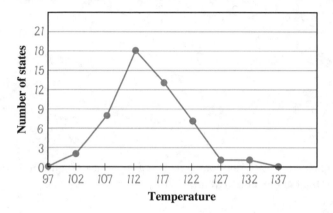

9. How does the frequency polygon compare to your histogram? Write down any thoughts you have on the value of drawing both. Feel free to be critical. It won't hurt my feelings one bit. Well, maybe a little. But I'll get over it.

   *Answers vary. For this type of data, there's really not much of an advantage to drawing a frequency polygon if you have a histogram. We kind of want students to draw that conclusion to set up the next question.*

So you may be wondering at this point: why bother with frequency polygons? Aren't they pretty much the same thing as histograms? Good question. There actually IS a point, though, as we will now see. The two grouped frequency distributions below come from data gathered in two calculus classes that I taught in Spring of 2015. One is for percentage on the final exam; the other is for overall percentage in the course. Then we see a frequency polygon for each data set.

**Final Exam Percentage**

| Percentage | Frequency |
|------------|-----------|
| 40–49.9 | 3 |
| 50–59.9 | 2 |
| 60–69.9 | 13 |
| 70–79.9 | 14 |
| 80–89.9 | 14 |
| 90–99.9 | 12 |

**Overall Percentage**

| Percentage | Frequency |
|------------|-----------|
| 40–49.9 | 0 |
| 50–59.9 | 1 |
| 60–69.9 | 7 |
| 70–79.9 | 20 |
| 80–89.9 | 19 |
| 90–99.9 | 11 |

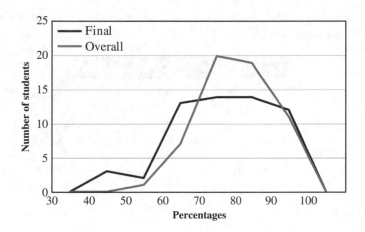

10. What would it look like if we tried to draw a single histogram that compares both data sets?

*If would be a complete mess. The bars for the histogram would be on top of each other, making if pretty much impossible to read.*

**11.** When are frequency polygons particularly useful?

*For comparing different data sets on the same graph.*

## Did You Get It

Try these problems to see if you understand the concepts we just studied. The answers can be found at the bottom of the portfolio page.

2. Draw a histogram for the data below, which is the number of losses by the team that won the NCAA men's basketball championship for the years from 1939–2012.

| Losses | Frequency |
|--------|-----------|
| 0–1 | 13 |
| 2–3 | 28 |
| 4–5 | 18 |
| 6–7 | 9 |
| 8–9 | 3 |
| 10–11 | 3 |

3. Draw a frequency polygon for the same data.

## Time Series Graphs

A **time series graph** can be drawn for data collected over a period of time. This type of graph is ideal for recognizing trends, like prices rising or falling, for the time period. We'll close this lesson by drawing and analyzing this type of graph.

## Drawing a Time Series Graph

**Step 1:** Label the horizontal axis with the time units and the vertical axis with a scale (beginning at zero) that's appropriate for the given data.

**Step 2:** Plot the points from the table and connect them with line segments.

12. The table shows the number of violent crimes committed per 100,000 citizens for selected years from 2000 to 2012. Draw a time series graph for the data.

| Year | Violent crimes per 100,00 citizens |
|------|------------------------------------|
| 2000 | 506.5 |
| 2002 | 494.4 |
| 2004 | 463.2 |
| 2006 | 479.3 |
| 2008 | 458.6 |
| 2010 | 404.5 |
| 2012 | 387.8 |

© Comstock/PunchStock RF

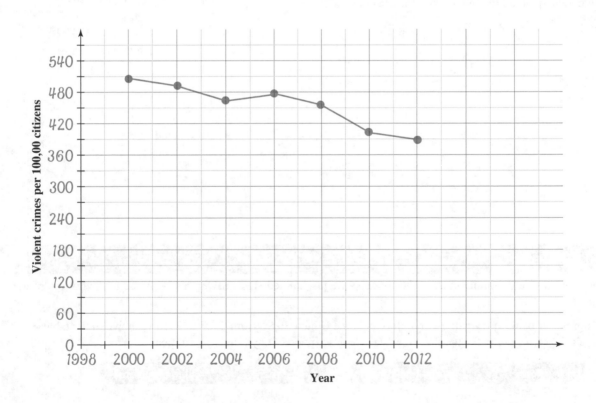

13. Overall, would you say that violent crime is getting worse or better? Explain.

    *It appears to be improving, as the number of violent crimes per 100,000 people shows a general downward trend.*

14. When did violent crime increase in the 21st century?

    *There was an increase from 2004 to 2006.*

15. In what two-year span did the biggest decrease occur?

    *The graph shows the largest drop from 2008 to 2010.*

> **Math Note**
>
> In case you're wondering about Excel, we'll learn how to draw line graphs later in this unit. Excel can draw histograms, but it's a very involved process. There's a video in the resources for this lesson that illustrates the procedure.

## Did You Get It   **?**

Try this problem to see if you understand the concepts we just studied. The answer can be found at the bottom of the portfolio page.

4. The number of bankruptcy filings (in millions) in the United States from 2003 to 2014 is shown in the table. Draw a time series graph for the data, then write a description of any trends you notice.

| Year | Filings (millions) | Year | Filings (millions) |
|------|--------------------|------|--------------------|
| 2003 | 1.66 | 2009 | 1.47 |
| 2004 | 1.60 | 2010 | 1.59 |
| 2005 | 2.08 | 2011 | 1.41 |
| 2006 | 0.62 | 2012 | 1.22 |
| 2007 | 0.85 | 2013 | 1.07 |
| 2008 | 1.12 | 2014 | 0.91 |

**4-2** **Portfolio**

Name _____

Check each box when you've completed the task. Remember that your instructor will want you to turn in the portfolio pages you create.

### Technology

**1.** ☐ Being able to draw the types of graphs we've studied in this lesson is certainly useful, if for no other reason than creating graphs is the best way to really understand them. On the other hand, this IS the 21st century, so maybe we should let our friend the computer do the work for us. Use a spreadsheet to recreate the graphs you drew in Questions 3 and 6 of the Class portion of this lesson. The template in the online resources has the data preloaded. There's a tab for each data set.

### Online Practice

**1.** ☐ Include any written work from the online assignment along with any notes or questions about this lesson's content.

### Applications

**1.** ☐ Complete the applications problems.

### Reflections

Type a short answer to each question.

**1.** ☐ Discuss the value of illustrating data with a graph after it's been gathered and organized.
**2.** ☐ When is a pie chart appropriate for illustrating data? When is a pie chart not appropriate?
**3.** ☐ What type of data is illustrated using a histogram and/or frequency polygon? Why?
**4.** ☐ Take another look at your answer to Question 0 at the beginning of this lesson. Would you change your answer now that you've completed the lesson? How would you summarize the topic of this lesson now?
**5.** ☐ What questions do you have about this lesson?

### Looking Ahead

**1.** ☐ Complete the Lesson 4-3 Prep Skills and read the opening paragraph in Lesson 4-3 carefully, then answer Question 0 in preparation for that lesson.

### Answers to "Did You Get It?"

Graphs can be found at the end of the Applications pages. Observations will vary.

## 4-2   Applications

Name _____

In Questions 1–6, write if a bar graph, pie chart, or time series graph would be the most appropriate way to represent the given data.

1. The number of students enrolled at a local college each year for the last 5 years

   *Time series graph*

2. The budget for the student activities department at your college

   *Pie chart*

3. The number of students who get to school by automobile, bus, train, or by walking

   *Bar graph*

4. The record high temperatures of a city for the last 30 years

   *Time series graph*

5. The areas of the five lakes in the Great Lakes

   *Bar graph*

6. The amount of each dollar spent for wages, advertising, overhead, and profit by a corporation

   *Pie chart*

In Questions 7–11, we'll use the types of graphs we studied in this lesson to study the issue of climate change.

7. Most climate experts agree that the release of carbon dioxide gas into the atmosphere is a significant factor in rising global temperatures. So where is all that $CO_2$ coming from? The first table below displays the total $CO_2$ emissions in kilotons for the top five producers. The second shows per capita emissions for these same producers, which is the number of tons emitted for each resident. Draw a separate bar graph for the data in each table, then write at least three things you can observe from your graphs.

| Producer | $CO_2$ emissions (kt) |
|---|---|
| China | 10.5 million |
| United States | 5.3 million |
| European Union | 3.4 million |
| India | 2.3 million |
| Russia | 1.8 million |

| Producer | Tons per capita |
|---|---|
| China | 7.6 |
| United States | 16.5 |
| European Union | 6.7 |
| India | 1.8 |
| Russia | 12.4 |

# 4-2 Applications

Name _____

**7. (Con't)**

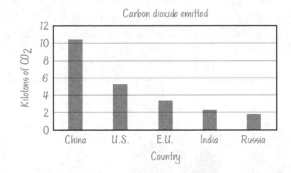

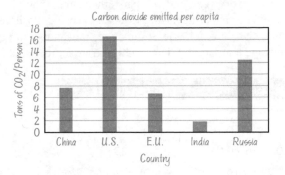

China produces by far the most $CO_2$, but in terms of amount per person, the U.S. and Russia are quite a bit worse. India's amount is quite low given its population.

**8.** Americans' attitudes toward climate change have been evolving very rapidly over the last few years. The tables below show responses to the survey question "From what you've read and heard, is there solid evidence that the temperature on earth has been getting warmer over the past four decades?" first in Spring of 2010, then again in Fall of 2015. Use the information to draw two pie charts, then discuss the results.

| Spring 2010 | |
|---|---|
| **Response** | **%** |
| Yes | 52 |
| No | 36 |
| Not sure | 12 |

| Fall 2015 | |
|---|---|
| **Response** | **%** |
| Yes | 70 |
| No | 16 |
| Not sure | 14 |

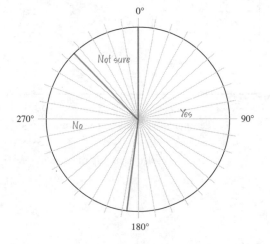

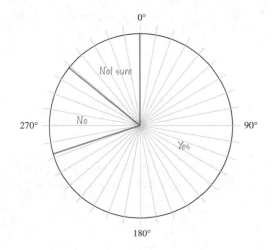

Discussions vary.

## 4-2    Applications

Name _____

9. Now let's look at global temperatures. The National Oceanic and Atmospheric Administration tracks the average global temperature every year, and compares the result to the average temperature for all years in the 20th century. They report the results in terms of departure from that average. Positive results mean warmer than average, negative cooler. The frequency distribution below summarizes the number of years from 1881 to 2015 that fell into each range of departure from average temperature. Draw a histogram for the data.

| Class | Frequency |
|---|---|
| −0.45 to −0.31 | 13 |
| −0.30 to −0.16 | 29 |
| −0.15 to −0.01 | 28 |
| 0 to 0.14 | 27 |
| 0.15 to 0.29 | 11 |
| 0.30 to 0.44 | 8 |
| 0.45 to 0.59 | 11 |
| 0.60 to 0.74 | 8 |

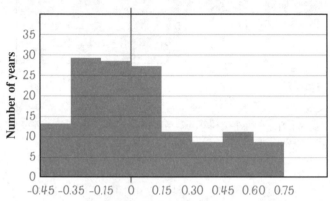

10. The next frequency distribution is drawn from the same data, but includes only the years from 1970 to 2015. Draw a frequency polygon, and write any observations you have from comparing the two temperature deviation graphs.

| Class | Frequency |
|---|---|
| −0.45 to −0.31 | 0 |
| −0.30 to −0.16 | 0 |
| −0.15 to −0.01 | 3 |
| 0 to 0.14 | 6 |
| 0.15 to 0.29 | 10 |
| 0.30 to 0.44 | 8 |
| 0.45 to 0.59 | 11 |
| 0.60 to 0.74 | 8 |

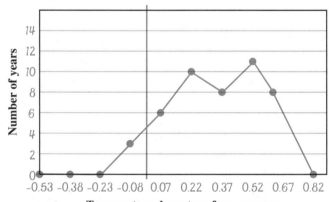

*Answers vary but the obvious conclusion is that looking at data over 135 years makes it look like cooler years are more likely, but if you start in 1970, it's easy to see that warmer years have become far more common.*

## 4-2 Applications

Name _____

**11.** Write about something you learned in this activity that you find interesting or compelling in some way.

*Answers vary.*

---

### ? Answers to "Did You Get It?"

**1.**

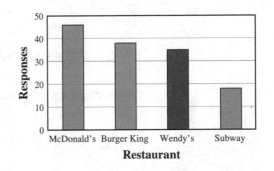

**2.**

Losses by the NCAA Basketball Champion

**3.**

Losses by the NCAA Basketball Champion

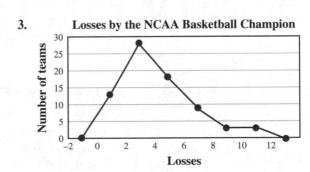

**4.**

Bankruptcy Filings by Year

# Lesson 4-3   Prep Skills

This is a short review of skills that will come in handy in the next lesson. In each case, answer the question, then rate your confidence level by checking one of the boxes. If you feel like you're struggling with these skills, consult the online resources provided by your instructor for extra practice.

**SKILL 1: ORDERING A LIST OF NUMBERS**

1. Arrange the list of numbers below in order from least to greatest.

   2.4   3.7   1.7   1.7   2.3   3.1   1.2   2.4   1.3   1.7   2.5   2.4   2.8   2.1   1.3   2.5

**SKILL 2: COMPUTING LENGTHY SUMS**

2. Find the sum of the numbers in the list above.

**SKILL 3: ORDER OF OPERATIONS**

Complete each calculation below.

3. $\dfrac{8 + 11 + 13 + 5 + 6}{5}$

4. $\dfrac{2 \cdot 98 + 4 \cdot 112 + 12 \cdot 13 + 10 \cdot 59 + 6 \cdot 80}{34}$

**SKILL 4: INTERPRET SUBSCRIPT NOTATION**

5. If we use the symbols $X_1$, $X_2$, $X_3$, and so on to represent the numbers in the list in Question 1, what number corresponds to $X_7$? (In the original list, not the ordered list.)

6. Refer to Question 5. If the entire list is written as $X_1$, $X_2$, $X_3$, . . . $X_n$, what number is represented by $n$?

# Lesson 4-3   **An Average Joe**   (Measures of Average)

**LEARNING OBJECTIVES**

☐ 1. Compute measures of average for given data.

☐ 2. Interpret the story told by measures of average.

☐ 3. Compute and interpret the mean for grouped data.

☐ 4. Compute weighted grades.

☐ 5. Use technology to compute measures of average.

© Ryan McVay/Getty Images RF

*The average dog is a nicer person than the average person.*
　　　　　　　—Andy Rooney

Are you an average college student? What does that even mean? According to a variety of sources found on the Web, the average college student is 20 years old, lives on campus and works off campus during the school year. She is female, talks to her parents every day, and comes from a family with an annual income between $50,000 and $100,000. She sleeps 6 hours a night, has $2,700 in credit card debt, and will leave college with $21,000 in total debt.

　　If this doesn't sound exactly like anyone you know, don't feel bad. As we will learn in this lesson, the word average is ambiguous—there are a variety of ways to describe an average. So what one source considers average might not match someone else's thoughts, and with so many different facets to a person, it's possible that nobody exactly meets all of the average criteria.

　**0.** After reading the opening paragraph, what do you think the main topic of this lesson will be?

## 4-3   Group

Our goal in this lesson will be to understand the different measures of average. In casual terms, average means the most typical case, or the center of where the values in a data set are distributed. Measures of average include the mean, median, mode, and midrange.

　　Let's suppose that an individual, let's just call him George, is about to finish college and step out into the work force. George finds a small company, Vandelay Industries, which he's considering going to work for. While researching this company, George finds a flier on which that company advertises that its average employee makes almost $150,000 per year. This sounds pretty darn good to George, so he accepts an entry-level position at a low salary, betting on quick advancement to that alleged average.

　　Shortly after starting his career, while emptying the recycling bin in the copy room (just one of George's glamorous duties), he stumbles across a list of salaries for all employees at his new company. Let's investigate just how true the company's average salary claim is.

Here's the salary list for Vandelay Industries, which we'll use to study measures of average, which are more technically called **measures of central tendency.**

| Employee | Salary |
|---|---|
| Jerry | $58,000 |
| Kramer | $65,000 |
| Newman | $944,000 |
| George | $20,000 |
| Elaine | $52,000 |
| Susan | $51,000 |
| Tim | $53,000 |
| Estelle | $55,000 |
| Frank | $50,000 |

> The "balance point" analogy for the mean, in the paragraph below, is an ideal opportunity for a class demonstration. Coins, a ruler or yardstick, and half of a toilet paper tube work nicely.

## The Mean

There's a pretty good chance that when you think of "average" in a math class, what you're thinking of is actually called the **mean.** The mean, also known as the arithmetic average, is found by adding the values of the data and dividing by the total number of values. Here's a good way to think of the mean: If all of the numbers were equal weights put on a number line, the mean is where the number line could be balanced without tipping in one direction or the other.

The Greek letter $\Sigma$ (sigma) is used to represent the sum of a list of numbers. If we use the letter $X$ to represent data values, then $\Sigma X$ means to find the sum of all values in a data set. Using this notation, we can write a formula for finding the mean.

---

The **mean** is the sum of values in a data set divided by the number of values. If $X_1, X_2, X_3, \ldots, X_n$, are the data values (which means there are $n$ of them), we use the symbol $\overline{X}$ to represent the mean, and

$$\overline{X} = \frac{X_1 + X_2 + X_3 + \ldots + X_n}{n} = \frac{\Sigma X}{n}$$

The symbol $\overline{X}$ is read "$X$ bar."

---

1. Find the mean salary for the company.

   $$\frac{58 + 65 + 944 + 20 + 52 + 51 + 53 + 55 + 50}{9} = 149.8 \quad \text{Mean salary is } \$149,800.$$

2. Newman owns the company, and obviously pays himself a handsome salary. If we ignore Newman's salary, what is the new mean? Based on this, do you feel like the mean is a good measure of what the typical employee makes?

   $$\frac{58 + 65 + 20 + 52 + 51 + 53 + 55 + 50}{8} = 50.5, \text{ so the mean salary is } \$50,500.$$

   *The second mean is a good measure, but not the first. The one super-large salary inflates the mean way higher than what we'd think of as the typical salary.*

## Did You Get It

Try this problem to see if you understand the concepts we just studied. The answer can be found at the bottom of the portfolio page.

1. The total areas, in thousands of square miles, of the 15 largest states in the U.S. are provided in the list below. Find the mean area for these 15 states.

| 665 | 269 | 164 | 147 | 122 | 114 | 111 | 104 |
|-----|-----|-----|-----|-----|-----|-----|-----|
| 98 | 98 | 97 | 87 | 85 | 84 | 82 | |

## The Median

According to the National Organization of Realtors, the mean selling price for existing homes nationally in August of 2015 was $271,600. The **median** selling price, on the other hand, was $228,700. Since both of these are measures of central tendency, how can they be so far apart? What exactly is the median? In this case, the median tells us that half of all homes sold during that month were priced above $228,700, and half were priced below that amount. In short, the median of a data set is the value in the middle if all values are arranged in order. The median will either be a specific data value in the set, or will fall in between two values. Here's how we find a median:

3. Arrange all of the salaries at Vandelay Industries in order from smallest to largest.

$20,000, $50,000, $51,000, $52,000, $53,000, $55,000, $58,000, $65,000, $944,000

4. Find the salary that's right in the middle of your ordered list. That's the median salary. How does it compare to the mean?

$20,000, $50,000, $51,000, $52,000, $53,000, $55,000, $58,000, $65,000, $944,000

   1     2     3     4     5     6     7     8     9

The value in the middle is the fifth one, which is $53,000. This is WAY less than the mean. Barely a third as large, in fact.

5. If there is an even number of values in a data set, there will be two values in the middle, not one like in Question 4. How do you think you'd find the median in that case?

We split the difference of the two values in the middle, choosing the median to be the number halfway between them (Which is the mean of those two numbers).

## Finding the Median of a Data Set

**Step 1:** Arrange the data in order, from smallest to largest. (Actually, largest to smallest is fine too. Whatever makes you happy.)

**Step 2:** If the number of data values is odd, there will be one value in the middle of the ordered list. That's the median. If the number of data values is even, there will be two numbers in the middle of the list: the median is the mean of these two values.

**6.** Find the median of the salaries at Vandelay Industries (without Newman's). How does it compare to the median of the salaries with Newman's included?

$20,000, $50,000, $51,000, $52,000, $53,000, $55,000, $58,000, $65,000
  1        2         3          4          5          6          7          8

*The values in the middle are $52,000 and $53,000, so the median is $52,500. It's almost the same with or without Newman's salary.*

**7.** What does this tell you about median when there are **outliers** (sample data values that are very far away from the majority of values)?

*It's barely affected at all, unlike the mean, in which the one huge salary almost tripled the mean.*

**8.** Find the median of the salaries at Vandelay Industries (without Newman's) if Kramer quits to start his own company (The Peterman Reality Tour). What can you observe?

$20,000, $50,000, $51,000, $52,000, $53,000, $55,000, $58,000
  1        2         3          4          5          6          7

*The value in the middle $52,000. Even throwing away the TWO biggest salaries, the median isn't affected all that much.*

© Columbia TriStar Television/Everett Collection

## Did You Get It

Try these problems to see if you understand the concepts we just studied. The answers can be found at the bottom of the portfolio page.

2. Find the median of the land areas provided in Did You Get It 1. Compare to the mean, and discuss the difference. Try to come up with an explanation of the discrepancy.
3. Find the mean and median if you throw out Alaska, which has the largest area by far. What does this tell you?

## The Midrange

The **midrange** is another measure of average. The advantage of the midrange is that it's very quick and easy to calculate. The disadvantage is that it totally ignores most of the data values, so it's not a particularly reliable measure. But in a pinch, it can give you a rough idea of average.

9. Find the number halfway between the lowest and highest salaries at Vandelay Industries (including Newman's). That's the midrange.

Lowest $20,000, highest $944,000. Halfway between: $\dfrac{\$20,000 + \$944,000}{2} = \$482,000$

### Finding the Midrange of a Data Set

**Step 1:** Find the smallest and largest values in the data set.

**Step 2:** Find the mean of those two values.

10. Find the midrange of the salaries at Vandelay Industries (excluding Newman's). How does it compare to the midrange of all salaries?

Lowest $20,000, highest $68,000. Halfway between: $\dfrac{\$20,000 + \$68,000}{2} = \$44,000$. It's less than one tenth as much!

11. Explain why the midrange isn't very reliable as a measure of central tendency.

it's HUGELY affected by the one very large salary. $482,000 is a ridiculous measure of average here, as there's not a single salary within $400,000 of that number.

### Did You Get It

Try this problem to see if you understand the concepts we just studied. The answer can be found at the bottom of the portfolio page.

4. Find the midrange area for the top fifteen largest states from Did You Get It 1.

## The Mode

The third measure of average is called the mode. The **mode** is sometimes said to be the most typical case.

**12.** These data represent the duration (in days) of the final 20 U.S. space shuttle voyages. Which number of days appears most often on the list? That's the mode.

11  12  13  12  15  12  15  13  15  12  12  15  13  10  13  15  11  12  15  12

*12 appears 7 times, so it's the mode.*

**13.** How does the mode compare to the mean? Which do you think describes the typical case best?

*The mean is 12.9. Second part is an opinion.*

Source: NASA

---

The **mode** is the value that occurs most often in a data set.

---

A data set can have more than one mode (if two or more values are tied for most appearances), or no mode at all (if every value appears only once). While modes aren't extremely useful for small data sets with numerical data, we'll begin there to help get an understanding of what the mode is about.

**14.** The number of wins in a 16-game season for the Cincinnati Bengals from 1996–2014 is listed below. Find the mode.

8  7  3  4  4  6  2  8  8  11  8  7  4  10  4  9  10  11  10

*Four and eight wins, which both appear on the list four times.*

**15.** How does the mode compare to the mean? Discuss again. Include a description of which measure of central tendency you think is more reliable in general, and why.

*The mean is about 7.1 wins. Second question is again an opinion.*

**16.** Do the employee salaries at Vandelay Industries have a mode? Why or why not?

*They do not. Every employee has a different salary.*

The mode is probably most useful when data are classified by groups or categories. In fact, it's the only measure of central tendency that even makes sense when the data values aren't numbers.

**17.** A survey of the junior class at Fiesta State University shows the following number of students majoring in each field. Find the mode.

| Major | Number |
|---|---|
| Computer Science | 632 |
| Liberal Arts | 878 |
| Business | 1,425 |
| General Studies | 95 |
| Education | 471 |

*The mode is majoring in business.*

This is a GREAT example to discuss when the mode is useful. Students will focus on the numbers and want to say that there is no mode. Point out that you can't find an "average" of something qualitative, like major, but the mode makes perfect sense in that setting.

**18.** Now let's evaluate the "average salary" claim made by Vandelay Industries at the beginning of this lesson. How truthful do you think that claim was? Use the measures of average you found in this lesson to discuss whether or not you think they were being deceptive in any way.

*Answers vary. Of course, the point is that if you take "average" to mean "mean," then the claim is technically truthful, but it's still deceiving in terms of what a reasonable person would think of as the average salary.*

## Did You Get It

Try this problem to see if you understand the concepts we just studied. The answer can be found at the bottom of the portfolio page.

5. The table below lists the average high temperature in degrees Fahrenheit for each month of the year on the island of Antigua (which is delightful, by the way). Find the mode and the median.

| Month | Jan | Feb | Mar | Apr | May | Jun | Jul | Aug | Sep | Oct | Nov | Dec |
|---|---|---|---|---|---|---|---|---|---|---|---|---|
| High | 81 | 82 | 82 | 83 | 85 | 86 | 87 | 87 | 87 | 86 | 84 | 82 |

## Did You Get It

Try this problem to see if you understand the concepts we just studied. The answer can be found at the bottom of the portfolio page.

6. Five hundred college graduates were asked how much they donate to their alma mater on an annual basis. Find the mode of their responses, summarized in the table.

| Amount | Number |
|---|---|
| $500 or more | 45 |
| Between $0 and $500 | 150 |
| Nothing | 275 |
| Declined to answer | 30 |

# 4-3   Class

We now return to the mean, this time in a situation that's a bit more complicated: when we have grouped data in a frequency distribution. The procedure for finding the mean for grouped data uses the midpoints and the frequencies of the classes. This procedure will give only an approximate value for the mean, so it's typically used in two situations. One is when the data set is very large and calculating the exact mean using all the data is impractical. The other is when the original raw data are unavailable but have been grouped by someone else.

## Finding the Mean for Grouped Data

**Step 1:** Find the midpoint of each class in the grouped data.
**Step 2:** Multiply the frequency for each class by the midpoint of that class.
**Step 3:** Add up all of the products from step 2.
**Step 4:** Divide by the sum of all frequencies (which is the total number of data values).

If you prefer formulas to procedures:

$$\overline{X} = \frac{\Sigma(f \cdot X_m)}{n}$$

where $f$ is the frequency for each class, $X_m$ is the midpoint of each class, and $n$ is the sum of all frequencies.

1. Here's another look at the grouped frequency distribution for the record high temperature in each state from earlier in this unit. Find the mean of these high temperatures. Begin by filling in the midpoints for each class.

| Class | Midpoint | Frequency |
|---|---|---|
| 100–104 | 102 | 2 |
| 105–109 | 107 | 8 |
| 110–114 | 112 | 18 |
| 115–119 | 117 | 13 |
| 120–124 | 122 | 7 |
| 125–129 | 127 | 1 |
| 130–134 | 132 | 1 |

$$\frac{2 \cdot 102 + 8 \cdot 107 + 18 \cdot 112 + 13 \cdot 117 + 7 \cdot 122 + 127 + 132}{2 + 8 + 18 + 13 + 7 + 1 + 1} = 114.2°$$

**2.** Explain why this formula only gives an approximation to the mean, not the actual mean.

*Because we're not actually using all of the data values. By using the midpoint of each class, we're basically changing every value in that class to the midpoint. This of course has an effect on the mean.*

*This is a tough question. I give extra credit for groups that get it in my classes.*

> ## Math Note
>
> Thinking of the mean as a "balance point" is really helpful in understanding why this way of approximating the mean makes sense. Think of stacking a number of coins corresponding to the frequency at the center of each class on a seesaw.

Finding the mean for grouped data is similar to finding a **weighted mean.** We can illustrate the concept by finding a student's average score in a course where different components contribute different amounts toward the final grade. For example, let's look at the grading structure for one course:

Homework average: 50 points
Four tests: 30 points each
Final exam: 50 points
Group project: 20 points
Attendance/Participation: 10 points

Tong had an 87% homework average, got 91%, 82%, 86%, and 94% on the four tests, 88% on the final exam, 92% on the group project, and 100% of attendance/participation points. We can treat this as a weighted mean problem to find her overall average percentage. The number of points assigned to each component of the course acts as the frequencies for each class, and the percentage earned on each component plays the role of the midpoints for each class. Then we can use our procedure for approximating the mean for grouped data.

**3.** With that in mind, what role does the sum of the points for each component play in the weighted mean calculation? Why?

*The sum of the points corresponds to the total number of data values, or n, in the formula. Since each number of points corresponds to a frequency, the sum of points is the sum of all frequencies.*

**4.** Use the mean for grouped data formula to find Tong's average for the course.

$$\frac{50 \cdot 0.87 + 30 \cdot 0.91 + 30 \cdot 0.82 + 30 \cdot 0.86 + 30 \cdot 0.94 + 50 \cdot 0.88 + 20 \cdot 0.92 + 10 \cdot 1}{50 + 4 \cdot 30 + 50 + 20 + 10} = 0.887$$

*Her average is 88.7%. Note that you can also use the scores in percentage form rather than decimal form.*

## Did You Get It

Try this problem to see if you understand the concepts we just studied. The answer can be found at the bottom of the portfolio page.

**7.** The data below is the number of losses by the team that won the NCAA men's basketball championship for the years from 1939–2012. Find the mean number of losses.

| Losses | Frequency |
|--------|-----------|
| 0–1    | 13        |
| 2–3    | 28        |
| 4–5    | 18        |

| Losses | Frequency |
|--------|-----------|
| 6–7    | 9         |
| 8–9    | 3         |
| 10–11  | 3         |

**5.** What are the pros and cons of each of the measures of average we studied?

*Answers vary. Our answers are summarized at the end of the lesson in the colored box.*

**6.** (This is my favorite question in the whole lesson.) Look back at the description of the "average" college student in the opening paragraph. For each characteristic listed, write which measure of average you think was used.

*Answers can vary. Our guesses: 20 years old—mean. Lives on campus—mode. Works off campus—mode. Female—mode. Talks to parents every day—mode. Family income—median. Sleeps 6 hours a night—mean. Has $2,700 in credit card debt—median. Leave with $21,000 in total debt—median.*

## Using Technology to Compute Measures of Central Tendency

Technology is certainly a useful tool in computing measures of average, so let's have a look at using spreadsheets and graphing calculators to do the heavy lifting for us. (For what it's worth, when a list of data has just a few numbers on it, it's probably quicker to find the measures of average by hand. It's the large data sets that make technology incredibly useful.)

To illustrate these features, we'll use the following data set. According to deathpenaltyinfo.org, there were 12 death row inmates that were exonerated and freed in 2003. The table below shows the number freed each year since then.

| Year | '03 | '04 | '05 | '06 | '07 | '08 | '09 | '10 | '11 | '12 | '13 | '14 | '15 |
|--------|-----|-----|-----|-----|-----|-----|-----|-----|-----|-----|-----|-----|-----|
| Number | 12  | 6   | 2   | 1   | 3   | 4   | 9   | 1   | 1   | 3   | 1   | 7   | 6   |

## Excel

There are built-in commands for finding the mean and median in Excel. There's no midrange command, but we can build one, and ordering the list allows us to find the mode.

First, the data should be entered into a single column, as shown in Figure 1. To calculate the mean, choose an empty cell and enter "= AVERAGE(". Then use the cursor to select all of the cells containing the data, enter a close parenthesies, and hit enter. This displays the mean, shown in cell B15. To find the median, use the same routine, but enter "MEDIAN" rather than "AVERAGE." This is in cell B16.

There's no direct command for midrange, but there are commands to find the highest and lowest numbers on the list; we can embed them in a simple calculation that finds the midrange. The string we need to enter looks like

$$= (MAX(range) + MIN(range))/2$$

where "range" represents the range of cells that the data lives in. Again, the simplest way to enter that range is to just use the cursor to select it after typing "MAX(" and "MIN(". The resulting midrange in shown in cell B17.

To find the mode, we'll first sort the list. Select the cells containing the data (B1 through B13 in this case), then choose "Sort. . ." from the "Data" menu. You can choose to sort in either ascending or descending order. The result, shown in Figure 2, makes it a simple matter to find the value or values that occur most often. Notice that (as we'd hope) sorting didn't affect mean, median, or midrange. Figure 3 shows the commands entered for finding the mean, median, and midrange.

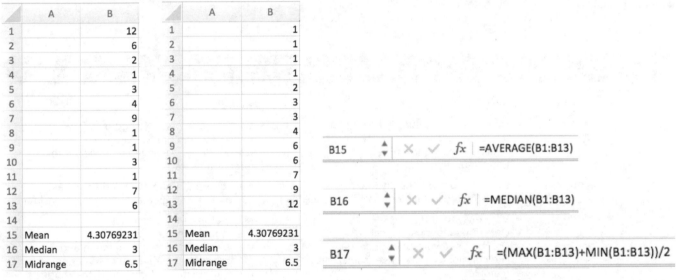

| **Figure 1** | **Figure 2** | **Figure 3** |

## TI-84 Graphing Calculator

In order to find measures of average for a group of numbers, the first step is entering those numbers in a list. To do this, we need to use the list editor: hit the STAT key, then choose 1. Enter the numbers one at a time, hitting ENTER after each. The above data is shown entered in Figure 4 below (most of it, anyhow). Then hit STAT again, and use the right arrow to select CALC at the top of the screen, and pick choice 1: 1-Var Stats (Fig. 5). After hitting ENTER twice, you get the 1-Variable Stats menu, shown in Figures 6 and 7.

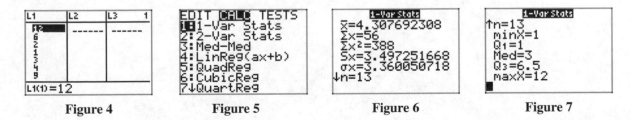

| **Figure 4** | **Figure 5** | **Figure 6** | **Figure 7** |

There's actually quite a bit more information on this screen than we're looking for, and some of it will be discussed in later lessons. For now, the mean is the very first thing on the list: x̄ = 4.307692308. Using the down arrow to scroll down, we find the median: Med = 3 (Fig. 7). The midrange isn't displayed, but minX = 1 and maxX = 12 provide the lowest and highest values. When you have those, it's simple to add them and divide by 2 to get the midrange of 6.5.

As with Excel, there's no specific command for finding the mode, but the calculator will order the data, which makes it a lot easier to find the mode. Hit the STAT key again and choose 2, which is SortA (for "sort ascending"). Then you need to tell it which list to sort. Since we entered the data in list L1, enter that by hitting 2nd 1 (Fig. 8). After you press ENTER, the calculator displays Done, and the list is ordered. When you go back to the list editor, you can easily find which value or values appear most often, giving you the mode (Fig. 9).

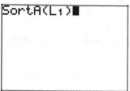

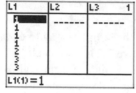

To approximate the mean for grouped data, enter the midpoint of each class in list L1, and the associated frequency in list L2. Then choose 1-Var Stats, but before hitting ENTER, key in L1,L2 (which is 2nd 1, 2nd 2). Then hit ENTER. See the Lesson 4-3-1 and 4-3-2 Using Tech videos in class resources for further instruction.

**Figure 8**          **Figure 9**

Earlier, we asked for your thoughts on the pros and cons of each measure of central tendency. We'll summarize the lesson with our thoughts.

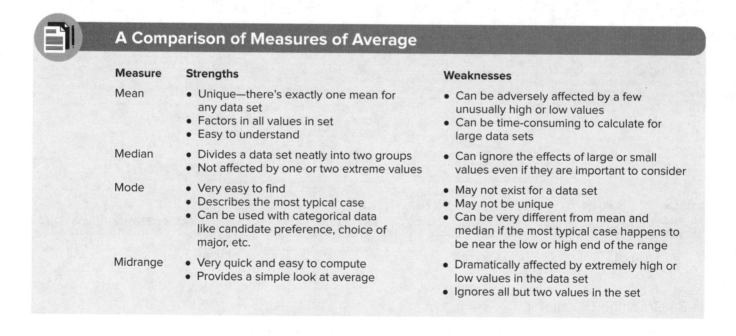

## A Comparison of Measures of Average

| Measure | Strengths | Weaknesses |
|---|---|---|
| Mean | • Unique—there's exactly one mean for any data set<br>• Factors in all values in set<br>• Easy to understand | • Can be adversely affected by a few unusually high or low values<br>• Can be time-consuming to calculate for large data sets |
| Median | • Divides a data set neatly into two groups<br>• Not affected by one or two extreme values | • Can ignore the effects of large or small values even if they are important to consider |
| Mode | • Very easy to find<br>• Describes the most typical case<br>• Can be used with categorical data like candidate preference, choice of major, etc. | • May not exist for a data set<br>• May not be unique<br>• Can be very different from mean and median if the most typical case happens to be near the low or high end of the range |
| Midrange | • Very quick and easy to compute<br>• Provides a simple look at average | • Dramatically affected by extremely high or low values in the data set<br>• Ignores all but two values in the set |

## 4-3 | Portfolio

Name _____

Check each box when you've completed the task. Remember that your instructor will want you to turn in the portfolio pages you create.

### Technology

1. ☐ In the last problem of the Applications homework, you'll approximate the mean for a grouped data set using the procedure within this lesson. The tech template for this lesson has the full data set, and your job is to use Excel to calculate the true mean, the median, the mode, and the midrange using commands from the tech box in the lesson. Then answer these questions: 1. How accurate was the approximation using grouped data? 2. Why was it so useful to use technology to get the true mean? 3. Describe what you can learn from looking at all four measures of average for this data set.

### Online Practice

1. ☐ Include any written work from the online assignment along with any notes or questions about this lesson's content.

### Applications

1. ☐ Complete the applications problems.

> Encourage students to use technology to find the measures of average in this assignment!

### Reflections

Type a short answer to each question.

1. ☐ What did this lesson do to change your view of what the word "average" means?
2. ☐ Which measure of average do you think is the most consistent and the best to use? Why?
3. ☐ Which measures of average are more reliable when you have extreme outliers in the data set?
4. ☐ Take another look at your answer to Question 0 at the beginning of this lesson. Would you change your answer now that you've finished the lesson? How would you summarize the topic of this lesson now?
5. ☐ What questions do you have about this lesson?

### Looking Ahead

1. ☐ Complete the Lesson 4-4 Prep Skills and read the opening paragraph in Lesson 4-4 carefully, then answer Question 0 in preparation for that lesson.

### Answers to "Did You Get It?"

**1.** 155,133 sq. mi.    **2.** 104,000 sq. mi.; the one extremely large state raises the mean considerably    **3.** Mean: 118,714 sq. mi.; median: 101,000 sq. mi.; that one large value did in fact skew the mean upward    **4.** 373,500 sq. mi.    **5.** Modes: 82° and 87°; median: 84.5°    **6.** Nothing    **7.** 3.7 losses

## 4-3  Applications

Name _____

For Questions 1–4, describe which measure of average—mean, median, or mode—was most likely to have been used in each situation. Provide a brief justification.

1. Half of the factory workers make more than $11.37 per hour and half make less than $11.37 per hour.

   *Median: describes the value in the middle of the spread*

2. The average number of children per family in the Plaza Heights is 1.8.

   *Almost certainly mean. It can't be mode because it's not a whole number, and unlikely to be median because it's not halfway between two whole numbers.*

3. Most people prefer red convertibles over any other color.

   *Has to be mode. There's no numerical information to find mean or median.*

4. The average age of college professors is 42.3 years.

   *Could be either mean or median. If ages are listed as whole numbers, it's most likely mean. But ages could be broken down into years and months, in which case it could be either.*

For Questions 5 and 6, find the mean, median, mode, and midrange. Then decide which you think is the most meaningful measure of average for that data set.

5. The table displays the number of murders in the United States for the years from 2000 to 2014.

| Year | 2000 | 2001 | 2002 | 2003 | 2004 | 2005 | 2006 | 2007 |
|---|---|---|---|---|---|---|---|---|
| Murders | 15,586 | 16,037 | 16,229 | 16,258 | 16,148 | 16,740 | 17,309 | 17,128 |

| Year | 2008 | 2009 | 2010 | 2011 | 2012 | 2013 | 2014 |
|---|---|---|---|---|---|---|
| Murders | 16,465 | 15,399 | 14,722 | 14,661 | 14,886 | 14,319 | 14,249 |

*Source: FBI Uniform Crime Reports*

*Mean, 15,742 murders. Median: 16,037 murders. Mode: None. Midrange: 15,779 murders. Most meaningful is an opinion.*

## 4-3 Applications

Name _____

**6.** The 12 states with the highest unemployment rates in December 2015 and their rates of unemployment are given below:

| State | Rate |
|-------|------|
| New Mexico | 6.8 |
| West Virginia | 6.6 |
| Nevada | 6.5 |
| Alaska | 6.4 |
| Louisiana | 6.3 |
| Mississippi | 6.0 |

| State | Rate |
|-------|------|
| Arizona | 6.0 |
| Alabama | 6.0 |
| Oregon | 5.7 |
| North Carolina | 5.7 |
| Illinois | 5.7 |
| California | 5.7 |

*Source: U.S. Bureau of Labor Statistics*

Mean: 6.12%. Median: 6.0%. Mode: 5.7%. Midrange: 6.25%. Most meaningful is an opinion.

Forty new automobiles were tested for fuel efficiency (in miles per gallon) by the Environmental Protection Agency. The individual MPG values are displayed below. Use this information for Questions 7–12.

37   27   20   30   24   17   32   26   17   32   25   28   20   18   27   32   36   25   9   26
34   30   25   23   25   24   20   13   31   20   20   25   20   22   37   27   27   25   37   30

**7.** Find the mean miles per gallon.

25.6 MPG

**8.** Complete the frequency distribution.

| Class | Frequency |
|-------|-----------|
| 8–12 | 1 |
| 13–17 | 3 |
| 18–22 | 8 |
| 23–27 | 15 |
| 28–32 | 8 |
| 33–37 | 5 |

**4-3   Applications**

Name _____

9. Use the frequency distribution to approximate the mean. How does your approximation compare to the actual mean?

   *Approximation = 25.1 mpg. This is a pretty good approximation of the actual mean.*

10. Find the median, mode, and midrange of this data set.

    *Median = 25 mpg       Mode = 20 mpg       Midrange = 23 mpg*

11. Which measure of central tendency would a government official choose to show if she wanted to make the case that gas mileage was getting better for newer vehicles? Why?

    *She would want to pick the largest measure of average in order to give the appearance that gas mileage was improving. She would probably go with the actual mean of 25.6 mpg.*

12. Which measure of central tendency would an environmental lobbyist choose to show if he wanted to make the case that gas mileage was still not very good for newer vehicles? Why?

    *He would want to pick the smallest measure of average in order to give the appearance that gas mileage still had room to improve. He would probably go with the mode of 20 mpg.*

## 4-3 Applications

Name _____

13. Eighty randomly selected compact fluorescent light bulbs were tested to determine their lifetimes (in hours). The grouped frequency distribution was obtained as shown. The full data set for this distribution is in the technology template for this lesson. You'll further analyze this data in the technology assignment. Use the frequency distribution to approximate the mean. Write a sentence explaining what your answer means. Be sure to include units.

| Class | Frequency |
|-------|-----------|
| 651–800 | 6 |
| 801–950 | 12 |
| 951–1,100 | 25 |
| 1,101–1,250 | 18 |
| 1,251–1,400 | 14 |
| 1,401–1,550 | 5 |

The approximate mean is 1,094.9 hours. This means that the average light bulb should last for a touch less than 1,095 hours before burning out.

# Lesson 4-4   **Prep Skills**

This is a short review of skills that will come in handy in the next lesson. In each case, answer the question, then rate your confidence level by checking one of the boxes. If you feel like you're struggling with these skills, consult the online resources provided by your instructor for extra practice.

### SKILL 1: FIND THE MEAN

1. Find the mean for the list of numbers below.

   26   32   18   65   12   51   162   30

### SKILL 2: COMPUTING SUMS OF SQUARES

2. Compute the sum:

   $(8 - 13)^2 + (22 - 13)^2 + (13 - 13)^2 + (20 - 13)^2 + (7 - 13)^2$

### SKILL 3: COMPUTE SQUARE ROOTS

3. Find the square root of each number. Round to two decimal places.

   112    14,873

### SKILL 4: USE SUMMATION NOTATION

4. If $x_1 = 18$, $x_2 = 23$, $x_3 = 50$, and $x_4 = 19$, find $\Sigma x_i$.

# Lesson 4-4  **Your Results May Vary**  (Measures of Variation)

## LEARNING OBJECTIVES

☐ 1. Compute measures of variation for a given data set.

☐ 2. Interpret standard deviation for a data set.

☐ 3. Make meaningful comparisons of standard deviation for two data sets.

☐ 4. Analyze the procedure for computing standard deviation.

© Tim Davis/Corbis

*Research shows that there is only half as much variation in student achievement between schools as there is among classrooms in the same school. If you want your child to get the best education possible, it is actually more important to get him assigned to a great teacher than to a great school.*

—Bill Gates

© Chris Collins/Corbis

Now we know quite a lot about measures of average. But just how much information are we getting when we study measures of average? Take a look at the two pictures of dogs on this page. If we look only at measures of average, particularly the mean, we might be fooled into thinking that the two groups are very similar, when clearly they are not. The difference, of course, is that all of the dogs in the first picture are of similar size, while those in the second picture have many different weights. Because there are some small dogs and one very large one, the mean weight in both groups is probably similar. This leads us to the conclusion that there's a lot more to the story told by a data set than simply measures of average. There can be a lot of variation within a group.

**0.** After reading the opening paragraph, what do you think the main topic of this lesson will be?

## 4-4 Class

The simplest measure of variation that we'll study is the **range.**

The **range** of a data set is the difference between the largest and smallest values in the set.

    Range = Largest value − Smallest value

1. The first list below is the weights of the dogs in the first picture, and the second is the weights of the dogs in the second picture. Find the mean and range for each list.

First picture:  70  73  58  60
Second picture:  30  85  40  125  42  75  60  55

*First: Mean 65.3 lbs, range 15 lbs*

*Second: Mean 64 lbs, range 95 lbs*

2. Describe what you notice about the range and mean for each group of dogs.

*The means are very similar, but the range shows that the dogs in the second picture have weights that vary much more widely.*

3. Why is the range somewhat limited as a measure of variation for a data set? (Not these particular data sets: ANY data set.)

*It has to be limited based on the fact that it only uses the smallest and largest values in the data set, and completely ignores all others.*

## Did You Get It?

Try this problem to see if you understand the concepts we just studied. The answer can be found at the bottom of the portfolio page.

1. The monthly high temperatures from January to December in Aruba and St. Louis are shown below. Find the median and range for each, then write any observations you make based on this information.

   Aruba: 85°  85°  86°  87°  88°  89°  88°  89°  89°  89°  87°  85°
   St. Louis: 38°  45°  55°  66°  77°  86°  91°  88°  81°  69°  54°  42°

## Standard Deviation

The range is a limited measure of variation because it ignores all the data except the highest and lowest values. If most of the values are similar, but there's just one unusually high value, the range will make it look like there's a lot more variation than there actually is. For this reason, we will next study **standard deviation,** which is a much more reliable (and commonly used) measure of variation.

Standard deviation is a little tricky to compute. Eventually, we'll learn how to use technology to handle the computation, which will allow us to focus on interpretation. But first, we'll develop a procedure for computing standard deviation by hand. This turns out to be useful even if you never actually DO compute it by hand, as it really helps you to understand what exactly standard deviation measures. This is a bit of an oversimplification, but it's still very useful in understanding what standard deviation is designed to measure: *standard deviation essentially describes the average distance that each data value is away from the mean.*

4. Read the description of standard deviation in italics above carefully again. Why does standard deviation provide a very reasonable way of describing how spread out a data set is?

*Since the mean is kind of the "center" of the data values, finding how far away most values are from the mean is exactly what you'd typically think of when considering how spread out the values are.*

## Interpretation of Standard Deviation

A standard deviation that's large relative to the mean tells us that the data values vary pretty widely from the mean. A relatively small standard deviation means that most data values are clustered fairly close to the mean.

Standard deviation comes in two delightful flavors: population and sample. As we saw in Lesson 4-1, in many cases, data are based not on every single member of a population, but rather a representative sample. When the standard deviation is computed for a data set derived from an entire population under study, it's called the **population standard deviation.** When it's based on data derived from a representative sample of a larger population, it's called the **sample standard deviation.**

As we begin our efforts to develop a formula that accomplishes what we want standard deviation to do, try to focus not so much on just doing the arithmetic, but the interpretation of what each step is accomplishing. The plan is to find the standard deviation for the weights of the eight dogs pictured in the lesson opener.

**Step 1.** Find the mean weight.

5. Find the mean of the dog weights: (Or, better still, copy it from Question 1.)

30 85 40 125 42 75 60 55

*The mean is 64 lbs.*

**Interpretation:** Standard deviation is a measure of how far the data values vary from the mean, so it makes sense to begin by computing the mean.

**Step 2:** Subtract the mean from each data value.

6. Fill in the table below by subtracting the mean weight from each value.

| X | $X - \bar{X}$ |
|---|---|
| 30 | $-34$ |
| 85 | $21$ |
| 40 | $-24$ |
| 125 | $61$ |

| X | $X - \bar{X}$ |
|---|---|
| 42 | $-22$ |
| 75 | $11$ |
| 60 | $-4$ |
| 55 | $-9$ |

**Interpretation:** We are literally measuring exactly how far each data value is from the mean. We'd like to average them, which means we'd like to first add them. But if we try, something bad happens . . .

7. Add up all of the differences from the mean. Why is the result not helpful in finding an average deviation from the mean?

*The sum is zero. If you think about it, that will always happen. Obviously, getting zero all the time isn't going to tell us anything useful about the spread of data. It's a good critical thinking exercise to ask students to figure out if the sum will always be zero, and why.*

**Step 3:** Square the differences.

8. Fill in the table below by squaring all of your results from the table in Question 6.

| X | $(X - \bar{X})^2$ |
|---|---|
| 30 | $1{,}156$ |
| 85 | $441$ |
| 40 | $576$ |
| 125 | $3{,}721$ |

| X | $(X - \bar{X})^2$ |
|---|---|
| 42 | $484$ |
| 75 | $121$ |
| 60 | $16$ |
| 55 | $81$ |

**Interpretation:** Squaring gets rid of the negatives so that the sum is no longer zero. It also makes the differences too big, and changes the units (our values are no longer in pounds), but we'll deal with that later.

**Step 4:** Add up the squares of the differences.

9. Add your answers from Question 8.

   $1,156 + 441 + 576 + 3,721 + 484 + 121 + 16 + 81 = 6,596$

**Interpretation:** In this and the next step, we're calculating an approximate average of the squares of the differences, so we want to first add them.

**Step 5:** Divide by $n - 1$, which is the number of data values in the sample minus 1.

10. Divide your result from Question 9 by one less than the number of dogs.

   $6,596/7 = 942.29$

**Interpretation:** It seems like dividing by the number of values ($n$) here is a good idea, but it turns out that when we're using a sample from a larger population to compute mean and standard deviation, dividing by $n - 1$ makes the sample standard deviation more likely to be a true reflection of the population standard deviation. In any case, at this point we have an approximate average of the squares of the individual variations from the mean.

**Step 6:** Calculate the square root of the approximate average.

11. Find the square root of your answer from Question 10. This is the sample standard deviation.

   $\sqrt{942.29} \approx 30.70$

**Interpretation:** This is the step that "undoes" the squaring we did in Step 3. When we squared the results earlier, it changed the units from pounds to pounds squared: the square root returns the units to pounds, giving us a good measure of how far the typical data value varies from the mean.

---

### Did You Get It

Try this problem to see if you understand the concepts we just studied. The answer can be found at the bottom of the portfolio page.

2. Find the sample standard deviation for the four dogs in the first picture at the beginning of the lesson. How does it compare to the standard deviation for the dogs in the second picture? Explain why this makes sense.

   70   73   58   60

12. Carefully describe exactly what your answer to Question 11 tells you about the dogs in that picture.

*On average, the dogs' weights are a little less than 31 pounds away from the mean weight of 64 pounds. That tells us that the weights vary quite a lot.*

13. Briefly describe how the step-by-step procedure helps to answer Question 12.

*Answers vary. Basically, this should be a summary of the 'interpretation' comments in the development of standard deviation.*

The formulas below summarize how to find sample standard deviation, and also show how to find population standard deviation. For population, the only difference in the procedure is dividing by the total number of data values, rather than one less like we did in finding sample standard deviation.

## Formulas for Sample and Population Standard Deviation

**Sample:** $s = \sqrt{\dfrac{\Sigma(X - \overline{X})^2}{n - 1}}$ 　　　　 **Population:** $\sigma = \sqrt{\dfrac{\Sigma(X - \mu)^2}{N}}$

$X$ represents each data value.
$\overline{X}$ is the mean of the sample.
$\mu$ is the mean of the population.
$n$ is the number of data values in the sample.
$N$ is the number of data values in the population.

## Math Note

The square of the standard deviation is called the *variance* for a data set.

## 4-4 | Group

Now that we have a handle on not only WHAT standard deviation tells us, but WHY it tells us that, we'll look at using technology to do the calculation for us. This allows us to expend more mental energy on interpreting the result. The procedures are summarized in the box below.

### Using Technology: Finding Standard Deviation

**TI-84 Calculator**

The 1-Var Stats screen, which we used to compute the mean and median in Lesson 4-3, also calculates the standard deviation. Below is another look at a screen shot from Lesson 4-3, where the data on death row exonerations were entered in the list editor, and then the 1-Variable Stats command was chosen. The quantities we're interested in are Sx and σx: these are the sample standard deviation (Sx) and the population standard deviation (σx).

```
1-Var Stats
 x̄=5.538461538
 Σx=72
 Σx²=1022
 Sx=7.206656467
 σx=6.923931571
↓n=13
```

**Excel**

To use Excel to calculate standard deviation, the data are entered in a single column, just like we did for computing measures of average in Lesson 4-3. Here are sample calculations for the second group of dog weights from Question 1 in this lesson, with the formulas used to calculate each statistic illustrated to the right.

| | A | B |
|---|---|---|
| 1 | | 30 |
| 2 | | 85 |
| 3 | | 40 |
| 4 | | 125 |
| 5 | | 42 |
| 6 | | 75 |
| 7 | | 60 |
| 8 | | 55 |
| 9 | | |
| 10 | Range | 95 |
| 11 | Sample st. dev. | 30.696673 |
| 12 | Population st. dev. | 28.714108 |

Range

| B10 | ⬍ | ✕ ✓ | *fx* | =MAX(B1:B8)-MIN(B1:B8) |

Sample Standard Deviation

| B11 | ⬍ | ✕ ✓ | *fx* | =STDEV(B1:B8) |

Population Standard Deviation

| B12 | ⬍ | ✕ ✓ | *fx* | =STDEVP(B1:B8) |

*See the Lesson 4-4-1 and 4-4-2 Using Tech videos in class resources for further information.*

**A word on notation:** We use a lowercase *s* to represent the sample standard deviation for a data set; the symbol Sx is simply what's used on the calculator screen. Similarly, we use a lowercase Greek sigma ($\sigma$) to represent population standard deviation, not $\sigma$x.

1. The table below shows the number of arrests in the United States for possession of marijuana, in thousands, for the years from 2005 to 2014. All data was gathered from the annual Uniform Crime Report published by the Federal Bureau of Investigation. Find the mean and sample standard deviation for the number of arrests. Include units.

| Year | 2005 | 2006 | 2007 | 2008 | 2009 | 2010 | 2011 | 2012 | 2013 | 2014 |
|------|------|------|------|------|------|------|------|------|------|------|
| Arrests (Thousands) | 569 | 547 | 640 | 620 | 620 | 614 | 541 | 543 | 503 | 516 |

We get 571.3 and 48.7, so the mean is about 571,300 arrests, and the standard deviation is about 48,700 arrests.

2. Why was it appropriate to find sample standard deviation, rather than population?

Because the data came from a sampling of years, not every year ever.

Standard deviation is easiest to interpret when compared to the size of the mean. For example, a standard deviation of 10 in a data set with mean 20 indicates a much wider spread than a standard deviation of 10 in a data set with mean 200. To help make this easier, we can find the **relative standard deviation** (also known as the **coefficient of variation**). This number, usually denoted $c_v$, is the standard deviation divided by the mean: it's literally what percent of the mean the standard deviation is. In symbols:

## The Coefficient of Variation

$c_v = \dfrac{s}{\overline{X}}$ for sample data, and $c_v = \dfrac{\sigma}{\mu}$ for population data.

3. Find the coefficient of variation for the arrest data above. What percent of the mean is the standard deviation?

$c_v = 48.7/571.3 \approx 0.085$. The standard deviation is 8.5% of the mean.

**4.** Do you think the standard deviation and coefficient of variation for this data set would be more likely to be used in an argument by someone that is in favor of legalizing marijuana, or against? Explain.

*This is an opinion. You could kind of use it to argue on both sides. The consistency in these numbers could be interpreted to mean that the war on drugs is a complete failure, or it could be interpreted to mean that marijuana use remains a big societal problem.*

**5.** Find the coefficient of variation for the 8 dogs from Questions 5–11 in the Class portion. Compare it to your answer to Question 3 on the previous page. What can you conclude?

*30.7/64 ≈ 0.48. The standard deviation for the dogs is 48% of the mean, while the standard deviation for the arrests is only 8.5% of the mean. This shows that the dog data is much more spread out than the arrest data.*

> Key point of emphasis here: Comparing 30.7 pounds and 48.7 arrests is meaningless. But we can make an intelligent comparison of the two spreads by comparing the coefficient of variation.

## Did You Get It

Try this problem to see if you understand the concepts we just studied. The answer can be found at the bottom of the portfolio page.

3. The numbers below are the percentage of all drug possession arrests that were for marijuana for the years from 2005 to 2014. Find the sample mean, standard deviation, and coefficient of variation.

   37.7   39.1   42.1   44.3   45.6   45.8   43.3   42.4   40.6   39.7

For Questions 6–8, identify the data set that is likely to have a larger standard deviation. Make sure you EXPLAIN your reasoning. Like with sentences and stuff.

**6.** Data set 1: 12   15   13   10   16   13   12   13

Data set 2: 5   26   31   2   10   25   6   33

*Data set 2. The values in set 1 are all within 6 units of each other, while the ones in set 2 are very spread out.*

**7.** Data set 1: 40-yard dash times for starting running backs in the National Football League
Data set 2: 40-yard dash times for every student in your math class

*Data set 2. Everyone that becomes a professional running back has to be at least reasonably fast, so you'd expect the times to be pretty consistent. But a group of students in a math class would most likely have some pretty fast runners, and some dreadfully slow runners.*

**8.** Data set 1: Average monthly high temperature in Chicago
Data set 2: Average monthly high temperature in Los Angeles

*Data set 1. Los Angeles has a very consistent climate, and is fairly warm even in winter. Chicago, on the other hand, gets very warm in the summer and very cold in the winter, so the average high will vary a lot.*

## Did You Get It

Try this problem to see if you understand the concepts we just studied. The answer can be found at the bottom of the portfolio page.

4. Which data set would be likely to have the larger standard deviation? EXPLAIN.

Data set 1: Weights of all dogs at a golden retriever rescue shelter

Data set 2: Weights of all dogs for sale in a pet store

**9.** A professor has two sections of Math 115 this semester. The 8:30 A.M. class has a mean score of 74% with a standard deviation of 3.6%. The 2 P.M. class also has a mean score of 74%, but a standard deviation of 19.2%. What can we conclude about the students' averages in these two sections?

*The first class has a very, very low coefficient of variation, meaning the scores are really consistent. You're going to see a boatload of Cs, with relatively few As or Fs. The second class has much more variation, so you'd see more As and Fs, with grades spread across the spectrum.*

**10.** In the Technology portion of the Portfolio, you'll be analyzing the heights of every student in your class, so before class is over make sure that you collect that data. Record heights in inches, and make sure you indicate whether each height is a male or female.

## 4-4 Portfolio

Name _____

Check each box when you've completed the task. Remember that your instructor will want you to turn in the portfolio pages you create.

### Technology

1. ☐ Enter the heights in inches of all students in your class in three separate columns of a spreadsheet: in column A, include everyone. In column B, list only the males, and in column C list only the females. Then use formulas to calculate the mean and sample standard deviation for each data set. Explain any differences you notice in the standard deviations. A template to help you get started can be found in the online resources for this lesson. It has a text box set up where you can enter your discussion of the results.

### Online Practice

1. ☐ Include any written work from the online assignment along with any notes or questions about this lesson's content.

### Applications

1. ☐ Complete the applications problems.

### Reflections

Type a short answer to each question.

1. ☐ If someone asked you informally to describe what standard deviation is, what would you say?
2. ☐ In many ways, standard deviation is most useful when you're comparing the standard deviations of two data sets. Explain why this is reasonable.
3. ☐ What do the mean and standard deviation together tell you about a data set? What do they not tell you?
4. ☐ Take another look at your answer to Question 0 at the beginning of this lesson. Would you change your answer now that you've finished the lesson? How would you summarize the topic of this lesson now?
5. ☐ What questions do you have about this lesson?

### Looking Ahead

1. ☐ Complete the Lesson 4-5 Prep Skills and read the opening paragraph in Lesson 4-5 carefully, then answer Question 0 in preparation for that lesson.

### Answers to "Did You Get It?"

1. Aruba, median 87.5°, range 4°; St. Louis, median 67.5°, range 53°; Aruba has a much more consistent climate.     2. 7.37 lbs; much less; the dogs are similar in size
3. Mean 42.06%, standard deviation 2.76%, coefficient of variation 0.066
4. Data set 2: all of the dogs in the first set are the same breed, so you'd expect them to be reasonably similar in size.

## 4-4  Applications

Name _____

The table shows the number of class periods missed over the last 10 courses by two students. Use this information for Questions 1–5.

| Helena | 3 | 4 | 3 | 2 | 2 | 4 | 3 | 2 | 2 | 3 |
|--------|---|---|---|---|---|---|---|---|---|---|
| Juanita | 0 | 9 | 2 | 1 | 0 | 6 | 0 | 4 | 0 | 8 |

1. Find the mean number of classes missed for each student.

   Helena: 2.8 classes

   Juanita: 3.0 classes

2. Find the range of the number of classes missed for each student.

   Helena: 2 classes

   Juanita: 9 classes

3. Without doing the calculations, how do you think the standard deviations compare for the two students? Explain.

   Clearly the numbers for Juanita are much more spread out, so we'd expect a considerably larger standard deviation.

4. Now calculate the standard deviation for these two students. Do these values agree with your thoughts from Question 3?

   Helena: 0.79 classes

   Juanita: 3.53 classes

   This is just what we expected. We're pretty smart.

5. Which is a better student in your opinion? What does that say about the importance of measures of average compared to measures of variation in some situations?

   Opinion question. But a good answer should certainly point out that you need measures of variation to decide since the means are essentially the same.

## 4-4    Applications

Name _____

When playing golf, in most cases the player will want to get the ball as close as possible to the hole when hitting a shot approaching the green. Suppose that two players hit 10 approach shots to a green, and their results are as shown in the two figures. The black dot is the hole, and the white dots are where each shot ended up. Use the diagram for Questions 6–8.

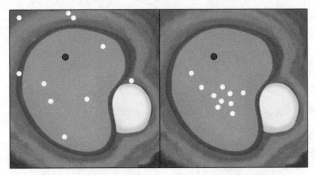

Pat's shots            Ron's shots

6. If you were to "average" the locations of all of the results for each player, where would you estimate the average shot would be for each?

   *Pat's average shot is pretty close to the hole, while Ron's is right in the middle of the green where most shots are clustered.*

7. How would you describe the measures of variation for each of the players?

   *Pat's variation would be much higher than Ron's. His shot locations are very consistent, while Pat's are spread out all over the place, with many missing the green entirely.*

8. Which is a better player in your opinion? What does that say about the importance of measures of average compared to measures of variation in some situations?

   *Opinion question, but the point is that Pat's average is practically in the hole, so based strictly on that you'd say that she's the better player. But Ron is much more consistent.*

## 4-4   Applications

Name _____

The heights in inches of nine army recruits (first list) and nine randomly selected people walking through a mall (second list) are shown below. Use these data for Questions 9–13.

List 1: 78   72   68   73   75   69   74   73   72
List 2: 32   75   54   48   70   63   67   46   66

9. Compute the mean, range, and standard deviation for the heights of the recruits.

   Mean: 72.7 inches

   Range: 10 inches

   Standard deviation: 3 inches

10. Compute the mean, range, and standard deviation for the heights of the mall shoppers.

    Mean: 57.9 inches

    Range: 43 inches

    Standard deviation: 13.9 inches

11. How do the means compare? What does this mean?

    The mean for recruits is much greater. For one, this is because all of the army recruits are adults, while it looks like some of the mall shoppers were children. There are also size standards for military recruits.

12. How do the ranges compare? What does this mean?

    The recruits' range is way smaller. This really confirms the idea that some of the mall shoppers are most likely children, while the recruits obviously are all adults.

13. How do the standard deviations compare? What does this mean?

    The recruits' standard deviation is very small in general, and especially compared to the mall shoppers. Similar ages and military physical standards make it totally reasonable that there's not a lot of variance in the recruits' heights. But if you pick nine people totally randomly in a mall, you would expect all shapes and sizes.

## 4-4   Applications

Name _____

14. The standard deviation for Juanita's number of classes missed (Question 1) was ___3.53 classes___. The standard deviation for the heights of the randomly selected shoppers in a mall was ___13.9 inches___. Explain why comparing these two numbers is meaningless. (Hint: Did you include units?)

    *The units tell the story here: these standard deviations measure two completely different things, classes missed and inches. Also, the standard deviation is only meaningful when we know what the mean is, and the means for the two data sets are very different.*

15. Find the coefficient of variation for Juanita's number of classes missed and the mall shoppers' heights.

    *Missed classes by Juanita: 3.53/3.0 ≈ 1.18, or 118%*

    *Mall shoppers' heights: 13.9/57.9 ≈ 0.24 or 24%*

16. The numbers from Question 15 CAN be compared in a meaningful way. Explain what comparing them tells us.

    *Even though the actual standard deviation for the shoppers' heights is more than three times as large, the coefficient of variation shows that the variation in their heights is nowhere near as significant as the variation in the number of classes missed by Juanita.*

# Lesson 4-5   Prep Skills

This is a short review of skills that will come in handy in the next lesson. In each case, answer the question, then rate your confidence level by checking one of the boxes. If you feel like you're struggling with these skills, consult the online resources provided by your instructor for extra practice.

### SKILL 1: FIND PERCENT OF A WHOLE

1. If 35 people in a class of 50 score lower than you on a final exam, what percent of people scored lower than you?

2. What percent of people scored higher than you?

### SKILL 2: COMPUTING A GIVEN PERCENTAGE OF AN AMOUNT

3. If 36% of days in March last year were rainy, how many days were rainy? How many were not?

### SKILL 3: FINDING A MEDIAN

4. A math class recorded the following scores, out of 200, on a final exam. What was the median score?

   189   186   183   179   177   175   168   167   166   163   161   158
   156   154   153   152   148   146   144   137   122   119   108   87

5. How does the median change if we throw out the lowest score?

# Lesson 4-5 Where Do You Rank? (Measures of Position in a Data Set)

## LEARNING OBJECTIVES

☐ 1. Compute percentile ranks.

☐ 2. Find data corresponding to a given percentile rank.

☐ 3. Use percentiles to compare data from different sets.

☐ 4. Compute quartiles and use them to analyze spread.

☐ 5. Draw and interpret box plots.

© Comstock Images/Jupiterimages RF

*Grades are almost completely relative, in effect ranking students relative to others in their class. Thus extra achievement by one student not only raises his position, but in effect lowers the position of others.*
—James S. Coleman

So you managed to survive your college years and escape with that long-awaited diploma. But maybe the thought of entering the mythical "real world" starts to look a little less appealing, and you realize that a couple more years of college might suit you. Next step: take the GRE (Graduate Record Examination), which is like the SAT for grad school. When you get your score back, you see that it's 1120. How do you know if that's a good score? The quickest way is to look at the percentile rank on the report, which in this case would probably be 60%. Does this mean that you only got 60% of the questions right? That wouldn't be a very good score, now would it? In fact, that's not at all what it means, and you did just fine.

When raw scores (or other data) are hard to interpret, it's useful to see where certain values rank within the data set, and that's what we'll study in this lesson.

**0.** After reading the opening paragraphs, what do you think the main topic of this lesson will be?

**4-5** **Class**

The term *percentile* is used in statistics to measure the position of a data value in a data set.

> A **percentile,** or percentile rank, of a data value indicates the percent of data values in a set that are less than that particular value.

In the case of the GRE score, your percentile rank of 60% means that 60% of all students who took the GRE scored lower than you did. Not bad! Scores on standardized tests are one of the most common uses for percentiles because they help you to put a raw score like 1120 into context.

1. Percentiles are used very commonly in health care, especially pediatrics. To monitor a child's development, doctors compare the child's height, weight, and head size at a certain age to measurements of other children at the same age. What do you think the medical value of doing this is?

   *If any of the child's characteristics are very unusual, it could indicate some underlying condition that might not be otherwise apparent. And in medicine, when there's a problem, the earlier it's detected, the more fixable it is.*

   **Math Note**

   Some books define a percentile as the percentage of data values less than or equal to a certain value, instead of just "less than."

Percentiles were originally used to analyze data sets with 100 or more values. But when statistical techniques were developed for smaller data sets, the percentile concept came into use for those sets as well. There are several methods that can be used for computing percentiles, and sometimes the answers vary slightly, especially with small data sets. In this lesson, we'll use a basic method that works well for smaller data sets, and rely on technology to handle bigger sets.

## Finding a Percentile Rank

The percentile rank for a given data point in a set with $n$ total values can be calculated using this formula:

$$\text{Percentile of a Value } x = \frac{\text{Number of data values less than } x}{n} \cdot 100$$

The result should be rounded to the nearest whole number.

2. Suppose you score 77 on a test in a class of 20 people, with the 20 scores listed below. What was your percentile rank? (Hint: It's not necessary to put the data values in order, but it surely doesn't hurt.)

   93  82  64  75  98  52  77  88  90  71  78  55  62  99  91  83  89  61  73  80

   *The ordered list:*

   *52  55  61  62  64  71  73  75  77  78  80  82  83  88  89  90  91  93  98  99*

   *Eight scores are less than 77, so the percentile rank is 8/20 times 100, or 40th percentile.*

## Did You Get It

Try this problem to see if you understand the concepts we just studied. The answer can be found at the bottom of the portfolio page.

1. The weights in pounds for the 12 members of a college gymnastics team are below. Find the percentile rank of the gymnast who weighs 97 pounds.

   101  120  88  72  75  80  98  91  105  97  78  85

Finding the percentile rank for a certain data value, as we've seen, can give us some useful perspective on how high or low that data value is. But what about the opposite question? Suppose that a researcher is interested in studying the homework habits of students that rank at the 80th percentile in their classes. How do you find the score that corresponds to a certain percentile? Let's see.

Here are the exam scores from your hypothetical class again. The goal is to find the score that corresponds to the 80th percentile.

93  82  64  75  98  52  77  88  90  71  78  55  62  99  91  83  89  61  73  80

**3.** Arrange the scores in order from smallest to largest.

52  55  61  62  64  71  73  75  77  78  80  82  83  88  89  90  91  93  98  99

**4.** The 80th percentile means that we want 80% of the scores to be less than the one we're looking for. With that in mind, how many scores do we want to have LESS than the score we're trying to identify?

*80% of 20 is 16, so we want 16 scores less.*

> You might let students know that our method for computing a percentile depends on having no repeated values in the data set, and that the percentiles that Excel calculates account for repeated data values. This plays a role later in the lesson.

**5.** Find the score that has 80% of the data below it.

*91*

This seems like a reasonable way to find the data value we're looking for, but there's a minor problem. If you're at the 80th percentile, you should have 80% of the scores below you, and 20% above you, right? But in this case . . .

**6.** How many scores are above the score you found in Question 5? What percentage is that of the total number of scores? What can you conclude?

*There are 3, which is 15% of the total number. Our method doesn't work exactly as you might expect, since the 80th percentile doesn't have 20% of values above it.*

Now we see the problem. For really large data sets, this isn't much of an issue. For example, if there were 200 scores rather than 20, the 80th percentile would have 80% of them below it (which is 160 scores), and 39 above it. This corresponds to 19.5%, which is pretty close to the 20% we'd want. But for smaller data sets, we don't have "enough" data above the one we're choosing for a certain percentile. The box below describes a slightly modified procedure to address this issue.

### Finding the Data Value that Corresponds to a Percentile

**Step 1:** Arrange the data values in order from smallest to largest.

**Step 2:** Count the total number of data values, then multiply that number by the percentile rank we're looking for, written as a percentage in decimal form. We'll call this number the *index,* and represent it with the letter $L$.

**Step 3:** If $L$ is a whole number, then the data value corresponding to our given percentile is halfway between the value in the $L$th position from the bottom and the next higher value.

**Step 4:** If $L$ is not a whole number, round it up to the next whole number. Then the data value at the given percentile is the $L$th value from the bottom on the list.

7. For the test score data in Questions 3–6, what would be the data value at the 80th percentile using this procedure? (Note that you already calculated $L$ in Question 4. You just didn't realize it at that point.)

*$L$ is 16, and the value in that position is 90. The next higher value on the list is 91, so we would say that 90.5 is at the 80th percentile.*

8. The disadvantage of the data value we got in this case is that it's NOT one of the actual data values on the list. The advantage? You tell me by answering this question: How many data values on the list are now below the value at the 80th percentile? How many are above? What percent is each of those of the total number of values?

*Now there are 16 values below 90.5, which is 80% of the data, and 4 above, which is 20% of the data. Splendid!*

9. Use the procedure in the box to find the score that's at the 62nd percentile.

   *62% of 20 is 12.4, which we round up to 13. The value in the 13th position is 83, so that's the value at the 62nd percentile.*

### Did You Get It

Try this problem to see if you understand the concepts we just studied. The answer can be found at the bottom of the portfolio page.

2. The number of homicides for the years from 2000 to 2014 in Columbus, OH is shown in the table. Which year is at the 25th percentile?

| '00 | '01 | '02 | '03 | '04 | '05 | '06 | '07 | '08 | '09 | '10 | '11 | '12 | '13 | '14 |
|-----|-----|-----|-----|-----|-----|-----|-----|-----|-----|-----|-----|-----|-----|-----|
| 67  | 82  | 81  | 110 | 89  | 103 | 102 | 79  | 109 | 83  | 105 | 93  | 90  | 92  | 91  |

Percentile ranks are really useful for comparing data that come from two different sets. Here's a great example of that: Two students are competing for one remaining spot in a law school class. Miguel ranked 51st in a graduating class of 1,400, while Dustin ranked 27th in a class of 540.

10. Would it be fair to award the spot to Dustin because he ranked closer to first in his class? Why or why not? Explain your answer.

    *Not necessarily, because Miguel's class was much bigger.*

11. Which has the better ranking if you compute percentiles within the class? Does that surprise you? Discuss. (That means write more than "yes" or "no".)

    *Miguel: 51st out of 1,400, so there are 1,349 students below him: 1,349/1,400 ≈ 0.963, so Miguel is at the 96th percentile.*

    *Dustin: 27th out of 540, so there are 513 students below him: 513/540 = 095, so Dustin is at the 95th percentile. Both are excellent students, but Miguel is ranked a bit higher. Whether you're surprised or not is an opinion.*

## Did You Get It

Try this problem to see if you understand the concepts we just studied. The answer can be found at the bottom of the portfolio page.

3. In the 2011–2012 school year, the University of Arkansas finished the season ranked fifth out of 120 teams in football and ninth out of 297 teams in baseball. Based on percentile rank, which team had the better ranking?

## 4-5 Group

1. Discuss this question in your group and see if you can come up with a good answer: What does the median (which we studied in Lesson 4-3) have to do with percentiles?

*The median is defined to be the value that has half of the data values below it and half above. That makes the median the same thing as the value at the 50th percentile.*

> Check that each group has a correct answer to this question, then refer back to it after students reach the quartile summary box on the next page.

## Quartiles

Quartiles divide a data set into four equal parts; that is, four intervals that contain the same amount of data. This isn't the same thing as four intervals of the same length relative to the data. For the test score data we've been studying, the highest score is 99 and the lowest is 52, so the range is 47 points. If we divided the data in categories of equal length, each would cover 11.75 points, and the categories would be 52–63.75, 63.75–75.50, 75.50–87.25, and 87.25–99.

2. How many data values would fall into each of those categories? You put the data in order in Question 3 of the Class portion of this lesson, which will help. The data is repeated below if you want it for reference.

93  82  64  75  98  52  77  88  90  71  78  55  62  99  91  83  89  61  73  80

| Category | # Values |
|---|---|
| 52–63.75 | 4 |
| 63.75–75.50 | 4 |
| 75.50–87.25 | 5 |
| 87.25–99 | 7 |

**3.** If, instead, we divide the data so that the same number of data values fall into each of four categories, how many data values will be in each category? (Don't think too hard—this is NOT a hard question.)

*Five: 20 values, four categories.*

Here's a visual that illustrates what quartiles are about:

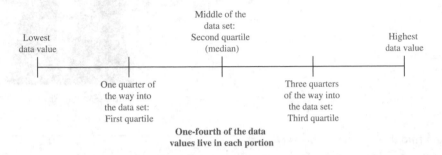

We use the symbol $Q_1$ to represent the first quartile, $Q_2$ to represent the second (which is also the median), and $Q_3$ for the third. This is a nice way to think of what these symbols mean:

### Interpretation of Quartiles

$Q_1$ (first quartile): 25% of data values are less than this, and 75% are greater than it.

$Q_2$ (second quartile): 50% of data values are less than this, and 50% are greater than it.

$Q_3$ (third quartile): 75% of data values are less than this, and 25% are greater than it.

**4.** While quartiles break the data into four equal portions, percentiles break data into 100 equal portions. If we use the symbol $P_{60}$ to represent the 60th percentile, how would we represent the first and third quartiles as percentiles using this notation? What about the median? (Note: There were three questions there.)

*First quartile: $P_{25}$. Third quartile: $P_{75}$. Median: $P_{50}$*

The data below are the percentages of total electricity generated that comes from nuclear power for the nations with the 12 largest economies in the world, listed by size of economy. Our goal is to find the quartiles.

19.5   2.4   0   15.8   17.2   76.9   2.9   0   3.7   18.6   16.8   0

5. Arrange the data in order from least to greatest.

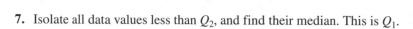

0   0   0   2.4   2.9   3.7   15.8   16.8   17.2   18.6   19.5   76.9

6. Find the median. This is $Q_2$.

*The median is halfway between the two values in the middle, which are 3.7 and 15.8. So $Q_2 = 9.75\%$.*

© Brand X Pictures RF

7. Isolate all data values less than $Q_2$, and find their median. This is $Q_1$.

*The median of the first six values is halfway between 0 and 2.4, so $Q_1 = 1.2\%$.*

> We're waving our hands a bit here because of the repeated data values. But because those values are all zero, this has very minimal effect on the quartiles.

8. Find the median of all data values greater than $Q_2$. This is $Q_3$.

*The median of the top six values is halfway between 17.2 and 18.6, so $Q_3 = 17.9\%$.*

---

### Did You Get It   ?

Try this problem to see if you understand the concepts we just studied. The answer can be found at the bottom of the portfolio page.

4. The data below are the number of cattle on farms in the United States (in millions) for each year that begins a decade from 1910 to 2010. Find the quartiles.

59.0   70.4   61.0   68.3   78.0   96.2   112.4   111.2   95.8   98.2   93.9

---

## The Interquartile Range

The **interquartile range**, or IQR, is a measure of variation that is often used when median is used as your measure of center. IQR measures the spread of the middle 50% of the data.

$$IQR = Q_3 - Q_1$$

**9.** Find the IQR for the nuclear power energy data set from Questions 5–8.

$$IQR = Q_3 - Q_1 = 17.9\% - 1.2\% = 16.7\%$$

When studying measures of average in Lesson 4-3, we learned that median is a more reliable measure of average than mean when there are a few values in the data set that are way higher or lower than the others. In other words, median tends to be resistant to the effects of a few aberrational data values, and for that reason it is called a **resistant measure**.

**10.** IQR is considered to be a resistant measure of variation. Discuss why you think that is reasonable.

In a way, it's similar to median. It focuses on the 50% of data that's in the middle of the spread, so it will not be affected by any unusually large or small data values.

One of the most useful applications of quartiles is using them to draw a **box plot** (sometimes called a box and whisker plot). This is a graphical way to evaluate the spread of a data set. In particular, a box plot makes it easy to identify data points that are *outliers*—those that appear to be aberrational in some way. (We'll learn more about outliers in just a bit.) Below is an example of a box plot for a group of test scores. (The labeling in purple is not typically included in a box plot: it's there to help you understand what the plot is displaying.)

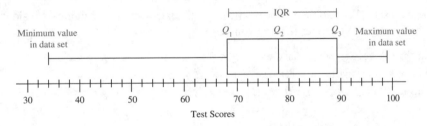

**11.** Use the box plot to fill in all of the requested information for the test scores it illustrates.

Lowest score ____34____          Third Quartile ____89____

First Quartile ____68____          Highest score ____99____

Median ____78____                    Interquartile Range ____21____

The first five numbers you found in Question 11 make up what's known as the **five number summary** for a data set. This is a good way to show how data is distributed in a concise way. In essence, a box plot is a graphical representation of the five number summary.

12. Write the five number summary for the nuclear power data we've been studying. Write it in this format, which is a typical way to write the summary: {Minimum, $Q_1$, $Q_2$, $Q_3$, Maximum}. (You've already found the quartiles.)

   *(0, 1.2, 9.75, 17.9, 76.9)*

13. Draw a box plot for the data.

   | Note that the dashed line is a fence that will be added in Question 17. |

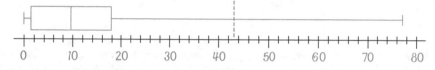

14. What does the box plot tell you about the data set? Write some observations. In particular, what do the numbers inside the box represent? Is the median closer to $Q_1$ or $Q_3$? What does that tell you?

   *Answers vary. Some observations: 1) Half of the data values are roughly between 1 and 18. This is what the numbers inside the box represent. 2) Most of the values are quite a bit less than the maximum value. 3) The highest value is very aberrational since it's so far outside the spread of the other values. 4) The median is a bit closer to $Q_1$ than $Q_3$, which means that there are more values in the middle half on the lower end.*

Data values are considered to be **outliers** if they are more than 1.5 times the interquartile range below the first quartile, or more than 1.5 times the interquartile range above the third quartile. The numbers $Q_1 - 1.5 \cdot$ IQR and $Q_3 + 1.5 \cdot$ IQR are called **fences**. They indicate that any data values outside of them are aberrational somehow. We can draw additional vertical boundaries on our box plot to identify the fences.

15. Find the length corresponding to 1.5 times the IQR for the nuclear power data.

   *The IQR is 16.7, and 1.5 times 16.7 is 25.05.*

16. Subtract that length from $Q_1$ and add it to $Q_3$. Are there any outliers? They would be data values that are outside the range of numbers you just found.

    $Q_1 - 25.05 = 1.2 - 25.05 = -23.85$. This is not relevant because no nation can generate a negative percentage of their electricity from nuclear power. $Q_3 + 25.05 = 17.9 + 25.05 = 42.95$. Looking back at the data set, we see that there is an outlier: the max value of 76.9%.

17. Go back and draw vertical boundaries on your box plot corresponding to the fences (if possible). If not, explain why. Fences are often drawn as dotted or dashed lines.

    We can draw a boundary at the upper fence, but not the lower. It's way off of the plot because it's so low, but that's okay because it represents a data value that's impossible given the context.

After identifying outliers, typically we would investigate those values. In some cases, they might be mistakes in the data gathering process. In others, they indicate values that are exceptionally high or low compared to the others (and therefore might be likely to skew some measures of average or variation—those that are not resistant.) If you find any outliers, it's worth taking some time to check if they're mistakes in the data. If not, you should consider how they might affect things like measures of average. In many cases, outliers are ignored when evaluating a data set.

18. To identify extreme outliers, we can find **outer fences**. These are values that are three times the IQR below $Q_1$ and above $Q_3$. Is the maximum value in our nuclear power data set an extreme outlier? Discuss how you might view that data value in relation to the rest of the set when evaluating how reliant most nations with large economies are on nuclear power.

    We already know that there's no point in looking well below $Q_1$: $Q_3 + 3 \cdot IQR = 17.9 + 3(16.7) = 68$. The highest value is an extreme outlier. Since all of the other values are so much lower, if we're interested in evaluating reliance on nuclear power in the world's largest economies, it would be reasonable to basically ignore the extreme outlier and focus on the other 11 data values.

19. Are there any outliers among the scores that generated the box plot you studied in Question 11? How can you tell?

    The fences are $68 - 1.5(21) = 36.5$ and $120.5$. Again, one of the fences is meaningless because nobody could score 120.5% on a test. The lower fence, on the other hand, is a bit above the minimum value, so we know that there is at least one outlier.

## Did You Get It

Try this problem to see if you understand the concepts we just studied. The answer can be found at the bottom of the portfolio page.

5.  Draw a box plot for the data in Did You Get It 4. Are there any outliers? If so, what are they?

## Using Technology: Finding Percentiles and Quartiles

There are Excel commands that will find all of the information we studied in this lesson. It's all about knowing the syntax. The example below shows the test scores that were used for the box plot sample on page 389. The list was already sorted using the SORT command.

| | A | B |
|---|---|---|
| 1 | Test Scores | 34 |
| 2 | | 62 |
| 3 | | 65 |
| 4 | | 66 |
| 5 | | 66 |
| 6 | | 68 |
| 7 | | 71 |
| 8 | | 73 |
| 9 | | 75 |
| 10 | | 77 |
| 11 | | 78 |
| 12 | | 80 |
| 13 | | 82 |
| 14 | | 83 |
| 15 | | 88 |
| 16 | | 89 |
| 17 | | 90 |
| 18 | | 91 |
| 19 | | 93 |
| 20 | | 98 |
| 21 | | 99 |
| 22 | | |
| 23 | Median | 78 |
| 24 | 1st Quartile | 68 |
| 25 | 3rd Quartile | 89 |
| 26 | | |
| 27 | 65th Percentile | 83 |
| 28 | 20th Percentile | 66 |

- We already know the median command.
- To find the first quartile:
    =QUARTILE(cell range,1)
  where cell range is the first and last cell on the list with a colon between them.
- To find the third quartile:
    =QUARTILE(cell range,3)
- To find a given percentile:
    =PERCENTILE(cell range,percentile)
  where the percentile is written as a percentage in decimal form.

$fx$ | =MEDIAN(B1:B21)

$fx$ | =QUARTILE(B1:B21,1)

$fx$ | =QUARTILE(B1:B21,3)

$fx$ | =PERCENTILE(B1:B21,0.65)

$fx$ | =PERCENTILE(B1:B21,0.2)

> If you want to talk about the fact that repeated data values affect percentiles, you can use Excel in class to calculate the percentiles for the nuclear power generation data on page 390. The results are slightly different than our hand calculations.

*See the Lesson 4-5 Using Tech video in class resources for further information.*

## 4-5 | Portfolio

Name _____

Check each box when you've completed the task. Remember that your instructor will want you to turn in the portfolio pages you create.

### Technology

1. ☐ It should be pretty obvious that for large data sets, using technology to compute percentiles and quartiles is a pretty darn good idea. The technology template for this lesson contains the net worth as of 2015 for all 538 members of the United States Congress. In Column F, use formulas to compute the statistics that are listed next to each cell in Column E. Then draw a box plot for the data by hand, and submit to your instructor. You can either turn it in on paper, or scan and submit in the same way you submit spreadsheets. Finally, write a short essay analyzing the information provided by your box plot.

### Online Practice

1. ☐ Include any written work from the online assignment along with any notes or questions about this lesson's content.

### Applications

1. ☐ Complete the applications problems.

### Reflections

Type a short answer to each question.

1. ☐ Why are percentiles useful in interpreting things like standardized test scores?
2. ☐ Explain what the five number summary tells us about a data set. You should describe each of the numbers and what its significance is, as well as give an overview of what the entire summary is useful for.
3. ☐ If you knew someone whose child scored in the 70th percentile on a standardized test, how would you explain to them what exactly that means?
4. ☐ Take another look at your answer to Question 0 at the beginning of this lesson. Would you change your answer now that you've finished the lesson? How would you summarize the topic of this lesson now?
5. ☐ What questions do you have about this lesson?

### Looking Ahead

1. ☐ Complete the Lesson 4-6 Prep Skills and read the opening paragraph in Lesson 4-6 carefully, then answer Question 0 in preparation for that lesson.

### Answers to "Did You Get It?"

1. 58th percentile    2. 2001    3. Baseball (97th percentile compared to 96th)
4. $Q_1 = 68.3$, $Q_2 = 93.9$, $Q_3 = 98.2$    5. There are no outliers.

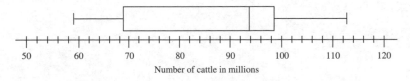

Number of cattle in millions

## 4-5   Applications

Name _____

It wasn't that long ago that it was reasonably unusual for a college football player to weigh more than 300 pounds, but those days are long gone. Listed below are the average weights for the starting offensive line at each of the 14 schools in the Southeastern Conference during the 2015 season. We'll be studying these weights in this activity.

| School | Avg. Weight |
| --- | --- |
| Arkansas | 321.1 |
| Mississippi | 313.4 |
| South Carolina | 310.4 |
| Vanderbilt | 309.5 |
| Kentucky | 308.3 |
| Louisiana State | 307.8 |
| Alabama | 303.6 |

| School | Avg. Weight |
| --- | --- |
| Tennessee | 303.3 |
| Mississippi State | 302.5 |
| Auburn | 300.6 |
| Texas A&M | 295.8 |
| Florida | 295.3 |
| Georgia | 291.1 |
| Missouri | 289.5 |

1. Find the percentile rank for Vanderbilt's offensive line.

   They rank 4th out of 14 teams, so there are ten teams below them. Their rank is 10/14 times 100, or at the 71st percentile.

2. Which school is at the 15th percentile?

   Fifteen percent of 14 is 2.1. We round this up to 3, and the team at the 15th percentile is the third from the bottom. That's Florida.

3. After seven weeks of the 2015 season, *USA Today* had Kentucky ranked 49th out of 128 teams. Which is higher: their percentile rank for offensive line weight in their conference, or their percentile rank among all 128 teams according to *USA Today?*

   49th out of 128 means 79 teams below them. 79/128 times 100 gives us 61.7%, which rounds to 62. Ranking-wise, Kentucky was at the 62nd percentile.

   Weight: Nine teams below them. 9/14 times 100 gives us 64.3%, which rounds to 64. Weight-wise, Kentucky is at the 64th percentile. Close, but they were heavier than they were good.

# 4-5 Applications

Name _____

4. Analyze the weight data by drawing a box plot. Feel free to use a spreadsheet to help with the calculations. Make sure you find the interquartile range and fences (and include any that are reasonable to draw on your plot), decide if there are any outliers, then write a paragraph describing any observations you have based on your results.

Median: 303.45. $Q_1$: 295.8. $Q_3$: 309.5. IQR = 309.5 − 295.8 = 13.7

Upper fence: 309.5 + 1.5(13.7) = 330.05. Lower fence: 295.8 − 1.5(13.7) = 275.25

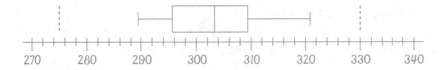

There are no outliers. Observations will vary, but one thing the plot shows is that there's not a terribly wide range. It also skews a bit toward the lower end, with the largest value not an outlier but still unusually large. Half of the offensive lines have average weights that are between 296 and 310.

5. You probably wouldn't be surprised to find that most members of Congress are really rich. But how rich? In the Technology portion of the homework, you'll be analyzing the net worth of every member of the House and Senate as of 2015. Senator Kay Hagan (D-NC) and Representative John Fleming (R-LA) both had net worths right around $9 million. Senator Hagan ranked 13th out of 100 senators, while Congressman Fleming ranked 29th out of 435 members of the House. Based on percentiles, which was richer relative to their congressional body? What do you think that says about the House compared to the Senate?

Hagan: 87/100 gives us 87th percentile. Fleming: 406/435 gives us 93rd percentile. Since Fleming ranks higher among representatives than Hagan does among senators, and they have the same net worth, we can conclude that in general senators are richer than representatives.

# Lesson 4-6    Prep Skills

This is a short review of skills that will come in handy in the next lesson. In each case, answer the question, then rate your confidence level by checking one of the boxes. If you feel like you're struggling with these skills, consult the online resources provided by your instructor for extra practice.

### SKILL 1: INTERPRET A HISTOGRAM

Use the histogram to answer Questions 1 and 2. It represents a distribution of the toll required (in cents) at various toll booths on American roads.

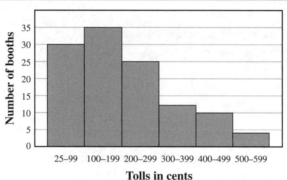

1. What range of tolls is most common?

2. How many toll booths have a toll $4 or more?

### SKILL 2: PROBABILITY AND PERCENT CHANCE

3. If there's a 12% chance of a hurricane making landfall in Florida this year, what's the probability of that occurring?

### SKILL 3: ESTIMATE AN ENCLOSED AREA

4. If the area enclosed by all boxes in the histogram above is 15 square centimeters, estimate the area enclosed by the first two boxes.

### SKILL 4: FIND PERCENT OF A WHOLE

5. There are 712 people watching a play in a theater with 850 seats. What percentage of the seats are filled?

# Lesson 4-6  Just a Normal Day  (Normal Distributions and Z Scores)

## LEARNING OBJECTIVES

☐ 1. Recognize characteristics of data that are normally distributed.

☐ 2. Understand the connection between area under a normal curve, percentage, and probability.

☐ 3. Make an educated guess about the empirical rule, then use the rule to calculate percentages and probabilities.

☐ 4. Compare data values from different sets using Z scores.

*To study the abnormal is the best way of understanding the normal.*
— William James

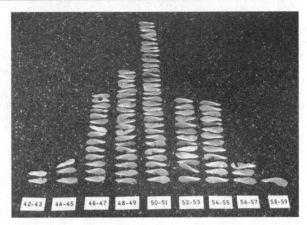

Courtesy of David Sobecki

If you grew up anywhere near maple trees, you're probably familiar with the seed pods they drop by the thousands in the spring. Like almost all living things, the individual pods vary in size—on any given tree, there's a typical size, with some pods bigger and some smaller.

On a beautiful spring day, I gathered 100 pods from the maple in my back yard, measured each, then grouped them according to their length. The smallest was 42 mm, the largest 59 mm, and in the photo they're grouped in classes 42–43, 44–45, 46–47, etc. An interesting thing happened—we see that the largest number of pods have lengths somewhere in the middle of the range, and the classes further away from the center have less pods. A wide variety of quantities in our world tend to exhibit this same phenomenon. In fact, it's so common that frequency distributions of this type came to be known as *normal distributions*. That means that if we get really good at studying normal distributions, we'll be able to analyze tons of interesting things in our world.

**0.** After reading the opening paragraphs, what do you think the main topic of this lesson will be?

## 4-6  Class

**1.** List some things that you think might be normally distributed. Try not to focus strictly on physical sizes.

*Answers vary. You'll probably want to pitch in on this one.*

Suppose a researcher selects a random sample of 100 adult women, measures their heights, and constructs a histogram. The researcher would probably get a graph similar to the one shown below.

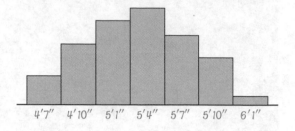

> Histograms were introduced in the Applications for Lesson 4-1. If you haven't discussed those questions, now would be a good time to go over them and talk about histograms.

**2.** Notice that we omitted a scale on the horizontal axis. Put in a scale that you think seems reasonable based on the description of this histogram. What do you think the value right in the middle of the horizontal axis represents?

*Sample answers shown. Inches are the better way to label, but most students will probably think in terms of feet, which is fine. The value in the middle should represent the mean height.*

Next, the researcher decides to go big or go home, and she chooses "big." She dramatically increases the number of women in the sample, and since she has more data to go on, makes the classes narrower as well. Happy with the results, she adds even more women to her sample, and makes the classes even narrower. The results would most likely look like the next two graphs.

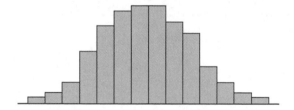 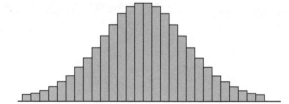

**3.** Now let's use some imagination. Suppose that our researcher has magical powers, and can continue adding data and improving her histogram until there are infinitely many data points. Wow, that's a lot. Instead of drawing boxes, draw a smooth curve that you think the histogram would become in the long run.

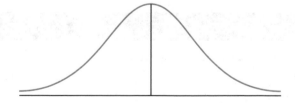

**4.** If all went well, you've just drawn your first normal probability distribution. (We'll see plenty of examples in the remainder of the lesson if you're unsure how well you did.) How does the drawing relate to the maple seed pod example from the opening paragraphs of this lesson?

*The shape is very similar. It shows that the greatest number of women will have heights somewhere close to the mean, and as you go outward to larger and smaller heights, there will be fewer women at those heights.*

To show that normal distributions are not even close to a purely mathematical topic, we're going to borrow our definition of normal distribution from an investment site called "Investopedia":

A probability distribution that plots all of its values in a symmetrical fashion and most of the results are situated around the probability's mean is called a **normal distribution.** Values are equally likely to plot either above or below the mean. Grouping takes place at values that are close to the mean and then tails off symmetrically away from the mean.

Next, we'll highlight some of the important features of a normal distribution (which, in turn, give us the key features of a data set that is normally distributed).

- The value in the middle of the distribution, which appears most often in the sample, is the mean.
- The distribution is symmetric about the mean. This means that the graph has two halves that are mirror images on either side of the mean value.
- (This is the key fact): The area under any portion of the curve is the percentage (in decimal form) of data values that fall between the values that begin and end that region.

Let's explore that last key point, because it's what makes normal distributions so useful in analyzing data. The graph below shows a normal distribution for heights of women in the United States. The numbers on the horizontal axis are heights in inches, and some areas are labeled for reference.

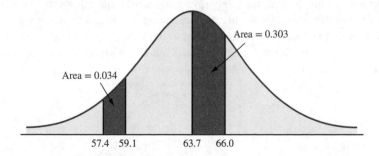

**5.** What is the mean height for American women?

*63.7 inches*

**6.** What percentage of American women are between 57.4 inches and 59.1 inches tall?

*3.4%*

**7.** If there are 31,806 women in the stands for a college football game, how many of them would you expect to be between 63.7 and 66.0 inches tall?

*30.3% of 31,806 is 9,637.*

> Good teaching moment: Discuss when it is and is not appropriate to include decimal parts of percent calculations. I'll bet you five American dollars that many of the students will answer 9,637.218. Feel free to make fun of them for including leftover body parts.

## Did You Get It

Try this problem to see if you understand the concepts we just studied. The answer can be found at the bottom of the portfolio page.

1. What percentage of American women are taller than 66 inches? (Hint: Half of all women are taller than 63.7 inches.)

So now we know that if we have data values that are normally distributed, and IF we can find the area under portions of the graph, we can find the percentage of data values that fall in a certain range. That leads to the big question: HOW in the world do you find areas under the graph? In this lesson, we'll rely on a known rule that allows us to quickly find a range in which most of the data values fall. It's known as the *empirical rule*. Before seeing the rule, let's make some educated guesses.

According to recent research, the mean height for women in the U.S. is 63.7 inches (which you already knew, right?), and the standard deviation is 2.7 inches. The normal graph below is marked with the mean and heights that are one and two standard deviations above and below the mean.

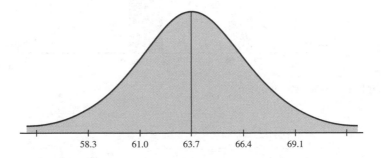

8. The total shaded area under the entire graph is 1, and this is true for ANY normal distribution. Explain why. Think carefully about what we know regarding area under a normal curve.

   *The area under any portion of the curve gives us the percentage of data values that fall within the vertical boundaries. If you look at the area under the entire curve, that should give you the percentage of values that fall somewhere between −∞ and +∞. Clearly, this is all values, or 100%. In decimal form, that's 1.*

9. Make an educated guess as to what percentage of the total shaded area is between 61.0 and 66.4. What does this tell us about women's heights?

   *Answers vary. In any case, what it tells us is the percentage of women in the population between 61.0 and 66.4 inches in height.*

10. Based on your answer to Question 9, estimate the percentage of area between 63.7 and 66.4 inches.

    *Whatever the student's answer to Question 9 is, this one should be half as much.*

11. Now make an educated guess on the percentage of total shaded area between 58.3 and 69.1 inches.

    *Answers vary. The actual percentage, of course, is about 95%.*

> Ask students to write their estimates for percentages on the board, then see how they did when the empirical rule is introduced.

Now it's time to see how you did.

## The Empirical Rule

When data are normally distributed, approximately 68% of the values are within 1 standard deviation of the mean, approximately 95% are within 2 standard deviations of the mean, and approximately 99.7% are within 3 standard deviations of the mean.

The graph to the right shows an illustration of the empirical rule. Recall that $\overline{X}$ is the mean, and $s$ is the standard deviation.

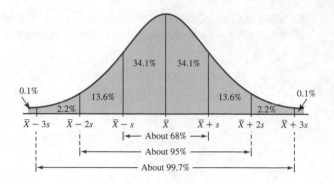

Man, I love M&M's. Can't get enough of them. When I buy a bag, the LAST thing I want is to get shorted. So how many M&M's is enough? According to a fascinating post on joshmadison.com, the mean number of M&M's in a standard vending machine bag is 54.6, with a standard deviation of 1.3.

12. Assuming that the number of M&M's per package is normally distributed (which, by the way, it more than likely is), fill in the blanks in the diagram below, which represents the distribution of M&M's in a standard package. Think number of M&M's.

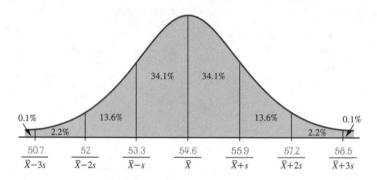

> **Math Note**
>
> In case you're wondering, to get the M&M data, some dude hand-counted over 2,600 M&M's from 48 packages. And I say "Good for him!"

13. If you buy 1,000 packages of M&M's (a number I assure you I've surpassed in my lifetime), how many bags would you expect to have between 53 and 56 M&M's in it?

*This should be roughly 68.2% of the bags, which would be 0.682 · 1,000 = 682.*

14. It's likely that over 99% of all bags have between ___50___ and ___59___ M&M's in them.

15. What percentage of bags would you expect to have at least 55 M&M's in them?

*Pretty close to half of them. You'd expect half to have more than 54.6, and since you can't have 0.6 M&M's, that would mean half should have 55 or more.*

16. What percentage of bags have less than 52 M&M's? How bad would that stink if you got one?

    *About 2.3%, and it would be devastating.*

17. How unusual would it be to get a bag with more than 58 M&M's, or less than 52? Explain.

    *It would be pretty unusual. These amounts cover the regions below 2 standard deviations under the mean and above 3 standard deviations above the mean. Collectively, this area is about 2.4% of the total area, meaning that less than 2.5% of all bags should have less than 52 or more than 58 M&M's.*

## Did You Get It?

Try this problem to see if you understand the concepts we just studied. The answer can be found at the bottom of the portfolio page.

2. Normal distributions are very commonly used for quality control in manufacturing. For example, a manufacturer of light bulbs would surely be interested in studying how long their bulbs last. In one case, the lifetime of one model of light bulb is normally distributed and has a mean $\mu = 1,600$ hours and a standard deviation of $\sigma = 300$ hours. What percentage of bulbs would you expect to last longer than 1,900 hours?

## 4-6   Group

The quantities we can study in relation to the normal distribution—things like sizes of seed pods, heights of human beings, and the number of M&Ms in a bag—are further examples of random variables (which we defined back in Lesson 3-5).

   If you're really sharp, you may have thought about the connection between the the percentages we've been calculating in this lesson and probability. If you haven't we're going to ask you to do so now. (There's a good reason that the normal is called a probability distribution, not a percentage distribution.)

1. Using what we know about area under a normal curve and percentage of data values, what does the area under the curve between two data values tell us about probability for a random variable?

    *It gives us EXACTLY the probability that a randomly selected data value will fall between those two values. We know we get the decimal form of the percent chance, which is the same thing as the probability.*

> This is a key idea in this lesson, so make sure that you circulate to all groups and check that they're clear on how to use area to find probabilities.

**2.** Based on the work you did earlier, what's the probability that the next bag of M&M's you get from a vending machine will have either 56 or 57 M&M's in it? Briefly describe how you got your answer.

*The probability is about 0.136. Those numbers cover all the possibilities between 1 and 2 standard deviations above the mean, and the empirical rule tells us that about 13.6 % of the data should live in that range. This corresponds to a probability of 0.136.*

### Did You Get It?

Try this problem to see if you understand the concepts we just studied. The answer can be found at the bottom of the portfolio page.

3. Refer back to the light bulb manufacturer in Did You Get It 2. On the packaging for this particular bulb, the manufacturer lists the expected life of the bulb as 1,000 hours. If you buy one of those bulbs, find the probability that the manufacturer's claim will be true.

## Z Scores

As you probably know, there are two main companies that offer standardized college entrance exams, ACT and SAT. Since each has a completely different scoring scale, it's really difficult to compare the scores of students that took different exams.

**3.** Do you think that scores for these exams are normally distributed? Discuss.

*They are, but answers can vary.*

One way to compare statistics drawn from different populations is to compare how far above or below the mean they are. The Z score is a statistical measure that was designed to do exactly that.

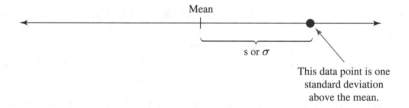

A Z score tells you how many standard deviations a data value is from the mean. The data value on the line above would have a Z score of 1 because it is 1 standard deviation above the mean. Data values that are below the mean would have negative Z scores.

**4.** Fill in the blanks in the diagram with Z scores, using the description at the bottom of the previous page.

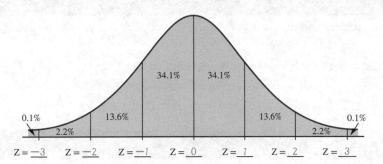

34.1%  34.1%

0.1%     13.6%          13.6%     0.1%
    2.2%                      2.2%

Z = $-3$   Z = $-2$   Z = $-1$   Z = $0$   Z = $1$   Z = $2$   Z = $3$

> Make sure that students have this diagram labeled correctly before moving on.

A standardized test of intelligence is scaled so that the mean IQ is 100, and the standard deviation is 15. We'll be using these facts for the next few questions.

**5.** Find the Z score for a person with an IQ of 85.

$-1$

**6.** Find the Z score for a person with an IQ of 115.

$1$

**7.** What's the probability that a randomly selected person has an IQ between 85 and 115?

*About 0.682*

**8.** If a data value has a Z score of ___0___, then half of the data are below that value, and half are above.

**9.** We know that the center of a normal distribution is the mean for a random variable. What does Question 8 tell you is also true about the center of the distribution?

*It's also the median! The fact that half of the data lives above and half lives below is the definition of median.*

**10.** A job applicant is told that their IQ score, measured in the screening process, is higher than 84% of the general population. What was their Z score, and their IQ?

*About 16% of the area is to the right of Z = 1, so their Z score is right around 1, making their IQ about 115.*

## Did You Get It

Try this problem to see if you understand the concepts we just studied. The answer can be found at the bottom of the portfolio page.

4. On a standardized IQ test, what's the Z score for a person with an IQ of 145?

## Computing Z Scores

For a data value from a sample with mean $\overline{X}$ and standard deviation $s$, or from a population with mean $\mu$ and standard deviation $\sigma$, the Z score is

$$Z = \frac{X - \overline{X}}{s} = \frac{X - \mu}{\sigma}$$

Some notes:

- A data point is greater than the mean if $z > 0$ and less than the mean if $z < 0$.
- Z scores have no units.
- Z scores are typically rounded to two decimal places.

One year the ACT had a mean score of 21.2 and a standard deviation of 5.1. That same year, the SAT had a mean score of 1,498 and a standard deviation of 347. Suppose that a scholarship committee is considering two students, one who scored 26 on the ACT and another who scored 1,800 on the SAT. Both are pretty good scores, but which one is better? That's not so easy to decide because the scales are totally different.

11. First instinct, which score sounds better to you?

*Opinion question, so answers vary.*

12. Find the Z score for each test score.

$$\text{ACT of 26: } Z = \frac{26 - 21.2}{5.1} = 0.94$$

$$\text{SAT of 1,800: } Z = \frac{1800 - 1,498}{347} = 0.87$$

### Math Note

Z scores are also used to approximate the area under any portion of a normal curve. This would allow you to compute probabilities more accurately than estimating based on the empirical rule.

**13.** Describe exactly what each Z score tells us.

*A Z score of 0.94 means that the ACT score of 26 was 0.94 standard deviations above the mean, while the Z score of 0.87 shows 1,800 on the SAT is 0.87 standard deviations above the mean.*

**14.** Based on the Z scores, which would you say was a better score? Why?

*The ACT score of 26 is better relative to other ACT scores, because it's further above the mean than the SAT of 1,800.*

## Did You Get It

Try this problem to see if you understand the concepts we just studied. The answer can be found at the bottom of the portfolio page.

5. I'm a 6′4″ male, and my wife is 5′10″. We're both pretty tall, but clearly I am taller. I can send you pictures if you don't believe me. Anyhow, based on Z scores, which of us is taller compared to the rest of our gender? (The mean and standard deviation for male heights in the U.S. are 69.1 in. and 2.9 in.)

Big sports fans tend to love arguing, and one of their favorite types of argument is "Who was better?" Michael or LeBron? Montana or Manning? Kershaw or Koufax? Blogs and airwaves are filled with arguments of this type. And what makes it so difficult to decide is that players and teams from different eras are hard to compare statistically because sports evolve, and what might have been an amazing statistic 50 years ago could be completely pedestrian today. Fortunately, this is EXACTLY the kind of thing that studying statistics analytically is good for.

The 1942 St. Louis Cardinals were an awesome baseball team. They won 106 games in an era when teams played only 154 games in a regular season. During the 1942 season, the mean number of games won by a National League team was 75.8 with a standard deviation of 20.5.

Another great Cardinals team was the 2004 squad, which won 105 out of 162 games. In 2004, the mean number of games won by a National League team was 80.9 with a standard deviation of 13.6.

© Associated Press

**15.** Based strictly on winning percentage (the percent of games won, that is), which was the better team?

*106/154 = 0.688, so the 1942 team won 68.8% of their games.*

*105/162 = 0.648, so the 2004 team won 64.8% of their games. That makes the 1942 team better in terms of winning percentage.*

16. Use information besides the winning percentages in the preceding paragraphs to make a good statistical argument about which team was better. Obviously, showing your work is a must. Write your final answer in the form of a few sentences, showing you know what you are talking about.

    *This question is intentionally left open-ended. Of course, any answer that doesn't compute and compare Z scores is no good. The Z scores work out to be*

    1942 team: $Z = \dfrac{106 - 75.8}{20.5} = 01.47$

    2004 team: $Z = \dfrac{105 - 80.9}{13.6} = 1.77$

17. Look back at your answer to Question 1 on the first page of this lesson. How did you do? Would you be able to come up with more examples now?

    *Answers vary.*

## 4-6 Portfolio

Name _____

Check each box when you've completed the task. Remember that your instructor will want you to turn in the portfolio pages you create.

### Technology

1. ☐ Spreadsheets can be used to efficiently do many comparisons between data values from different sets, because you can set up a formula to quickly calculate Z scores. The plan here is to build a Z score calculator that allows you to input mean and standard deviation for two different data sets, then use formulas to calculate the Z scores for different data values. In the template you can find in online resources for this lesson, there are a variety of ACT and SAT scores listed. Fill in the appropriate means and standard deviations from within the lesson, then use a formula to find Z scores and copy it down to find Z scores for all of the test scores for comparison. There are further instructions on the template.

### Online Practice

1. ☐ Include any written work from the online assignment along with any notes or questions about this lesson's content.

### Applications

1. ☐ Complete the applications problems.

### Reflections

Type a short answer to each question.

1. ☐ Describe a random variable that is normally distributed.
2. ☐ Why are measures of average and variation so important in studying normal distributions?
3. ☐ What's the connection between a normal distribution and probability?
4. ☐ In what setting are Z scores useful? Why?
5. ☐ Take another look at your answer to Question 0 at the beginning of this lesson. Would you change your answer now that you've finished the lesson? How would you summarize the topic of this lesson now?
6. ☐ What questions do you have about this lesson?

### Looking Ahead

1. ☐ Complete the Lesson 4-7 Prep Skills and read the opening paragraph in Lesson 4-7 carefully, then answer Question 0 in preparation for that lesson.

### Answers to "Did You Get It?"

**1.** 19.7%     **2.** About 16%     **3.** About 0.9765     **4.** 3     **5.** I am, by just a bit.

## 4-6   Applications

Name _____

The College Board reported that SAT scores in the early 2000s were normally distributed with mean 1,026 and standard deviation 210. Use this information for Questions 1–3.

1. Fill in the blanks in the diagram.

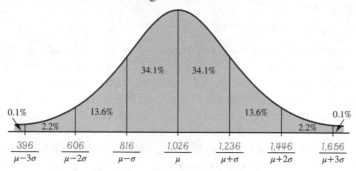

> **Math Note**
>
> Notice that in this case we're using $\mu$ and $\sigma$, which indicates that the mean and standard deviation are population, not sample, statistics.

2. What percentage of students scored over 606?

   About 97.7%

3. Out of every 500 students, how many would we expect to score between 816 and 1,236?

   About 68.2% of them, which is 341.

4. If a student from that era scored 1,400 on the SAT and her IQ was tested at 144, use Z scores to decide which test she did better on. Refer to Questions 5–10 in the Group portion of the lesson for information on IQ scores.

   $1{,}400$ SAT: $Z = \dfrac{1400 - 1026}{210} \approx 1.78$

   $144$ IQ: $Z = \dfrac{144 - 100}{15} \approx 2.93$

   She did MUCH better on the IQ test.

## 4-6 Applications

Name _____

According to 9monthsafter.com, the lengths of human pregnancies are normally distributed with mean 268 days and standard deviation 15 days. Use this for Questions 5–7.

**5.** Fill in the blanks in the diagram.

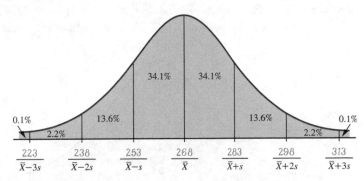

**6.** What is the probability that you were born more than 298 days after you were conceived?

*About 0.023.*

**7.** If a child is conceived on April 19, what is the probability that it will be born on or before January 27?

*11 days in April; 31 in May, July, August, October, and December; 30 in June, September, and November.*

$11 + 31 \cdot 5 + 30 \cdot 3 + 27 = 283.$ *Probability is 0.841.*

According to the label, a bag of Kettle brand Tias tortilla chips contains 8 ounces of chips. Suppose that the bagging process is normally distributed with a standard deviation of 0.14 ounce.

**8.** If the machine that does the bagging is set to put 8 ounces of chips in each bag, this would be the mean of the distribution, with standard deviation as mentioned above. What percentage of all bags would have less than the amount stated on the package in this case?

*50%*

**9.** Explain why it would be a bad idea for the manufacturer to set the bagging machine at 8 ounces.

*Half of every bag containing below the listed weight is a class-action lawsuit waiting to happen. At the very least, they risk a lot of unhappy customers.*

## 4-6 Applications

Name _____

10. If the manager wants there to be greater than a 97% chance that any given bag has at least 8 ounces, and the weight they set their filling machine for provides the mean weight, how should they set the machine? Complete the diagram as part of showing your work.

   *They would want 8 ounces to be at least 2 standard deviations below the mean, so that less than 3% of all bags will be likely to have less than 8 ounces. Two standard deviations below the mean would be 0.28 ounces, so he or she should set the machine to put 8.28 ounces in each bag.*

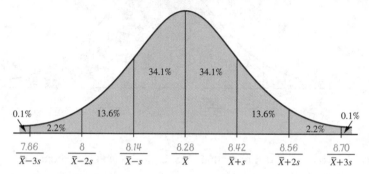

For Questions 11–14, we'll assume that the finishing times for a group of runners in a marathon race are likely to be normally distributed. The mean finish time for male marathon (26.2 miles) runners is 278.42 min with a standard deviation of 39.4 min. The mean finish time for female marathon runners is 294.45 min with a standard deviation of 39.9 min. At the 2014 Boston Marathon, Meb Keflezighi won the men's division with a time of 128.62 min and Rita Jeptoo won the women's division at 138.95 min.

11. Who finished faster, relative to their gender? Explain why. (Remember that in a race you want to finish in a short time.)

   $$\text{Meb: } Z = \frac{128.62 - 278.42}{39.4} \approx -3.80$$

   $$\text{Rita: } Z = \frac{138.95 - 294.45}{39.9} \approx -3.90$$

   *Rita's time is further below the mean than Meb's, so she had a better time relative to her gender than Meb did.*

## 4-6 Applications

Name _____

**12.** Out of 10,000 runners, where would you expect a woman who finishes in a time of 294.45 min to finish? Complete the diagram to help show your work.

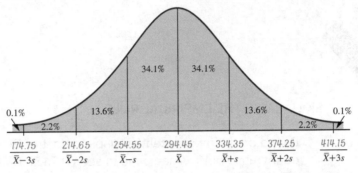

5,000th. Since 294.95 minutes is the mean, it's also the median, meaning half of the data values will be higher.

**13.** A man who finished in a time of three and a half hours would finish in the fastest __5__ percent of male racers. Complete the diagram to help you show your work. You'll have to make an estimate of area since that time doesn't correspond to one of the labeled times. (Interesting note after you have the percentage: This guy would finish well over an HOUR after the winner. Wow.) Hint: A time of 160.22 minutes means you're in the fastest 0.1%, so you finished before 99.9% of the runners.

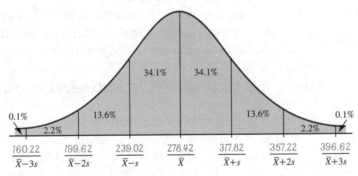

Three and a half hours, which is 210 minutes, is a fourth of the way between 199.62 and 239.02. Estimates will vary but any good answer at least has to be between 2.3% and 15.9%. I think something around 5% is a pretty good guess.

## Lesson 4-7   Prep Skills

This is a short review of skills that will come in handy in the next lesson. In each case, answer the question, then rate your confidence level by checking one of the boxes. If you feel like you're struggling with these skills, consult the online resources provided by your instructor for extra practice.

### SKILL 1: USE THE EMPIRICAL RULE

1. Based on the most recent available data, the Graduate Record Exam (GRE) quantitative portion had a mean score of 151.3 with a standard deviation of 8.7. What percentage of test-takers scored above 160?

2. The mean and standard deviation for the verbal portion were 150.8 and 8.5. In that year, 417,000 prospective grad students took the test. About how many scored between 133.8 and 159.3?

### SKILL 2: UNDERSTAND PERCENTILES

3. If a student got their GRE report and found that they scored in the 60th percentile, what does that mean?
   a.   They got 60% of the questions right.
   b.   60% of everyone that took the test did better than they did.
   c.   60% of everyone that took the test did worse than they did.
   d.   Six out of ten people taking the test earned a score similar to theirs.

### SKILL 3: USE TECHNOLOGY TO FIND MEAN AND STANDARD DEVIATION

4. Use either a graphing calculator or spreadsheet to find the mean and standard deviation of this list of GRE scores:
   133   133   137   138   139   140   140   142   144   144   145   146
   146   147   151   151   154   156   158   158   160   161   162   164

### SKILL 4: DRAW A HISTOGRAM

5. Draw a histogram for the score data above using six classes.

# Lesson 4-7 The Way the Cookie Crumbles (Applications of the Normal Distribution)

### LEARNING OBJECTIVES

☐ 1. Use normal distributions to find probabilities, percentages, and percentiles.

☐ 2. Learn how normal distributions are used in manufacturing and packaging.

☐ 3. Recognize data that are approximately normally distributed.

*I've never been very cookie cutter. If I choose something different from the status quo, it's my responsibility and my choice to live my life that way.*
—Sara Ramirez

© McGraw-Hill Education/John Flournoy, photographer

Surely there must be someone out there who doesn't like Oreos, but I haven't met him or her. A standard package of America's favorite cookie contains 510 grams of sweet temptation. Of course, when you buy a package, you expect every one of those 510 grams. But there's variation in just about everything, so some packages will have more than the intended weight, and some will have less. The folks running Nabisco aren't dummies, though—they know that if someone decides to check the weight and finds it to be less than 510 grams, they won't be a very happy customer. So what to do?

This is exactly the sort of situation where weights tend to be normally distributed. The company would likely design its production and packaging process so that the mean is somewhat larger than 510 grams, with a standard deviation that assures that the vast majority of packages will weigh at least 510 grams. We know a little bit about finding probability for random variables that are normally distributed. In this lesson, we'll learn a whole lot more and be able to carry out in-depth analysis on the related quantities.

**0.** After reading the opening paragraph, what do you think the main topic of this lesson will be?

## 4-7 Class

In Lesson 4-6, we were able to answer questions about the area under a normal curve because the values we were interested in just happened to be exactly 1, 2, or 3 standard deviations away from the mean. But what if we wanted to know how many men have heights that are between 1.2 and 1.8 standard deviations below the mean height? We'd need to be able to, find the area under the graph for that exact situation, which I can guarantee you is NOT easy. Worse still, if we then try to find how many people we'd expect to have an IQ between 1.2 and 1.8 standard deviations below the mean IQ, we're stuck with a similar problem, but the graph (and area calculations) will be different!

The point is that while all normally distributed data have the same general shape for their graph, areas under portions of the graph depend on how tall the curve is and how spread out it is. These characteristics in turn depend on what the mean and standard deviation are for that particular data set. This would require a different set of extremely difficult area calculations for every individual situation involving normally distributed data. Ouch!

Not to worry, though: The picture's not as grim as we've painted it. Statisticians found two ways to work around this problem. (1) Use tables. (2) Use technology. Using tables of Z scores and corresponding areas is a good way to get approximations for probabilities for normally distributed data. The areas have been calculated for a simple normal distribution with mean 0 and standard deviation 1; then a procedure was developed to apply those areas to other distributions.

Graphing calculators, spreadsheets, and other statistical software can perform these calculations easily and accurately. The user is left with the important part—interpreting the results. We'll develop the process for using a table, then show how to use technology and leave it up to your professor to decide which method to use.

## The Standard Normal Distribution

The special distribution used for tables is called the **standard normal distribution,** which is a normal distribution that has mean 0 and standard deviation 1. The standard normal distribution is shown below. The values under the curve, which should look very familiar, indicate the proportion of area in each section. For example, the area between the mean and 1 standard deviation above or below the mean is about 0.341, or 34.1%. Of course, these percentages come from the empirical rule, which we studied in Lesson 4-6.

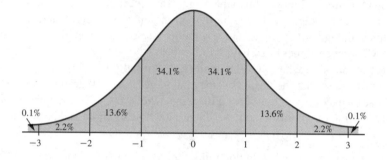

1. Now back to cookies, and not a moment too soon in my opinion. If the weights of Oreos in a package are normally distributed with mean 518 grams and standard deviation 4 grams, what percentage of packages will weigh less than the stated weight of 510 grams?

   *510 grams is two standard deviations below the mean, so only about 2.3% of packages will weigh less than 510 grams.*

   > Students may remember this question if they used our book *Pathways to Math Literacy*. If so, you can let them know that we'll be able to study the packaging in much greater depth than we did using only the empirical rule.

We were able to answer Question 1 without doing any calculations because we know the empirical rule, and because the weight we're interested in just happens to be exactly 2 standard deviations away from the mean. But what if the plant manager were interested in the probability that a package had a weight between 520 and 527 grams? Those weights don't correspond to whole-number multiples of the standard deviation away from the mean. So at the moment the best we could do is make a rough estimate of area from looking at the graph. I believe that we should be able to do better than a rough guess, so let's make it happen.

2. Based on the mean and standard deviation described in Question 1, label the normal graph on the next page with the appropriate weights.

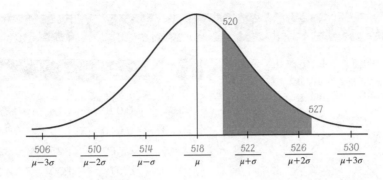

3. Label the two weights we're interested in (520 and 527 grams), and draw vertical bars from the axis along the bottom up to the normal curve. Then shade the area in between. This is the area we want, as it will give us the probability that a package weighs between 520 and 527 grams.

4. Find the Z score for each of those weights.

For 520 grams: $\dfrac{520 - 518}{4} = 0.5$

For 527 grams: $\dfrac{527 - 518}{4} = 2.25$

5. Use the table on page 418 to determine the area between 0 and the Z score associated with 520 grams.

A = 0.192

6. Use the table on page 418 to determine the area between 0 and the Z score associated with 527 grams.

A = 0.488

7. What do you need to do to these two areas to find the area we're looking for? Use the graph as a guide.

They need to be subtracted. The shaded area is the area between 0 and 527 grams with the portion between 0 and 520 grams thrown out.

8. Now you should be ready to answer the question. What is the probability that a randomly selected package of Oreos would weigh between 520 and 527 grams?

0.488 − 0.192 = 0.296

## Area Under a Normal Distribution Curve

The value in the *A* column of the table is the area under the standard normal curve between Z = 0 and each given positive value of Z.

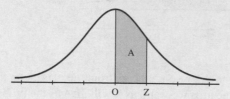

If you need the area for a Z score that isn't listed in this table, you can get an approximate area by choosing an area between areas in the table. In a bit, we'll learn how to use technology to get more accurate areas.

**Important notes:**

1. The area under any normal curve is divided into two equal halves at the mean. Each of the halves has area 0.500.

2. The area between Z = 0 and a positive Z score is the same as the area between Z = 0 and the negative of that Z score.

These facts are both consequences of the fact that normal distributions are symmetric about the mean.

| Z | A | Z | A | Z | A |
|------|-------|------|-------|-------|-------|
| 0.00 | 0.000 | 1.10 | 0.364 | 2.20 | 0.486 |
| 0.05 | 0.020 | 1.15 | 0.375 | 2.25 | 0.488 |
| 0.10 | 0.040 | 1.20 | 0.385 | 2.30 | 0.489 |
| 0.15 | 0.060 | 1.25 | 0.394 | 2.35 | 0.491 |
| 0.20 | 0.079 | 1.30 | 0.403 | 2.40 | 0.492 |
| 0.25 | 0.099 | 1.35 | 0.412 | 2.45 | 0.493 |
| 0.30 | 0.118 | 1.40 | 0.419 | 2.50 | 0.494 |
| 0.35 | 0.137 | 1.45 | 0.427 | 2.55 | 0.495 |
| 0.40 | 0.155 | 1.50 | 0.433 | 2.60 | 0.495 |
| 0.45 | 0.174 | 1.55 | 0.439 | 2.65 | 0.496 |
| 0.50 | 0.192 | 1.60 | 0.445 | 2.70 | 0.497 |
| 0.55 | 0.209 | 1.65 | 0.451 | 2.75 | 0.497 |
| 0.60 | 0.226 | 1.70 | 0.455 | 2.80 | 0.497 |
| 0.65 | 0.242 | 1.75 | 0.460 | 2.85 | 0.498 |
| 0.70 | 0.258 | 1.80 | 0.464 | 2.90 | 0.498 |
| 0.75 | 0.273 | 1.85 | 0.468 | 2.95 | 0.498 |
| 0.80 | 0.288 | 1.90 | 0.471 | 3.00 | 0.499 |
| 0.85 | 0.302 | 1.95 | 0.474 | 3.05 | 0.499 |
| 0.90 | 0.316 | 2.00 | 0.477 | 3.10 | 0.499 |
| 0.95 | 0.329 | 2.05 | 0.480 | 3.15 | 0.499 |
| 1.00 | 0.341 | 2.10 | 0.482 | 3.20 | 0.499 |
| 1.05 | 0.353 | 2.15 | 0.484 | 3.25* | 0.499 |

*For Z scores greater than 3.25, use A = 0.500.

## Did You Get It

Try this problem to see if you understand the concepts we just studied. The answer can be found at the bottom of the portfolio page.

1. Use the table to find the probability that a package of Oreos weighs less than 512 grams. Report the Z score you used as well.

## Using Technology: Computing Probabilities from a Normal Distribution

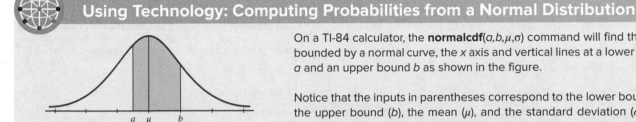

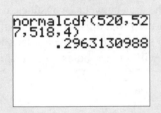

On a TI-84 calculator, the **normalcdf**($a,b,\mu,\sigma$) command will find the area bounded by a normal curve, the *x* axis and vertical lines at a lower bound *a* and an upper bound *b* as shown in the figure.

Notice that the inputs in parentheses correspond to the lower bound (*a*), the upper bound (*b*), the mean ($\mu$), and the standard deviation ($\sigma$). This eliminates the need to calculate Z scores: you just need the mean and standard deviation for the given random variable.

The normalcdf is used to find the probability that a given random variable takes any value between the lower and upper bounds. The screen shot shows a calculation for the probability that a package of Oreos weighs between 520 and 527 grams.

*See the Lesson 4-7-1 Using Tech video in class resources for further information.*

In order to use technology effectively, it's important to understand exactly what it's built to do. In this case, the calculator is built to have the user input two values for the random variable in addition to the mean and standard deviation. It calculates the probability that the random variable will be between those two values. If we want to find a probability that doesn't have two boundaries, like the probability that a package weighs more than 525 grams, we'll need to be clever.

9. Shade the area on the graph that corresponds to the probability that a package weighs more than 525 grams.

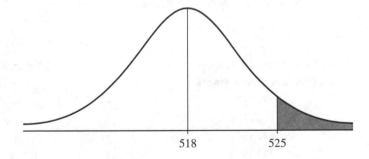

**10.** Use a calculator to find the probability that a package weighs between 525 and 540 grams. Round to six decimal places.

normalcdf(525, 540, 518, 4) = 0.040059

**11.** Use a calculator to find the probability that a package weighs between 525 and 1,000,000 grams. Round to six decimal places.

normalcdf(525, 1,000,000, 518, 4) = 0.040059

**12.** What can you conclude about a strategy for finding areas that only have one boundary using the **normalcdf** function?

You choose an upper or lower bound that's so high or low that no value is likely to be above or below it, then use the regular function with two boundaries.

Excel is set up to calculate normal probabilities differently. Instead of calculating the area between two values, it calculates the area to the LEFT of any value. This works fabulously well if you're interested in the probability of a randomly selected value being LESS than some number. For other types of probability, we'll need to do some arithmetic. First let's look at the syntax. The samples at the bottom show calculations for weights we've studied so far, with the formulas entered shown in the second graphic.

## Using Technology: Computing Probabilities from a Normal Distribution

The Excel command is =NORM.DIST. When you start typing =NORM.DIST in Excel here's what appears, as a guide to help you:

= NORM.DIST(x, mean, standard_dev, cumulative), where
- x is a value of the random variable.
- mean is the mean for the distribution.
- standard_dev is the standard deviation for the distribution.
- cumulative = TRUE; we won't use FALSE in this book.

|   | A | B |
|---|---|---|
| 1 | **X** | **Probability that a package weighs less than X grams** |
| 2 | 510 | 0.022750132 |
| 3 | 520 | 0.691462461 |
| 4 | 527 | 0.987775527 |
| 5 | 525 | 0.959940843 |

|   | A | B |
|---|---|---|
| 1 | **X** | **Probability that a package weighs less than X grams** |
| 2 | 510 | =NORM.DIST(A2,518,4,TRUE) |
| 3 | 520 | =NORM.DIST(A3,518,4,TRUE) |
| 4 | 527 | =NORM.DIST(A4,518,4,TRUE) |
| 5 | 525 | =NORM.DIST(A5,518,4,TRUE) |

*See the Lesson 4-7-2 Using Tech video in class resources for further information.*

Whether you are using tables or some form of technology, the best way to proceed with any of these problems is to start by drawing a graph. Don't ignore your graph when writing your final answer! As long as you keep in mind that the total area under the distribution is 1, you can visually check if your answer is reasonable.

13. Look back at the drawing you shaded on page 417. The Excel screen grabs on page 420 show the area under the normal curve up to each of 520 grams and 527 grams. Devise a strategy that uses that information to find the probability that a package weighs between 520 and 527 grams. You can use your answer from Question 8 to check that your strategy worked. (You can round all values to three decimal places.) Show your work please!

*The area between those two boundaries is the area up to 527 minus the area up to 520. Using values from the spreadsheet, we get 0.988 − 0.691 = 0.297. This is very close to what we got in Question 8.*

In Questions 14–17, find each area under the standard normal distribution to practice what we've learned so far. Use as many methods as you'd like (tables, calculator, Excel). Remember that "standard normal" means that the mean is 0 and the standard deviation is 1. We'll shade the figures for the first two: after that, it's up to you.

14. Between $Z = -1.75$ and $Z = 1.50$

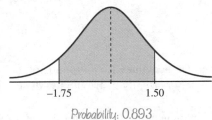

*Probability: 0.893*

15. To the right of $Z = 1.70$

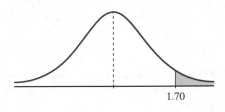

*Probability: 0.045*

16. To the left of $Z = -2.20$

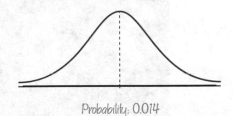

*Probability: 0.014*

17. To the left of $Z = 1.95$.

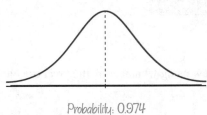

*Probability: 0.974*

Answers could vary just a bit depending on the method used. I used a TI-84 with 10 or −10 as upper or lower boundaries for one-sided regions.

Try this problem to see if you understand the concepts we just studied. The answer can be found at the bottom of the portfolio page.

2. Find the area under the standard normal distribution

   a. Between $Z = -3.2$ and $Z = -2.0$.
   b. Between $Z = -0.55$ and $Z = 1.6$.
   c. To the right of $Z = 0.25$.
   d. To the left of $Z = 0.1$.

## 4-7    Group

1. How many pounds of trash do you think you personally generate in one year? Discuss with your group and see how your guesses compare.

*Answers vary.*

Based on data in the 2012 Statistical Abstract of the United States, the average American generates 1,570 pounds of garbage per year. We'll assume that the number of pounds generated per person is approximately normally distributed with standard deviation 200 pounds.

In Questions 2–4, let's work on finding the probability that a randomly selected person generates between 1,250 and 2,050 pounds of garbage per year.

2. Draw and label a figure to represent the area we need to find.

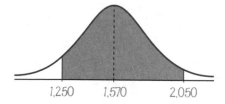

3. Find the area you drew using whatever method makes you happy.

*The area is 0.937.*

© Photodisc/Getty Images RF

**4.** Write a sentence or two describing exactly what your answer to Question 3 means.

*This tells us that if a person is selected at random, the probability that he or she generates between 1,250 and 2,050 pounds of garbage per year is 0.937. Or, if you like, there's a 93.7% chance that he or she generates an amount in that range.*

In Questions 5–7, let's work on finding the probability that a randomly selected person generates more than 2,050 pounds of garbage per year. When you interpret the area you find, think about how likely it is to find someone who generates that many pounds of garbage per year.

**5.** Draw and label a figure to represent the area we need to find.

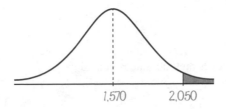

1,570     2,050

**6.** Find the area you drew using whatever method makes you happy.

*The area is 0.008.*

**7.** Interpret your answer from Question 6.

*The probability that a randomly selected person generates more than 2,050 pounds of garbage per year is 0.008, or 0.8%. This is less than one person out of 100 people, so you're not very likely to come across many people that generate that much trash.*

**Did You Get It**

Try this problem to see if you understand the concepts we just studied. The answer can be found at the bottom of the portfolio page.

3. The Statistical Abstract also indicates that of the 1,570 pounds of garbage generated by the average individual, 872 pounds will end up in a landfill. If these amounts are approximately normally distributed with standard deviation 160 pounds, find the probability that a randomly selected person generates

   a. Less than 600 pounds that end up in a landfill.
   b. Between 600 and 1,000 pounds that end up in a landfill.

The American Automobile Association reports that the average time it takes to respond to an emergency call is 25 minutes. It would be reasonable to assume that the response time is approximately normally distributed. Let's suppose that the standard deviation is 4.5 minutes.

In Questions 8–10, we'll work on finding the approximate number of calls out of 80 randomly selected calls that will have response times less than 15 minutes.

© Jeremy Hoare/Life File/Getty Images RF

**8.** Draw and label a figure to represent the area we need to find.

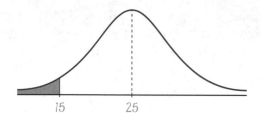

**9.** Find the area you drew using whatever method makes you happy.

*The area is about 0.013.*

**10.** Interpret your answer from Question 9. Reread the paragraph above Question 8, and think carefully about how you write your final answer.

*An area of 0.013 tells us that 1.3% of calls will have a response time of less than 15 minutes. Multiply the percentage by the number of calls in our sample: 1.3% of 80 calls = 0.013 · 80 = 1.04. About one call in 80 will have response time less than 15 minutes (1.04 calls doesn't make sense).*

Based on what we know so far, if the response time for one emergency call is 30 minutes, is that fast or slow? One way to answer that is to look at the percentile rank for 30 minutes, which we'll do in Questions 11–13.

**11.** Draw and label a figure to represent the area we need to find.

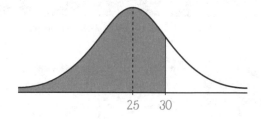

**12.** Find the area you drew using whatever method makes you happy.

*The area is about 0.867.*

**13.** Based on your answer to Question 12, in what percentile is a response time of 30 minutes? Explain your answer, and describe what this say about how good or bad that time is.

*An area of 0.864 means that 86.4% of calls will get a response time of less than 30 minutes, so the time of 30 minutes is in the 86th percentile. That puts a response time of 30 minutes in the slowest 14% of all calls, so that's not very good at all.*

## Did You Get It

Try this problem to see if you understand the concepts we just studied. The answer can be found at the bottom of the portfolio page.

4. The mean for a reading test given nationwide is 80, and the standard deviation is 8. The random variable is normally distributed. If 10,000 students take the test, find each.

   a. The number of students who will score above 90
   b. The number of students who will score between 78 and 88
   c. The percentile of a student who scores 94

The random variables we've studied so far in this lesson are described as being normally distributed. But how would you know that if you were gathering raw data? One way is to draw a histogram and see if it's bell-shaped, or close to it.

A random sample of 25 entrées served by a college cafeteria is tested to find the number of calories per serving, with the data in the list below.

| 845 | 460 | 620 | 752 | 683 | 1,088 | 785 | 575 | 580 |
|-----|-----|-----|-----|-----|-------|-----|-----|-----|
| 755 | 720 | 650 | 512 | 945 | 672 | 526 | 1,050 | 725 |
| 822 | 740 | 773 | 812 | 880 | 911 | 910 | | |

**14.** Draw a histogram for the data using the classes shown below.

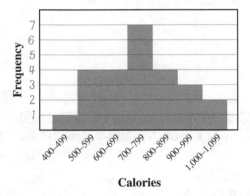

**15.** Based on your histogram, do the data appear to be normally distributed? Explain.

*The histogram doesn't look exactly like a normal curve, but it's close enough that it would be reasonable to guess that the data are approximately normally distributed. With only 25 data values, it would be silly to expect something that looks exactly bell-shaped.*

> Good opportunity here to point out that more data is better! It's tough to draw solid conclusions from a small data set.

**16.** Find the mean and standard deviation for the data. Technology strongly recommended.

*The mean is 751.6 and the standard deviation is 160.7.*

**17.** If the mean and standard deviation from the sample are reasonable values for the mean and standard deviation of all entrées served by that cafeteria, and we assume that the number of calories in all of the entrees are normally distributed, what percentage of their entrées have more than 700 calories? Include a sketch in your answer, please.

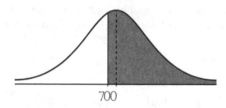

700

*The shaded area works out to be 0.626, so we can conclude that about 63% of entrees will have more than 700 calories.*

---

**Did You Get It** ?

Try this problem to see if you understand the concepts we just studied. The answer can be found at the bottom of the portfolio page.

5. The ages of 33 randomly selected inmates at a county jail are shown in the list.

18   18   20   24   26   26   27   29   30   30   31   33   34   34   36   37   37
38   38   38   39   41   42   42   43   43   46   47   49   49   52   54   55

Draw a histogram to show that the ages are approximately normally distributed, then find the mean and standard deviation and use that information to find how many of the jail's 1,148 inmates are likely to be under the age of 21.

## 4-7 Portfolio

Name _____

Check each box when you've completed the task. Remember that your instructor will want you to turn in the portfolio pages you create.

### Technology

1. ☐ We learned three methods for finding the area under a portion of a normal curve in this lesson, and for the most part when solving problems you're welcome to use the method you feel most comfortable with. However, in this assignment you'll need to do at least two of the questions in the Applications portion using Excel commands, then submit the spreadsheet you used to your instructor. So that's good news: In doing the Technology homework, by default you'll be working on Applications as well. You're welcome.

### Online Practice

1. ☐ Include any written work from the online assignment along with any notes or questions about this lesson's content.

### Applications

1. ☐ Complete the applications problems.

### Reflections

Type a short answer to each question.

1. ☐ Given a data set, how could you decide if the distribution of the data was approximately normal?
2. ☐ When you know that a random variable is approximately normally distributed, what do you need to find in order to calculate probabilities of the variable being in some range?
3. ☐ What are some advantages of using technology to find areas under a normal curve?
4. ☐ Take another look at your answer to Question 0 at the beginning of this lesson. Would you revise your answer now that you've completed the lesson? How would you summarize the topic of this lesson now?
5. ☐ What questions do you have about this lesson?

### Looking Ahead

1. ☐ Complete the Lesson 4-8 Prep Skills and read the opening paragraph in Lesson 4-8 carefully, then answer Question 0 in preparation for that lesson.

### Answers to "Did You Get It?"

1. $Z = -1.5$, probability is 0.067    2. **a.** 0.022    **b.** 0.654    **c.** 0.401    **d.** 0.540
3. **a.** 0.045    **b.** 0.743    4. **a.** 1,056    **b.** 4,400    **c.** 96th percentile
5. Histogram omitted; the mean is 36.5, the standard deviation is 10.0, and about 70 inmates would likely be under 21.

## 4-7   Applications

Name _____

For Questions 1–5, the average life of a brand of automobile tires is 30,000 miles, with a standard deviation of 2,000 miles. Assume the life of this brand of tire is normally distributed. If a tire is selected and tested, find the probability that it will have the given lifetime. Drawings are recommended, but it's up to you.

**1.** Greater than 30,000 miles

0.5

**2.** Greater than 35,000 miles

0.0062

**3.** Less than 33,000 miles

0.933

© Ingram Publishing/Alamy RF

**4.** Between 27,000 and 32,000 miles

0.775

**5.** If you worked at a tire shop, would you expect to see many sets of these tires that lasted 40,000 miles? Why or why not? Make sure your answer is backed up with math! Show the details.

You surely would not. The probability of a set lasting more than 40,000 miles is less than 0.0000003; less than 3 in 10 million sets will last that long.

## 4-7 Applications

Name _____

For Questions 6 and 7, the average waiting time at a local restaurant is 9.2 minutes, with a standard deviation of 2.6 minutes. When a customer arrives at the restaurant, find the probability that the customer will have to wait the given time. Assume the wait time is normally distributed.

**6.** Between 5 and 10 minutes

0.568

**7.** Less than 6 minutes or more than 9 minutes

Less than 6 minutes: $P = 0.109$

More than 9 minutes: $P = 0.531$

One or the other: $0.109 + 0.531 = 0.640$

**8.** For an advertised promotion, the manager of the restaurant decides to give a free appetizer to anyone waiting longer than 12 minutes. Was this a good idea? What percent of customers will be receiving an appetizer?

P(longer than 12 minutes) $= 0.141$. Probably not a great idea: they're giving away food to a little more than 14% of customers.

**9.** Suppose his team is able to cut the mean wait time down to 7.0 minutes with a standard deviation of 2.1 minutes. If he offers the same promotion, how many customers out of every 100 will get a free appetizer?

P(longer than 12 minutes) $\approx 0.009$. Now less than 1 of every 100 customers will get a free appetizer.

For Questions 10 and 11, the average time a person spends in each visit to a certain online social networking service is 62 minutes. The standard deviation is 12 minutes. If a visitor is selected at random, find the probability that he or she will stay on the networking service for the amount of time shown. Assume the times are normally distributed.

**10.** At least 180 minutes

This probability is so tiny that it's essentially zero: it works out to be about $4 \cdot 10^{-23}$.

**4-7**   **Applications**

Name _____

**11.** At least 50 minutes

0.841

**12.** Suppose that your grades have been slipping, and you impose a new rule on yourself: no more than 30 minutes at a time on social networking sites. What percentile would that put you in for this particular site?

P(less than 30) = 0.0038, so only 0.38% of all users will be on for less time than that. That puts you in the first percentile.

**13.** If you just can't stay away from social media as much as you planned and end up spending 45 minutes at a time, what would be the change in percentile rank from your answer in Question 12?

P(less than 45) = 0.078, so only 7.8% of all users will be on for less time than that. That puts you in the eighth percentile, and your rank went up by seven places.

A researcher is studying reaction times in adult subjects who are alcohol-impaired in an effort to study the effects of impairment on driving. The amount of time in seconds that 25 randomly selected adults took to react to a stimulus when they have a blood alcohol level of 0.08 was recorded and is displayed below. Use this information for Questions 14–18.

1.2   1.5   1.6   1.6   1.7   1.9   2.0   2.1   2.1   2.2   2.2   2.2   2.3
2.4   2.4   2.5   2.5   2.7   2.8   2.8   2.8   3.0   3.1   3.3   3.5

**14.** Build a frequency distribution for the data using five classes.

| Class | Frequency |
|-------|-----------|
| 1–1.5 | 2 |
| 1.6–2.1 | 7 |
| 2.2–2.7 | 9 |
| 2.8–3.3 | 6 |
| 3.4–3.9 | 1 |

## 4-7  Applications

Name _____

**15.** Draw a histogram for the data, and use it to explain why it's reasonable to assume that reaction times for all impaired adults would be normally distributed.

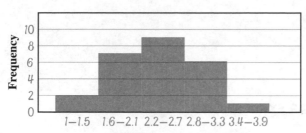

**Reaction time in seconds**

The histogram shows a shape very similar to a normal distribution. Also, this is the type of human characteristic that tends to be normally distributed, as we've seen.

**16.** Find the mean and standard deviation. Again, technology is pretty much a must.

Mean is about 2.3, standard deviation is about 0.6.

**17.** Assuming that reaction times are normally distributed, find the probability that a randomly selected driver with a blood alcohol level of 0.08 will take less than 1.5 seconds to react.

P(less than 1.5 seconds) ≈ 0.091

**18.** Find the probability that a randomly selected driver with a blood alcohol level of 0.08 will take between 2 and 4 seconds to react.

P(between 2 and 4 seconds) ≈ 0.689

# Lesson 4-8    Prep Skills

This is a short review of skills that will come in handy in the next lesson. In each case, answer the question, then rate your confidence level by checking one of the boxes. If you feel like you're struggling with these skills, consult the online resources provided by your instructor for extra practice.

### SKILL 1: EVALUATE A LINEAR EXPRESSION

1. For the equation $y = 4.3x - 7.2$, find the value of $y$ when:

$x = 10$

$x = 40$

$x = 19.2$

### SKILL 2: EVALUATE A LINEAR EXPRESSION IN CONTEXT

2. The equation $y = 179{,}840 + 3{,}250x$ can be used to approximate the value of a certain home in dollars $x$ years after it was built. If the house was built in 1982, approximate the value in 2016.

### SKILL 3: GRAPH A LINE

3. Draw the graph of the line that has equation $y = 126x + 1{,}400$. Make sure you choose a reasonable scale for each axis, and label the scales on your graph.

# Lesson 4-8  **Making Connections** (Correlation and Regression Analysis)

## LEARNING OBJECTIVES

☐ 1. Draw and analyze scatter plots for two data sets.

☐ 2. Define correlation coefficient, and decide if correlation coefficients are significant.

☐ 3. Find regression lines and use them to make predictions.

☐ 4. Recognize the difference between data sets being related and being linearly related.

*The price of soda in 20 years has gone down 40 percent while the price of whole foods, fruits and vegetables, has gone up 40 percent and obesity goes up right along that curve.*
—Tom Colicchio

Courtesy of David Sobecki

Unless you're a major shareholder in an oil company, chances are you're not at all fond of high gas prices. Is it possible that maybe prices like the ones shown in the photo aren't all bad? While doing some research for this book, I came across an interesting article online which was based on research a student in economics did for his PhD dissertation. The claim made in the paper is that rising gas prices have a strong connection to a decrease in the number of obese people in the United States. So what exactly does that mean? Do higher gas prices make people thinner? Superficially, those things appear to be totally unrelated. In order to study this claim, we'd want to find some data on both obesity and gas prices in a way that the data can be paired together for comparison. In this case, we could find obesity rates by year, as well as the average price of a gallon of gas in that year. Then we'll see if we can make a connection.

**0.** After reading the opening paragraph, what do you think the main topic of this lesson will be?

## 4-8  Class

Once we've found comparative data, we can then plot a graph designating one set of data as the *x* variable or **independent variable** and the other as the *y* variable or **dependent variable.** This graph is called a *scatter plot.*

A **scatter plot** is a graph of the ordered pairs (*x*, *y*) consisting of data from two data sets.

After a scatter plot is drawn, we can analyze the graph to see if there's a noticeable pattern. If there is, like the points falling in an approximately straight line, we can conclude that the two variables MIGHT be related somehow.

If there appears to be a reasonably clear relationship between the variables, we might study that relationship further by trying to find an equation that relates the variables. This is known as *regression analysis,* which we will learn about later in the lesson. For now, we'll focus on building a scatter plot.

Data on obesity rates in the United States were collected from the Center for Disease Control for various years. Data were also collected on the average price of a gallon of gas for those same years from a variety of online sources. This data is organized in the table below.

| Year | x, Avg. gas price per gallon ($) | y, Obesity rate (% of adult population) |
|---|---|---|
| 1961 | 0.27 | 10.7 |
| 1973 | 0.385 | 12.1 |
| 1978 | 0.65 | 12.7 |
| 1991 | 1.18 | 20.5 |
| 1999 | 1.30 | 27.7 |
| 2001 | 1.43 | 28.3 |
| 2003 | 1.56 | 31.7 |
| 2005 | 2.27 | 33.8 |
| 2007 | 2.81 | 32.5 |
| 2009 | 2.35 | 35.9 |

1. Draw a scatter plot for the data by plotting points based on the information in the table. Use the values from the gas prices column as first coordinates and obesity rates as second coordinates.

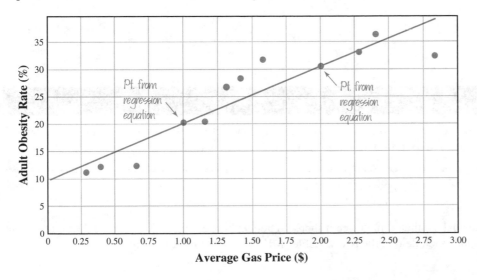

Make sure you emphasize the idea that the line of best fit may not go through any of the points. Give students a general idea of how to draw one, then walk around and see how they did. Also, show students how to make a simple straightedge by folding a sheet of paper in half.

2. Write a general description of trends you see on your scatter plot. Does this appear to support or refute the claim made in the opening paragraph of this lesson?

*The general trend goes from lower left to upper right, meaning that lower gas prices tend to match with lower obesity rates, and higher gas prices match with higher obesity rates. This is the opposite of the claim made by the researcher, who posited that higher gas prices would lower obesity rates.*

### Did You Get It

Try this problem to see if you understand the concepts we just studied. The answer can be found at the bottom of the portfolio page.

1. The data below represent the heights in feet and the number of stories of the tallest buildings in Pittsburgh. Draw a scatter plot for the data and describe the relationship.

| Height (x) | 485 | 511 | 520 | 535 | 582 | 615 | 616 | 635 | 728 | 841 |
|---|---|---|---|---|---|---|---|---|---|---|
| Stories (y) | 40 | 37 | 41 | 42 | 38 | 45 | 31 | 40 | 54 | 64 |

## Regression

When we draw a scatter plot and it looks like there might be a straight-line relationship between the data sets, we can analyze the data further by trying to find the equation of a line that goes through the data points. This line is known as a **regression line.**

If you look back at the scatter plot in Question 1, you can see a general trend among the points from lower left to upper right. They definitely don't line up exactly in a line, but you could probably put a straightedge down and draw what seems like the closest approximation to a line by "splitting the difference" between points that don't line up exactly. That's what a regression line does. But instead of guessing, we're finding the single line with a special property: the overall distance from each point to the line is a minimum. (For that reason, the regression line is also called the *line of best fit.)*

3. Lightly draw what your eyes tell you is the line of best fit on your scatter plot from Question 1.

*Actual regression line shown on graph. Guesses will vary.*

We know from our algebra background that the equation of a line in slope-intercept form is $y = mx + b$, where $m$ is the slope and $b$ is the $y$ intercept (that is, the point that has first coordinate zero). In statistics, the equation of the regression line is often written as $y = a + bx$, where $a$ is the $y$ intercept and $b$ is the slope. In this book, we'll write our equations in the form $y = ax + b$ since this is the form we'll get from the technology we use. Since we know what the equation looks like, and since $y$ and $x$ in the general formula are the variables, all we need to find in a given situation is specific values for $a$ and $b$.

There are formulas that can be used to compute the values of $a$ and $b$ by hand, but they're so cumbersome to work with that it's almost always necessary to use technology to do the final calculations. And if you're going to use technology anyhow, you may as well take full advantage of it, right? In this case, both graphing calculators and Excel have built-in commands for finding the line of best fit. These are described in the technology boxes on the next page. (The formulas and a description are included in an online supplement in case your professor wants you to learn how to use them.)

## Using Technology: Finding the Line of Best Fit

To find and graph a line of best fit for two data sets that appear to have an approximate linear relationship:

**Graphing Calculator**

1. Press **STAT** **ENTER** to get to the list editor.

2. Enter the data set you want to use as inputs (*x* values) under **L1.**

3. Use the right arrow key ❯ to access **L2,** then enter the data set you want to use as outputs (*y* values). When entering data from a table, make sure you enter the second list in the same order as the first.

4. Turn on **Plot1** by pressing **2nd** **Y=** **1**. Set up the screen, as shown below.

5. Press **Y=** and if the **Y =** screen isn't blank, move the cursor over any entered equations and press **CLEAR**.

6. Press **ZOOM** **9** which is the **Zoom Stat** option; this automatically sets a graphing window that displays all of the plotted points.

7. Press **STAT** followed by the right arrow key to access the **STAT CALC** menu, and choose the **LinReg** (for linear regression) option, which is choice 4. Then press **ENTER** to calculate the line of best fit.

8. Press **Y=** and enter the equation of the line of best fit, then press **GRAPH** to display the scatter plot along with the line of best fit.

> Students will likely need some help interpreting how the calculator displays the regression line. You should project an example and discuss if possible.

```
Plot1  Plot2  Plot3
On Off
Type: ⠿ ⠿ ⠿
        ⠿ ⠿ ⠿
Xlist:L₁
Ylist:L₂
Mark: ■ + ·
```

**Excel**

1. Enter the data in two columns and create a scatter plot.
2. Click on one of the points on the scatter plot, then choose "Add Trendline" from the **Chart** menu.
3. In the formatting dialog box that appears, click "Options," then click the checkbox for "Display equation on chart."

*See the Lesson 4-8-1 and 4-8-2 Using Tech videos in class resources for further Instruction.*

4. Find the equation of the regression line for the data in Question 1. You can use either a graphing calculator or a spreadsheet.

$y = 10.464x + 9.7261$

## Graphing the Regression Line

In order to graph your regression line on your scatter plot, start by choosing two $x$ values. These values can be pretty much any numbers between the max and min values of the data set that makes up the first coordinates on your scatter plot. It helps to make them as easy as possible to work with, though. You could choose something like 7.324, but it's more sensible to choose whole numbers.

5. List two $x$ values here that are between the min and max values for average gas prices. They don't have to be values from the table.

   *Sample answers: $1.00, $2.00*

6. Substitute each $x$ value from Question 5 into the regression equation to find the corresponding $y$ values.

   $y = 10.464(1) + 9.7261 = 20.1901$

   $y = 10.464(2) + 9.7261 = 30.6541$

7. Plot the two points you obtained in Questions 5 and 6 on the scatter plot and draw the line that passes through those two points. Then write a sentence or two analyzing how the line of best fit compares to your initial guess from Question 3.

   *Answers vary depending on initial guess.*

### Did You Get It

Try this problem to see if you understand the concepts we just studied. The answer can be found at the bottom of the portfolio page.

2. Find the equation of the regression line for the data in Did You Get It 1.

## Analyzing a Scatter Plot

There are several types of relationships that can exist between the $x$ values and the $y$ values in a scatter plot. These relationships can be identified by looking at the pattern of the points on the graphs. For the scatter plot that you drew, it was reasonable to guess that there was a linear relationship, but that may not always be the case.

In Questions 8–11, select the graph below that best represents each description and fill in any blanks.

8. A positive linear relationship exists when the points fall approximately in an ascending straight line from left to right. In this case as the x values are increasing, the y values are <u>increasing</u>. This relationship is best illustrated by graph <u>d</u>.

9. A negative linear relationship exists when the points fall approximately in a descending straight line from left to right. In this case as the x values are increasing, the y values are <u>decreasing</u>. This relationship is best illustrated by graph <u>b</u>.

10. A nonlinear relationship exists when the points fall in a curved line. The relationship is described by the nature of the curve. This relationship is best illustrated by graph <u>a</u>.

11. No relationship exists when there is no discernible pattern to the points. This relationship is best illustrated by graph <u>c</u>.

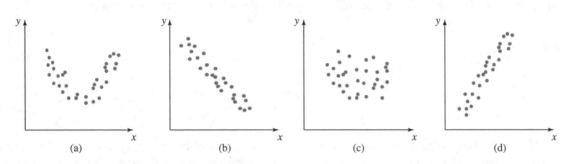

(a)          (b)          (c)          (d)

## The Correlation Coefficient

Deciding whether or not two data sets are related by simply looking at a scatter plot is a pretty subjective process, so it would be nice to have a way to quantify how strongly connected data sets are. The **correlation coefficient** is a number that describes how close to a linear relationship there is between two data sets. Correlation coefficients range from −1 (perfect negative linear relationship) to +1 (perfect positive linear relationship). The closer this number is to one in absolute value, the more likely it is that the data sets are linearly related. A correlation coefficient close to zero indicates that the data sets are most likely not linearly related. This could mean that they're related in some nonlinear way or that they're not related at all.

We use the letter r to represent the correlation coefficient. It doesn't depend on the units for the two data sets, and it also doesn't depend on which set you choose for the x variable.

12. The graphic below describes the scale of correlation coefficients. Make an estimate for r for each of the four graphs above.

*Answers vary. (d) should be close to 1, (b) should be close to −1. (c) should be close to zero. (a) is the tough one, but if they say close to zero that's sensible.*

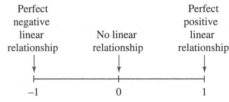

As with the regression line, there's a formula for calculating $r$, which you can find in the online supplement to this lesson. In terms of technology, you already know how to find the correlation coefficient, since both graphing calculators and spreadsheets automatically calculate $r$ when finding the regression line.

## Using Technology: Finding the Correlation Coefficient

**Graphing Calculator**
The correlation coefficient should display on the screen when you find the regression line. If it doesn't, go to the CATALOG menu (2nd 0), then scroll down and choose DiagnosticOn.

**Excel**
After finding the trendline, on the format trendline menu, click the box that says "Display R-squared value on chart." This finds the square of the correlation coefficient, so you can then use the formula "=SQRT(" to find $r$.

*See the Lesson 4-8-3 Using Tech video in class resources for further information.*

13. What's the correlation coefficient for the data in Question 1? What does that say about your answer to Question 2?

*$r \approx 0.918$; this shows a strong linear relationship, so if that was the conclusion drawn in Question 1, then good job.*

## Did You Get It

Try this problem to see if you understand the concepts we just studied. The answer can be found at the bottom of the portfolio page.

3. Find the correlation coefficient for the data in Did You Get It 1, and discuss what you think it indicates.

14. Based on what we've seen so far, would you say that an increase in gas prices led to an increase in obesity rates, or that an increase in obesity rates caused gas prices to rise?

*Hopefully not.*

All we know so far is that the two variables appear to be related in a linear way. This says exactly NOTHING about whether one is caused by the other. We'll discuss this very important issue later in the lesson.

## The Relationship between *r* and the Regression Line

Two things should be noted about the relationship between the value of *r* and the regression line. First, the value of *r* and the value of the slope (*b*) always have the same sign. Each indicates whether there's a positive or negative linear relationship between the variables. Second, the closer the value of *r* is to +1 or −1, the better the points will fit the line. In other words, the stronger the relationship, the better the fit.

**15.** Match each value of *r* with the appropriate graph.

$r = -1$:  _____d_____

$r = -0.9$:  _____b_____

$r = -0.5$:  _____f_____

$r = 0.5$:  _____a_____

$r = 0.9$:  _____e_____

$r = 1$:  _____c_____

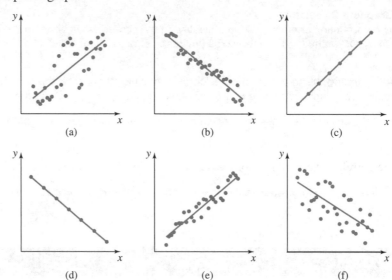

## 4-8  Group

**1.** A medical researcher selects a sample of small hospitals in his state and hopes to discover if there is a relationship between the number of beds and the number of personnel employed by the hospital. Draw a scatter plot on the next page for the data shown. Make sure you choose a reasonable scale for each axis, and clearly mark the scale on your graph.

| No. of beds (x) | 28 | 56 | 34 | 42 | 45 | 78 | 84 | 36 | 74 | 95 |
|---|---|---|---|---|---|---|---|---|---|---|
| Personnel (y) | 72 | 195 | 74 | 211 | 145 | 139 | 184 | 131 | 233 | 366 |

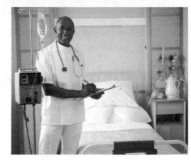

© Digital Vision/SuperStock RF

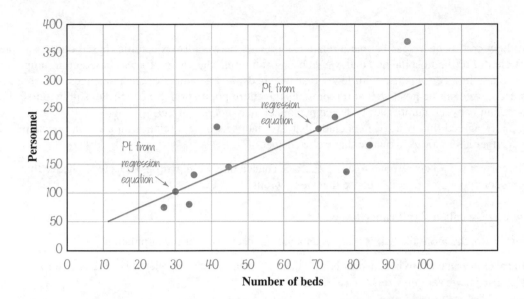

2. From simply looking at your scatter plot, describe the type of relationship (if any) that you think might exist between the number of beds and the number of personnel.

   *Answers vary.*

3. Find the equation of the regression line for these data.

   $y = 2.7077x + 20.118$

4. Graph the line of best fit on the scatter plot from Question 1 by choosing two $x$ values between 0 and 100 (so that the points will appear on the scatter plot).

   *Sample points:*
   $x = 30$:  $y = 2.7077(30) + 20.118 \approx 101$
   $x = 70$:  $y = 2.707(70) + 20.118 \approx 210$
   *Line shown on graph.*

5. Find the correlation coefficient for this data.

   $r = 0.748$

## Significance Levels

Next we'll tackle the issue of how confident we can be that a relationship exists between two quantities based on the sample size and the correlation coefficient. For the hospital bed data we've been examining, the value of $r$ was based on a sample of data. The population is all hospitals in a certain state with fewer than 100 beds, and a sample of such hospitals was chosen. When data from a sample is used, we can't be positive that it represents the entire population. So conclusions drawn, like the conclusion that there's a connection between numbers of beds and personnel, may not be correct.

Statisticians have traditionally agreed that when we conclude that two data sets have a relationship, we can be satisfied with that conclusion if there is either a 95% or 99% chance that we're correct.

6. A 95% chance that we're correct would correspond to a ____5____ % chance that we're wrong, and a 99% chance that we're correct would correspond to a ____1____ % chance that we're wrong.

These percentages of being wrong are called **significance levels.**

We know that the more data we have, the more likely it is that the data are representative of the population.

7. We would expect that the size of $r$ needed to be reasonably sure that two data sets are correlated is __larger__ for small sample sizes, and __smaller__ for large sample sizes.

In the following table, we see the minimum $r$ values needed, for different sample sizes, for us to have a 5% and 1% chance of being wrong when we conclude that two data sets are linearly related. (Actually, these are the minimum values for the absolute value of $r$, since it could be either negative or positive.)

| Sample Size | 5% | 1% | Sample Size | 5% | 1% |
|---|---|---|---|---|---|
| 4 | 0.950 | 0.990 | 17 | 0.482 | 0.606 |
| 5 | 0.878 | 0.959 | 18 | 0.468 | 0.590 |
| 6 | 0.811 | 0.917 | 19 | 0.456 | 0.575 |
| 7 | 0.754 | 0.875 | 20 | 0.444 | 0.561 |
| 8 | 0.707 | 0.834 | 21 | 0.433 | 0.549 |
| 9 | 0.666 | 0.798 | 22 | 0.423 | 0.537 |
| 10 | 0.632 | 0.765 | 23 | 0.412 | 0.526 |
| 11 | 0.602 | 0.735 | 24 | 0.403 | 0.515 |
| 12 | 0.576 | 0.708 | 25 | 0.396 | 0.505 |
| 13 | 0.553 | 0.684 | 26 | 0.361 | 0.463 |
| 14 | 0.532 | 0.661 | 27 | 0.312 | 0.402 |
| 15 | 0.514 | 0.641 | 28 | 0.254 | 0.330 |
| 16 | 0.497 | 0.623 | 29 | 0.179 | 0.234 |

Ideally, we'd want students to answer larger and smaller for Question 7, rather than just "large" and "small." You might need to coax them in that direction, talking about relative size being important here.

## Using Significant Values for the Correlation Coefficient

If |r| is greater than or equal to the value given in the table for either the 5% or 1% significance level, then we can reasonably conclude that the two data sets are linearly related.

Let's determine if the correlation coefficient found in Question 5 is significant at the 5% level.

**8.** What is the sample size?

$n = 10$

**9.** What is the minimum value of |r| needed for that sample size at the 5% level?

$|r| = 0.632$

**10.** How does that value of |r| compare to the value of |r| from Question 5? Interpret this result.

Since $|r| = 0.748$ is larger than $0.632$, there's at least a 95% chance that the data sets are linearly related.

**11.** Remember, the result of Question 9 doesn't guarantee that the data sets are actually related—there's still a ___5___ % chance that they're not related at all.

**12.** Is the correlation coefficient found in Question 5 significant at the 1% level? What does that mean?

We can't conclude that there is a linear relationship between the data sets at the 1% significance level since r would need to be greater than or equal to $0.765$. In this example, $|r| = 0.748$, which is less than $0.765$.

### Did You Get It

Try this problem to see if you understand the concepts we just studied. The answer can be found at the bottom of the portfolio page.

4. Test the significance of the correlation coefficient obtained from Did You Get It 3. Use 5%, and then 1%.

How should we choose whether to use the 5% or 1% significance level in a given situation? It depends on the seriousness of the situation and the importance of drawing a correct conclusion. Suppose that researchers think that a new medication helps patients with asthma to breathe easier, but that some patients have experienced side effects. A correlation study would probably be done to decide if there is a relationship between the medication and these particular side effects.

13. If the potential side effects are serious, like heart attacks or strokes, which significance level would be used? Why?

   *The 1% significance level would be used. Since the side effects are serious, we would want to minimize the chance of being wrong.*

14. If the side effects are mild, like headache or nausea, which significance level would be used? Why?

   *The 5% significance level would be used. Since the side effects are not as serious, we would be willing to accept a larger chance of being wrong.*

One of the most useful aspects of finding a regression line is that it can be used to make predictions for one of the variables given a value for the other. As part of graphing the line, we've already used the equation to make predictions for two points. **Important note:** If we hadn't already checked whether the correlation is significant, then it would be meaningless to make any predictions.

15. Use the equation of the regression line found in Question 3 to predict the approximate number of personnel for a hospital with 65 beds.

   *Substituting 65 for x into the equation $y = 2.7077x + 20.118$ we get 196.12.*

   *We predict that a hospital with 65 beds will have about 196 personnel.*

## Math Note

Never use a regression line to predict anything unless you've already checked that the correlation is significant! If it isn't significant, the regression line is meaningless.

For any data value from a set, the **residual** is the difference between the actual value and the predicted value that comes from the regression equation. Each point from the data set has one residual. As you'll verify in the Tech assignment, the sum and the mean of the residuals for a data set will be zero. That's a fancy way of saying that the regression line perfectly "splits the difference" between all of the points on a scatter plot.

Notice that the original data set didn't contain the $x$ value of 65 beds so we can't compute a residual for the value in Question 15.

**16.** Use the equation of the regression line found in Question 3 to predict the approximate number of personnel for a hospital with 42 beds.

$y = 2.7077(42) + 20.118 \approx 134$

**17.** What is the actual number of personnel for a hospital with 42 beds?

211

**18.** What is the residual for this value? Interpret this result.

$211 - 134 = 77$. This tells us that the hospital in the study with 42 beds had 77 more personnel than the model predicts.

**19.** What is the residual for the number of personnel in a hospital with 78 beds? Pay attention to the sign. Interpret this value.

$y = 2.7077(78) + 20.118 \approx 231$

The residual is $139 - 231 = -92$. This tells us that the hospital in the study with 78 beds had 92 fewer personnel than the model predicts.

## Did You Get It

Try this problem to see if you understand the concepts we just studied. The answer can be found at the bottom of the portfolio page.

5. Use the equation of the regression line found in Did You Get It 2 to predict the number of stories for a 582-foot building. Then compute the residual.

## Correlation and Causation

Here's a key phrase to remember when studying correlation and regression analysis: *correlation is not the same thing as causation.* Knowing that two variables are related doesn't say anything about whether or not one CAUSES changes in the other. Here are some possible interpretations when two variables are significantly correlated.

### Possible Relationships Between Data Sets

1. *There is a direct cause-and-effect relationship between two variables.* That is, *x* causes *y.* For example, water causes plants to grow, poison causes death, and heat causes ice to melt.

2. *There is a reverse cause-and-effect relationship between the variables.* That is, *y* causes *x.* Suppose that we find a correlation between excessive coffee consumption and nervousness. It would be tempting to conclude that drinking too much coffee causes nervousness. But it might actually be the case that nervous people drink a lot of coffee because they think it calms their nerves.

3. *The relationship between the variables may be caused by a third variable.* You could probably find a positive correlation between the amount of ice cream consumed per week and the number of drowning deaths for each week of the year. But this doesn't mean that eating ice cream causes you to drown. Both eating ice cream and swimming are more common during the summer months, and it stands to reason that more people will drown when more people are swimming. In this case, a third variable (seasonal weather) is affecting each of the original two variables.

4. *There may be a variety of complicated interrelationships among many variables.* For example, a researcher may find a significant relationship between students' high school grades and college grades. But there probably are many other variables involved, such as IQ, hours of study, influence of parents, motivation, age, and instructors.

5. *The relationship might simply be coincidental.* For example, historians have noticed that there is a very strong correlation between the party that wins a presidential election and the result of the Washington football team's final game before the election. But good old common sense tells us that this relationship has to be a coincidence.

20. Based on everything you learned in this lesson, write a description of the relationship between gas prices and obesity. Include your thoughts on which of the five relationships above is most likely to hold in this case.

*Answers vary. In my view, the third relationship is most likely. Each of those are things that have risen over time, so they appear to be connected to each other when EACH is connected to what year it is.*

# 4-8 Portfolio

Name _____

Check each box when you've completed the task. Remember that your instructor will want you to turn in the portfolio pages you create.

## Technology

**1.** ☐ Use a spreadsheet to compute the residuals for all 10 data values in the group part of this lesson. Then compute the sum and the mean of these values. Finally, write a paragraph that describes the significance of the sum of the values. A template to help you get started can be found in the online resources for this lesson.

## Online Practice

**1.** ☐ Include any written work from the online assignment along with any notes or questions about this lesson's content.

## Applications

**1.** ☐ Complete the applications problems.

## Reflections

Type a short answer to each question.

**1.** ☐ Describe the difference between correlation and causation, and explain why understanding the difference is so important.

**2.** ☐ If the correlation coefficient for two data sets is close to zero does that mean that they're not related at all? Think carefully about this one, and explain your answer.

**3.** ☐ Think of an example of two data sets that you'd expect to have a negative linear correlation.

**4.** ☐ Take another look at your answer to Question 0 at the beginning of this lesson. Would you revise your answer now that you've completed the lesson? How would you summarize the topic of this lesson now?

**5.** ☐ What questions do you have about this lesson?

## Looking Ahead

**1.** ☐ Complete the Lesson 4-9 Prep Skills and read the opening paragraph in Lesson 4-9 carefully, then answer Question 0 in preparation for that lesson.

## Answers to "Did You Get It?"

**1.**

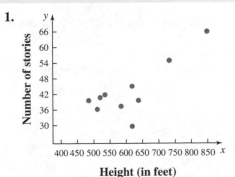

**Height (in feet)**

**2.** $y = 0.0685x + 1.646$

**3.** $r \approx 0.798$; there is likely a linear relationship between height of a building and number of stories.

**4.** Significant at both levels.

**5.** 42 stories; the residual is $-4$.

As height goes up, so does the number of stories.

## 4-8 Applications

Name _____

In Questions 1–4, for each pair of quantities, decide if they are likely to be positively correlated, negatively correlated, or uncorrelated. Explain your reasoning.

1. Total number of years of school completed and average annual salary

   *Positive. It's a documented fact that on average, more years of schooling leads to more earning potential.*

2. Number of class meetings missed by college students and their average scores in the course

   *Negative. Obviously if you miss more classes (i.e., number of misses goes up), your score is likely to go down.*

3. The age of a person and the probability that he or she wears glasses or contact lenses

   *Positive. Eyesight tends to get worse as people get older. Sigh.*

4. The height of adults and the amount of money they earn relative to their coworkers

   *There should be none, although there are some studies that show taller people do tend to make more money overall. Obviously my campus didn't get that memo.*

For the data sets in Questions 5–7,
   a. Draw a scatter plot.
   b. Find the value for $r$.
   c. Test the significance of $r$ at the 5% level and at the 1% level. If you conclude that $r$ is not significant at either level, be sure to explain why.
   d. Find the equation of the regression line and draw the line on the scatter plot, but only if $r$ is significant.
   e. Describe the nature of the relationship if one exists.
   f. If possible, make the requested prediction using your regression line.
   g. If possible, compute the requested residual and explain the meaning of the result.

## 4-8  Applications

Name _____

5.  A researcher hopes to determine if there is a relationship between the number of days an employee missed a year and the person's age. The following table displays information for 10 randomly selected employees at a large company. Predict the number of days missed by a 56-year-old employee. Compute the residual for the point (50,7).

| Age, x | 22 | 30 | 25 | 35 | 65 | 50 | 27 | 53 | 42 | 58 |
|--------|----|----|----|----|----|----|----|----|----|----|
| Days missed, y | 0 | 4 | 1 | 2 | 14 | 7 | 3 | 8 | 6 | 4 |

*a.*

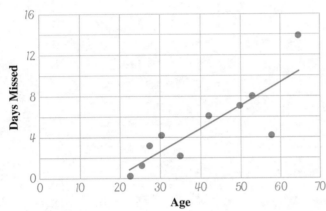

*b. r = 0.842*

*c. Yes, at both levels*

*d. y = 0.228x − 4.380*

*e. Age and days of work missed are positively correlated and significant at the 1% level.*

*f. The equation predicts that a 56-year-old employee will miss 8.4 days of work in a year.*

*g. The residual for the point (50,7) is −0.02. This means the observed value is 0.02 days less than the predicted value. In other words, it's right on the money.*

## 4-8 Applications

Name _____

6.  A researcher believes there is a connection between violent crime and the average high temperature in a city. He randomly selects 9 cities from a list of U.S. cities over 250,000 in population and records the average high temperature in April and the violent crime rate (per 100,000 residents). Predict the crime rate for a city with an average high temperature in April of 75°. Compute the residual for the point (63, 473).

| Avg. Apr. high, x | 62 | 70 | 80 | 64 | 65 | 63 | 60 | 84 | 67 |
|---|---|---|---|---|---|---|---|---|---|
| Crime rate | 458 | 1,122 | 841 | 795 | 1,185 | 473 | 1,334 | 1,060 | 1,685 |

a.

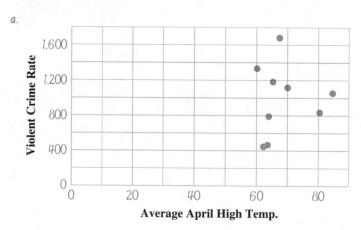

b. $r = 0.065$

c. Not significant at 5%. $r$ needed to be 0.666 or higher. Not significant at 1%. $r$ needed to be 0.798 or higher.

d. $r$ is not significant enough to justify creating a linear regression equation.

e. There is insufficient evidence to support a conclusion about the relationship between average high temperature and violent crime rates.

f. N/A

g. N/A

# 4-8 Applications

Name _____

7. Is there a connection between the unemployment rate in a state and the average household income there? The next table shows 2015 data for eight randomly selected states. Predict the average household income for a state with an unemployment rate of 4%. Predict the unemployment rate for a state with average household income of $62,500. (Careful about which variable represents which quantity.) Compute the residual for the point (4.8, 55,173).

| Unemployment %, x | 6.2 | 6.4 | 2.7 | 4.8 | 3.1 | 4.3 | 4.7 | 5.0 |
|---|---|---|---|---|---|---|---|---|
| Household income, y | 42,278 | 49,875 | 60,730 | 55,173 | 73,397 | 58,080 | 53,875 | 46,140 |

a.

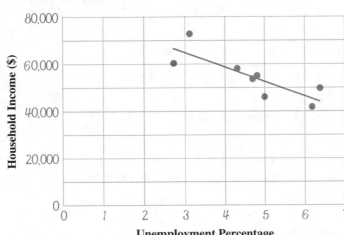

b. r = −0.825

c. Significant at 5% level, not significant at 1%. r needed to be −0.834 or lower.

d. y = − 6,079.2x + 83,212

e. Unemployment rate and household income are negatively linearly related at the 5% level.

f. The equation predicts an average household income of $58,895 for a state with an unemployment rate of 4%.

g. The residual for the point (4.8, 55173) is $1,141. This means the observed value is $1,141 more than the predicted value.

# Lesson 4-9   Prep Skills

This is a short review of skills that will come in handy in the next lesson. In each case, answer the question, then rate your confidence level by checking one of the boxes. If you feel like you're struggling with these skills, consult the online resources provided by your instructor for extra practice.

### SKILL 1: COMPUTE MEASURES OF AVERAGE

1. Find all four measures of average for this data set:

   12   18   21   18   9   33   97   20   19   25   13

### SKILL 2: COMPUTE RELATIVE DIFFERENCE

2. After a promising earnings report, the price of a tech stock jumps from $7.45 to $11.30 in one day. Find the change in price, and the relative change in price.

### SKILL 3: DRAW A BAR GRAPH

3. Draw a bar graph that illustrates the data in the table, which is the maximum depth in feet of each of the Great Lakes. The scale on the horizontal axis should go from zero to 1,500 feet.

| Lake | Superior | Erie | Michigan | Ontario | Huron |
|---|---|---|---|---|---|
| Max Depth | 1,333 | 210 | 923 | 802 | 750 |

### SKILL 4: GRAPH PAIRED DATA

4. The data in the table are the percentage of total power in the U.S. generated by wind for selected years from 2002 to 2014. Graph the data on a rectangular coordinate system with the year on the $x$ axis.

| Year | 2002 | 2005 | 2008 | 2011 | 2014 |
|---|---|---|---|---|---|
| Percent | 0.26% | 0.46% | 1.25% | 3.20% | 3.95% |

# Lesson 4-9 **Trust No One** (Misuses of Statistics)

## LEARNING OBJECTIVES

☐ 1. Identify misuses of sampling and evaluate their effect on statistical results.

☐ 2. Recognize and describe common misuses of compiling and reporting statistics that make them meaningless or deceiving.

☐ 3. Study ways that graphs can be manipulated to tell a desired story.

*There are two ways of lying. One, not telling the truth and the other, making up statistics.*

— Josefina Vazquez Mota

© Ed Araquel/TM and Copyright 20th Century Fox Film Corp/Everett Collection

"Trust No One" was the unofficial motto of the classic TV show *The X Files,* in which intrepid agent Fox Mulder and his faithful assistant Dr. Scully work to find the truth behind incredible events amid vast conspiracies. In the world of that show, things were rarely what they seemed, and the best course of action for the investigators (and viewers) was to assume that anything that anyone said may have been at best a stretching of the truth. In our modern world, there's a lot of wisdom in that approach. We are constantly bombarded with information and statistics, and it would be quite a leap to expect that most of the people disseminating that information have your best interests in mind. An educated adult knows that it's a good idea to view information suspiciously, and also knows how to recognize when statistics are being manipulated to tell the story that someone wants you to hear, not the truth. But, as Mulder was fond of pointing out, the truth is out there. You just have to want to find it.

**0.** After reading the opening paragraphs, what do you think the main topic of this lesson will be?

> This entire lesson is in Group format. It's all about students thinking for themselves about what does and does not make sense.

## 4-9 Group

Ideally, statistical research is used to provide knowledge and information to help us make intelligent decisions about our health and welfare, or maybe just to give us information about things we find interesting. But the world is a less-than-ideal place and there are people who will misuse statistics to sell us products that don't work; to attempt to prove something that isn't true; or to get our attention by using fear, shock, or outrage supported by bad statistics.

Just because we read or hear the results of a research study or an opinion poll in the media, this doesn't mean that these results are reliable or that they can be applied to any and all situations. For example, reporters sometimes leave out critical details like the size of the sample used or how the research subjects were selected. Without this information, you can't properly evaluate research and properly interpret the conclusions of a study or survey.

The purpose of this lesson is to show you some ways that statistics can be misused. The point isn't to make you reject any statistical study or result; it's to help you to recognize when information or conclusions you're being given might be presented in a biased or dishonest way. Throughout this unit, we've sprinkled in some information on ways that statistics can be misused; in this lesson, we'll compile and expand on those misuses.

## Suspect Samples

Since there are over 300 million people in the U.S. (and over 7 billion in the world), the vast majority of statistical studies you run across involve sampling: this is where any study is going to begin. That's why we started our study of statistics with sampling, and it's also why that's where we'll begin our look at statistical mischief.

### Unreported Sample Sizes

In the first part of the 21st century, there was a chewing gum brand that ran a large campaign claiming that "Four out of five dentists surveyed" would recommend their product. That sounds like a ringing endorsement. But what does it really mean?

1. By making this statement, what is the advertiser trying to imply? Calculate and use a percentage in your answer.

   *That 80% of all dentists in the country would recommend this particular product.*

2. How many dentists do you think there are in the United States? Make a guess.

   *Answers vary, but the actual number is about 98,000.*

3. How many dentists do you feel like they would have to survey in order to make this statistic meaningful?

   *This is an opinion. But it better be more than five.*

The bottom line is that the advertiser (of course) provided no information on how many dentists they actually surveyed. If they only surveyed five, their claim could still be technically true, but they may have stumbled across four that by coincidence would recommend their product, even if the vast majority of dentists would rather see their patients chewing razor blades. Worse still, they could easily have chosen to survey five that would be predisposed to recommend their product for one reason or another (like say a check with multiple zeroes on it).

If samples in a study are too small, the results could be completely meaningless. And if the size of a sample is conveniently left out, there's a pretty good chance that the person reporting the statistics would just as soon have you not know what that sample size was.

4. Why would an advertiser be likely to leave out the size of a sample on which a statistic is based?

   *If they're making a claim that is unlikely to hold true with a meaningful sample size, they'd be likely to use a smaller sample, and one improperly chosen. And in that case, obviously, they'd rather keep that quiet.*

## Did You Get It

Try this problem to see if you understand the concepts we just studied. The answer can be found at the bottom of the portfolio page.

1. Evaluate this claim by an advertiser: 60% of people surveyed prefer our brand of Cola over the leading national brand.

### Samples Relying on Volunteer Participation

5. Suppose that a national poll is conducted by telephone to gauge the favorability rating for a particular candidate for the presidency. What types of people will not be represented in this survey? List as many as you can think of.

*Some potential answers: people that don't have a phone. People that don't answer calls from numbers they don't recognize. People that answered the phone but declined to answer. People on the do-not-call list. People that work odd hours and aren't available to answer calls during normal hours.*

Studies using volunteers sometimes have a built-in bias because volunteers generally don't represent the population at large. Sometimes they are recruited from a particular socio-economic background. For example, unemployed people are far more likely to volunteer for research studies in order to get paid, and because they're likely to have more free time available to participate.

6. What groups of people would be available for studies that require the subjects to spend several days or weeks in an environment other than their home or workplace?

*Almost exclusively people that don't have a job with regular hours. People that don't have school-aged children would probably be overrepresented as well.*

People who are annoyed by unsolicited phone calls won't appear in a sample of people contacted by phone.

© Tracy Kahn/Corbis RF

7. In the past, many studies have used only men but have tried to generalize the results to both men and women. Do you think this is a good idea? Why? Does it depend on what is being studied?

*Opinion question.*

8. To conduct market research on their products, some companies will offer coupons, samples, or even cash to participate in a study. Comment on how you think this is likely to affect the outcome.

*Answers vary. First, it's a classic volunteer sample situation, which automatically cuts down on randomness. Second, the inducements are likely to bias many people in favor of the product. Inducements also give the recipients a general feeling of good will toward the company, and respondents are more likely to say what they think the company wants to hear, rather than what they really think.*

## Samples Relying on Convenience

It can be difficult and time-consuming to conduct a study involving a truly random sample. It's not uncommon for people to cut corners, and work with a sample that's easy to get to for one reason or another.

9. A sports reporter in Chicago is asked to write an article about the popularity of certain baseball teams in the Midwest. He decides that conducting a poll to gather some data is a fine idea, and while he's at it, he may as well enjoy a beverage and an appetizer. So he hops on the L (public transportation) and goes to a very popular sports bar on the north side of the city, then asks everyone that will pay attention to him which is their favorite baseball team. Over the course of four hours, he manages to gather information from over 300 people. Do you think this was a reasonable approach to gathering information? Explain.

© Cheryl Keegan

*It may have been convenient, but it's a ridiculous sample. The north side of Chicago is where the Chicago Cubs stadium is, and the vast majority of people he runs into there would likely choose the Cubs as their favorite team.*

A **convenience sample** is one where members of a preexisting group are selected. This can lead to bias because there may be something that connects all the members of that group.

10. An educational researcher wants some data on the number of hours per week that average college students study outside of class. She sends around an email asking colleagues to administer a short survey in their classes, and ends up surveying two 300-level chemistry courses and students in a senior-level physics course. List several different reasons why this is likely to be a nonrepresentative sample.

*First, the fact that both are upper-level courses is a bad idea. Next, both courses are in the hard sciences, so it's likely that the students will have a lot in common other than their class standing. Other answers are possible, of course.*

If you're trying to interpret the results of a study done using a small sample, a volunteer sample, or a convenience sample, you have to give a lot of thought to whether the characteristics of that sample make it representative of an entire population.

11. There are many sites on the Internet where college students can rate their professors in terms of teaching effectiveness. Suppose that one instructor has seven reviews at a site, with six of them describing the teacher as being a wonderful educator. Discuss how reliable you think that would be for a student deciding whether or not to take that instructor. Back up your conclusions with evidence based on the ideas in this lesson.

*Answers vary. There are many interpretations here. Some feel that only students that feel strongly one way or another will make the effort to fill out an evaluation, so it doesn't end up being a representative sample.*

## Did You Get It

Try this problem to see if you understand the concepts we just studied. The answer can be found at the bottom of the portfolio page.

2. In a study to determine how long it takes to fall asleep, would college students be a good sample of the overall population? Why?

## Ambiguous Averages

There was a time when we all thought that "average" meant one thing: the result of adding all data values and dividing by how many there are. But we know better now, don't we? When someone uses the term "average" in making some sort of claim instead of letting us know which measure of average (mean, median, mode, midrange) that they're using, it's time to trust no one and be suspicious.

We know that the values of these different measures of average sometimes differ quite a lot. People who know that there are several types of average can, without lying, select the one for the data that most lends evidence to support their position. For example, suppose a storeowner employs four salespeople. The number of years each has been employed by the store is 22, 10, 2, and 2.

12. What is the mean number of years of service for the four salespeople?

*Nine years*

13. What is the median?

*Six years*

**14.** What is the mode?

*Two years*

**15.** What about the midrange?

*Twelve years*

**16.** If the storeowner wanted to advertise the fact that his employees have many years of experience, which average do you think he would use? Why?

*In this case, he'd pick the midrange, since it's the highest of the four measures.*

## Faulty Survey Questions

Surveys and opinion polls obtain information by using questionnaires. There are two types of studies: interviews and self-administered questionnaires. The interview survey requires a person to ask the questions either in person or by telephone. Self-administered questionnaire surveys require the participant to answer the questions by mail, computer, or in a group setting, such as a classroom. When analyzing the results of a survey using questionnaires, you should be sure that the questions are properly written, since the way questions are phrased can often influence the way people answer them.

© Photographer's Choice/SuperStock RF

**17.** A group of people was asked two questions relating to gun control:

- Do you favor a waiting period before guns are sold?
- Do you favor a national gun-registration program costing about 20% of all dollars spent on crime control?

Both questions ask people if they're in favor of stricter gun restrictions. One question was answered "Yes" by 91% of respondents, and 6% said "No." The other was answered "Yes" by just 37% and "No" by 61%. Which is which? Explain why.

*The first was answered yes by 91%, the second only 37%. The second is a very biased question: it focuses on the negative aspects of the program, rather than simply asking if the respondents are in favor of the concept.*

When reading and interpreting the results obtained from questionnaire surveys, watch out for some of these common mistakes made in the writing of the survey questions.

- *Asking Biased Questions.* By asking a question in a certain way, the researcher can lead the respondents to answer the question the way the researcher wants them to.

- *Asking Double-Barreled Questions.* Sometimes two ideas are contained in one question, and the respondent may answer one or the other in his or her response.

- *Using Double Negatives.* Survey questions containing double negatives often confuse the respondent.

- *Using Confusing Words.* Using words in a survey question that are not well-defined or understood can invalidate the responses. Most people wouldn't admit that they don't understand a question, so they just answer it in some random way. Clearly, this is not optimal.

In Questions 18–21, consider each survey question. Why do you think each question is a poor one? Think about the common mistakes described above.

**18.** "Are you going to vote for Candidate Jones, even though the latest survey shows he will lose the election?"

*The question makes it less likely people will answer yes, because (1) people generally don't like being associated with the loser, and (2) the question will lead people to conclude that it's not worth their time to even vote.*

**19.** "Do you think people would live longer if they were on a diet?"

*What sort of diet? That word is not at all well-defined.*

**20.** "Are you in favor of a national health program and do you think it should be subsidized by a special tax as opposed to other ways to finance it, such as a national lottery?"

*There are two questions here. The first is a perfectly legitimate question, but it's tied to the second, which leads people to answer no, since it brings up the prospect of a national tax. The wording is also confusing.*

**21.** "Do you feel that it is not appropriate to have areas where people cannot smoke?"

*I wrote this question and I have to read it three times to figure out what it's asking. It's clearly designed to confuse the respondents.*

Other factors that could bias a survey would include anonymity of the participant, the time and place of the survey, and whether the questions were open-ended or closed-ended.

22. Participants will, in some cases, respond differently to questions based on whether or not their identity is known. Researchers try to ensure confidentiality rather than anonymity; however, many people will be suspicious in either case. List some types of issues that people might be surveyed on where lack of anonymity might affect their responses.

*Answers vary, but anything involving sexuality, morality, or self-reported criminal behavior is guaranteed to lead to biased responses if anonymity is not ensured.*

23. The time and place where a survey is taken can influence the results. For example, if a survey on airline safety is taken right after a major airline crash, the results may differ from those obtained in a year with no major airline disasters. Think of at least two other similar examples where time and/or place could bias results.

*Answers vary.*

### Did You Get It

Try this problem to see if you understand the concepts we just studied. The answer can be found at the bottom of the portfolio page.

3. Two "researchers" (by which we mean "spin doctors") conduct surveys on people's attitudes toward health care. One survey contains the question "Do you feel that the high cost of Obamacare is justified by what it accomplishes?" The other survey has the question "Are you in favor of expanding the Affordable Health Care Act so that even more families can get quality medical care?" Describe how each "researcher" wants those surveyed to respond.

## Convenient Use of Percentages

Another type of statistical distortion can occur when different values are used to represent the same data. For example, one political candidate who is running for reelection might say, "During my administration, expenditures increased a mere 3%." His opponent, who is trying to unseat him, might say, "During my opponent's administration, expenditures have increased a whopping $6,000,000." Both figures could be correct; but expressing $6,000,000 as "a mere 3%" makes it seem like a very small increase, while expressing the same increase as "a whopping $6,000,000" makes it sound like a very large increase. If you want to get to the truth, ask yourself, "Which measure best represents the data?"

© Jim Bourg/Reuters

24. In North Carolina, the individual income tax rate was 7.75% in 2013. In 2015, that rate dropped to 5.75%. What is the difference in the two tax rates? Answer as a percent.

    *The difference is 2%.*

25. What is the relative difference in the two tax rates?

    $$\frac{5.75\% - 7.75\%}{7.75\%} \approx -0.26$$

    *The relative difference is negative 26%.*

26. If someone earned $40,000 in income, what is the difference this tax cut had on that person's income?

    *7.75% of $40,000 is $3,100. 5.75% of $40,000 is $2,300. So the tax cut saved that person $800.*

27. Which of the three differences would be used by someone wanting to argue that this tax cut won't hurt the state's budget much?

    *Open to interpretation, but probably the 2%, which probably sounds the least significant.*

28. Which of the three differences would be used by someone wanting to argue that this tax cut will have a devastating effect on the state's budget?

    *Open to interpretation, but probably −26%, which shows that the state will lose over a quarter of income tax revenue.*

### Did You Get It

Try this problem to see if you understand the concepts we just studied. The answer can be found at the bottom of the portfolio page.

4. An upcoming school levy in my town would raise the property taxes on a $150,000 home from $248 per month to $280 per month. Calculate the annual increase and the percent increase, then pick which one of these numbers would most likely be publicized by an advocacy group that opposes the raise.

## Implied Connections

This one is a classic—if you look for it, you'll find it in advertising pretty much every day. Many claims imply that there's a connection between two variables without having any compelling evidence (or maybe any evidence at all) to back up that connection. To cover themselves legally, advertisers will use words like "may," "suggest," "some," etc. so that if the connection actually doesn't exist, they're not lying.

29. Explain why each of the following claims, found in online advertisements, are essentially meaningless.
    **a.** "Eating fish may help to reduce your cholesterol."

    *Or it MAY increase it. Or it MAY have no effect whatsoever.*

    **b.** "Studies suggest that using our exercise machine will reduce your weight."

    *Studies "suggest" isn't exactly a ringing endorsement. If a study PROVED it, that would mean something.*

    **c.** "Taking calcium will lower blood pressure in some people."

    *And in others? It could raise blood pressure, or have no effect.*

## Misleading Graphs

Graphs are great. We love them. In general, they're a fantastic way to illustrate information, making it easier to interpret. But there's a dark side to graphs. They can often be found hanging out with shady characters and committing crimes. Well, that's an exaggeration, but an inappropriately drawn graph can (either intentionally or not) misrepresent data and lead to false or misleading conclusions.

**30.** Draw a bar graph illustrating the change in North Carolina's tax rate on each of the axes below. Note that you'll be using the same information on each graph.

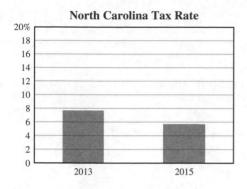

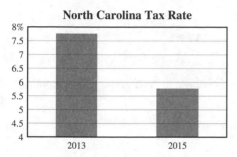

**31.** Which of the two bar graphs would be used by someone wanting to argue that this tax cut won't hurt the state's budget much? Why?

*The first graph makes it look like the two rates are pretty similar. You really have to read the scale carefully to see the significance in the tax cut.*

**32.** Which of the two bar graphs would be used by someone wanting to argue that this tax cut will have a devastating effect on the state's budget? Why?

*The second. It makes it look like the new tax rate is about half of the old rate, which is inaccurate.*

The average lifespan for Americans has been increasing for decades (although, to be fair, we still rank 34th in the world). The data below displays the average life expectancy for Americans according to the National Center for Health Statistics.

| Year | 1985 | 1990 | 1995 | 2000 | 2005 | 2010 | 2015 |
|---|---|---|---|---|---|---|---|
| Life Expectancy | 74.7 | 75.4 | 75.8 | 76.8 | 77.4 | 78.3 | 78.8 |

33. Draw a graph for the pairs of data on each graph below, with the year on the horizontal axis.

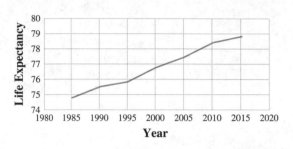  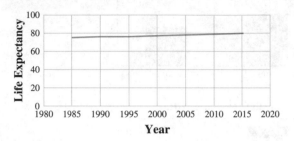

34. Describe how the life expectancy appears to be changing based on what you observe in each graph. (Two separate descriptions, please.)

    *The first graph makes it look like the increase in lifespan has been very dramatic. In the second graph, it pretty much looks negligible.*

35. Which graph would you show if you wanted to convince someone that the advances of modern medicine will soon have us living to be 150?

    *The first. The increase looks so dramatic, it naturally tricks you into thinking that average lifespan is headed toward the hundreds and beyond very quickly.*

36. Which graph would you show if you were arguing that we're really not living much longer than we were way, way back in 1985?

    *The second. With that scale, you have to look very closely to see any improvement at all.*

## 4-9 Portfolio

Name _____

Check each box when you've completed the task. Remember that your instructor will want you to turn in the portfolio pages you create.

### Technology

1. ☐ One of my favorite misuses of statistics is missing comparisons. For example, you might hear a claim like "Our brand of crackers has 1/3 fewer calories." That's completely meaningless if no comparison is given. One-third fewer calories than what? Someone else's crackers? An entire cow? Another common example is time comparisons: "Our aspirin works four times faster." Faster than what? The lady at the DMV? Your job is to search the Internet for an example of a missing comparison. Provide a link to the example, or upload a screen shot, then write an explanation of why their claim is completely ridiculous.

### Online Practice

1. ☐ Include any written work from the online assignment along with any notes or questions about this lesson's content.

### Applications

1. ☐ Complete the applications problems.

### Reflections

Type a short answer to each question.

1. ☐ Why is a truly representative sample so important in gathering data?
2. ☐ Write about an example you've seen or heard recently where someone made a fishy claim backed either by dubious evidence, misleading evidence, or maybe no evidence at all.
3. ☐ How can you use the ideas in this lesson throughout your lifetime?
4. ☐ Take another look at your answer to Question 0 at the beginning of this lesson. Would you change your answer now that you've finished the lesson? How would you summarize the topic of this lesson now?
5. ☐ What questions do you have about this lesson?

### Looking Ahead

1. ☐ Complete the Lesson 5-1 Prep Skills and read the opening paragraph in Lesson 5-1 carefully, then answer Question 0 in preparation for that lesson.

### Answers to "Did You Get It?"

**1–3.** Answers can vary. Talk to your group mates and instructor to make sure you understand the key ideas! **4.** Increase: $32; percent increase: 13%. Which the group might choose is an opinion. Justify yours!

## 4-9    Applications

Name _____

1. According to a pilot study of 20 people conducted at the University of Minnesota, daily doses of a compound called arabinogalactan over a period of 6 months resulted in a significant increase in the beneficial lactobacillus species of bacteria. Why can't it be concluded that the compound is beneficial for the majority of people?

   *First, 20 people is a very small sample. Second, we have no idea how those 20 were chosen. Are they representative of the general population, or did they all come from a group like college students? Do they vary by race, gender, age, eating habits, fitness level?*

2. Comment on this statement taken from a magazine advertisement: "In a recent clinical study, Cell-Tech was proved to be 1,950 percent better than creatine!"

   *Better in what way? At building muscle? At generating big profits for the manufacturer?*

3. In an ad for women, the following statement was made: "For every hundred women, 91 have taken the road less traveled." Comment on this statistic.

   *The road less traveled is at best vague. It could mean wildly different things to different people.*

4. In many ads for weight-loss products, under the product claims and in small print, the following statement is made: "These results are not typical." What does this say about the product being advertised?

   *It says that for most people, it doesn't work nearly as well as for the small handful of people highlighted in the ad.*

5. An article in a leading magazine stated that "When 18 people with chronic, daily, whiplash-related headaches received steroid injections in a specific neck joint, 11% had no more headaches." Think of a possible reason why the figure 11% was used.

   *The writer was probably hoping that the reader would mistake 11% of patients with 11 out of 18 patients. That's a huge difference, since 11% of 18 patients is 2 patients.*

**4-9** **Applications**

Name _____

**6.** "Vitamin E is a proven antioxidant and may help in fighting cancer and heart disease." Is there anything ambiguous about this claim?

*If it "may help," then it may also not help, or it may make these conditions worse.*

**7.** The results of a survey reported in *USA Weekend* stated that "9% would drive through a toll booth without paying," and "13% would steal cable television or inflate their resumes." Explain why these figures may not be representative of the population in general.

*Each of those behaviors is illegal, and people are a lot less likely to admit to doing something illegal or clearly wrong.*

**8.** In a recent year, there were 6,067 male fatalities in the workplace and 521 female deaths. A government official made this statement: "Over 90 percent of the fatal injuries the past year were men, although men accounted for only 54 percent of the nation's employment." Can we conclude that women are more careful on the job? Explain.

*No. It's entirely possible that men are more likely to work in high-risk jobs. Also, a fatality on the job may or may not have anything to do with being careful.*

**9.** At one point in the voting process for the 2015 baseball All-Star team, the Kansas City Royals had the leading vote getter for 7 of the 9 starting positions. Fans were allowed to vote online as many times as they wanted. Do you think it was likely that the vote was representative of the population as a whole? Why?

*Almost certainly not. First, people have to go out of their way to vote online. Second, people would be far more likely to vote for players from a team that they are excited about rooting for, which means teams that are winning a lot of games that year.*

**10.** A stats instructor has recorded the scores of a recent quiz worth 20 possible points below.

20  18  18  15  15  18  15  15  15  20  19  20  15  20  19  0  0  18  19  15

**a.** If he wanted to be a jerk and tell his students the average on the quiz was terrible, which measure of average is he likely to use? Give that value in your explanation.

*Because of the two zeroes, the midrange is 10, which is 50%. Ugh. That makes it seem like the scores were awful.*

## 4-9    Applications

Name _____

**b.** If he wanted to be a great guy and tell them the average on the quiz was fantastic, which measure of average is he likely to use? Give that value in your explanation.

*The median was 18—great job class! Most of the scores were high, but the two zeroes lowered all other measures of average.*

For Questions 11–14, explain why each survey question might lead to an erroneous conclusion. Also suggest a better question.

**11.** "How often do you run red lights?"

*Asking flat-out about something against the law would tend to lead people to underreport how often they do it. Something like "how many times per year does a light turn red before you clear an intersection" has two advantages: it specifies what's meant by "how often," and makes the activity sound much more reasonable and less illegal.*

**12.** "Do you think gun manufacturers should put safety locks on all guns sold even though it would increase the cost of the gun by 20%?"

*The focus of the question appears to be the cost, not what it's really asking about. It would be best to leave the cost part out, or at worst make it two separate questions: "Do you think gun manufacturers should put safety locks on all guns?" and "Would you still support that if it added 20% to the cost of a gun?"*

**13.** "Do you think that it is not important to give extra tutoring to students who are not failing?"

*The double-negative makes this question confusing. It should be worded "Do you think it is important to give extra tutoring to students who are passing?"*

**14.** "Which restaurant in town has the best food and the greatest service?"

*There are two questions here that may be unrelated. A lot of restaurants have fantastic food and shaky service, and many have great service and mediocre food. This should be two completely separate questions.*

## 4-9  Applications

Name _____

15. The two graphs below were used by President Obama's reelection campaign commission to illustrate certain aspects of domestic energy production during his presidency. Which graph is misleading and why?

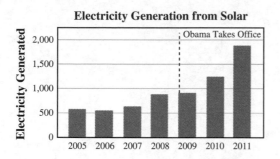

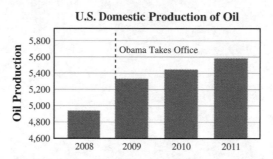

*The first is fine. The second has a scale on the vertical axis that doesn't start at zero, so it makes the growth in oil production look much more significant than it actually was. It only increased by about 14%, but the last bar is more than twice as tall as the first.*

# Unit 5
# Building Models

© Getty Images RF

## Outline

# Math In   Drug Administration

Have you ever looked at the dosage information on a bottle of aspirin and thought "It just doesn't seem reasonable to recommend the same dosage for all adults"? People come in all shapes and sizes, and the effect of a certain dosage is in large part dependent on the size of the individual. If a 105-pound woman and her 230-pound husband both take two aspirin the morning after their wedding reception, she is in effect getting more than twice as much medicine as he is.

Because there's a lot of variation in the world, the study of algebra was created based on a brilliantly simple idea: using a symbol, rather than a number, to represent a quantity that can change. Since the word "vary" is a synonym for change, we call such a symbol a variable. The use of variables is the thing that distinguishes algebra from arithmetic and makes it extremely useful to describe phenomena in a world in which very few things stay the same for very long. An understanding of the basics of algebra is, in a very real sense, the gateway to higher mathematics and its applications. Simply put, you can only go so far with just arithmetic. To model real situations, expressions involving variables are almost always required.

In this unit, we'll review some key ideas from algebra, but one thing we won't do is find $x$ just for the heck of it. A lot of students, maybe even most, believe that algebra was conceived as an abstract study, with early nerds sitting around simplifying expressions and solving equations on scrolls. Then a few centuries later, some genius said "Holy cow, we can use this stuff to find when two trains left San Francisco!"

Nothing could be farther from the truth. Algebra, and really all of classical math, was developed 100% as a tool for solving very real problems. So our study of algebra will focus on modeling, which is using algebra to represent situations in our world, like dosage calculations. You're accustomed to losing points when you make a mistake in a calculation, but outside the classroom, the stakes can be a LOT higher. The wrong dose of aspirin might upset your stomach, but more serious drugs carry with them more serious consequences. In many cases, an incorrect dosage could lead to death. Using the skills you learn in the chapter, you should be able to answer the following questions.

Suppose that a new pain-killing drug is being tested for safety and effectiveness in a variety of people. The recommended dosage for an average 5'10", 170-pound man is 400 mg. The manufacturer claims that the minimum effective dose for a person of that size is 250 mg, and that anything over 1,500 mg could be lethal. Two of the patients in the test are a 6'5", 275-pound college football player recovering from a major injury, and a 4'2", 65-pound girl being treated for sickle-cell disease. According to the manufacturer, dosages for this drug are proportional to body weight.

1. What would the recommended dosage be for each patient?
2. If the medications are mixed up and the recommended dosage for the football player is given to the child, is she in danger of dying?
3. Would the child's recommended dosage be at all effective for the football player?

For many medications, the effective dosage depends not just on body weight but also on body surface area (BSA), which accounts for the overall size of the patient. One model for body surface area is

$$BSA = \sqrt{\frac{wh}{3,600}}$$

where $w$ is weight in kilograms and $h$ is height in centimeters.

4. Find the ratio of body surface area for the football player compared to the girl. How does it compare to the ratio of their weights?
5. Find the body surface area for an average 5'10", 170-pound man.
6. If the dosages for the medication in the drug trial are based on body surface area rather than weight, rework Questions 2 and 3 to see if the child would be in danger, or if the medication would be at all effective for the football player.
7. Write any conclusions about using body surface area rather than weight when doing dosage calculations.

# Lesson 5-1 Prep Skills

This is a short review of skills that will come in handy in the next lesson. In each case, answer the question, then rate your confidence level by checking one of the boxes. If you feel like you're struggling with these skills, consult the online resources provided by your instructor for extra practice.

### SKILL 1: REDUCE FRACTIONS

Write each fraction in lowest terms:

1. $\dfrac{70}{100}$

2. $\dfrac{6}{10}$

3. $\dfrac{18}{48}$

### SKILL 2: MULTIPLY A WHOLE NUMBER BY A FRACTION

Perform each multiplication.

4. $\dfrac{9}{14} \cdot 7$

5. $y \cdot \dfrac{11}{y}$

### SKILL 3: SOLVE A LINEAR EQUATION

Find all solutions to each equation.

6. $8x = 30$

7. $-4(2x - 3) = 10$

# Lesson 5-1  **Keeping Things in Proportion**  (Ratios and Proportions)

**LEARNING OBJECTIVES**

☐ 1. Compare two quantities using ratios.

☐ 2. Describe the value of using ratios to compare quantities rather than differences.

☐ 3. Solve proportions.

☐ 4. Solve problems that involve proportional reasoning.

© Digital Vision/SuperStock RF

*One of the tricks of life is to have sense and money in roughly equal proportions.*
          —Craig Brown

The most obvious way to compare the sizes of two numbers is to subtract them. But is that the best way? Suppose you're comparing the cost of an item at two different stores, and you find that the item is a dollar more at Target than at Wal-Mart. If that item is a bottle of Coke, and the prices are $1 and $2, that dollar difference is significant. You'd most likely feel pretty strongly about buying from the cheaper store.

But if the item is a 60-inch flat-screen TV and the prices are $1,201 and $1,200, would you really care? Those two prices are essentially the same. It's still a dollar difference, but that difference just feels inconsequential. If you divide the prices rather than subtract them, however, something interesting happens:

$$\text{Coke: } \frac{\$2}{\$1} = 2 \quad \text{TV: } \frac{\$1,201}{\$1,200} = 1.0008$$

Do you see the point? For the Coke, a dollar more is twice as much—kind of a big deal. For the TV, when you divide the prices, you basically get 1, meaning the two prices are pretty much the same. Conclusion? The most meaningful way to compare the sizes of two numbers is to divide them, forming what we call a *ratio*. The study of ratios as a means of comparing numbers will lead us into a type of equation that can be used in a lot of modeling situations, the *proportion*.

  **0.** After reading the opening paragraphs, what do you think the main topic of this lesson will be?

## 5-1  Class

### Ratios

A **ratio** is a comparison of two quantities using division. For example, according to a 2015 survey reported in the *New York Daily News*, for every 76 people that reported some religious affiliation, there were 24 that did not. We would say that the ratio of those with an affiliation to those without is 76 to 24.

  Ratios are typically written in two different ways: using a colon between the quantities, or in fractional form. So we could write the ratio in the previous paragraph as either

$$76{:}24 \text{ or } \frac{76}{24}$$

In this course, we'll mostly use fractional form so that we can do arithmetic and algebra with ratios. Notice that if you perform the division in the ratio 76/24, you get about 3.2 in decimal form (rounded to one decimal place). This shows us that there are a little more than 3 times as many Americans that have a religious affiliation as those who do not. And this brings us full circle on what the point of ratios is: comparing sizes of quantities. Nice.

1. From 1969 through 1977, 4 of the teams in Major League Baseball made the playoffs each year, while 20 did not. Now, 10 make the playoffs and 20 do not. Write the ratio of teams making the playoffs to the total number of teams in 1969 and today. Write each ratio in fractional form, then reduce the fraction if you can.

$$1969: \frac{4}{24} = \frac{1}{6} \qquad\qquad Today: \frac{10}{30} = \frac{1}{3}$$

2. Describe what those ratios tell us about how likely a given team is to make the playoffs now as compared to in the mid-70s.

   *Since 1/3 is exactly half of 1/6, it tells us that a team today is twice as likely to make the playoffs as the teams between 1969 and 1977.*

3. Why was it useful to reduce the ratios?

   *In reduced form, it was a lot easier to compare the results. Looking at 4/24 and 10/30 is no more helpful than just saying 4 out of 24 made the playoffs before and 10 out of 30 make it now.*

4. A sub shop advertises a new 18-inch sandwich. Big! Not to be outdone, a rival chain comes out with a 2-foot long sandwich. Explain why writing the ratio below to compare the size of the sandwiches is deceiving:

   $$\frac{2}{18}$$

   *It makes it look like the 2-foot sandwich is a whole lot smaller, when in fact it's bigger.*

5. How should you write the ratio in order to make it meaningful as a size comparison? What does this tell us about the importance of units when writing ratios?

*We could write it either as $\frac{24}{18}$ or $\frac{2}{1.5}$. Since the point of using ratios in this way is comparing the sizes of numbers, it's crucial that the numbers are written in the same units, or the comparisons will be deceiving.*

## Did You Get It

Try this problem to see if you understand the concepts we just studied. The answer can be found at the bottom of the portfolio page.

1. Write each ratio as a fraction and reduce if possible. Think about consistency of units before writing!

   a. A Gallup poll conducted in 2015 indicated that 12 out of 100 Americans did not have health insurance. Write the ratio of those that have health insurance to those that do not.
   b. Write the ratio of 40 ounces to 2 pounds.

## Proportions

A **proportion** is an equation stating that two ratios are equal. In some cases involving only numbers, a proportion can be obviously true. For example, you most likely know that the ratios 1/2 and 4/8 are identical: if something occurs four out of every eight times, that means the same as saying that it occurs one out of every two times. In other words,

$$\frac{1}{2} = \frac{4}{8}$$

This is a simple example of a proportion that happens to be true.

Proportions are a bit more interesting when they contain variable quantities. We know that when you flip a coin, on average it will land on heads half the time. So if you flip a coin 80 times, how many times would you expect it to land on tails? If you said 40, that's great. Here's what that question would look like in proportion form:

$$\frac{1}{2} = \frac{t}{80}$$

where $t$ represents the number of times that tails would come up. The solution to this equation (which is a value of the variable quantity $t$ that makes the equation true) is the number of times we'd expect to get tails.

It turns out that there's a simple method for solving proportions that contain a variable quantity, and this method will come in really handy when we get to the key idea in this lesson, which is using proportions to solve applied problems. So before we get to the applied part, we'll practice the algebra part.

The goal will be to solve the proportion below, and we'll develop a simple method for doing so along the way.

$$\frac{12}{60} = \frac{3}{y}$$

6. A foolproof way to solve ANY equation that involves fractions is to multiply both sides of the equation by a common denominator for all fractions involved. In this case, $60y$ is a common denominator, so multiply both sides of the equation by $60y$. Then reduce fractions on each side of the equation.

$$60y \cdot \frac{12}{60} = \frac{3}{y} \cdot 60y \Rightarrow 12y = 180$$

7. Why is the resulting equation so much easier than the original one?

   *The resulting equation is easier because there are no fractions in it.*

8. Draw lines connecting the parts of the original equation that you ended up multiplying to get the simpler equation at the end of Question 6.

$$\frac{12}{60} \diagdown \!\!\! \diagup \frac{3}{y}$$

Congratulations! You've just discovered the shortcut method we can use to solve proportions. It's known as **cross-multiplying** because you're multiplying each part of the equation by the one diagonally across from it.

9. Use cross-multiplying to solve the proportion.

$$\frac{12}{60} = \frac{3}{y} \Rightarrow 12y = 180 \Rightarrow y = \frac{180}{12} = 15$$

10. Use cross-multiplying to solve this proportion: $\dfrac{x-5}{10} = \dfrac{x+2}{20}$

$$\frac{x-5}{10} = \frac{x+2}{20} \Rightarrow 20(x-5) = 10(x+2) \Rightarrow 20x - 100 = 10x + 20$$
$$20x - 100 = 10x + 20 \Rightarrow 10x = 120 \Rightarrow x = 12$$

**11.** How can you check to see if you solved the proportion in Question 10 correctly? Explain, then do it.

*You can substitute 12 back into the original equation and see if it's a true statement.*

$$\frac{12-5}{10} = \frac{12+2}{20} \Rightarrow \frac{7}{10} = \frac{14}{20}$$ *This is a true statement.*

---

### Did You Get It

Try this problem to see if you understand the concepts we just studied. The answer can be found at the bottom of the portfolio page.

2. Use cross-multiplying to solve the proportion:

$$\frac{x+6}{15} = \frac{x-2}{5}$$

---

## 5-1 Group

If it doesn't make you uncomfortable, exchange the following information with the classmates in your Unit 5 group. This will be your small group for the fifth unit. It would be a good idea to schedule a time for the group to meet to go over homework, ask/answer questions, or prepare for exams. You can use this table to help schedule a mutually agreeable time.

| Name | Phone Number | Email | Available times |
|------|--------------|-------|-----------------|
|      |              |       |                 |
|      |              |       |                 |
|      |              |       |                 |
|      |              |       |                 |
|      |              |       |                 |

## Applications of Proportions

The reason that we practiced solving proportions, and in fact the reason this lesson is even in the course, is that there are TONS of applied problems that can be solved by setting up and solving a proportion. In fact, proportions have been around for a really long time in one form or another—a written record of their use goes back at least to 400 BCE or so, but most math historians feel that the idea is almost as old as formal numeric thought. That doesn't happen unless a topic is legitimately useful.

Here's the first problem we'll study: While on a spring break trip, a group of friends burns 12 gallons of gas in the first 228 miles, then stops to refuel. If they have 380 miles yet to drive, and their SUV has a 21-gallon tank, can they make it without refueling again?

Keep in mind that a proportion is an equation stating that two ratios are equal. Keep in mind also that ratios are used to compare the sizes of quantities. So a good way to recognize when proportions might help to solve a problem is to identify situations that are comparing the sizes of related quantities. That's certainly the case here: there's a comparison between gas used and miles traveled. There's also a comparison between the distance traveled in the first segment of the trip, and the distance that can be traveled after refueling. If we start writing some comparisons, maybe we'll be able to write an equation.

1. Write a ratio (in fraction form) comparing the amount of gas burned in the first portion of the trip to the distance driven.

$$\frac{12 \text{ gallons}}{228 \text{ miles}}$$

© Jack Star/PhotoLink/Getty Images RF

2. If we use the symbol $m$ to stand for the variable quantity representing the number of miles they can drive in the second portion of the trip, write a ratio comparing the amount of gas burned in the second portion to the distance driven. Make sure that you put the amount of gas on the same side of the fraction bar as you did in Question 1.

$$\frac{21 \text{ gallons}}{m \text{ miles}}$$

3. Explain why the two ratios that you wrote in Questions 1 and 2 should have the same value. Then set the two ratios equal to each other and solve the resulting proportion.

*Both represent a comparison between fuel burned and miles driven for the same vehicle. Unless the driving conditions change dramatically, which you wouldn't expect on a long trip, the two ratios should be the same.*

$$\frac{12 \text{ gallons}}{228 \text{ miles}} = \frac{21 \text{ gallons}}{m \text{ miles}} \Rightarrow 12m = 4{,}788 \Rightarrow m = 399$$

**4.** Use your result to decide if our friends can make the rest of the trip without refueling. Write a sentence explaining your reasoning.

*They can. They have 380 miles to go and we found that they have enough gas to cover 399 miles. That's kind of cutting it close, but they can make it.*

The procedure outlined in Questions 1–4 is a pretty darn good model for how to solve proportion problems: it's usually about writing ratios by finding information that compares the sizes of quantities, and recognizing that there's a connection between ratios allowing you to set them equal to each other.

In order to decide that a certain species is endangered, biologists have to know how many individuals are in a population. But how do they do that? It's actually an interesting application of proportions illustrated in our next example problem.

As part of a research project, a biology class plans to estimate the number of fish living in a lake thought to be polluted. They catch a sample of 37 fish, tag them, and release them back into the lake. A week later, they catch 80 fish and find that 6 of them are tagged. About how many fish live in the lake?

**5.** Using the letter $f$ to represent the total number of fish in the lake, write a ratio comparing the total number of fish in the lake to the number that are tagged.

$$\frac{f \; total}{37 \; tagged}$$

**6.** Write a ratio that compares the number of fish that were caught a week later to the number that were tagged.

$$\frac{80 \; total}{6 \; tagged}$$

Photo by Scott Bauer, USDA-ARS

**7.** Explain why the two ratios that you wrote in Questions 5 and 6 should have the same value. Then set the two ratios equal to each other and solve the resulting proportion.

*Both ratios are a comparison between the number of fish total (in either the whole lake or a sample) and the number that are tagged.* $\frac{80 \; total}{6 \; tagged} = \frac{f \; total}{37 \; tagged} \Rightarrow 6f = 2{,}960 \Rightarrow f \approx 493$

8.  Use your result to answer the original question posed in this problem. Make sure your answer makes sense in the problem!

*Since the symbol f stands for the variable quantity total number of fish in the lake, there are about 493 fish living in the lake.*

## Math Note

One good way to make sure that your answer to an application problem makes sense is to write your answer in the form of a sentence by rephrasing the original question. Do that here!

---

### Did You Get It

Try this problem to see if you understand the concepts we just studied. The answer can be found at the bottom of the portfolio page.

3.  In 2012, roughly 13 of every 100 people in the United States were African-American. A marketing company wants to select a group of 250 people that accurately reflects the racial makeup of the country. How many African-Americans should be included?

---

There are 39 grams of sugar in one 12-oz. can of Coca Cola. If you're like most Americans, that doesn't come as much of a surprise. Not because you have a good perspective on how much sugar they pack in there—because you have no idea how much sugar that is. Let's check it out.

9.  There are just about 21 grams of sugar in 4 teaspoons of regular granulated sugar. How many teaspoons of sugar are in one can of Coke? To find out, set up and solve a proportion.

*Compare grams of sugar per teaspoon in granulated sugar:* $\frac{21\,g}{4\,tsp}$. *Use C to represent teaspoons of sugar in one can. Then compare grams of sugar per teaspoon in a can of Coke:* $\frac{39\,g}{C\,tsp}$

$$\frac{21\,g}{4\,tsp} = \frac{39\,g}{C\,tsp} \Rightarrow 21C = 156 \Rightarrow C \approx 7.4$$

*There are almost seven and a half teaspoons of sugar in one 12 oz can of Coke. Ugh!*

> Demonstrate this proportion for students, leaving the units in. Tell them that it's not algebraically necessary to leave in the units when setting up and solving a proportion, but it makes it much easier to decide how to set it up.

**10.** How many grams of sugar would you ingest if you drank exactly one can of Coke every day for an entire year?

39 grams per day · 365 days = 14,235 grams

**11.** One hundred grams is just about 0.22 pounds. How many 5-pound bags of sugar would you ingest in a year if you drank that single can of Coke each day? Show all work, and make sure you're using a proportion, seeing as that's like, the point.

$$\frac{100\ g}{0.22\ lb} = \frac{14,235\ g}{x\ lb} \Rightarrow 100x = 3,131.7 \Rightarrow x = 31.317\ lb$$

Dividing by 5, we get 6.2634 5-pound bags of sugar.

**12.** There are about 12.5 grams of sugar in one standard-sized Reese's peanut butter cup. How many of those would you have to eat in a year to get the same amount of sugar that you get in a daily can of Coke?

$$\frac{12.5\ g}{1\ cup} = \frac{14,235\ g}{x\ cups} \Rightarrow 12.5x = 14,235 \Rightarrow x = 1,138.8$$

You'd need to eat about 1,139 Reese's cups.

---

## Did You Get It

Try this problem to see if you understand the concepts we just studied. The answer can be found at the bottom of the portfolio page.

4. According to a poll conducted by the Gallup Corporation in 2014, the metropolitan areas with the highest and lowest proportions of obese adults were Baton Rouge, LA, and Colorado Springs, CO, respectively. In Baton Rouge, for every 321 people who were not obese, there were 179 who were. In Colorado Springs, for every 49 obese people, there were 201 who were not obese. At that time, the estimated populations were 825,478 for Baton Rouge and 686,908 for Colorado Springs. How many more obese people were there in the Baton Rouge area than in the Colorado Springs area?

Understanding ratios can be really helpful in making sure that you've set up a proportion problem correctly. We'll illustrate the idea with one final example.

Based on a combination of worldwide surveys conducted from 2008 to 2011 and reported at Gallup.com, for every 29 people that would be happy to stay in the country they live in, 71 would prefer to emigrate to a different country. At the time, the population of the world was very close to 7 billion. Based on these results, how many of those people were happy where they lived?

First, we write a ratio based on the survey:

$$\frac{\text{Want to stay}}{\text{Want to leave}} \quad \frac{29}{71}$$

> **Math Note**
>
> When writing a ratio, writing it first in words is a really great way to keep track of what it represents.

If we use the letter $h$ to represent the variable quantity representing the number of people worldwide that are happy in the country where they live, it would seem reasonable to write the ratio

$$\frac{h}{7 \text{ billion}}$$

13. This is a fine ratio. It's delightful. But it won't help answer the question. Write the ratio in word form, like the one above, and explain why.

   *It compares people that want to stay to 7 billion people in the world. This ratio doesn't compare those that want to stay to those that want to leave, like the first one. It compares those that want to stay to EVERYONE.*

To avoid inconsistency in setting up proportions, we can use a snazzy rule:

 **The Rule of Matching Parts**

> When setting up a proportion, read the numbers straight across the numerators. There should be a connection between the pieces of information they represent. Repeat for the denominators. Then read up and down on each side of the equation—the same should be true.

If we set up a proportion using the two ratios above and apply the rule of matching parts, we can see that we've made a mistake.

$$\begin{array}{ccc} & \text{Numbers} & \\ & \text{from} & \text{Overall} \\ & \text{survey} & \text{population} \end{array}$$

$$\text{Want to stay} \longrightarrow \frac{29}{71} = \frac{h}{7 \text{ billion}} \begin{array}{l} \longleftarrow \text{Want to stay} \\ \longleftarrow \text{Total people} \end{array}$$

Reading up and down, we're good: both parts on the left are numbers from the survey, and both parts on the right are numbers from the overall population. Reading across the numerators, we're also good: both numbers represent folks that want to stay in their country. It's reading across denominators that we find our mistake: on the left, we have people that want to leave, on the right we have total people. The easiest fix? Change the 71 in the left-side denominator to 100, which represents a total from the survey ($29 + 71 = 100$). We'll ask you to make this change then answer the question in the Applications.

## 5-1 Portfolio

Name _____

Check each box when you've completed the task. Remember that your instructor will want you to turn in the portfolio pages you create.

### Technology

1. ☐ One very common use of ratios is unit pricing. For example, if you buy a 21.7 oz box of Froot Loops for $3.98, the unit price is $\frac{\$3.98}{21.7 \text{ oz}} \approx 0.183 \frac{\$}{\text{oz}}$. This makes it easy to compare prices of items that come in different sizes. Spreadsheets can be a very effective tool for easily computing unit prices. In this exercise, the goal is to build a spreadsheet that computes unit prices to easily decide which item is a better buy. The template provided in online resources lists a number of buying choices. In each case, set up a unit price calculator, then use a background cell color to highlight the item that is the best choice.

### Online Practice

1. ☐ Include any written work from the online assignment along with any notes or questions about this lesson's content.

### Applications

1. ☐ Complete the applications problems.

### Reflections

Type a short answer to each question.

1. ☐ Why is it more useful to compare the sizes of quantities using division than subtraction?
2. ☐ What kinds of problems are likely to be solvable using proportions?
3. ☐ Describe why units are so important in writing ratios.
4. ☐ Take another look at your answer to Question 0 at the beginning of this lesson. Would you change your answer now that you've completed the lesson? How would you summarize the topic of this lesson now?
5. ☐ What questions do you have about this lesson?

### Looking Ahead

1. ☐ Complete the Lesson 5-2 Prep Skills and read the opening paragraph in Lesson 5-2 carefully, then answer Question 0 in preparation for that lesson.

### Answers to "Did You Get It?"

**1. a.** $\frac{22}{3}$ **b.** $\frac{5}{4}$ **2.** $x = 6$ **3.** Either 32 or 33 **4.** 160,887 people

**5-1**  **Applications**

Name _____

In Questions 1–3, a comparison of two quantities is given. Write a ratio and reduce if possible. Make sure the comparisons are consistent in terms of units.

1. 3 pounds to 12 ounces

   Either $\dfrac{3\ lb}{3\frac{1}{4}\ lb}$ which can be rewritten as $\dfrac{4}{1}$, or $\dfrac{48\ oz}{12\ oz}$ which can also be rewritten as $\dfrac{4}{1}$.

   > Point out to students that each of these can be done two ways, but in each case one way leads to an easier ratio to simplify.

2. 12 years to 2 decades

   Either $\dfrac{12\ yr}{20\ yr}$ which can be rewritten as $\dfrac{3}{5}$, or $\dfrac{12\ decade}{2\ decade}$ which can also be rewritten as $\dfrac{3}{5}$.

3. 5 feet to 30 inches

   Either $\dfrac{5\ ft}{2.5\ ft}$ which can be rewritten as $\dfrac{2}{1}$, or $\dfrac{60\ in}{30\ in}$ which can also be rewritten as $\dfrac{2}{1}$.

Near the end of this lesson, we began to study this question: For every 29 people that would be happy to stay in the country they live in, 71 would prefer to emigrate to a different country. At the time, the population of the world was very close to 7 billion. Based on these results, how many of those people were happy where they lived?

4. Review the work we did on page 484 and use it to solve this problem.

   $\dfrac{29\ want\ to\ stay}{100\ total} = \dfrac{h\ want\ to\ stay}{7\ billion\ total} \Rightarrow 100h = 203\ billion \Rightarrow h = 2.03\ billion$

   Only 2.03 billion out of 7 billion people would stay in the country they live in. Wow.

Among those in the survey that said they wanted to leave their current country, 24 out of 71 said they'd like to move to the United States. The two next-highest proportions were for Canada and Great Britain, each at 7 of 71.

5. About how many people in the world want to move to another country? How many of those would choose the United States?

   7 billion − 2.03 billion = 4.97 billion want to move to another country.

   $\dfrac{24\ want\ U.S.}{71\ want\ to\ move} = \dfrac{x\ want\ U.S.}{4.97\ billion\ want\ to\ move} \Rightarrow 71x = 119.28\ billion \Rightarrow x = 1.68\ billion$ want to move to the United States.

## 5-1 Applications

Name _____

**6.** How many more people want to move to the United States than to Canada and Great Britain combined?

$\dfrac{14 \text{ want Can or GB}}{71 \text{ want to move}} = \dfrac{x \text{ want Can or GB}}{4.97 \text{ billion want to move}} \Rightarrow 71x = 69.58 \text{ billion} \Rightarrow x = 0.98 \text{ billion}$ want to move to Canada or Great Britain. So 1.68 billion − 0.98 billion = 0.7 billion, which is 700 million, more people want to move to the United States than to Canada and Great Britain combined.

**7.** A true story about how I recently used a proportion: My car has one of those touch-screen thingies for maps, music, and so forth, and you can upload your own picture to be the background screen. The catch is that the size of the picture has to be 800 pixels wide by 384 pixels high, or it gets all stretched out and looks goofy. Actually, the picture doesn't have to be EXACTLY those dimensions: it just has to have the same ratio of width to height. The most recent picture I chose to use as background screen had a native width of 1,164 pixels. To what height did I need to crop it?

$\dfrac{800 \text{ wide}}{384 \text{ high}} = \dfrac{1,164 \text{ wide}}{x \text{ high}} \Rightarrow 800x = 446,976$

$x \approx 559$

The picture was cropped to a height of 559 pixels. And it looks GOOD.

Courtesy of Dave Sobecki

**8.** A small college has 1,200 students and 80 professors. The college is planning to increase enrollment to 1,500 students next year. How many new professors should be hired to keep the ratio of students to professors the same?

Let $x =$ the number of new professors to hire.

$\dfrac{1,200 \text{ students}}{80 \text{ profs}} = \dfrac{1,500 \text{ students}}{80 + x \text{ profs}} \Rightarrow 1,200(80 + x) = 120,000 \Rightarrow 80 + x = 100 \Rightarrow x = 20$

They need to hire 20 new professors.

# Lesson 5-2   Prep Skills

This is a short review of skills that will come in handy in the next lesson. In each case, answer the question, then rate your confidence level by checking one of the boxes. If you feel like you're struggling with these skills, consult the online resources provided by your instructor for extra practice.

### SKILL 1: EVALUATING EXPRESSIONS FOR A GIVEN INPUT

1. Evaluate each expression for the given values of $x$.

    $2x + 12$; $x = -10, 0, 10$

    $700 - 0.3x$; $x = 0, 350, 1{,}100$

    $x^2 + 7x - 3$; $x = -3, 0, 5$

    $-2x^2 + 400$; $x = 0, 10, 20$

### SKILL 2: SOLVING LINEAR EQUATIONS

2. Find all solutions to each equation.

    $2x + 12 = 0$

    $0 = 700 - 0.3x$

### SKILL 3: WRITING INEQUALITIES

3. Write each statement as an inequality.

    $x$ is a number less than 140.

    $y$ is a number greater than or equal to $-10$.

    $z$ is a number between 4 and 12.

# Lesson 5-2    **Making Some Extra Cash**    (The Basics of Graphing Functions)

### LEARNING OBJECTIVES

☐ 1. Demonstrate an understanding of the significance of a rectangular coordinate system.

☐ 2. Describe what the graph of an equation is.

☐ 3. Use and interpret function notation.

☐ 4. Graph and interpret linear functions.

☐ 5. Graph and interpret quadratic functions.

*A dead tree, cut into planks and read from one end to the other, is a kind of line graph, with dates down one side and height along the other, as if trees, like mathematicians, had found a way of turning time into form.*

—Alice Oswald

Pretty much everyone I know has been in a situation at least once in their lives where they really need some quick cash. When you find yourself in that position, what to do? Picking up a temporary job would certainly be one way to raise some funds. In a lot of locations, business owners pay people to stand near a busy intersection to advertise the services offered by their company. Sometimes workers hand out flyers or coupons that are designed to encourage customers to stop in. Of course, the boss would want to know that the time he or she is paying for is being well-spent, so it would be reasonable to keep track of how many customers they get from their investment. In turn, this might affect how much money you could make from the job. If you're handing out coupons for $2 off at a local restaurant, your pay would most likely depend on how many of those coupons get used by actual customers.

This is the type of situation that the field of math modeling was designed to study. What does the relationship between the number of coupons used and the amount of money you earn look like? In this lesson, after reviewing some basic graphing skills, we'll dive into the study of math modeling by studying questions about how the size of one quantity affects another.

**0.**  After reading the opening paragraph, what do you think the main topic of this lesson will be?

> In an ideal world most, if not all, of this lesson would be review for students in a college-level course. We felt that it was important to remind students of the key ideas involved in modeling.

## 5-2  |  Class

We've already talked about scatter plots in this course, but before we dive in on graphing equations, let's review some basic facts about the rectangular coordinate system.

## The Rectangular Coordinate System

The foundation of graphing in math is a system for locating data points using a pair of perpendicular number lines. We call each one an **axis.**

**1.**  The horizontal number line is called the ___x axis___, the vertical number line is called the ___y axis___, and the point where the two intersect is called the ___origin___.

Collectively, they form what is known as a **rectangular coordinate system,** sometimes called the **Cartesian plane.** The two axes divide the plane into four regions called **quadrants,** which we number using Roman numerals I, II, III, and IV as shown below.

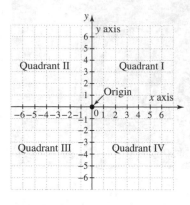

When visualizing data, it's often natural to have two quantities paired together (like the number of coupons that get used and the amount of money you make). We can associate pairs of numbers in a rectangular coordinate system with points by locating each number on one of the two number lines that make up the coordinate system. We call the two numbers **coordinates** of a point. Together they form an **ordered pair,** and we write them as $(x, y)$, where the first numeral describes a number on the $x$ axis and the second describes a number on the $y$ axis.

2. The coordinates of the origin are ____(0,0)____.

3. A point $P$ whose $x$ coordinate is 2 and whose $y$ coordinate is 5 is written as $P = (\,\underline{2}\,,\,\underline{5}\,)$.

4. The point in Question 3 is plotted by starting at the origin and moving two units ___right___ and five units ___up___.

5. Negative coordinates correspond to negative numbers on the axes, so a point like $(-5, -4)$ is plotted by starting at the origin, moving five units ___left___ and four units ___down___.

6. Plot and label the points from Questions 3 and 5 on the figure to the right.

For Questions 7–11, fill in the blanks in these key observations about the rectangular coordinate system:

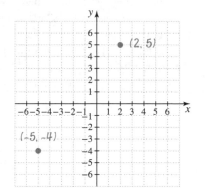

7. If both coordinates of a point are positive, the point is located in quadrant ___I___.

8. If $x$ is negative and $y$ is positive, the point is located in quadrant ___II___.

9. If $x$ and $y$ are both negative, the point is located in quadrant ___III___.

10. If $x$ is positive and $y$ is negative, the point is in quadrant ___IV___.

11. If $x = 0$, the point is on the ___y___ axis, and if $y = 0$, the point is located on the ___x___ axis.

## Linear Functions

Suppose you get offered six bucks to stand on a street corner and hand out flyers for a restaurant, plus an extra $2 for every customer that brings your flyer into the restaurant and orders a meal. If we use variable $x$ to represent the number of customers ordering a meal with your flyer, and variable $y$ to represent the amount of money you make, we could write an equation to describe $y$: $y = 2x + 6$. Verbally, this says that you make $2 times the number of flyers returned, plus $6. If we choose a pair of numbers to substitute into this equation for $x$ and $y$, exactly two things can happen: the resulting equation is either true or false.

12. Substitute $x = 4$ and $y = 14$ into the equation $y = 2x + 6$. Is the resulting statement true or false? Be sure to show your work.

    *The equation is $14 = 2(4) + 6$, which is a true statement.*

13. Substitute $x = 14$ and $y = 4$ into the equation $y = 2x + 6$. Is the resulting statement true or false? Be sure to show your work.

    *The equation is $4 = 2(14) + 6$, which is not a true statement.*

14. Based on your answers to Questions 12 and 13 we call the pair (___4___, ___14___) a **solution** to the equation, and say that the pair of numbers **satisfies** the equation. On the other hand, the pair (___14___, ___4___) is not a solution to the equation.

Here's a list of some pairs that satisfy the equation $y = 2x + 6$:

   $(0, 6), (1, 8), (2, 10), (3, 12), (4, 14)$

15. Plot the points corresponding to these pairs. What do you notice?

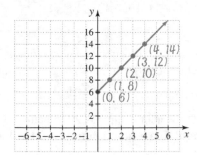

   *The points line up in what appears to be a straight line.*

Hopefully, you noticed that all of the points appear to line up in a straight line pattern. This is not a coincidence. In fact, for this reason, equations like $y = 2x + 6$ are called **linear equations.** (More on that later.)

16. Connect the points you plotted above with a line.

17. Explain why in this case it's appropriate to include an arrow on the right end of the line you drew, but NOT the left end.

*Hopefully you'll end up with more than six customers turning in flyers that you handed out, so the line would continue to the right. But they can't turn in a negative number of flyers, so we want the graph to have a distinct beginning at x = 0.*

> This is a CRUCIAL point in modeling: you always need to think about when the mathematical model does and does not make sense in the context of a situation.

The result of plotting some sample points and then making an educated guess on how to fill in the gaps is called the *graph of the equation*. This is one of the most important ideas in all of math, so it deserves a cool definition box:

> The **graph of an equation** is a way to geometrically represent every pair of numbers that is a solution to the equation. Each of those pairs corresponds to a point on the graph.

We may not have realized it, but we've been working with a really important concept in math for quite some time now. Finally, we'll give it a name and symbols.

> A **function** is a relationship between two quantities where each input produces a unique output.

In the case of that job handing out flyers, for every possible number of those bad boys that can be redeemed at the restaurant, there corresponds a specific amount of money that you'll make. In this case, the number of flyers redeemed is the input, and the resulting output is your pay. In order to make it clear that a given equation actually defines a function, we use *function notation*.

 **Function Notation**

> For a given input $x$, the output of a function named $f$ is described by the symbol $f(x)$, which is read "$f$ OF $x$," NEVER "$f$ TIMES $x$."

The use of the word "of" is to indicate that every output for a function is a result **OF** applying that function to a given input. The symbol $f(x)$ does NOT indicate multiplication; it's a way to indicate that the function $f$ determines the output for a given input $x$.

18. For example, the function describing your pay from handing out $x$ flyers could be written as $f(x) =$ ___$2x + 6$___.

19. In that case, $f(20)$ represents the output of the function (amount of money you make) when the input is 20 (meaning 20 flyers get handed out and turned in). Compute the value of $f(20)$. This is called **evaluating a function for a particular value of the input.** Then describe what your result means in context.

*$f(20) = 2(20) + 6 = 46$; If 20 flyers get turned in, you'll make $46.*

Another advantage of function notation is efficiency. By writing $f(8) = 22$, we can communicate a bunch of information in one clean notation.

**20.** Write a sentence explaining what is meant by $f(8) = 22$ in the context of this problem.

*If 8 flyers get turned in, you'll make $22.*

> Point out to students that understanding the *context* is the crucial difference between studying algebraic topics in this course, and studying algebraic topics in a traditional algebra course.

## Did You Get It

Try this problem to see if you understand the concepts we just studied. The answer can be found at the bottom of the portfolio page.

1. The tuition at a community college is based on a flat fee of $200, plus an additional $120 for each credit hour you register for. The cost of registering for $x$ hours can then be modeled by $T(x) = 200 + 120x$. Find $T(3)$ and $T(15)$ and describe what each result means.

## Using Technology: Using the Table Feature to Find Ordered Pairs

The table feature on a graphing calculator can be used to quickly find points on a graph.

1. Enter the equation next to **Y1** on the **Y =** screen.
2. Access the Table Setup by pressing **2nd, WINDOW.** Decide on the lowest input value you want an output for, and enter it next to **TblStart.** Then decide on the distance you want between input values, and enter it next to **ΔTbl** for your input values
3. View the table by pressing **2nd GRAPH.**
4. Selecting **Ask** next to **Indpnt** in the **TABLE SETUP** screen will allow you to input any $x$ values and have the calculator calculate the corresponding $y$ values. Hey, that's probably why it's called a calculator!

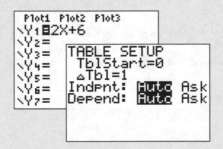
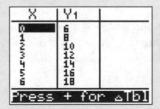
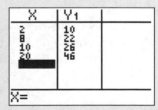

*See the Lesson 5-2-1 Using Tech video in class resources for further information.*

## Intercepts

When drawing the graph of an equation, the first thing you need to decide is how to scale the two axes. A good way to help decide is to find the key points where the graph crosses each axis.

21. The point where a graph crosses the __x__ axis is called the $x$ intercept, and the point where a graph crosses the __y__ axis is called the $y$ intercept.

22. Every point on the $x$ axis has $y$ coordinate __0__, and every point on the $y$ axis has $x$ coordinate __0__, so we get the following rules.

### Finding Intercepts

To find the $x$ intercept, substitute zero for $y$ and solve the equation for $x$.

To find the $y$ intercept, substitute zero for $x$ and solve the equation for $y$.

23. Find the $x$ intercept for the equation $y = 2x + 6$. Explain the significance of this point in the context of handing out flyers, or explain why it doesn't have one.

    Plugging in zero for $y$, we get $0 = 2x + 6$, $2x = -6$, $x = -3$. The $x$ intercept is $(-3, 0)$. This has no meaning in the context because you can't have a negative number of flyers turned in.

    > We decided to leave it to the instructor to decide how rigid you want to be in terms of writing intercepts as points. That's my preference, so that's what you'll see in the answers.

24. Find the $y$ intercept for the equation $y = 2x + 6$. Explain the significance of this point in the context of handing out flyers, or explain why it doesn't have one.

    Plugging in zero for $x$, we get $y = 2(0) + 6 = 6$. The $y$ intercept is $(0, 6)$. Since you're getting six bucks plus extra for each flyer turned in, it makes perfect sense that if none get turned in, your pay is $6.

### Did You Get It

Try this problem to see if you understand the concepts we just studied. The answer can be found at the bottom of the portfolio page.

2. Find both intercepts for the function describing tuition in Did You Get It 1, then explain the significance of each in the context of the problem, or explain why it doesn't have one.

# 5-2 Group

So far, we've looked at an example of a linear function. Linear functions are particularly convenient to work with because they're easy to recognize, both from the graph and from the equation.

- All linear functions can be written in the form $f(x) = mx + b$ where $m$ and $b$ are real number constants.

- The graph of every linear function is a straight line. (Which explains why they're called linear functions.)

1.  In the general form $f(x) = mx + b$, what letter represents the input of the function? What letter represents the output?

    x is the input, and f is the output.

In using function notation, math folks often use letters other than $f$ for the name of the function. Sometimes we use letters to help us remember what the function stands for. In the next function we study, we'll use the capital letter $C$ to represent the cost of a mobile phone plan.

The function $C(x) = 15x + 80$ represents the cost of a cell phone plan, where $x$ represents the number of megabytes the user goes over their 6 gigabyte data allowance.

2.  Complete the table of ordered pairs, and use it to draw the graph of $C(x)$.

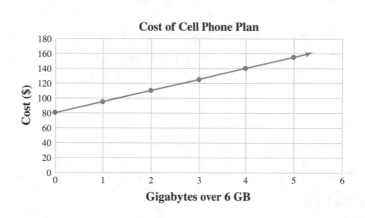

| x | C(x) |
|---|------|
| 0 | 80 |
| 1 | 95 |
| 2 | 110 |
| 3 | 125 |
| 4 | 140 |
| 5 | 155 |

**Cost of Cell Phone Plan**

3.  Fill in the blank. $C(3) = \underline{125}$. Explain what both numbers in this statement mean.

    When you go over your 6 GB limit by 3 GB, then your cost for this plan will be $125.

## Math Note

According to Juniper Research, the average American mobile phone customer used 2.5 gigabytes of data per month in the first quarter of 2015, up from 1.8 GB the year before.

4. Complete the blank. $C(\underline{\phantom{5}}5\underline{\phantom{5}}) = 155$. Explain what both numbers in this statement mean.

   *When you go over your 6 GB limit by 5 GB, then your cost for this plan will be $155.*

5. Explain the conditions for which the cost of this phone plan would be more than $140.

   *The cost of this plan will be more than $140 if you go over the 6 GB limit by more than 4 GB.*

6. Write the question and the answer to Question 5 in symbols.

   *Question: $C(x) > 140$    Answer: $x > 4$*

   > Students will likely need some guidance here, but we didn't want to flat-out tell them to use an inequality.

7. Find the $x$ intercept for $C(x)$ and describe if it has meaning in the context of the problem.

   *$0 = 15x + 80$, so we get $15x = -80$ and $x = -80/15$. The x intercept is $(-80/15, 0)$, which has no meaning here because you can't use a negative amount of data. (But if you could your plan would be free, so you'd have that going for you.)*

8. Find the $y$ intercept for $C(x)$ and describe if it has meaning in the context of the problem.

   *The y intercept is $(0, 80)$. If you don't go over your data limit, the monthly cost is $80.*

   > This is a good place to see if students are THINKING. If not, they'll find the intercept algebraically, and you can use that as a lesson on not just memorizing procedures.

9. As the $x$ (input) values increase from 0 to 1, the $y$ (output) values change from __80__ to __95__, which is an increase of __15__.

10. As the $x$ (input) values increase from 3 to 4, the $y$ (output) values change from __125__ to __140__, which is an increase of __15__.

11. Summarize what you observe about how the *y* values change compared to the *x* values. A good answer will include units.

*Every time the input increases by 1 GB, the output goes up by $15.*

> We'll deal with the interpretation of slope as rate of change a lot in the next lesson. This is just setting that idea up.

## Did You Get It

Try this problem to see if you understand the concepts we just studied. The answer can be found at the bottom of the portfolio page.

3. The function $C(x) = 2.40x + 3.60$ represents the cost of a taxi ride of length *x* miles.

   a. Complete the table and draw the graph of the function.

   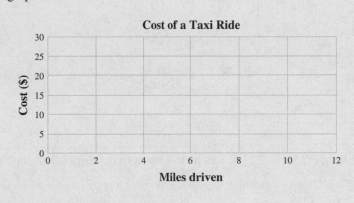

   | x | C(x) |
   |---|------|
   | 0 | |
   | 2 | |
   | 4 | |
   | 6 | |
   | 8 | |
   | 10 | |

   **Cost of a Taxi Ride**

   b. Find the intercepts and explain the meaning of each, if there is one.
   c. Fill in the blanks and explain the meaning of each resulting ordered pair.

   $$C(2) = \underline{\hspace{1cm}} \qquad C(\underline{\hspace{1cm}}) = 22.80$$

   d. Explain the conditions for which the cost of a ride in this taxi would be less than $13.20 and write this question and answer in symbols.

## Quadratic Functions

Linear functions are useful in a lot of different settings, but they're not the only game in town. Next, we'll turn our attention to the graph of a *quadratic function*. A function of the form $f(x) = ax^2 + bx + c$, where *a*, *b*, and *c* are real numbers and $a \neq 0$, is called a **quadratic function.** The $a \neq 0$ part provides the distinguishing feature of quadratic functions: The highest power of the variable that appears is two. The graph of a quadratic function is called a **parabola.** If you toss a ball across a room and think of the path it would take if viewed from the side, then you're thinking of a parabola.

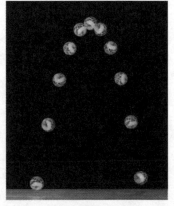

© Custom Life Science Images/ Alamy

After hiring an economic consultant, the owner of a small business is informed that the profit from producing and selling $x$ model toys per week can be approximated by the function $P(x) = -x^2 + 70x - 600$.

12. Complete the table of ordered pairs. (Using some form of technology might be a good idea.) Then plot the points and complete the graph by connecting the points with a smooth line. If you found and plotted all of the points correctly, you should get a shape similar to the time-lapse photo on page 497—a parabola. Think about whether it is or is not appropriate to put arrows on the ends of your graph.

| $x$ | $P(x)$ |
|---|---|
| 0 | −600 |
| 5 | −275 |
| 10 | 0 |
| 15 | 225 |
| 20 | 400 |
| 25 | 525 |
| 30 | 600 |

| $x$ | $P(x)$ |
|---|---|
| 35 | 625 |
| 40 | 600 |
| 45 | 525 |
| 50 | 400 |
| 55 | 225 |
| 60 | 0 |

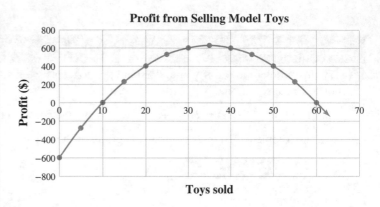

13. Fill in the blank. $P(5) =$ ___−275___. Explain what both numbers in this statement mean.

    $P(5) = -275$: When you sell 5 model toys in a week, you'll lose $275.

14. Complete the blank. $P(\underline{20 \text{ or } 50}) = 400$. If there's more than one correct answer for this blank, give them all. Explain what all numbers in this statement mean.

    When you sell either 20 or 50 model toys in a week, you'll profit $400.

15. What has to happen for the weekly profit for this business to be more than $600?

    The weekly profit for this business would be more than $600 if they sell between 30 and 40 model toys in a week.

16. Write the question and the answer to Question 15 in symbols.

    Question: $P(x) > 600$   Answer: $30 < x < 40$

> This question provides an opportunity to review writing intervals as a three-part inequality, which we saw back in Unit 4.

**17.** Do you see any *x* intercepts on your graph? If so, what are they and what do they mean?

*There are two x intercepts: (10, 0) and (60, 0). This tells us that if the company makes and sells either 10 or 60 toys per week, they'll break even.*

**18.** Do you see a *y* intercept on your graph? If so, what is it and what does it mean?

*There's a y intercept at (0, −600). This tells us that if the company doesn't sell any toys in a given week, they'll lose $600.*

## Summary of Linear and Quadratic Functions

**Linear Function**

**Algebraically:** $f(x) = mx + b$

**Graphically:** Straight line

**Example:** $f(x) = -2x + 3$

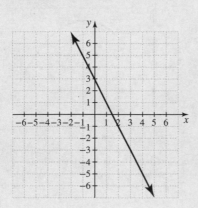

**Quadratic Function**

**Algebraically:** $f(x) = ax^2 + bx + c$

**Graphically:** Parabola

**Example:** $f(x) = x^2 - 4$

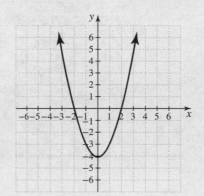

## Using Technology: Graphing Lines and Parabolas

The thing that makes a graphing calculator a graphing calculator is the ability to draw graphs. Here's a quick look at how.

1. Press **Y=** and enter the equation to be graphed.
2. Press **WINDOW** and adjust the viewing window to display the portion of the graph that you're interested in seeing. The two screen shots show settings and the result for the flyer problem and the profit problem from this lesson. Notice how the **Xmin** and **Xmax** settings match the least and greatest $x$ values displayed on the graphs you drew earlier, and the **Xscl** setting matches the width of each box on the grid in the horizontal direction. Likewise, the **Ymin, Ymax,** and **Yscl** settings reflect the lowest and highest values on the $y$ axis as well as the height of each box on the grid.
3. Press **GRAPH.**

   **Note:** If you don't see anything when you press graph, the most likely issue is that you have bad settings on the **WINDOW** screen.

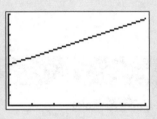

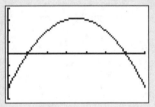

*See the Lesson 5-2-2 Using Tech video in class resources for further information.*

## 5-2 Portfolio

Name _____

Check each box when you've completed the task. Remember that your instructor will want you to turn in the portfolio pages you create.

### Technology

**1.** ☐ While Excel doesn't have a graphing function that allows you to just key in an equation and generate a graph, you can use the scatter plot function and some ingenuity to draw graphs using Excel. You can use the equation as a formula to quickly generate a table of values, then use the "Scatter with smooth lines" command to generate the graph. Easy peasy. In the Applications assignment, you'll be drawing two graphs by hand. In this Technology assignment, you'll use Excel to draw the same two graphs as a way to check your work. There's a template to help you get started in the online resources for this lesson.

### Online Practice

**1.** ☐ Include any written work from the online assignment along with any notes or questions about this lesson's content.

### Applications

**1.** ☐ Complete the applications problems.

### Reflections

Type a short answer to each question.

**1.** ☐ What do you think the term "math modeling" means?
**2.** ☐ Explain what the point of drawing the graph of an equation is in a modeling situation.
**3.** ☐ Take another look at your answer to Question 0 at the beginning of this lesson. Would you revise your answer now that you've completed the lesson? How would you summarize the topic of this lesson now?
**4.** ☐ What questions do you have about this lesson?

### Looking Ahead

**1.** ☐ Complete the Lesson 5-3 Prep Skills and read the opening paragraph in Lesson 5-3 carefully, then answer Question 0 in preparation for that lesson.

### Answers to "Did You Get It?"

**1.** $T(3) = 560$, $T(15) = 2,000$. It would cost \$560 to register for 3 hours, and \$2,000 for 15 hours.
**2.** The $x$ intercept is $(-5/3, 0)$, which has no meaning in context, and the $y$ intercept is $(0, 200)$, which means that you'll pay \$200 to be a student without taking any hours.
**3. a.** Table and graph are on the last page of the applications pages.      **b.** The $x$ intercept is $(-1.5, 0)$ which has no meaning. The $y$ intercept is $(0, 3.6)$, which means that it costs \$3.60 just to get into the cab.      **c.** $C(2) = 8.4$, and $C(8) = 22.8$. A cab ride of 2 miles costs \$8.40, while riding for 8 miles costs \$22.80.      **d.** Any ride less than 4 miles will cost less than \$13.20; Question: $C < 13.2$; Answer: $x < 4$.

## 5-2 Applications

Name _____

For skydivers, it is recommended that the parachute is opened by the time they reach an altitude of 2,500 ft. Once a parachute opens, skydivers fall at approximately 22 ft/sec. Assuming the chute opens at 2,500 ft, the height in feet of a skydiver can be modeled by the function $H(x) = 2,500 - 22x$, where $x$ is the number of seconds after the chute opens.

1. Would you describe this as a linear function or a quadratic function? Explain.

   *This is a linear function. It is in the form $f(x) = mx + b$.*

2. Complete the table of ordered pairs.

© Purestock/SuperStock RF

| x | H(x) |
|---|---|
| 0 | 2,500 |
| 15 | 2,170 |
| 30 | 1,840 |
| 45 | 1,510 |
| 60 | 1,180 |
| 75 | 850 |
| 90 | 520 |
| 105 | 190 |
| 120 | −140 |

3. Do all of the ordered pairs make sense in the context of this problem?

   *I certainly hope not. . . . Even if the parachute doesn't open, you'd expect to not reach an altitude of −140 feet.*

4. Find the $y$ intercept and explain what it means in the context of this problem.

   *(0, 2,500) At the time the chute opens, the altitude is 2,500 ft.*

5. Find the $x$ intercept and explain what it means in the context of this problem.

   *(113.6, 0) It takes 113.6 seconds from the time the chute opens to reach the ground.*

## 5-2 Applications

Name _____

6. Using the intercepts and a few of the ordered pairs from the table, draw the graph of $H(x)$.

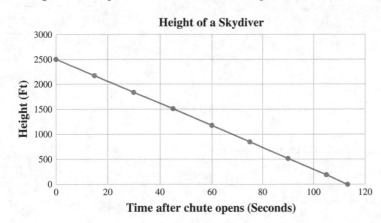

**Height of a Skydiver**

7. Should we put arrows on either end of the graph? Explain.

   *No. We don't know anything about the height before the chute opens, so we have nothing to model for negative inputs. And our skydiver won't continue underground even under the worst of circumstances, so any negative outputs won't make sense in context.*

8. Fill in the blank. $H(12) = $ __2,236__. Explain what both numbers in this statement mean.

   *Twelve seconds after the parachute opens, the height of the skydiver is 2,236 feet.*

9. Fill in the blank. $H($ __90__$) = 520$. Explain what both numbers in this statement mean.

   *Ninety seconds after the parachute opens, the height of the skydiver is 520 feet.*

# 5-2   Applications

Name _____

10. Explain when the height of the skydiver would be less than 850 ft. Write the question and the answer in symbols.

*Between 75 and 113.6 seconds after the parachute opens, the skydiver will be below 850 feet.*

*Question: $H(x) < 850$.    Answer: $75 < x < 113.6$*

The profit for a company that produces discount sneakers can be modeled by the function $P(x) = 4x^2 - 32x - 210$, where $x$ is the number of pairs of sneakers sold.

11. Would you describe this as a linear function or a quadratic function? Explain.

*This is a quadratic function. It's in the form $f(x) = ax^2 + bx + c$.*

12. Complete the table of ordered pairs and use them to draw a graph of $P(x)$.

| x | P(x) |
|---|------|
| 0 | −210 |
| 2 | −258 |
| 4 | −274 |
| 6 | −258 |
| 8 | −210 |
| 10 | −130 |
| 12 | −18 |
| 14 | 126 |
| 16 | 302 |

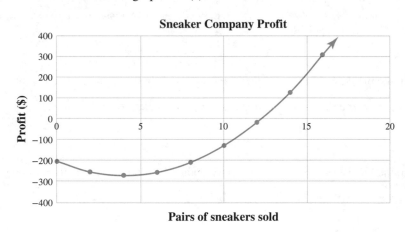

**Sneaker Company Profit**

13. Do all of the ordered pairs make sense?

*They do, because profit can be negative.*

14. Find the $y$ intercept and explain what it means in the context of this problem.

*$(0, -210)$. If the company sells no sneakers, they'll lose 210 dollars.*

## 5-2   Applications

Name _____

15. Write the equation you would need to solve to find the $x$ intercept. Then use the graph to approximate this $x$ intercept and explain what it means in the context of this problem.

    Equation: $4x^2 - 32x - 210 = 0$; Approximate x intercept (12.2, 0). When they sell 12 pairs, they'll come close to breaking even.

16. Should arrows be placed at either end of this graph? Explain.

    At the left end, no, because they can't sell a negative number of pairs. On the right side, yes: sales can continue to go up. You might discuss the fact that at some point the model (like most) will no longer be realistic.

17. Fill in the blank. $P(11) = \underline{-78}$. Explain what both numbers in this statement mean.

    Selling 11 pairs of sneakers will result in a loss of $78.

18. Fill in the blank. $P(\underline{16}) = 302$. Explain what both numbers in this statement mean.

    Selling 16 pairs of sneakers will result in a profit of $302.

19. Look over your graph. There should appear to be a point on the graph that is lower than all other points. Write a statement containing both coordinates of this point using function notation. Explain the meaning of that statement in the context of this problem.

    The point is (4, −274). This can be written as $P(4) = -274$: The worst this company can do is lose $274. This happens if they sell 4 pairs of sneakers.

**Answers to "Did You Get It?"**

| x | 0 | 2 | 4 | 6 | 8 | 10 |
|------|------|------|-------|-------|-------|-------|
| C(x) | 3.60 | 8.40 | 13.20 | 18.00 | 22.80 | 27.60 |

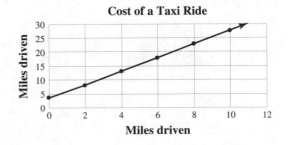

Cost of a Taxi Ride

# Lesson 5-3   **Prep Skills**

This is a short review of skills that will come in handy in the next lesson. In each case, answer the question, then rate your confidence level by checking one of the boxes. If you feel like you're struggling with these skills, consult the online resources provided by your instructor for extra practice.

### SKILL 1: FIND THE INTERCEPTS OF A LINE

1. Find all intercepts for the function $f(x) = -12x + 300$.

### SKILL 2: EVALUATE QUADRATIC FUNCTIONS

2. For each quadratic function, find the requested outputs.

   $K(x) = 3x^2 + 14x - 12$; find $K(0)$, $K(-3)$, and $K(10)$

   $f(x) = -0.2x^2 - 1.4x + 5.4$; find $f(4.125)$ and $f(11.9)$

### SKILL 3: INTERPRET A CORRELATION COEFFICIENT

3. A trendline is calculated for two different data sets. For the first set, the correlation coefficient $r$ is 0.359. For the second set, $r = -0.873$. Which of the two sets is more accurately modeled by a linear function?

### SKILL 4: USE THE DISTRIBUTIVE PROPERTY

4. Simplify each expression using the distributive property.

   $3x(x + 15)$

   $-16x(4x - 10)$

# Lesson 5-3   **A Slippery Slope**   (Modeling with Linear and Quadratic Functions)

**LEARNING OBJECTIVES**

☐ 1. Calculate slope and interpret as rate of change.

☐ 2. Identify quantities that are and are not good candidates to be modeled with linear or quadratic functions.

☐ 3. Solve problems using linear and quadratic modeling, both algebraically and using technology.

© Grant V Faint/Getty Images RF

*When I see a slippery slope, my instinct is to build a terrace.*
                                                   —John McCarthy

In the movie *The Shawshank Redemption,* there's a character who was released from prison after being locked away for a very long time. The first thing that jumped out at him after going back out into the world was how quickly everything and everyone seemed to move. In a letter back to his friends in prison, he wrote "The world went and got itself in a big damn hurry." Things do change very quickly in our modern world, and those who can't adapt to change get left behind. So far, we've studied math modeling from kind of a static viewpoint: the information we get from points is like a snapshot of what happened at a particular point. In order to study our changing world, we'll be interested in studying relationships between different points in a math model. One of the most common, and most useful, ways of doing so is studying the rate at which a quantity changes, which happens to be the best reason for studying the concept of slope.

Next, we'll turn our attention to key information that can be learned from a quadratic model if you learn a bit more about the behavior of a quadratic graph, which allows us to study how the quantity it models changes.

0. After reading the opening paragraphs, what do you think the main topic of this lesson will be?

## 5-3 ▮ Class

Now that we've reviewed graphing lines and parabolas, and used each to model situations, we'll study these graphs and the types of functions that generate them in greater depth to increase our understanding of the usefulness of math modeling.

## More About Linear Functions

### Slope

Once you know a single point on any line, all you need to get the rest of the line is what direction it heads in. This makes the steepness of a line one of its key characteristics geometrically. Eventually we'll see that this provides much more than just geometric information, but for now we'll focus on graphs. Loosely defined, *slope* is a number that indicates how steep a line is. Understanding how slope is calculated, and why that calculation makes perfect sense, is key to understanding the most important stuff we'll be using slope for in modeling, so let's start there.

The slope of a line on a graph is very much like the slope (or steepness) of a road. Look at the two roads in the figure.

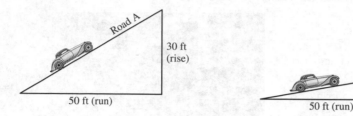

1. If we want slope to measure the steepness of a line, which should have a bigger slope? Why?

   *Road A is clearly steeper.*

   > The key part of the development of slope in this lesson is students figuring out that rise over run is the only reasonable way to define it if we want slope to measure how steep a line is. You can't emphasize this understanding enough.

2. A good way to define steepness of each road is to compare the change in height (sometimes called the *rise*) and the horizontal distance covered (the *run*). And the best way to compare the sizes of two numbers is with a ratio. The question is: which distance should be put in the numerator? Use your answer from Question 1 to decide whether we want to divide change in height by horizontal distance, or horizontal distance by change in height.

   *If we put the change in height in the numerator, we'll get a larger result when the change in height is big compared to the run, which is exactly what we want.*

3. Summary: to find the slope of a line, we divide _____the change in height_____ by _____the horizontal distance covered_____. In terms of coordinates on a graph, we divide the change in __y__ coordinate by the change in __x__ coordinate.

4. Find the slope of each road above; make sure that your results make sense based on your answer to Question 1.

   Road A: $\dfrac{30}{50} = \dfrac{3}{5}$   Road B: $\dfrac{10}{50} = \dfrac{1}{5}$

In my humble opinion, you'd be best off thinking of slope in the way you described it in Question 3. But if you want to think of it more in terms of a formula, here's what we get:
   The **slope** of a line (designated by $m$) is

$$m = \frac{y_2 - y_1}{x_2 - x_1} \quad \frac{\text{Change in } y \text{ coordinate}}{\text{Change in } x \text{ coordinate}}$$

where $(x_1, y_1)$ and $(x_2, y_2)$ are two points on the line. In words, the slope of a line can be calculated by subtracting the $y$ coordinates (the vertical height) of two points and dividing that difference by the difference obtained from subtracting the $x$ coordinates (the horizontal distance) of the same two points.

Let's think back to the cell phone problem in Lesson 5-2. The completed graph and table are reproduced here for convenience.

| X | C(x) |
|---|------|
| 0 | 80 |
| 1 | 95 |
| 2 | 110 |
| 3 | 125 |
| 4 | 140 |
| 5 | 155 |

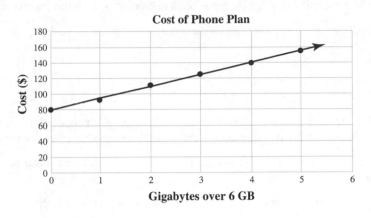

**Cost of Phone Plan**

5. Choose any two points on this line and perform the calculation to find the slope.

   *Calculation varies depending on points chosen, but the slope is 15.*

6. Choose two completely different points and calculate the slope again.

   *Ditto*

7. Explain why it makes no difference which two points you choose.

   *Because the graph is a line and never changes direction. Any portion of if has the same slope as any other portion.*

### Did You Get It

Try this problem to see if you understand the concepts we just studied. The answer can be found at the bottom of the portfolio page.

1. In Did You Get It 3 of Lesson 5-2, you completed the table below, which describes the cost of a cab ride in terms of miles driven. Find the slope of the line that describes the cab fare.

| X | 0 | 2 | 4 | 6 | 8 | 10 |
|------|------|------|-------|-------|-------|-------|
| C(x) | 3.60 | 8.40 | 13.20 | 18.00 | 22.80 | 27.60 |

8. At this point, we know that the slope of the line describing the cell phone charge compares the change in $y$ coordinate to the change in $x$ coordinate. What two quantities is it comparing in the context of the function?

   *It compares the change in cost (numerator) to the change in the number of gigabytes over 6 used (denominator).*

A comparison like the one you described in Question 8 is called a **rate of change.** In this case, we would say that the slope represents the rate at which the monthly cost is changing as the number of gigabytes of data used changes.

9. In the case of the cost of the cell phone plan, we can say that the cost is increasing by __$15__ for each additional GB over the 6 GB limit.

10. You already answered this question in the previous lesson, but what is the $y$ intercept of this line?

   *It's (0, 80)*

**Slope-Intercept Form**

The $y = mx + b$ form we've been using is called the **slope-intercept** form of a linear equation with a slope $m$ and $y$ intercept $(0, b)$. This is very useful information because the slope and $y$ intercept can be observed directly from the equation.

11. The linear function $C(x) = 15x + 80$ that models the phone plan problem in the graph above is also in slope intercept form. Does this make sense with what you've written in Questions 9 and 10? Explain.

   *It does. Based on the slope-intercept form, the slope is 15 and the y intercept is (0, 80).*

Now here is the key point: when we have a linear equation in the form $y = mx + b$, we know the slope (the coefficient of $x$), and the $y$ intercept (the constant term). But it works the other way around, too: if we know the slope and the $y$ intercept for a linear equation, then we can write the equation!

12. A physical therapist made \$43,000 per year at the time she was hired, and her salary has been increasing by \$2,700 each year. Write a linear function $P(x)$ that describes her salary, where $x$ represents the number of years since she was hired.

   *$P(x) = 2,700x + 43,000$*

> One of the key reflections questions asks students about the two ways we can use slope-intercept form in modeling. Emphasize those two ways when covering Questions 11 and 12.

## Did You Get It

Try these problems to see if you understand the concepts we just studied. The answers can be found at the bottom of the portfolio page.

2.  What are the slope and $y$ intercept of the line that has equation $y = -43x - 210$?

3.  Write the equation of a line that has slope $\frac{11}{2}$ and $y$ intercept $(0, 15)$.

## More about Quadratic Functions

When we studied quadratic functions in Lesson 5-2, we got the general shape but left out two details that can be useful in analyzing quadratic models—finding the vertex and finding the $x$ intercepts.

13.  Recall that a function of the form $f(x) = ax^2 + bx + c$, where $a$, $b$, and $c$ are real numbers and $a \neq 0$, is called a ____quadratic_____function____, and the graph of a quadratic function is called a ____parabola____.

When a parabola decreases in height, reaches a low point, and then increases, we say that it *opens upward*. (See the first graph below.) This occurs when $a$, the coefficient of $x^2$, is positive. When a parabola increases in height, reaches a high point, then decreases, as in the second graph below, we say that it *opens downward*. This occurs when $a$ is negative.

One of the key features that makes a parabola a parabola is the fact that it changes direction at some point. The point where this occurs is crucial in studying quantities modeled by quadratic function. It's called the **vertex** of the parabola, and it represents either the lowest or highest point on the entire graph, depending on whether the parabola opens up or down.

Every parabola has two distinct halves, with the divider being a vertical line through the vertex. We call this line the **axis of symmetry.** It's not part of the parabola, but a guide to help us draw one. We say that a parabola is **symmetric** about its axis of symmetry, meaning that the parts of the parabola on either side are mirror images of each other. Two representative parabolas are shown in the figure below.

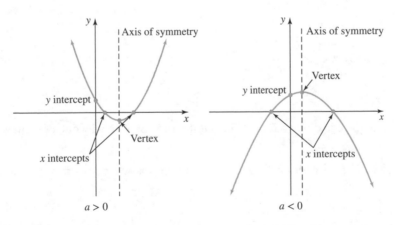

14.  How many $x$ intercepts does a parabola have? (This is a harder question than you might think: Give it some thought, and maybe draw a few sample parabolas.)

It depends on where the vertex is. It can have none (if the vertex is below the x axis for a parabola that opens down, or above the x axis for a parabola that opens up). It could have one if the vertex lives on the x axis. Or it could have two, like the ones in the graphs above.

If a parabola has $x$ intercepts, they are places where the output is zero. So we can find them by substituting zero in for the output, then solving the equation for $x$. (This is how we found $x$ intercepts for linear functions in Lesson 5-2.) In order to do that efficiently, we'll need to be able to solve equations of the form $ax^2 + bx + c = 0$. There are different methods for solving quadratic equations, but there's one that we'll focus on because it works for EVERY equation of that form: the *quadratic formula*. This is a formula that provides all solutions to any quadratic equation. The only catch is that it HAS TO BE in the form $ax^2 + bx + c = 0$.

## The Quadratic Formula

To solve an equation in the form $ax^2 + bx + c = 0$, where $a$ is not zero, identify the coefficients $a$, $b$, and $c$, then substitute them into the formula

$$x = \frac{-b \pm \sqrt{b^2 - 4ac}}{2a}$$

The $\pm$ symbol indicates that there are two possible solutions: one where you add the value of the radical, and one where you subtract it. If the number inside the radical is negative then there are no solutions, and the graph of the quadratic has no $x$ intercepts.

15. The photo back on page 497 shows that a ball flying through the air travels in a parabolic arc. One particular ball is tossed and its path can be modeled by the function $H(x) = -0.1x^2 + x + 2$, where $H$ is the height of the ball when its horizontal position is $x$ feet from where it was thrown. Use the quadratic formula to find how far away from where it was thrown the ball hits the ground. (Hint: This happens when the height is zero.)

$-0.1x^2 + x + 2 = 0;\ a = -0.1,\ b = 1,\ c = 2$

$x = \dfrac{-1 \pm \sqrt{1^2 - 4(-0.1)(2)}}{2(-0.1)} = \dfrac{-1 \pm \sqrt{1.8}}{-0.2} \approx -1.7,\ 11.7$

It lands 11.7 feet from where it was thrown.

16. There are two solutions to the equation you solved in Question 15. Explain why one of them is irrelevant to answering the question.

One solution is $-1.7$: this would mean the ball went backward and landed behind where it was tossed, which doesn't make any sense.

The fact that parabolas are symmetric can provide a really clever way to find the vertex. If you know any two points that live at the same height—like, say, the $x$ intercepts—the symmetry guarantees that the vertex has to be halfway in between. Rearranging the quadratic formula just a bit:

$$x = \frac{-b}{2a} + \frac{\sqrt{b^2 - 4ac}}{2a}, \qquad x = \frac{-b}{2a} - \frac{\sqrt{b^2 - 4ac}}{2a}$$

**17.** Explain why $x = \frac{-b}{2a}$ is halfway between the two $x$ intercepts. You'll need the information at the bottom of the previous page.

*One of the intercepts is* $-b/2a$ *PLUS a number, and the other is* $-b/2a$ *MINUS that same number. If you start someplace on a number line then go a certain distance in each direction, the place you started has to be right in the middle.*

## Finding the Vertex of a Parabola

To find the vertex of a parabola:

**Step 1.** Make sure that the equation is written in the form $y = ax^2 + bx + c$.

**Step 2.** Use the formula $x = \frac{-b}{2a}$ to find the first coordinate of the vertex.

**Step 3.** Substitute that input into the equation to find the second coordinate.

## Did You Get It

Try this problem to see if you understand the concepts we just studied. The answer can be found at the bottom of the portfolio page.

   4.  For the quadratic function $f(x) = 2x^2 + 12x - 1$, find the $x$ intercepts and the vertex.

Remember the quadratic function $P(x) = -x^2 + 70x - 600$ that represents the profit in dollars from selling $x$ model toys in a week for a small business from Lesson 5-2? Let's see about finding the intercepts and the vertex for this function without first making a table or a graph.

**18.** The $y$ intercept is pretty simple. Use the function and show your work to find it.

   *$P(0) = -600$; the $y$ intercept is $(0, -600)$.*

**19.** The $x$-intercept is a little more complicated. Use the quadratic formula (or factoring if you're good at it) to find the two $x$ intercepts. Do your answers agree with your observations from the graph and table?

   *Using either factoring or the quadratic formula, the $x$ intercepts work out to be $(10, 0)$ and $(60, 0)$. These are the same results we got from the table and graph in Lesson 5-2. That's a good thing.*

**20.** Use the formula to find the vertex. Then describe what exactly it tells us about the toy company. Make sure you talk about how the profit CHANGES.

$x = -70/-2 = 35$; $P(35) = 625$. The vertex is $(35, 625)$. This tells us that the profit will get bigger as they make more toys, but it reaches a highest value of $625, which occurs if they make and sell 35 toys. If they continue to make more toys after that, the profit declines.

## 5-3   Group

The standard fare for a taxi in one city is $3.25, plus $1.80 per mile. Our goal is to write a linear function that describes the cost of a cab ride in terms of the length of the ride in miles.

**1.** Identify the quantity in that description that is a rate of change (slope).

$1.80 per mile. It describes how the cost changes (goes up) as the number of miles for the trip changes.

**2.** Identify the quantity that is a fixed or starting value ($y$ intercept).

You pay $3.25 to begin the trip, regardless of the number of miles driven.

**3.** Use your answers to Questions 1 and 2 to write the linear function that describes the cost of the ride. You can use whatever letters you want to represent the cost and the number of miles, but make sure you identify what each letter stands for.

$C(x) = 1.80x + 3.25$, where C represents the cost and x represents the number of miles driven.

© Steve Mason/Getty Images RF

**4.** Show work and use your function to find the cost of a 6-mile ride, an 8.5-mile ride, and a 12-mile ride.

$C(6) = 1.80(6) + 3.25 = $14.05$
$C(8.5) = 1.80(8.5) + 3.25 = $18.55$
$C(12) = 1.80(12) + 3.25 = $24.85$

**Math Note**

When writing a function to model a situation, it's ALWAYS important to clearly identify what quantity each variable represents.

**5.** Use the table in a spreadsheet or a calculator to check your work from Question 4.

*Yep, same answers alright.*

**6.** Show work and use your function to find the length of a ride that costs $10.90. This will involve setting up and solving an equation.

$10.90 = 1.80x + 3.25$

$1.80x = 7.65x$

$x = 4.25$  *A ride of 4.25 miles costs $10.90.*

---

## Did You Get It

Try this problem to see if you understand the concepts we just studied. The answer can be found at the bottom of the portfolio page.

5. The cost of a medium cheese pizza at Mario's Campus Pizzeria is $6.75, and each additional topping costs $0.35.
   a. Write a linear function that describes the cost of a pizza in terms of the number of toppings.
   b. Use your function to find the cost of a pizza with three toppings and one with five toppings.
   c. Use your function to find the number of ingredients on a pizza that costs $8.85.

---

 ## Using Technology: Solving an Equation Using the Intersect Feature

We've already covered how to use the table feature to create ordered pairs. Now, we'll show how to use the intersect feature to solve equations.

1. Enter the left side of the equation next to **Y1**.
2. Enter the right side of the equation next to **Y2**.
3. Adjust the window until you can see where the two graphs cross.
4. Press **2nd TRACE** and select option 5. Then press **ENTER** twice to select the two curves. Before pressing **ENTER** a third time, it might be necessary to move the cursor close to the intersection you are trying to find.
5. The *x* value displayed is a solution to the equation. If the graphs cross more than once, repeat to find additional solutions.

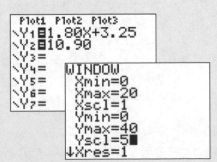

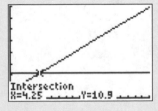

Students can (ideally) solve all of the equations in this lesson algebraically, but this sets up more complicated equations we can use for modeling in Lesson 5-4.

*See the Lesson 5-3 Using Tech video in class resources for further information.*

A family buys a new puppy because puppies are awesome. They plan to fence in a rectangular portion of their backyard for an exercise area. They buy 60 feet of fencing, and plan to put the fenced area against the house so that fencing is needed on only three sides. The goal will be to write a quadratic function that describes the area enclosed, and use it to find the dimensions that will enclose the largest area.

7. Using the diagram below as a guide, if the sides perpendicular to the house are 10 feet long, how long will the side parallel to the house be? SHOW YOUR WORK. That's important.

© Comstock Images/Alamy RF

60 feet total − 2(10) = 40 feet

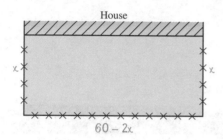

8. Let's use the letter $x$ to represent the length of the two sides perpendicular to the house. Label the diagram using that variable. Then use the same line of reasoning you did in Question 7 to label the length of the side parallel to the house.

9. Write a function $A(x)$ that describes the area enclosed by the fence. Use the dimensions in the diagram.

$A(x) = x(60 − 2x)$

10. Multiply out the parentheses in your function so that it's in the form $A(x) = ax^2 + bx + c$.

$A(x) = −2x^2 + 60x$

> Point out to students that it's okay to have $c = 0$ in a quadratic function.

11. Use our vertex formula to find the dimensions that will provide the largest area for the fuzzy puppy to roam around in.

$x = −60/(−4) = 15$

We were asked for the dimensions so we don't need the second coordinate of the vertex. The area will be greatest when the sides perpendicular to the house are 15 feet long, and the side parallel to the house is 30 feet long.

### Did You Get It

Try this problem to see if you understand the concepts we just studied. The answer can be found at the bottom of the portfolio page.

6. Suppose the family from Questions 7–11 decides to move the dog pen away from the house, so that fence is needed on all four sides. What dimensions will provide the largest area?

When we know that the rate of change of some quantity doesn't change, like the $1.80 per mile in the cab problem, we can use algebra to find an equation for describing that quantity. But what if we don't know if a linear model will fit? Or what if we suspect a quadratic model might work? In that case, we can take advantage of the regression skills we learned in Lesson 4-8. Both graphing calculators and spreadsheets can find linear and quadratic models.

The table below shows the median price for all homes sold in the United States in January for each year from 2003 to 2015. Then we see two scatter plots: the first is for home prices from 2003 to 2009, and the second from 2010 to 2015.

| Date | Median Price |
|------|-------------|
| 2003-01-01 | $181,700 |
| 2004-01-01 | $209,500 |
| 2005-01-01 | $223,100 |
| 2006-01-01 | $244,900 |
| 2007-01-01 | $254,400 |
| 2008-01-01 | $232,400 |
| 2009-01-01 | $208,600 |
| 2010-01-01 | $218,200 |
| 2011-01-01 | $240,100 |
| 2012-01-01 | $221,700 |
| 2013-01-01 | $251,500 |
| 2014-01-01 | $269,800 |
| 2015-01-01 | $292,000 |

*Source: Federal Reserve Bank of St. Louis*

12. Which of the two types of models we studied in this lesson appears to be a good fit for the 2002–2009 data? What about for the 2010–2015 data?

*Quadratic looks like a good choice for the 2002–2009 data; linear seems like a better choice for 2010–2015.*

13. Use a graphing calculator or spreadsheet to find the models that you decided on in Question 12. For best results, don't use years as input: use years after 2003. So the median price in 2003 will match up with $x = 0$, the price in 2004 will match up with $x = 1$ and so on. If you need a review, a description of how to find a line of best fit is on page 436. To find a quadratic regression equation, choose "QuadReg" on a graphing calculator, or choose "Polynomial" under Trendline Options in Excel, then select 2 in the "Order" drop-down menu.

2002–2009: $y = -5{,}483.3x^2 + 38{,}536x + 177{,}762$

2010–2015: $y = 13{,}940x + 116{,}453$

14. What's the value of the correlation coefficient for each model that you found? Explain if these results back up the choices you made in Question 12.

2002–2009: $r = 0.968$

2010–2015: $r = 0.915$

These are both very close to one, which indicates that we made good choices.

> There's so much good stuff to discuss from this problem. Most notably, getting two different accurate models from different years within the same data set is a great way to illustrate what an inexact science modeling with real data can be.

15. Using past data to predict future behavior is a dicey proposition because trends change all the time. Do an Internet search for the median price for new home sales in the United States in January of the current year, then see if either of the models you found in Question 13 provides an accurate prediction.

Answers vary by year.

## 5-3  Portfolio

Name _____

Check each box when you've completed the task. Remember that your instructor will want you to turn in the portfolio pages you create.

### Technology

1. ☐ Near the end of this lesson, we studied median home prices from 2002 to 2015, and found that two different models were appropriate for two different time periods. Each of the data sets we used were very limited, though: either six or seven median prices. The tech template for this lesson has a slightly more extensive data set on home prices: median prices for every month from January 1963 to December 2015, a total of more than 600 data points. Use all of this data to find both a linear and a quadratic model, then write a description of which you think is a more appropriate model. Include EVIDENCE, not just your opinion.

### Online Practice

1. ☐ Include any written work from the online assignment along with any notes or questions about this lesson's content.

### Applications

1. ☐ Complete the applications problems.

### Reflections

Type a short answer to each question.

1. ☐ What is meant by the term "rate of change," and what does that have to do with slope?
2. ☐ Describe two different ways that we can use slope-intercept form in studying data that can be modeled with a linear function.
3. ☐ Discuss the value of finding the vertex for a quadratic model.
4. ☐ Take another look at your answer to Question 0 at the beginning of this lesson. Would you revise your answer now that you've completed the lesson? How would you summarize the topic of this lesson now?
5. ☐ What questions do you have about this lesson?

### Looking Ahead

1. ☐ Complete the Lesson 5-4 Prep Skills and read the opening paragraph in Lesson 5-4 carefully, then answer Question 0 in preparation for that lesson.

### Answers to "Did You Get It?"

1. $m = 2.4$     2. slope: $-43$; $y$ intercept: $(0, -210)$     3. $y = \frac{11}{2}x + 15$
4. $x$ intercepts: $(-6.08, 0)$ and $(0.08, 0)$; vertex: $(-3, -19)$     5. a. $C(x) = 0.35x + 6.75$, where $C$ is the cost and $x$ is the number of toppings.     b. $C(3) = \$7.80$, $C(5) = \$8.50$     c. 6
6. 15 feet on all sides

## 5-3 Applications

Name _____

The United States Census Bureau uses demographic information to set a poverty threshold that is used to determine how many Americans are living in poverty based on annual income. For an individual on her own, the poverty threshold was $4,190 in 1980, and has increased by about $220 per year since then.

1. Which piece of information in the problem is a rate of change? What would that represent in a linear function modeling the poverty threshold?

   *$220 per year, which will be the slope in our model.*

2. When modeling information that changes with time, we almost never use the actual time—whether it's clock time or year—as input. Instead, we choose a beginning time for the problem and call that $x = 0$. In this case, we would decide that $x = 0$ corresponds to 1980, since that's the earliest time we have information for. In that case, what is the $y$ intercept for our function?

   *(0, 4,190)*

3. Write a linear function that describes the poverty threshold in dollars in terms of years after 1980. Then use your function to estimate the poverty threshold in 2010, and the year that it will pass $15,000 per year.

   *$T(x) = 220x + 4,190$*
   *$T(30) = 220(30) + 4,190 = \$10,790$*
   *$15,000 = 220x + 4,190 \Rightarrow 220x = 10,810 \Rightarrow x = 49.1.$ It should pass $15,000 in 2030.*

   *(Need to round up since it won't quite reach $15,000 in 2029.)*

4. Use the Internet to find the most recent poverty threshold as set by the census bureau, and discuss how accurately your model predicted that value.

   *Answers vary depending on year. For 2016, the model says $12,110, the feds say $11,770, which is actually not bad at all.*

The next problem is similar to the one you just solved, but this time instead of stepping you through it, we'll just state the problem and you're on your own. If you need to, using Questions 1–3 as a guide will be helpful. Make sure that you clearly identify what the letters you use in your model represent.

## 5-3   Applications

Name _____

5. A contestant on The Biggest Loser starts out weighing 345 pounds and loses weight steadily at the rate of 7 pounds per week. Write a linear function that describes his weight in terms of weeks, and use it to find how long it will take him to reach his goal of 175 pounds.

*x will stand for weeks after the contest began, and W will stand for the contestant's weight.*

$W(x) = -7x + 345$

$175 = -7x + 345 \Rightarrow \quad -7x = -170 \quad x \approx 24.3$

*It will take a little more than 24 weeks at his current pace.*

When an object is launched or thrown from some height $h_0$ (in feet) with an initial upward velocity $v_0$ (in feet per second), the height in feet of that object $t$ seconds later is given by the function $h(t) = -16t^2 + v_0 t + h_0$. (This ignores the effects of friction and air resistance, which can be negligible for an object like a ball bearing and significant for an object like a paper airplane.) Suppose that a bowling ball is launched upward from the top of a 230-foot building with initial velocity 60 ft/sec. (Legal disclaimer: If you try this, you're a jerk.)

6. In this case, what numbers would correspond to $v_0$ and $h_0$ in the function? Use that information to write the specific function describing the height of the bowling ball.

$v_0 = 60$ *and* $h_0 = 230$

$h(t) = -16t^2 + 60t + 230$

7. Find the vertex of the parabola, then describe what it tells us physically about the situation.

$t = \dfrac{-60}{2(-16)} = 1.875;\ h(1.875) = 286.25;\ \ The\ vertex\ is\ (1.875,\ 286.25).$

*The ball reaches its highest point 1.875 seconds after launch, and it reaches a maximum height of 286 feet and 3 inches.*

8. Find any $x$ intercepts, and describe what they tell us physically about the situation. (You can call them $t$ intercepts if you like, since we're using $t$ as the input.)

$t = \dfrac{-60 \pm \sqrt{60^2 - 4(-16)(230)}}{2(-16)} \approx -2.35,\ 6.10$

*The first has no physical meaning because the ball is incapable of going backward in time. The second tells us that it takes 6.10 seconds for the ball to reach the ground.*

## 5-3   Applications

Name _____

**9.** In a calculus class, you would learn that if the height of the ball is given by $h(t) = -16t^2 + 60t + 230$, then its velocity at any time $t$ is modeled by $v(t) = -32t + 60$. How fast would the ball be going when it hits the ground?

$v(6.10) = -32(6.10) + 60 = -135.2$

*The ball will be going 135.2 feet per second, which goes a long way toward describing why you're a jerk if you launch a bowling ball off the top of a building.*

**10.** Why can't the information we've used in this problem tell us how far away from the building the bowling ball will land?

*Because the input of the function is time, not horizontal distance. The only information we can get from the function is either height or time.*

**11.** A decent major league pitcher can throw a ball at 90 miles per hour, which is 132 feet per second. How high could one of these guys throw a ball straight up, and how long do they have to get out of the way to avoid getting hit in the melon when it comes back down? (Let's say the pitcher is 6 feet tall, and he releases the ball from a point a foot above his head.) Again, you're on your own this time, but you can use Questions 6–8 as a guide.

$v(t) = -16t^2 + 132t + 7$

Find vertex for max. height: $t = \dfrac{-132}{2(-16)} = 4.125$; $h(4.125) = 279.25$

*He can throw the ball 279.25 feet straight up. (This is like throwing it to the top of a 22-story building.)*

Find x intercepts for time to come back down: $t = \dfrac{-132 \pm \sqrt{132^2 - 4(-16)(7)}}{2(-16)} \approx -0.05, 8.3$

*He'll have 8.3 seconds to get out of the way.*

# Lesson 5-4   Prep Skills

This is a short review of skills that will come in handy in the next lesson. In each case, answer the question, then rate your confidence level by checking one of the boxes. If you feel like you're struggling with these skills, consult the online resources provided by your instructor for extra practice.

### SKILL 1: EVALUATE EXPRESSIONS WITH EXPONENTS

1. Find the value of each expression.

$$100(1.15)^{15} \qquad 31{,}000\left(1+\frac{0.04}{12}\right)^{24}$$

### SKILL 2: FIND INTERCEPTS FOR A FUNCTION

2. Find all intercepts for $f(x) = -23x + 70$.

### SKILL 3: SOLVE EQUATIONS USING RADICALS

3. Find all solutions to the equation $y^2 = 144$.

4. Find all solutions to the equation $x^3 = 90$.

### SKILL 4: SOLVE LINEAR EQUATIONS

5. Solve the equation: $12 + 3x = 40$

6. Solve the equation: $-7.3 - 2.3f = 11.1$

# Lesson 5-4 **Phone a Friend** (Modeling with Exponential and Log Functions)

### LEARNING OBJECTIVES

☐ 1. Identify quantities that are and are not good candidates to be modeled with exponential equations.

☐ 2. Solve problems by exponential modeling, both algebraically and using technology.

☐ 3. Define logarithms as inverses of exponentials.

☐ 4. Solve problems by logarithmic modeling, both algebraically and using technology.

© McGraw-Hill Education

*Every time one person gets a piece of information, the likelihood of that information being exposed grows exponentially. It's no longer two people. It's two people squared.*
—Jon Cryer

I'll admit it—I'm a bit of an Apple nerd. I jumped on the iPod bandwagon in the early days, and I do whatever I can to hear about the latest cool technology coming down the pike. It seems pretty quaint now, but I clearly remember back in 2006 when I excitedly told my wife about a rumor I'd read about iPods: that the next ones to come out wouldn't have any physical control buttons—the whole front would be a video display, and controls would pop up when you touched the screen. That sounded like science fiction then, but the introduction of the iPod touch and iPhone in 2007 changed the tech world seemingly overnight. By the end of 2012, not everyone in America had an iPhone—it just seemed that way. The growth in iPhone sales increased so rapidly that the types of functions we've modeled with so far aren't very effective: we'll need to develop a different type of function that allows for a rapidly increasing growth rate. Does that ring a bell? Think about ways to grow your fortune . . .

**0.** After reading the opening paragraph, what do you think the main topic of this lesson will be?

> This Class portion is probably "classier" than most: students will almost certainly need extra guidance. This is one of the few lesson portions that I treat almost like a worksheet in a more traditional lecture course.

## 5-4 Class

A bar graph of iPhone sales between 2007 and 2012 shows one striking feature: it starts low, and grows in a BIG hurry.

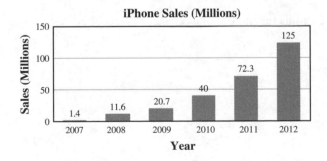

Every one of the functions we've studied so far in this book has one thing in common: all the exponents are numbers. Functions that model rapid growth, like we're seeing in the iPhone sales graph, often have the variable in an exponent. This changes almost everything in terms of the behavior of the function, so the functions known as *exponential functions* merit some special attention. These functions are very useful in modeling situations we've examined in previous units like investments and loans. They are also useful for modeling depreciation, growth and decay, and population changes.

To understand these functions, we'll look at some of the same key characteristics we've studied about linear and quadratic functions. We'll also look at some new ones.

---

An **exponential function** has the form $f(x) = c \cdot b^x$, where $b$ is a positive real number, but not 1, and $c$ is any nonzero real number.

**1.** Which of the following are examples of exponential functions?

   **a.** $f(x) = 2^x$     **b.** $g(x) = 200 \cdot 10^x$     **c.** $h(x) = 5\left(\frac{1}{3}\right)^x$     **d.** $y(x) = (0.5)^x$

   *All of them!*

> ## Math Note
>
> If $b = 0$, then $f(x) = c \cdot b^x$ always has output zero. If $b = 1$, the output is always $c$. If $b$ is negative, we get a MESS: the graph has infinitely many holes in it!

Let's start by looking back at a situation we've already studied—compound interest.

The formula $A = P(1 + r)^t$ tells us how much an account that starts at $P$ dollars is worth after $t$ years at an interest rate $r$, where interest is compounded annually.

**2.** For an account that currently has $5,000 in it and grows at a rate of 3% compounded annually, write a function $A(t)$ that describes the value of this account after $t$ years.

   *$A(t) = 5,000(1.03)^t$*

One of the things we typically find when graphing a function is the $y$ intercept. For exponential functions, this is pretty simple, as we will see shortly.

**3.** For the function you wrote in Question 2, to find the $y$ intercept, we substitute zero for ___*t*___ and find the value of ___*A*___.

**4.** Perform that calculation now and write the $y$ intercept for this function, then plot your $y$ intercept on the graph at the top of the next page.

   *$A(0) = 5,000(1.03)^0 = 5,000$*

   *The y intercept is (0, 5,000).*

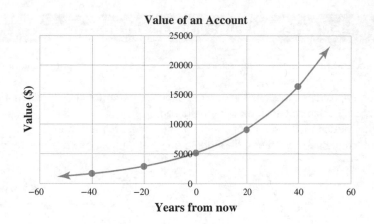

**Value of an Account**

Another key fact we'd like to know is whether there are any $x$ intercepts.

5. In the context of the problem, what would it mean if there was an $x$ intercept?

   *That would be a time when the account reached value zero.*

6. Use a calculator or a spreadsheet to complete the table of values. Then plot these points on the graph.

| t | A(t) |
|------|------|
| −500 | 0.0019 |
| −40 | 1,532.78 |
| −20 | 2,768.38 |
| 0 | 5,000 |
| 20 | 9,030.56 |
| 40 | 16,310.20 |
| 500 | $1.3 \times 10^{10}$ |

7. What does a time of −40 mean in the context of this problem?

   *Forty years ago.*

   > Students tend to really struggle with negative values of time, probably because we don't use them very often. Point out that the original statement said there's $5,000 in the account *currently*; it doesn't say at the time it was opened.

8. Now insert −500 at the top of the $t$ column and 500 at the bottom. Evaluate the function using these two new values. What do you observe?

   *For −500 the output is tiny, and for 500 it's huge. Gigantic, I tell you. It's a veritable leviathan of outputs.*

9. Based on your answers to Questions 7 and 8, do you think this function has an $x$ intercept? Describe what you think happens if you trace the graph further and further in each direction.

   *It does not. As you trace out to the left, the height of the graph keeps getting closer and closer to zero.*

   *As you trace out to the right, the graph keeps getting higher and higher.*

## Summary of Exponential Function Graph Features

- For any acceptable value of $b$, the expression $b^0 = 1$, so every exponential function of the form $f(x) = c \cdot b^x$ has $y$ intercept $(0, c)$.
- The graph approaches the $x$ axis in one direction but never touches it. When this happens, we say that the $x$ axis is a **horizontal asymptote** of the graph.
- In the other direction, the height of the graph increases without bound.
- The graph can have two shapes, depending on whether the base $b$ is greater or less than 1.

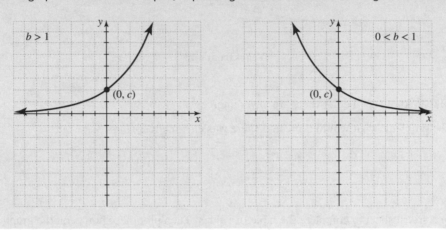

Since all of the exponential functions have the same basic shape, we can draw the graph by plotting a handful of points and drawing a curve similar to the ones in the figures above.

**10.** Use this knowledge to complete your graph of the exponential function on page 527.

When investing a certain amount of money, like say $5,000 at 3% interest compounded annually, it certainly would be reasonable to wonder how long it would take the investment to grow to a certain amount. Let's see what that would look like.

**11.** If we wanted to know how many years it took until the account was worth $10,000, what equation would we need to solve? Write it down. Don't try solving it yet. We'll get there.

$$10{,}000 = 5{,}000(1.03)^t$$

**12.** Use the graph you drew to estimate the solution to this equation.

*Answers can vary, but it looks like maybe 23 years or so.*

**13.** Use the **Intersect** feature on your calculator to get a really good approximation for the solution to this equation. (This command was introduced in Lesson 5-3.)

*$t \approx 23.45$ years*

**14.** We're ready to start solving the equation. First, divide both sides of the equation by 5,000. What's left?

$2 = 1.03^t$

Now we have a problem. In order to solve the equation, we'll need a way to get the variable out of the exponent, and none of our usual algebraic tools can do that. A lesser scholar might quit at this point, but not you! In much the same way that we use roots to "undo" powers when solving equations, we can use a group of functions called **logarithms** to "undo" exponentials.

Roots are actually a really good analogy for understanding logarithms, or logs for short. There are many different powers: square, cube, fourth power, etc., so there are many different roots: square root, cube root, fourth root, etc. Exponential functions have many potential bases, so there are many different logarithms, depending on the base. For example, the logarithm function with base 3, written $\log_3 x$, is the function that "undoes" an exponential with base 3. That is,

$$\log_3(3^x) = x \qquad \text{Compare this to } \sqrt[3]{x^3} = x.$$

For any base $b$ that is positive but not 1, the **logarithm function with base $b$**, denoted $\log_b x$, is a function with the following property: for any real number $x$, $\log_b(b^x) = x$.

**15.** Now we should be able to solve the equation you wrote in Question 14. To undo the exponential and get $t$ alone on one side of the equation, we'll apply the log function that undoes the exponential base 1.03 to both sides:

$$\log_{1.03}(2) = \log_{1.03}(3^t)$$

Use what you just learned about logs to simplify the right side of that equation. What's the solution?

The solution is $t = \log_{1.03}(2)$.

Now we have an answer, but we can't do much to interpret it until we go to a calculator. The fact that there are many different logarithms (infinitely many, in fact) presents a problem when programming a calculator. You can't put infinitely many log buttons on a calculator: You can try, but you would not be successful. Most calculators have a button for log base 10, which is simply denoted log (if there's no base listed, it means the base is 10). Fortunately, there's a formula that allows us to change the base of a logarithm. Shockingly, it's called the **change of base** formula.

### The Change of Base Formula

For any acceptable base $b$ and any positive real number $x$,
$$\log_b x = \frac{\log x}{\log b}$$

16. Use the change of base formula to put your answer to Question 15 in terms of log base 10. Then use the log button on a calculator to find a decimal equivalent.

$$\log_{1.03} 2 = \frac{\log 2}{\log 1.03} \approx 23.45$$

*Finally,* we have an answer to the question about how long it will take until our $5,000 is worth $10,000.

17. How does your answer compare to the visual estimate and the calculator approximation?

It's close to the visual estimate, and identical to the calculator approximation.

18. Using this same situation, find how long it will take the $5,000 to be worth $16,000. Check your answer using the graph and the intersect feature on your calculator.

$$16,000 = 5,000(1.03)^t$$

$$(1.03)^t = \frac{16}{5}$$

$$t = \log_{1.03} \frac{16}{5} = \frac{\log \frac{16}{5}}{\log 1.03} \approx 39.35 \quad \text{It will be worth } \$16,000 \text{ in a little more than 39 years.}$$

19. Now find when the $5,000 was worth $2,000. Check your answer using the graph and the intersect feature on your calculator.

$$2,000 = 5,000(1.03)^t$$

$$(1.03)^t = \frac{2}{5}$$

$$t = \log_{1.03} \frac{2}{5} = \frac{\log \frac{2}{5}}{\log 1.03} \approx -31 \quad \text{It was worth } \$2,000 \text{ about 31 years ago.}$$

## Did You Get It

Try these problems to see if you understand the concepts we just studied. The answers can be found at the bottom of the portfolio page.

1. For an account that currently has $8,000 and grows at a rate of 2.5% compounded annually, write a function $A(t)$ that describes the value of this account after $t$ years.
2. How much will the account be worth in 6 years?
3. How long will it take for this account to grow to $19,000?

## 5-4 Group

Riverside County, California, is one of the five fastest-growing counties in the United States. One estimate uses the function $P(t) = A_0(1.04)^t$ to model the population, where $A_0$ is the population at time $t = 0$ and $t$ is the time in years. The population in 2007 reached 2,000,000 for the first time.

1. Write a specific model for the population of Riverside County in terms of years after 2007.

$P(t) = 2,000,000(1.04)^t$

2. Use the model to predict the population in 2027.

$P(20) = 2,000,000(1.04)^{20} \approx 4,382,246$

3. Use the model to predict when the population will reach 3,000,000.

$3,000,000 = 2,000,000(1.04)^{20}$

$(1.04)^t = \dfrac{3}{2}$

$t = \log_{1.04}\dfrac{3}{2} = \dfrac{\log\frac{3}{2}}{\log 1.04} \approx 10.3$   *The population was predicted to reach 3 million in 2017.*

## Did You Get It

Try this problem to see if you understand the concepts we just studied. The answer can be found at the bottom of the portfolio page.

4. Another estimate was released in early 2012 with a less optimistic projection for growth due to economic factors. This predicts a model of $P(x) = A_0(1.02)^t$, where $A_0$ is the population at time $t = 0$, and $t$ is time in years. The county had grown to 2,189,000 by 2012. What does this model predict the population will be in 2027? Use the model to predict when the population will reach 3,000,000.

As we saw in Unit 2, interest on a savings account can be compounded annually, semiannually, quarterly, or daily. The formula for compound interest is given by the formula

$$A = P\left(1 + \frac{r}{n}\right)^{nt}$$

where $A$ is the amount of money, which includes the principal plus the earned interest, $P$ is the principal (amount initially invested), $r$ is the yearly interest rate in decimal form, $n$ is the number of times the interest is compounded each year, and $t$ is the time in years that the principal has been invested.

    After being injured in an accident with a driver who was texting while driving, Maureen is awarded an \$80,000 settlement. She wants to invest the money so that she has \$100,000 to put toward a home. If the investment draws 6% interest compounded monthly, how long will it take for her to reach that goal?

4. Use the formula above to write a function describing the amount of Maureen's investment $t$ years from now.

$$A(t) = 80{,}000\left(1 + \frac{0.06}{12}\right)^{12t} \quad or \quad 80{,}000\,(1.005)^{12t}$$

5. How much interest will the investment earn in the first year? Use that to make an educated guess on how long it will take to grow to \$100,000.

$$A(1) = 80{,}000\,(1.005)^{12} \approx 84{,}934.22$$

She'll earn \$4,934.22 in the first year. Educated guesses will vary on how educated the guesser is.

6. Set up and solve an equation to find how long it will take for the investment to reach \$100,000. Be careful after applying a log to get the variable out of the exponent: you won't quite be done solving at that point.

$$100{,}000 = 80{,}000\,(1.005)^{12t}$$

$$(1.005)^{12t} = \frac{5}{4}$$

$$12t = \log_{1.005}\frac{5}{4} \Rightarrow t = \frac{\log_{1.005}\frac{5}{4}}{12} \approx 3.7$$

It will take 3.7 years.

**Did You Get It**

Try this problem to see if you understand the concepts we just studied. The answer can be found at the bottom of the portfolio page.

5. If Maureen finds an investment that offers 7.5% interest compounded daily, how much sooner will she have the $100,000 she's hoping for?

---

Carbon-14 is a radioactive isotope found in all living things. It begins to decay when an organism dies, and scientists can use the proportion remaining to estimate the age of objects derived from living matter, like bones, wooden tools, or textiles. The function

$$f(x) = A_0 2^{-0.0175x}$$

describes the amount of carbon-14 in a sample, where $A_0$ is the original amount and $x$ is the number of centuries (100 years) since the carbon-14 began decaying. A wooden bowl was unearthed at an archaeological dig in Peru, and when analyzed, it was found to have 62% of the amount of carbon-14 found in a living sample of that type of wood.

7. If $A_0$ is the amount of carbon-14 that was originally in the sample, write an expression for the amount left in the bowl (which is 62% of the original amount).

$0.62A_0$

8. Using your answer to Question 7, set up an equation whose solution will tell you the age of the wood in the bowl.

$0.62A_0 = A_0 2^{-0.0175x}$

© age fotostock/Alamy

9. Solve the equation. How old is the bowl?

$0.62 = 2^{-0.0175x}$

$\log_2 0.62 = -0.0175x$

$x = \dfrac{\log_2 0.62}{-0.0175} \approx 39.4$

Remember that x represents the number of centuries, so the bowl is about 3,940 years old.

This is an outstanding place to remind students of how important it is to clearly identify what all of the variables in a function represent. If you can do it nicely, make fun of them when they say that the bowl is 39 years old.

## Did You Get It

Try this problem to see if you understand the concepts we just studied. The answer can be found at the bottom of the portfolio page.

6. It's very common for archaeological digs to have several layers of artifacts from different eras. An ax handle found above the wooden bowl in Questions 7–9 has 72% of the original amount of carbon-14 remaining. How much later was it made than the bowl?

We've studied logarithmic functions only from the standpoint of using them to solve exponential equations, but they can be used to model things in our world as well. One example comes from the world of chemistry, where the pH scale is used to measure the hydrogen ion concentration in a solution. Distilled water has a pH of 7, acids have a pH of less than 7, and bases have a pH of more than 7. The formula for the pH of a solution is

$$pH = -\log(H^+)$$

where $H^+$ measures the concentration of hydrogen ions in moles per liter (mol/L).

10. The hydrogen ion concentration of a well-known brand of light beer, that may or may not get hauled around on a cart pulled by very large horses with fuzzy white feet, is measured at $1.58 \times 10^{-5}$ mol/L. What is its pH?

$$pH = -\log(1.58 \times 10^{-5}) = 4.8$$

11. The best-selling soft drink in the world, on the other hand, which might come in a red can with a white stripe, has a hydrogen ion concentration of 0.00316 mol/L. Find the pH.

$$pH = -\log(0.00316) = 2.5$$

## 5-4 | Portfolio

Name _____

Check each box when you've completed the task. Remember that your instructor will want you to turn in the portfolio pages you create.

### Technology

1. ☐ In the Applications questions, you'll use the exponential regression command on a graphing calculator to find an exponential curve of best fit for some data. In this assignment, you'll do that as well. But you'll also use Excel to find an exponential curve of best fit, and you'll find that the curves come in two different forms: the calculator uses a base that corresponds to the initial value of the data, while Excel always uses base $e$ (which we encountered back in Lesson 2-4). You'll then use Excel to compute residuals for both models and compare. The models will be based on the iPhone sales data that began this lesson. There's a template to help you get started in the online resources for this lesson.

### Online Practice

1. ☐ Include any written work from the online assignment along with any notes or questions about this lesson's content.

### Applications

1. ☐ Complete the applications problems.

### Reflections

Type a short answer to each question.

1. ☐ What types of quantities are likely to be modeled well with exponential functions. Why?
2. ☐ What is a logarithm? Why are there many different logarithms? Why are logarithms useful in this lesson?
3. ☐ Take another look at your answer to Question 0 at the beginning of this lesson. Would you revise your answer now that you've completed the lesson? How would you summarize the topic of this lesson now?
4. ☐ What questions do you have about this lesson?

### Looking Ahead

1. ☐ Complete the Lesson 6-1 Prep Skills and read the opening paragraph in Lesson 6-1 carefully, then answer Question 0 in preparation for that lesson.

### Answers to "Did You Get It?"

1. $A(t) = 8,000(1.025)^t$    2. $A(6) = \$9,277.55$    3. About 35 years
4. 2,946,105; near the end of 2028    5. About 0.7 years, or a bit less than 8 1/2 months
6. About 1,230 years

## 5-4 Applications

Name _____

When a drug is administered to a patient, doctors and nurses must be aware of the minimal effective concentration, which is the concentration below which the drug doesn't have the desired effect. One way health professionals talk about this concentration is the half-life of elimination, which is the amount of time it takes for the concentration to be cut in half. The data below is based on theophylline, an antiasthma drug, where the time is the number of hours after the medication peaks and starts to decline in the bloodstream.

| Time (hrs) | Concentration (mg/L) |
|:---:|:---:|
| 0 | 10 |
| 8 | 5 |
| 16 | 2.5 |
| 24 | 1.25 |

© Terry Vine/Blend Images LLC RF

1. Many drugs are known to leave the body exponentially. Determine the exponential regression equation of best fit using **ExpReg** on a graphing calculator. The process for doing this is identical to that for linear and quadratic regression from earlier in this unit.

    $y = 10(0.977)^x$

2. Graph the points from the table and the curve of best fit. In this case it should be a perfect fit.

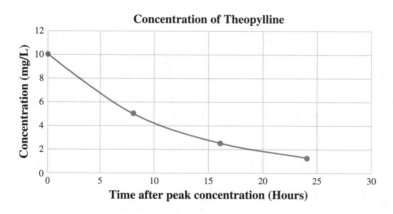

3. Use your equation to find the concentration of this asthma medicine after 4 hours. Does this agree with your graph?

    $y = 10(0.977)^4 \approx 7.07 \, mg/L$    This looks like it matches the graph pretty well.

## 5-4 Applications

Name _____

**4.** What is the concentration after 32 hours? If you're clever, you won't need your equation.

$0.625$ mg/L

**5.** Use your equation to find exactly how long it will take for the concentration to reach the minimal effective concentration of 4 mg/L for this medication. Does your answer match your graph?

$$10(0.977)^x = 4 \Rightarrow (0.977)^x = \frac{2}{5} \Rightarrow x = \log_{0.977}\frac{2}{5} = \frac{\log\frac{2}{5}}{\log 0.977} \approx 10.6$$

It will take 10.6 hours. This also matches the graph very well.

The population growth of an emerging African nation is defined by the function $P(t) = A_0(1.4)^t$, where $A_0$ is the present population and $t$ is the time in decades. The present population is 4,200,000.

**6.** Write a specific function that describes the population of that nation in terms of decades from now.

$P(t) = 4,200,000(1.4)^t$

**7.** Find the population in 5 years. Pay close attention to what $t$ represents!

$P(0.5) = 4,200,000(1.4)^{0.5} \approx 4,969,507$

**8.** If the population continues growing at the same rate, how long will it take to reach 6 million?

$$4,200,000(1.4)^t = 6,000,000 \Rightarrow (1.4)^t = \frac{60}{42} = \frac{10}{7} \Rightarrow t = \log_{1.4}\frac{10}{7} \approx 1.06$$

It will take about $10\frac{1}{2}$ years to reach 6 million.

## 5-4  Applications

Name _____

Questions 9 and 10 use the compound interest formula, $A = P\left(1 + \frac{r}{n}\right)^{nt}$.

**9.** Facing some stiff gambling debts, Lucky Louie turns to a quick loan from a local loan shark. Louie borrows $2,500 at 70% interest compounded daily. The friendly neighborhood loan shark informs Louie that his thumbs will be broken unless he pays the loan off in full in exactly 1 year. How much will he owe at that point?

$$A = 2,500\left(1 + \frac{0.7}{365}\right)^{365(1)} \approx \$5,031.01$$

**10.** Louie decides that in the interest of avoiding broken thumbs, he'd just as soon stay well away from the 1-year deadline. Instead, after hitting a winning streak, he decides to pay the loan back when the balance reaches $3,500. When should he pay?

$$2,500\left(1 + \frac{0.7}{365}\right)^{365t} = 3,500 \Rightarrow (1.002)^{365t} = 1.4 \Rightarrow 365t = \log_{1.002}(1.4)$$

$$t = \frac{\log_{1.002}(1.4)}{365} \approx 0.46$$

He should pay in 0.46 years, which is about 168 days.

Questions 11 and 12 use the carbon dating formula, $f(x) = A_0\, 2^{-0.0175x}$. Recall that $A_0$ is the original amount of carbon-14 in a specimen, and $x$ is the number of centuries since the specimen died.

**11.** In 2003, Japanese scientists announced the beginning of an effort to bring the long-extinct woolly mammoth back to life using modern cloning techniques, a goal that I think we can all agree is pretty cool. Their efforts were focused on an especially well-preserved specimen discovered frozen in the Siberian ice. Nearby samples of plant material were found to have 28.9% of the amount of carbon-14 in a living sample. If $A_0$ is the amount of carbon-14 originally in the specimen, write an expression that describes how much was left in 2003.

$0.289\, A_0$

© Leonello Calvetti/Stocktrek Images/Getty Images RF

## 5-4 Applications

Name _____

**12.** What was the approximate age of these samples?

$$0.289\,A_0 = A_0 2^{-0.0175x} \Rightarrow 2^{-0.0175x} = 0.289 \Rightarrow -0.0175x = \log_2(0.289)$$

$$x = \frac{\log_2(0.289)}{-0.0175} \approx 102.3$$

102.3 centuries is 10,230 years.

You probably know that when an earthquake is reported, how powerful it was (known as the magnitude) is given as a decimal number somewhere between 0 and 10. The scale used to measure the magnitude is known as the Richter scale, named in honor of a seismologist in California who devised the first version of the scale in 1935. Magnitude is given by the function

$$M(E) = \frac{2}{3}\log\frac{E}{10^{4.4}}$$

where $E$ is the amount of energy released by the quake. Use this information for Questions 13 and 14.

**13.** On March 11, 2011, a massive earthquake struck off the coast of Japan. The quake and the resulting tsunami killed over 15,000 people and resulted in a well-publicized nuclear emergency when three power plants were damaged. The quake released $7.94 \times 10^{17}$ joules of energy. What did it measure on the Richter scale?

$$M(7.94 \times 10^{17}) = \frac{2}{3}\log\frac{7.94 \times 10^{17}}{10^{4.4}} \approx 9.0$$

**14.** The largest and most powerful nuclear weapon ever detonated was tested by the Soviet Union on October 30, 1961, on an island in the Arctic Sea. The blast was so powerful that there were reports of windows breaking in Finland over 700 miles away. The detonation released about $2.1 \times 10^{17}$ joules of energy. What would be the magnitude of an earthquake that released that much energy?

$$M(2.1 \times 10^{17}) = \frac{2}{3}\log\frac{2.1 \times 10^{17}}{10^{4.4}} \approx 8.6$$

# Unit 6
# The Joy of Sets

© John Lund/Blend Images LLC RF

## Outline

Lesson 1: Setting Up (The Basics of Working with Sets)

Lesson 2: Busy Intersections, More Perfect Unions (Operations on Sets)

Lesson 3: Worlds Collide (Studying Sets with Two-Circle Venn Diagrams)

Lesson 4: A Dollar for Your Thoughts (Using Sets to Solve Problems)

# Math In  **Diversity**

Demography is the statistical study of the changing characteristics of people in a population. If there's one thing we can guarantee for certain in this field, it's that the racial makeup of the United States population has undergone a radical shift in recent years, and that shift is only expected to speed up.

The bar graph below shows the percentage of the total population that fell into four distinct categories in 1960 and 2011, and what those percentages are projected to be in 2050 by the Pew Research Center, an organization that ranks among the world leaders in population statistics.

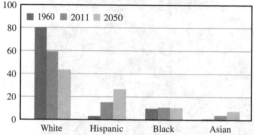

There's a lot going on here: the percentage of whites decreases dramatically, with Asians and Hispanics both showing significant gains, and blacks staying more or less the same.

No matter how you slice it, our society is becoming more and more diverse every year, to the point where even defining what we mean by "race" isn't so easy anymore. The most common racial groups referred to in population statistics are white, black, Asian, and Hispanic, but of course there are many people that fall into more than one category (including the 44th President of the United States!). Actually, it's even more confusing than that: "Hispanic" isn't really a race, but rather an ethnic group, and many Hispanics also report themselves as either white or black. (For the data in the bar graph, "white" means "non-Hispanic white.")

Sorting it all out to get any sort of meaningful picture of what we as Americans look like isn't easy, and the techniques of set theory are very useful tools in trying to do so. In this chapter, we'll define what we mean by sets and study sets and how they can be used to organize information in an increasingly complex world. The concept of sets has been used extensively since people began studying mathematics, but it wasn't until the late 1800s that the theory of sets was studied as a specific branch of math. One of the major tools that we will use to study sets, the Venn diagram, was introduced in an 1880 paper by a man named John Venn. These diagrams enable us to picture complicated relationships between sets of objects, like people of certain races.

Because race and ethnicity are self-reported in a variety of different ways, it's very difficult to find detailed data on the breakdown of races, but there are some reasonable estimates out there. The following estimates were cobbled together from a number of different sources. In a group of 1,000 randomly selected Americans, 783 would self-report as white, 132 as black, and 199 as Hispanic. In addition, 17 would self-report as black and white, 13 as black and Hispanic, and 136 as white and Hispanic. Finally, 8 would self-report as all three. Based on these estimates, after completing this chapter, you should be able to answer the following questions:

1. How many of the original 1,000 report as white only, black only, and Hispanic only?
2. How many report as Hispanic and black, but not white?
3. How many report as either Hispanic or black?
4. How many report as none of white, black, or Hispanic?
5. Based on the bar graph to the left, which set will have more elements in 2050: the set of Americans reporting as white, or those reporting as nonwhite?

# Lesson 6-1  Prep Skills

This is a short review of skills that will come in handy in the next lesson. In each case, answer the question, then rate your confidence level by checking one of the boxes. If you feel like you're struggling with these skills, consult the online resources provided by your instructor for extra practice.

### SKILL 1: CLASSIFY NUMBERS INTO CATEGORIES

For each number, decide if it is an integer, a whole number, an even number, or an odd number. Most will fall into more than one category.

1. 53

2. −8

3. 16

4. 0

### SKILL 2: RECOGNIZE NUMBERS IN A GIVEN LIST

5. Would 23 be on the list described by 1, 4, 7, 10, 13, . . .?

6. Is 56 on a list of even integers between 12 and 56?

# Lesson 6-1   **Setting Up**   (The Basics of Working with Sets)

**LEARNING OBJECTIVES**

☐  1. Define sets and use different methods to represent them.

☐  2. Identify when sets are equivalent.

☐  3. Study cardinality for finite and infinite sets.

*"Individual commitment to a group effort—that is what makes a team work, a company work, a society work, a civilization work."*
                                  —Vince Lombardi

© Vetta/Getty Images RF

Have you ever thought about the role that grouping things plays in everyday life? Think of all the subgroups just within the people you know: you have a group of close friends, a group of Facebook friends, a group of family members, a group of casual acquaintances, a group of classmates, a group of professors, a group of coworkers. . . . You also have a group of keys, groups of clothes, electronics, foods, TV shows, and many others. Our entire world is divided into groups of things, or what we call *sets*. So studying sets from a mathematical standpoint is a good opportunity to study how math is used in our world. Our entire study of sets will be set up by the topics in this lesson. Set up—get it? You don't get that quality of bad humor in most textbooks.

**0.**  After reading the opening paragraph, what do you think the main topic of this lesson will be?

## 6-1   Class

Election laws specify who is allowed to vote in an election. They have to be very specific in order to make an election fair and legal. Consider this group of citizens from a town, let's just call it Springfield: Homer, Marge, Edna, Bart, Ned, Apu, Moe, and Mr. Burns. Homer, Marge, Edna, Ned, and Moe are all registered to vote. Mr. Burns isn't registered, Apu is not a legal citizen, and Bart is ten years old. This group of people is referred to in Questions 1, 2, 4, 5, and 6.

© FOX/Getty Images

**1.**  List the citizens from the above group that are eligible to vote in the next election.

Homer, Marge, Edna, Ned, Moe

In general, a **set** is a collection of objects. For our purposes, we will focus on *well-defined sets*. A set is **well-defined** if for any given object, we can objectively decide whether it is or is not in the set. In short, to be well-defined, the definition of what is or is not in a set has to be based on facts, not opinions.

2. Is the set of people in the paragraph at the beginning of the lesson who are allowed to vote in the next election a well-defined set? Explain, including thoughts on what the requirements are to vote.

    *Yes. There are very specific laws governing who can vote. You have to be a legal adult citizen and registered.*

3. Is the set of funny characters in the paragraph at the beginning of the lesson a well-defined set? Explain.

    *It is not, because who is or is not funny is subjective.*

4. There are many other laws that might affect certain sets, like the set of businesses in a certain industry. These laws need to clearly define the set the law applies to. Why is it important that the set of businesses that a certain law applies to is well-defined?

    *In law, it's particularly important. Laws cannot be enforced unless it's absolutely clear who they apply to and what the circumstances are.*

## Did You Get It?

Try this problem to see if you understand the concepts we just studied. The answer can be found at the bottom of the portfolio page.

1. Write an example of a set that IS well-defined, and an example of one that is not.

Each object in a set is called an **element** or a **member** of the set.

One method of designating a set is called the **roster method,** in which elements are listed between braces, with commas between the elements. The order in which we list elements isn't important: {2, 5, 7} and {5, 2, 7} are the same set. Often, we will name sets by using a capital letter.

5. The set of citizens from the paragraph at the beginning of the lesson who are allowed to vote in that district of Springfield in the next election could be written using the roster method as:

    $V = \{$ <u>Homer</u> , <u>Marge</u> , <u>Edna</u> , <u>Ned</u> , <u>Moe</u> $\}$

**6.** Write the set of Simpsons characters in the paragraph at the beginning of the lesson whose names begin with a letter that comes before M in the alphabet. Is this set well-defined? Why or why not?

*(Homer, Edna, Bart, Apu, Mr. Burns) Whether or not the set is well-defined depends on your perspective. Are we going by first name or last? All of the characters except for Mr. Burns are listed by first name.*

> ### Math Note
> The commas between elements make it clear that the elements of the set are the names, not the individual letters.

In math, the set of counting numbers or natural numbers is defined as $N = \{1, 2, 3, 4, \ldots\}$. (When we are designating sets, the three dots, or ellipsis, mean that the list of elements continues indefinitely in the same pattern.) The set $E = \{2, 4, 6, 8, \ldots\}$ is the set of even natural numbers and the set $O = \{1, 3, 5, 7, \ldots\}$ is the set of odd natural numbers.

**7.** Use the roster method to write the set of natural numbers less than 6.

*(1, 2, 3, 4, 5)*

> ### Math Note
> You can list an element of a set more than once if it means a lot to you, but it's common to choose not to list repeats. For example, the set of letters in the word letters is written as $\{l, e, t, r, s\}$.

**8.** Write the set of odd natural numbers greater than 4.

*(5, 7, 9, 11, 13, . . .)*

Students often wonder how many elements of a set to write before ending with an ellipsis. The correct answer is "seven." Just kidding—there is no set rule. Just make sure to include enough initial numbers so that the pattern is clear. For Question 8, just writing $\{5, 7, \ldots\}$ would leave any number of possible interpretations: $\{5, 7, 8, 10, 11, 13, 14, 16, \ldots\}$, $\{5, 7, 10, 14, \ldots\}$ are two that come to mind.

---

### Did You Get It?

Try these problems to see if you understand the concepts we just studied. The answers can be found at the bottom of the portfolio page.

2. Write the set of months that end with the letter y.

3. Write each set, using the roster method.
   a. The set of even natural numbers from 80 to 90.
   b. The set of odd natural numbers greater than 10.

The symbol ∈ is used to show that an object is a member or element of a set.

9. For example, if *A* is the set of days of the week, we could write Monday ∈ *A*, and read this as "___Monday___ is an element of set ___A___."

10. Likewise, we could write ___Friday___ ∈ ___A___ to indicate that "Friday is an element of set *A*."

When an object is not a member of a set, we use the symbol ∈.

11. Since "Icecreamday" is not a day of the week (although it probably should be), write a statement using symbols that means "Icecreamday is not an element of *A*."

    Icecreamday ∈ A

> **Math Note**
>
> Be sure to use correct symbols when you show membership in a set. For example, the notation {6} ∈ {2, 4, 6} is incorrect since the set {6} is not a member of this set: only the number 6 is.

For Questions 12–14, decide whether each statement is true or false.

12. Oregon ∈ *A*, where *A* is the set of states west of the Mississippi River.

    False. Oregon is a state, and is west of the Mississippi, so it is in set A.

13. 29 ∈ {1, 5, 9, 13, 17, . . .}

    True. Even though 29 is not specifically written in brackets, if we continue the pattern, the next numbers are 21, 25, and 29.

14. z ∈ {v, w, x, y, z}

    False. z is specifically listed as an element of the set, so it's false to say that z is not an element of the set.

The **descriptive method** is a second way to describe a set. It uses a short statement to describe the set. To see a couple of examples, look back at Questions 7 and 8: we used the descriptive method to define a set that you were then asked to write using the roster method.

15. Use the descriptive method to describe the set *B* containing 2, 4, 6, 8, 10, and 12.

    B is the set of even whole numbers starting at 2 and ending at 12. (One possible answer.)

## Did You Get It?

Try these problems to see if you understand the concepts we just studied. The answers can be found at the bottom of the portfolio page.

4. Decide whether each statement is true or false.
   a. July $\in A$, where $A$ is the set of months between Memorial Day and Labor Day.
   b. $21 \in \{2, 5, 8, 11, \ldots\}$
   c. map $\in \{m, a, p\}$
5. Use the descriptive method to describe the set $A$ containing $-3, -2, -1, 0, 1, 2, 3$.

The third method of designating a set is **set-builder notation,** which uses variables. Recall that a variable is a symbol that can represent different elements of a set. We usually use letters for variables, but any symbol that's not a numeral will do.

Set-builder notation uses a variable, braces, and a vertical bar | that is read as "such that." For example, the set $\{1, 2, 3, 4, 5, 6\}$ can be written in set-builder notation as $\{x \mid x \in N \text{ and } x < 7\}$. Let's break this down and see how we would read it aloud.

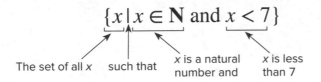

$$\{x \mid x \in N \text{ and } x < 7\}$$

The set of all $x$    such that    $x$ is a natural number and    $x$ is less than 7

> **Math Note**
>
> Actually, a variable is something that can vary, not the symbol that we use to represent something that can vary. But we often use the term variable to describe the symbol used as well as the variable quantity or object itself.

16. Write how this set would be described aloud: $K = \{x \mid x \in O \text{ and } 9 \leq x \leq 39\}$

    *K is the set of all x such that x is an odd number and x is greater than or equal to 9 and less than or equal to 39.*

A note on using an ellipsis: If a set contains enough elements that it's cumbersome to list them all, we can again use an ellipsis to represent the missing elements as long as we illustrate a clear pattern. For example, the set in Question 16 could be written as $\{9, 11, 13, 15, \ldots, 39\}$. Likewise, the set $\{a, b, c, \ldots, x, y, z\}$ includes all the letters of the alphabet.

Use set-builder notation to write the set in Questions 17 and 18, then write how your answer would be read aloud.

**17.** The set $R$ contains the elements 2, 4, and 6.

*$R = \{x \mid x \in E$ and $1 < x < 7\}$. $R$ is the set of all $x$ such that $x$ is an even number and $x$ is between 1 and 7.*

**18.** The set $W$ contains the elements red, yellow, and blue.

*$W = \{x \mid x$ is a primary color$\}$. $W$ is the set of primary colors. Or, if you want to be a wise guy, the set of colors in the flag of, say, Colombia.*

In Questions 19–21, designate the set $S$ with elements 32, 33, 34, 35, . . . using the given method.

**19.** The roster method.

*$S = \{32, 33, 34, 35, \ldots\}$*

**20.** The descriptive method.

*$S$ is the set of whole numbers that are 32 or greater.*

**21.** Set-builder notation.

*$S = \{x \mid x \in N$ and $x \geq 32\}$*

**22.** Discuss which you think is the most efficient way to write this particular set.

*This is completely an opinion.*

---

### Did You Get It?

Try this problem to see if you understand the concepts we just studied. The answer can be found at the bottom of the portfolio page.

   6. Use set-builder notation to designate each set, then write how your answer would be read aloud.
      a. The set $K$ contains the elements 10, 12, 14, 16, 18.
      b. The set $W$ contains the elements Democrat and Republican.

**23.** As of 2015 the set of Asian-American Presidents of the United States would contain how many elements?

*Zero*

A set with no elements is called an empty set or null set. The symbols used to represent the empty set are { } or ∅. So if we were asked to write the set of all Asian-American U.S. Presidents, our answer would look like this: ∅.

**24.** Which of the following sets are empty?
   **a.** The set of woolly mammoth fossils in museums
   **b.** $\{x \mid x$ is a living woolly mammoth$\}$
   **c.** { }
   **d.** $\{x \mid x$ is a natural number between 1 and 2$\}$

   *Sets b, c, and d are all empty.*

> **Math Note**
>
> Make sure you don't write the empty set as {∅}. This set isn't empty: it's the set containing the empty set, so it has one element.

## 6-1   Group

Now that we're into Unit 6, we're hoping that you're familiar with the idea of exchanging information with your new group mates. Exchange away!

### Cardinal Numbers

**1.** Earlier in the lesson, we looked at the set $K = \{x \mid x \in O$ and $9 \le x \le 39\}$. How many elements are in the set?

   *The set contains 31 elements.*

So what is a cardinal number? It's 11, because the St. Louis Cardinals have won 11 World Series titles. Note: That's completely untrue. (Not the 11 World Series part—that's true.) The **cardinal number** (or **cardinality**) of a set is the number of elements in that set. For a set $A$ the symbol for the cardinality is $n(A)$, which is read as "$n$ of $A$."

**2.** Use this notation for cardinal number, and your answer from Question 1, to write the cardinality of the set $K$.

   $n(K) = 31$

In Questions 3–6, find the cardinal number of each set, and write it using $n(A)$ notation.

**3.** $A = \{5, 10, 15, 20, \ldots, 50\}$

$n(A) = 10$

**4.** $B = \{x \mid x \in \mathbf{N} \text{ and } x < 16\}$

$n(B) = 15$

**5.** $C = \{\varnothing\}$

$n(C) = 1$

> I'll bet you upwards of five American dollars that students will want to answer zero here. Make sure you point out that the set containing the empty set is not the same as the empty set.

**6.** $D = \{\}$

$n(D) = 0$

## Finite and Infinite Sets

Sets come in two delightful flavors: *finite* and *infinite*. A set is called **finite** if it has no elements, or has cardinality that is a natural number. A set that is not finite is called an **infinite** set.

**7.** Why do you think we didn't define an infinite set to be a set with cardinality $\infty$?

Because the cardinality of a finite set is zero or a natural number, and infinity is neither of those.

**8.** The set $K = \{x \mid x \in \mathbf{O} \text{ and } 9 \leq x \leq 39\}$ is ___finite___ because it contains ___31___ elements. The set $J = \{x \mid x \in \mathbf{O} \text{ and } x \geq 39\}$ is ___infinite___ because it has an unlimited number of elements.

In Questions 9–12, classify each set as finite or infinite.

**9.** $Z = \{x \mid x \in \mathbf{N} \text{ and } x > 100\}$.

Infinite

**10.** $U$ is the set of all stars in the universe.

Finite

**11.** $D = \{100, 102, 104, 106\}$

Finite

**12.** $S$ is the set of songs that can be written.

This one can be debated, but the prevailing wisdom is infinite.

**Did You Get It?**

Try this problem to see if you understand the concepts we just studied. The answer can be found at the bottom of the portfolio page.

7. Find the cardinality of each set, or classify it as infinite.
   a. $\{1, 3, 5, 7, 9\}$     b. $\{x \mid x \in \mathbf{E}$ and $x$ is between 1 and 19$\}$     c. $\{x \mid x \in \mathbf{N}$ and $x > 1,000,000\}$

## Equal and Equivalent Sets

As we study sets in this unit, it's important to understand the concepts of *equal sets* and *equivalent sets*. Two sets $A$ and $B$ are **equal** (written $A = B$) if they have exactly the same elements. Two finite sets are said to be **equivalent** (written $A \cong B$) if they have the same number of elements ($n(A) = n(B)$).

13. The sets $A = \{$Mars, Saturn, Venus, Uranus$\}$ and $B = \{$Uranus, Mars, Saturn, Venus$\}$ are ___equal___ because ___they contain the exact same elements___.

14. The sets $A = \{$Mars, Saturn, Venus, Uranus$\}$ and $B = \{$Mercury, Neptune, Jupiter, Pluto$\}$ are ___equivalent___ because ___they have the same cardinality___.

In Questions 15–20, decide if the two given sets are equal, equivalent, both, or neither.

15. $\{p, q, r, s\}$; $\{a, b, c, d\}$

    Equivalent

> On the next page, we'll ask students to observe that equal sets are equivalent, but not the other way around.

16. $\{8, 10, 12\}$; $\{12, 8, 10\}$

    Both

17. $\{213\}$; $\{2, 1, 3\}$

    Neither

18. $\{1, 2, 10, 20\}$; $\{2, 1, 20, 11\}$

    Equivalent

19. $\{$even natural numbers less than 10$\}$; $\{2, 4, 6, 8\}$

    Both

20. $\{4, 5, 6\}$; $\{4, 4, 5, 6\}$

    Both

**21.** Based on your observations, are equal sets also equivalent, or are equivalent sets also equal?

*Equal sets are equivalent, but not the other way around.*

It can be very interesting to study trends in the top college majors in terms of degrees awarded over some time period. In this case, we have the number of bachelor's degrees awarded for the top ten majors between 1999 and 2009. There's a lot of information in this table, and using sets to analyze some of it can be useful.

| Major | 1999 | 2004 | 2009 |
|---|---|---|---|
| Business | 240,947 | 307,149 | 347,985 |
| Social sciences and history | 124,658 | 150,357 | 168,500 |
| Health professions | 85,214 | 73,934 | 120,488 |
| Education | 107,086 | 106,278 | 101,708 |
| Psychology | 73,636 | 82,098 | 94,271 |
| Visual and performing arts | 54,404 | 77,181 | 89,140 |
| Biological and biomedical sciences | 64,608 | 61,509 | 80,756 |
| Communication | 51,384 | 70,968 | 78,009 |
| Engineering | 58,260 | 63,558 | 69,133 |
| English | 49,800 | 53,984 | 55,462 |

*Source: http://nces.ed.gov/programs/digest/d10/tables/dt10_282.asp*

**22.** List the set of majors that increased in popularity every year listed.

*(Business, Social sciences and history, Psychology, Visual and performing arts, Communication, Engineering, English)*

**23.** List the set of majors that didn't increase in popularity from 2004 to 2009.

*(Education)*

**24.** List the set of majors that increased in popularity by at least 30% from 1999 to 2009. (Recall that percent increase was covered in Lesson 2-1.)

*(Business, Social sciences and history, Health professions, Visual and performing arts, Communication)*

## 6-1   Portfolio

Name _____

Check each box when you've completed the task. Remember that your instructor will want you to turn in the portfolio pages you create.

### Technology

**1.** ☐   As we continue our study of the theory of sets, we'll be making use of a graphical way of studying sets called the Venn diagram. Do a Google image search for the phrase "Venn diagram," then copy and post a diagram that you find either interesting, relevant, or maybe just fun. Describe what the diagram is trying to illustrate.

### Online Practice

**1.** ☐   Include any written work from the online assignment along with any notes or questions about this lesson's content.

### Applications

**1.** ☐   Complete the applications problems.

### Reflections

Type a short answer to each question.

**1.** ☐   What's the difference between equal and equivalent sets?
**2.** ☐   Describe what it means for a set to be well-defined, as well as a situation in which something not being well-defined would lead to negative consequences.
**3.** ☐   Write an example of an infinite set and describe how you know it's infinite.
**4.** ☐   Take another look at your answer to Question 0 at the beginning of this lesson. Would you revise your answer now that you've completed the lesson? How would you summarize the topic of this lesson now?
**5.** ☐   What questions do you have about this lesson?

### Looking Ahead

**1.** ☐   Complete the Lesson 6-2 Prep Skills and read the opening paragraph in Lesson 6-2 carefully, then answer Question 0 in preparation for that lesson.

### Answers to "Did You Get It?"

**1.** Answers vary widely.     **2.** {January, February, May, July}
**3. a.** {80, 82, 84, 86, 88, 90}     **b.** {11, 13, 15, 17, 19, . . .}
**4. a.** True     **b.** False     **c.** True
**5.** One answer: The set of integers that are between −4 and 4.
**6. a.** $\{x \mid x \text{ } \mathbf{E} \text{ and } 9 < x < 19\}$; the set of all $x$ such that $x$ is an even number between 9 and 19.
   **b.** $\{x \mid x \text{ is one of the major American political parties}\}$; the set of all $x$ such that $x$ is one of the major American political parties     **7. a.** 5     **b.** 9     **c.** Infinite

## 6-1   Applications

Name _____

For Questions 1–4, write each set using the roster method. You may have to do a little Internet research, which is a good thing.

1.  *R* is the set of odd natural numbers between 2 and 16.

    {3, 5, 7, 9, 11, 13, 15}

2.  *B* is the set of integers that are less than –4.

    {–5, –6, –7, –8, –9, –10, . . .}

3.  *C* is the set of the seven mainland countries in Central America.

    {Belize, Costa Rica, El Salvador, Guatemala, Honduras, Nicaragua, Panama}

4.  *O* is the set of colors in the flags of the states whose names begin with the letter O.

    {red, white, blue, tan, green, black, yellow}

For Questions 5–8, decide if the set is well-defined or not, and explain your reasoning.

5.  The set of all Americans

    Not well-defined. Who qualifies as an American? Legal definition? By birth? Living in the United States? North America? South America?

6.  The set of all lawyers in Alaska

    In order to be a lawyer in Alaska, you have to be a member of the Alaska bar. That's well-defined.

7.  The set of luxury cars in the 2017 model year

    Not well-defined. "Luxury car" is subjective.

# 6-1 Applications

Name _____

**8.** The set of all mothers

*Not well-defined. Mother could mean different things: biological, adoptive, foster, house . . .*

Identity theft is one of the most costly types of crime committed in the United States, and younger adults are often the targets. In 2014 alone, over 1.3 million people under the age of 25 were victims of I.D. theft. The following charts show types of identity theft fraud reported in 2014, and the percentage of victims by age. Use this information for Questions 9–16.

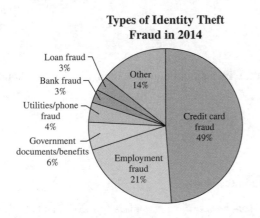

**Types of Identity Theft Fraud in 2014**

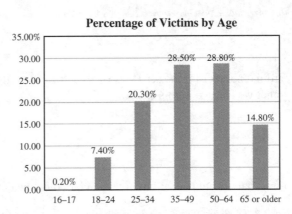

**Percentage of Victims by Age**

**9.** List the set of types of identity fraud that made up less than 20% of all reported cases.

*{Other, Loan fraud, Bank fraud, Utilities/phone fraud, Government document/benefits}*

## 6-1 | Applications

Name _____

**10.** List the set of age groups that made up less than 20% of I.D. theft victims.

*(16–17, 18–24, 65 or older)*

**11.** List the set $\{x \mid x$ is a percentage for an age group of those 35 and over who are victims of I.D. theft$\}$.

*(28.50%, 28.80%, 14.80%)*

**12.** Write the set {Other, Employment fraud, Credit card fraud} using set-builder notation.

*(x | x is a type of fraud that made up over 10% of I.D. theft cases)*

**13.** Find the cardinal number for the set $F = \{x \mid x$ is type of I.D. theft with a percentage less than 40$\}$. Use the notation for cardinality that we learned in this lesson.

*$n(F) = 6$*

**14.** Write two sets that are equivalent but not equal based on the data in the charts.

*There are many potential answers to this question. One potential answer is (age groups with a percentage over 20%) and (I.D. theft types that made up less than 5% of cases).*

**15.** Write the set of identity theft types that made up more than 50% of all reported claims.

*∅*

**16.** Are the two sets listed below equal, equivalent, or neither?

$A = \{x \mid x$ is an I.D. theft victim less than 65 years old$\}$
$B = \{y \mid y$ is an age group that did not have an I.D. theft percentage between 10% and 20%$\}$

*Neither. The first set describes actual victims, not the age categories.*

## Lesson 6-2   Prep Skills

This is a short review of skills that will come in handy in the next lesson. In each case, answer the question, then rate your confidence level by checking one of the boxes. If you feel like you're struggling with these skills, consult the online resources provided by your instructor for extra practice.

### SKILL 1: USE THE ROSTER METHOD

1. Write the set of days of the week using the roster method.

2. Write the set of even integers greater than 5 using the roster method.

### SKILL 2: USE SET-BUILDER NOTATION

3. Write the set {4, 5, 6, 7, 8, 9, 10} using set-builder notation.

4. Write the set {e, f, g, h, i, . . . , y, z} using set-builder notation.

### SKILL 3: USE INDUCTIVE REASONING

5. Use inductive reasoning to predict the next three numbers on each list.

   4, 8, 16, 32, 64, _____, _____, _____

   10, 30, 50, 70, _____, _____ , _____

### SKILL 4: CALCULATE POWERS OF TWO

6. Compute each power of two:

   $2^4$

   $2^7$

# Lesson 6-2   **Busy Intersections, More Perfect Unions** (Operations on Sets)

**LEARNING OBJECTIVES**

☐ 1. Find the complement and all subsets for a given set.

☐ 2. Evaluate set statements involving subset notation.

☐ 3. Perform and apply set operations: union, intersection, subtraction.

© McGraw-Hill Education

*What is the intersection between technology, art and science?*
*Curiosity and wonder, because it drives us to explore, because*
*we're surrounded by things we can't see.*
 —Louie Schwartzberg

We've seen that set theory is about identifying relationships between things that are grouped together for some reason. Taking that idea a little further, sets often have relationships with other sets, and that's when things get a bit complicated. In that case, a system for displaying and studying those relationships will come in handy, which ultimately is kind of the main point of studying set theory. So far, we've just scratched the surface. For example, you are a member of both the set of college students and the set of students taking a college math course. You could be in the set of sophomores or the set of juniors, but not in both. You might be in the set of students living off campus and the set of students who walk to class. Maybe you're in the set of students that eats lunch in the cafeteria and the set of students that think the french fries are too soggy, but not in the set of people who load on the ketchup and eat the lousy things anyhow. Let's see what we can do about organizing all of these complicated connections between sets.

**0.** After reading the opening paragraph, what do you think the main topic of this lesson will be?

## 6-2 | Class

To begin we'll need to introduce a new concept called a *universal set*.

> The **universal set** is the set of all objects in the universe.

   Just kidding. (No harm in trying to have a little fun in a math class.) We now return to our regularly scheduled definition:

> The **universal set** for a given situation, symbolized by *U*, is the set of all objects that are reasonable to consider in that situation.

For example, all of the sets described in the opening paragraph contain people, so theoretically we could use the set of all human beings as *U*. But it would be much more reasonable to assign *U* = {College students}.

Once we define a universal set in a given setting, we are restricted to considering only elements from that set. If $U = \{1, 2, 3, 4, 5, 6, 7, 8\}$, then the only elements we can use to define other sets in this setting are the integers from 1 to 8. In the remainder of this chapter, we'll use a clever method for visualizing sets and their relationships called a Venn diagram (so named because it was developed by a man named John Venn in the 1800s).

Here is an example of a Venn diagram.

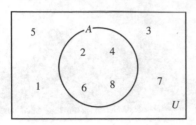

You can get a lot of information from this simple diagram. A set called $A$ is being defined.

1. The universal set from which elements of $A$ can be chosen is

   $U = \{\underline{\;1\;}, \underline{\;2\;}, \underline{\;3\;}, \underline{\;4\;}, \underline{\;5\;}, \underline{\;6\;}, \underline{\;7\;}, \underline{\;8\;}\}$.

2. The set $A = \{\underline{\;2\;}, \underline{\;4\;}, \underline{\;6\;}, \underline{\;8\;}\}$, and the elements not in $A$ are $\{\underline{\;1\;}, \underline{\;3\;}, \underline{\;5\;}, \underline{\;7\;}\}$.

We call the elements in $U$ that are not in $A$ the **complement of $A$,** and denote it $A'$. This is a good opportunity to review set-builder notation.

3. For a given set $A$,

   $A' = \{x \mid x \in \underline{\;U\;} \text{ and } x \notin \underline{\;A\;}\}$

In a Venn diagram, the complement of a set $A$ is all the things inside the rectangle that are not inside the circle representing set $A$.

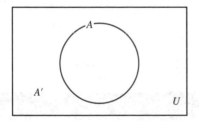

## Math Note

The complement of the empty set is the universal set, and the complement of the universal set is the empty set.

| TOP 25 TEAMS, WEEK 10 | | |
|---|---|---|
| RANK | TEAM | RECORD |
| 1 | Ohio State | 8–0 |
| 2 | Baylor | 7–0 |
| 3 | Clemson | 8–0 |
| 4 | Louisiana State | 7–0 |
| 5 | Texas Christian | 8–0 |
| 6 | Michigan State | 8–0 |
| 7 | Alabama | 7–1 |
| 8 | Notre Dame | 7–1 |
| 9 | Stanford | 6–1 |
| 10 | Iowa | 8–0 |

Here we have listed the top 10 teams from the AP Top 25 College football teams for the week of Nov. 1, 2015. Let $U$ be the set of teams in the top ten, represented by the school's initials. Note that a record of 8–0 means a team has won 8 games and lost none.

$U = \{$OSU, BU, CU, LSU, TCU, MSU, UA, UND, SU, UI$\}$. Now we'll define a new set:

$D = \{$UA, UND, SU$\}$

4. Find $D'$. Make sure you use proper set notation.

$D' = \{$OSU, BU, CU, LSU, TCU, MSU, UI$\}$

5. Give a verbal description of set $D$. (Look carefully at the information provided in the graphic, not just the team names.)

$D$ is the set of teams in the top ten that have lost a game.

6. Give a verbal description of set $D'$.

$D'$ is the set of teams in the top ten that have not lost a game.

7. Draw a Venn diagram that illustrates all of the sets in this example.

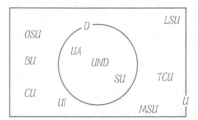

You have to be a little careful here since the elements contain letters: Notice that we put the letters $D$ and $U$ on the borders to indicate that they're set names rather than elements.

---

## Did You Get It

Try this problem to see if you understand the concepts we just studied. The answer can be found at the bottom of the portfolio page.

1. Let $U = \{10, 20, 30, 40, 50, 60, 70, 80, 90\}$ and $A = \{10, 30, 50\}$. Find $A'$ and draw a Venn diagram that illustrates these sets.

## Subsets

At the beginning of the lesson, we pointed out that you're in both the set of college students and the set of students taking a college math course. Notice that everyone in the second set is automatically in the first one. (Obviously, if you're taking a college math course, then you have to be a college student.) We could say that the set of students taking a college math course is contained in the set of all college students. When one set is contained in a second set, we call the smaller set a *subset* of the larger one.

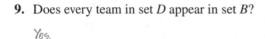

If every element of a set *A* is also an element of a set *B*, then *A* is called a **subset** of *B*. The symbol ⊆ is used to designate a subset; in this case, we write *A* ⊆ *B*.

There are many subsets of this set of spring breakers: the subset of female students, the subset of guys hitting on those female students, the subset of students who had their fake I.D. confiscated by the police, and so on.

Speaking of college, back to football. Look back at your verbal description of set *D*.

8. If we define set *B* as the list of teams in the top ten but not the top four, list set *B*.

$B = \{TCU, MSU, UA, UND, SU, UI\}$

© McGraw-Hill Education/Barry Barker, photographer

9. Does every team in set *D* appear in set *B*?

Yes.

10. What does this mean in terms of subsets? Write an answer in words and symbols.

It means that $D$ is a subset of $B$, which we would write as $D \subseteq B$.

11. Does every team in set *D* appear in set *D*? No this is not a typo. Just think and answer yes or no.

Yes they surely do.

12. What does this mean in terms of subsets? Write an answer in words and symbols.

It means that $D$ is a subset of itself. We can write $D \subseteq D$.

Having run out of lemon (no big deal) and blueberry (now THAT'S a problem), a snow cone stand is offering only grape, cherry, and lime today. So the set of flavors is $S = \{$Grape, Cherry, Lime$\}$. The goal of Questions 13–19 will be to find all subsets of this set, which is all the choices of flavors we could make if we're undecided on how many snow cones we feel like choking down.

13. Set $S$ contains ___3___ elements.

14. We could choose all three flavors, which would almost certainly lead to brain freeze. That would be the set:

    {Grape, Cherry, Lime}

15. We could choose two of the three flavors. List each subset containing exactly two flavors.

    {Grape, Cherry}, {Grape, Lime}, {Cherry, Lime}

© Jill Fromer/Getty Images RF

16. We could choose only one flavor. List each subset containing one flavor.

    {Grape}, {Lime}, {Cherry}

17. We could decide we don't want a snow cone. That could be represented by the set:

    ∅

18. The set $S$, which has 3 elements, has a total of ___8___ subsets.

19. How many subsets are not equal to the original set $S$?

    7

These subsets that aren't equal to the original set are called *proper subsets* of $S$. The Venn diagram for a proper subset is shown below. In this case, $U = \{1, 2, 3, 4, 5\}$, $A = \{1, 3, 5\}$, and $B = \{1, 3\}$.

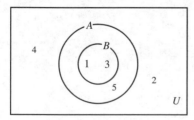

If a set *A* is a subset of a set *B* and is not equal to *B*, then we call *A* a **proper subset** of *B*, and write A ⊂ B. That is, A ⊆ B and A ≠ B.

**20.** More blanks to fill in: the set {Grape, Lime} is a proper subset of {Grape, Cherry, Lime} because

{Grape, Lime} _⊂_ {Grape, Cherry, Lime} and _Cherry_ ∈ {Grape, Lime}.

**21.** The two longest-running "reality" shows on American television, at least as of late 2015, are included in the set *T* = {The Real World, Survivor}. Write all of the subsets of this set. You may want to look back at Questions 13–19 to help make sure you don't miss any.

*{The Real World, Survivor}, {The Real World}, {Survivor}, Ø*

**22.** What does the group of subsets you found in Question 21 describe about these shows? Write in plain English, not using set terminology.

© Monty Brinton/CBS/Getty Images

*This could be answered in a number of ways. One way would be in terms of shows you could choose to watch in any given week. You could watch both shows, one or the other, or neither.*

**23.** How many of the subsets you found are proper subsets?

*Three of the four.*

## Did You Get It

Try these problems to see if you understand the concepts we just studied. The answers can be found at the bottom of the portfolio page.

2. List all subsets of the set *D* from Questions 4–7.
3. How many proper subsets does the set {♦, ♥, ♠, ♣} have? List them.

To indicate that a set is not a subset of another set, the symbol ⊄ is used. The symbol ⊄ is used to indicate that the set is not a proper subset.

**24.** Decide if each statement is true or false. If false, briefly explain why.

**a.** {1, 3, 5} ⊂ {1, 3, 5, 7}

*True.*

**b.** {a, b} ⊂ {a, b}

*False. (a, b) is a subset of itself, but not a proper subset.*

**c.** {x | x ∈ **E** and x > 10} ⊂ **N**

*True.*

**d.** {r, s, t} ⊄ {t, s, r}

*True.*

**e.** {Lake Erie, Lake Huron} ⊄ The set of Great Lakes

*False. Those are two of the Great Lakes, so they form a proper subset of the set of Great Lakes.*

**f.** ∅ ⊂ {5, 10, 15}

*True.*

**g.** {u, v, w, x} ⊆ {x, w, u}

*False. The first set has an element that isn't in the second set.*

**h.** {0} ⊆ ∅

*False. The first set has an element, so it has an element not in the empty set.*

> ## Math Note
>
> Make sure you don't confuse subsets and elements. The statement 6 ∈ {2, 4, 6} is true, since 6 is an element of that set. And the statement {6} ⊆ {2, 4, 6} is true for the same reason. But {6} ∈ {2, 4, 6} isn't. The number 6 is an element of that set, but the set containing 6 is not.

**25.** Since every set is a subset of itself, a set with no elements still has ___*1*___ subset(s).

**26.** A set with one element has how many subsets? Describe them.

*Two: the set itself, and the empty set.*

**27.** We've already seen that if a set has two elements, there are ___*4*___ subsets, and if a set has three elements, there are ___*8*___ subsets. This is an excellent opportunity to use the inductive reasoning that we practiced in Unit 1!

**28.** Complete the table as much as possible using the information from the previous questions.

| Number of Elements | 0 | 1 | 2 | 3 | 4 | 5 |
|---|---|---|---|---|---|---|
| Number of Subsets | *1* | *2* | *4* | *8* | *16* | *32* |

**29.** Based on this pattern, make a conjecture about the number of subsets of a set with 4 elements. What about 5 elements? Add your answers to the table.

**30.** Write a formula for the number of subsets of a set with $n$ elements.

*$2^n$*

**31.** Use that formula to verify the results in the table above for each value of $n$.

*$2^0 = 1$; $2^1 = 2$; $2^2 = 4$; $2^3 = 8$; $2^4 = 16$; $2^5 = 32$*

**32.** Describe the relationship between the number of proper subsets of a set and the total number of subsets.

*The number of proper subsets is one less than the total number of subsets.*

**33.** Write a formula for the number of proper subsets of a set with $n$ elements.

*$2^n - 1$*

**34.** Use that formula to predict the number of proper subsets of a set with 9 elements.

*$2^9 - 1 = 511$*

## Did You Get It

Try this problem to see if you understand the concepts we just studied. The answer can be found at the bottom of the portfolio page.

4.  Find the number of subsets and number of proper subsets for the set $D'$ from Question 4.

# 6-2 | Group

## The Intersection and Union of Sets

At the beginning of this lesson, we pointed out that you might be in both the set of students living off campus and the set of students who walk to class. We will identify objects that are common to two or more sets by using the term *intersection*.

The **intersection** of two sets $A$ and $B$, symbolized by $A \cap B$, is the set of all elements that are in both sets. In set-builder notation, $A \cap B = \{x \mid x \in A \text{ and } x \in B\}$.

For example, if $A = \{10, 12, 14, 15\}$ and $B = \{13, 14, 15, 16, 17\}$, then the intersection $A \cap B = \{14, 15\}$, since 14 and 15 are the only elements that are common to both sets. The Venn diagram for $A \cap B$ is shown below. Notice that the elements of $A$ are placed inside the circle for set $A$, and the elements of $B$ are inside the circle for set $B$. The elements in the intersection are placed into the portion where the circles overlap: $A \cap B$ is the shaded portion.

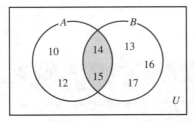

1.  Look back at the set $D$ from Question 4 in the Class portion of this lesson, and also at set $B$ from Question 8. Write a verbal description of the set $D \cap B$, then list out the set using the roster method.

    *This set is the teams that had lost a game, and were in the top ten but not the top four. $D \cap B = \{UA, UND, SU\}$*

Intersection is an example of a **set operation**—a rule for combining two or more sets to form a new set. The intersection of three or more sets consists of the set of elements that are in every single set. Note that the word *and* is sometimes used to indicate intersection; A ∩ B is the set of elements in *A* and *B*.

If *A* = {Cleveland, Indianapolis, Chicago, Des Moines, Detroit}, *B* = {New York, Los Angeles, Chicago, Detroit}, and *C* = {Seattle, Los Angeles, San Diego}, find each requested set in Questions 2–4.

2. *A* ∩ *B*

   *(Chicago, Detroit)*

3. *B* ∩ *C*

   *(Los Angeles)*

4. *A* ∩ *B* ∩ *C*

   ∅

### Did You Get It

Try this problem to see if you understand the concepts we just studied. The answer can be found at the bottom of the portfolio page.

5. If $A = \{5, 10, 15, 20, 25\}$, $B = \{0, 10, 20, 30, 40\}$, and $C = \{30, 50, 70, 90\}$, find $A \cap B$, $B \cap C$, and $A \cap B \cap C$.

When the intersection of two sets is the empty set, the sets are said to be **disjoint**. For example, the set of students who stop attending class midway through a term and the set of students earning A's are disjoint, because you can't be a member of both sets. The Venn diagram for a pair of disjoint sets *A* and *B* is shown below. It's pretty easy to recognize: if the sets have no elements in common, the circles representing them don't overlap at all.

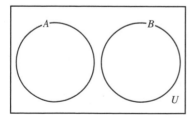

Another way of combining sets to form a new set is called *union*.

---

The **union** of two sets A and B, symbolized by A ∪ B, is the set of all elements that are in set A or set B (or both). In set-builder notation, A ∪ B = {x | x ∈ A or x ∈ B}.

---

For example, if $A = \{5, 10, 15, 20\}$ and $B = \{5, 20, 30, 45\}$, then the union $A \cup B = \{5, 10, 15, 20, 30, 45\}$. Even though 5 and 20 are in both sets, we list them only once in the union. The Venn diagram for $A \cup B$ is shown below. The set $A \cup B$ is the shaded area consisting of all elements in either set.

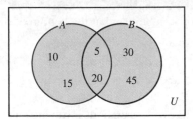

5. Why do you think the words "intersection" and "union" were chosen for these operations? An answer based on Venn diagrams would be especially appreciated.

   'Intersection' has a connotation of where things meet or cross, and the intersection of the two circles represents the intersection of the sets. As for union, you get the union by joining together all of the elements in the set, and in essence joining together the circles.

Three experimental medications are being evaluated for safety. Each has a list of side effects that has been reported by at least 1% of the people trying the medication. This a blind trial, so the medications are simply labeled *A*, *B*, and *C*. The side effects for each are listed below.

   $A = \{$nausea, night sweats, nervousness, dry mouth, swollen feet$\}$
   $B = \{$weight gain, nausea, nervousness, blurry vision, fever, trouble sleeping$\}$
   $C = \{$dry mouth, nausea, blurry vision, fever, weight loss, eczema$\}$

For Questions 6–8, find each requested set. Then provide a verbal description of what the set represents.

6. $A \cup B$

   {nausea, night sweats, nervousness, dry mouth, swollen feet, weight gain, blurry vision, fever, trouble sleeping} This is the set of side effects reported by more than 1% of subjects taking either medication A or B.

7. $A \cup C$

   {nausea, night sweats, nervousness, dry mouth, swollen feet, blurry vision, fever, weight loss, eczema} This is the set of side effects reported by more than 1% of subjects taking either medication A or C.

**8.** $A \cup B \cup C$

(nausea, night sweats, nervousness, dry mouth, swollen feet, weight gain, blurry vision, fever, trouble sleeping, weight loss, eczema). This is the set of side effects reported by more than 1% of subjects taking any of the three medications.

## Did You Get It?

Try this problem to see if you understand the concepts we just studied. The answer can be found at the bottom of the portfolio page.

6. If $A = \{a, b, c, d, e\}$, $B = \{a, c, e, g, i\}$, and $C = \{b, d, f, h, j\}$, find $A \cup B$, $A \cup C$, and $A \cup B \cup C$.

What about operations involving more than two sets and more than one operation? Just like with operations involving numbers, we use parentheses to indicate an order of operations.

For Questions 9–11, use the sets of side effects from Questions 6–8. Find the requested set, and again describe verbally what it represents.

**9.** $(A \cup B) \cap C$

(dry mouth, nausea, blurry vision, fever). This is the set of side effects common to medication C and either A or B.

> Starting here, it can get pretty complicated to find these sets. Encourage the students to take them in stages, and to pay attention to parentheses.

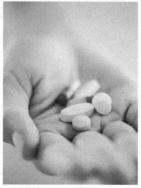

© JGI/Jamie Grill/Blend Images LLC RF

**10.** $A \cap (B \cup C)$

(nausea, dry mouth, nervousness). This is the set of side effects common to medication A and either B or C.

**11.** $(A \cap B) \cup C$

(nausea, nervousness, dry mouth, blurry vision, fever, weight loss, eczema). This is the set of side effects reported either by users of medication C, or both users of A and users of B.

When combining union and intersection with complements as we will do next, we'll have to be extra careful. Pay particular attention to the parentheses and to whether the complement symbol is inside or outside the parentheses. And remember to do any operation in parentheses first! For example, to find $(A \cap B)'$, you would first find the intersection of $A$ and $B$, then find all elements of the universal set not in that intersection.

Going back to our sets of side effects, recall that these were reported by at least 1% of users. The universal set below is the set of all side effects reported by ANY users. Use this to find the sets requested in Questions 12–14.

$U$ = {nausea, night sweats, nervousness, dry mouth, swollen feet, weight gain, blurry vision, fever, trouble sleeping, weight loss, eczema, motor mouth, darting eyes, uncontrollable falling down}

**12.** $A' \cap C'$

$A'$ = (weight gain, blurry vision, fever, trouble sleeping, weight loss, eczema, motor mouth, darting eyes, uncontrollable falling down); $C'$ = (night sweats, nervousness, swollen feet, weight gain, trouble sleeping, motor mouth, darting eyes, uncontrollable falling down)

$A' \cap C'$ = (weight gain, trouble sleeping, motor mouth, darting eyes, uncontrollable falling down)

**13.** $(A \cap B)' \cap C$

(dry mouth, blurry vision, fever, weight loss, eczema)

**14.** $B' \cup (A \cap C')$

(night sweats, swollen feet, dry mouth, weight loss, eczema, motor mouth, darting eyes, uncontrollable falling down, nervousness)

> ## Math Note
> Don't forget: the complement of a set $A$ is all of the elements in the universal set that are not in $A$, not all of the objects in the universe that are not in $A$.

---

## Did You Get It   ?

Try this problem to see if you understand the concepts we just studied. The answer can be found at the bottom of the portfolio page.

7. Let $U = \{1, 2, 3, 4, 5, 6, 7, 8\}$, $A = \{1, 3, 5, 7\}$, $B = \{2, 4, 6, 8\}$, and $C = \{2, 3, 5, 7\}$. Find each set.
   a. $A \cup (B \cap C)$    b. $(A \cup B)'$

---

Union and intersection are very applicable concepts, even when you don't necessarily realize that you're using them. In Questions 15 and 16, describe each set verbally.

**15.** The intersection of U.S. citizens older than 17 and the set of U.S. citizens that have not been convicted of a felony.

People who are eligible to vote in United States federal election in every state.

© Momentum Creative Group/Alamy
RF

**16.** The union of your mother's parents and your father's parents.

*Your grandparents*

## Set Subtraction

Another set operation we can study is the *difference* of sets. If you're in the set of students that live off campus but not in the set of students that walk to school, then you're in the difference of those two sets.

---

The **difference** of two sets $A$ and $B$, symbolized by $A - B$, is the set of all elements that are in $A$ but not in $B$. In set-builder notation, $A - B = \{x \mid x \in A \text{ and } x \in B\}$.

---

**17.** While it's often most natural to think of the difference of two sets in terms of set subtraction, you can actually describe the difference of sets $A$ and $B$ using operations that we studied earlier in the lesson. How? (Hint: The description of difference in set-builder notation is VERY helpful.)

*$A \cap B'$*

**18.** For the side effect sets $A$, $B$, and $C$ from earlier in the lesson, find the differences $A - B$ and $B - C$, and describe what each represents.

*$A - B =$ (night sweats, swollen feet, dry mouth). This is the set of side effects experienced by at least 1% of the subjects taking medication A, but not experienced by at least 1% of those taking medication B.*

*$B - C =$ (nervousness, weight gain, trouble sleeping). This is the set of side effects experienced by at least 1% of the subjects taking medication B, but not experienced by at least 1% of those taking medication C.*

# 6-2 Portfolio

Name _____

Check each box when you've completed the task. Remember that your instructor will want you to turn in the portfolio pages you create.

## Technology

1. ☐ The quote at the beginning of this lesson talks about the intersection of technology, art, and science. Do an Internet search for the string of "The intersection of" and find an example of someone describing an intersection that you find interesting. Provide the URL where you found it, quote the part that references an intersection, then describe what the writer is trying to say.

## Online Practice

1. ☐ Include any written work from the online assignment along with any notes or questions about this lesson's content.

## Applications

1. ☐ Complete the applications problems.

## Reflections

Type a short answer to each question.

1. ☐ Describe each of these important terms in your own words: subset, union, intersection, complement.
2. ☐ Write your own example of a union problem, and an intersection problem. No abstract sets! Explain the context.
3. ☐ Take another look at your answer to Question 0 at the beginning of this lesson. Would you revise your answer now that you've completed the lesson? How would you summarize the topic of this lesson now?
4. ☐ What questions do you have about this lesson?

## Looking Ahead

1. ☐ Complete the Lesson 6-3 Prep Skills and read the opening paragraph in Lesson 6-3 carefully, then answer Question 0 in preparation for that lesson.

## Answers to "Did You Get It?"

1. $A' = \{20, 40, 60, 70, 80, 90\}$   2. {UA, UND, SU}, {UA, UND}, {UA, SU}, {UND, SU}, {UA}, {UND}, {SU}, ∅   3. 15: {♦, ♥, ♠}, {♦, ♥, ♣}, {♦, ♠, ♣}, {♥, ♠, ♣}, {♦, ♥}, {♦, ♠}, {♦, ♣}, {♥, ♠}, {♥, ♣}, {♠, ♣}, {♦}, {♥}, {♠}, {♣}, ∅   4. 128 and 127
5. $A \cap B = \{10, 20\}$ ; $B \cap C = \{30\}$; $A \cap B \cap C = \emptyset$
6. $A \cup B = \{a, b, c, d, e, g, i\}$; $A \cup C = \{a, b, c, d, e, f, h, j\}$; $A \cup B \cup C = \{a, b, c, d, e, f, g, h, i, j\}$
7. **a.** $A \cup (B \cap C) = \{1, 2, 3, 5, 7\}$   **b.** $(A \cup B)' = \emptyset$

Diagram for 1

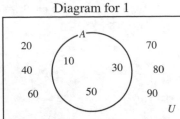

## 6-2   Applications

Name _____

1. The U.S. Department of Health and Human Services recommends that everyone healthy enough to exercise should get either 150 minutes of moderate physical activity (like walking or stretching) per week or 75 minutes of vigorous activity (like running or biking) per week. Let's say that the gym at your campus has treadmills, stationary bikes, and elliptical machines. You can choose none, some, or all of those as part of a workout plan. Write all the possible choices you could make, then explain what in the world that has to do with our study of sets in this lesson.

   *You could choose all three, treadmill and stationary bike, treadmill and elliptical, stationary bike and elliptical, treadmill only, stationary bike only, elliptical only, or none of those. This represents all subsets of the set (treadmill, stationary bike, elliptical).*

© JGI/Jamie Grill/Blend Images LLC RF

2. When playing five-card poker, players are originally dealt five cards (because six would just be silly), and can choose to discard any number of them from none to all five. How many different choices do you have of discards after the original draw? Your explanation in Question 1, and a formula you developed in this lesson will help.

   *$2^5 = 32$. This is the number of subsets of those five cards.*

3. This personal ad was posted on Craigslist: "Wife wanted, must be able to dig and clean worms or be able to clean fish. Must have own boat with motor. Please send photograph of motor boat." Write a statement involving three sets, intersection, and union that describes this fine gentleman's requirements for a life partner.

   *Set D is women able to dig and clean worms, set C is women able to clean fish, and set B is the set of women that have a motorboat. Our friend is looking for a woman in $B \cap (D \cup C)$.*

In Questions 4–6, write a description of the complement of each set. You'll need to decide on an appropriate universal set, so make sure you describe that as well.

4. Your Facebook friends (If you're not on Facebook, play along and pretend that you are.)

   *It depends on what you define as the universal set. If you think of it as all people on Facebook, then the complement is everyone on Facebook that you're not friends with. If the universal set is everyone you know, the complement is people you know that you're not friends on Facebook with. If the universal set is everyone in the world, then the complement is everyone on the planet except your Facebook friends.*

## 6-2  Applications

Name _____

5. The courses you'll need to take to fulfill your degree requirements.

*If the universal set is all courses offered by your school, then the complement is all courses you don't have to take to fulfill your degree requirements. If the universal set is all the courses you'll take, then the complement is the electives.*

6. NASA missions that resulted in a successful launch.

*If the universal set is all scheduled NASA launches, then the complement is missions where the launch was scrubbed or was unsuccessfully executed. If the universal set is all launches that were attempted, the complement is just those that were unsuccessfully executed.*

Questions 7–13 use the following sets. For each question, write a verbal description of the set.

$U$ = the set of all people who have been charged with a felony
$A$ = the set of people who are on trial or awaiting trial on felony charges
$B$ = the set of people who have been convicted of a felony
$C$ = the set of people who have been convicted of a felony and have been released from prison
$D$ = the set of people who were charged with a felony and found not guilty
$E$ = the set of people who were charged with a felony and had charges dropped before standing trial

7. $B \cup D$

*The set of all people who were charged with a felony and were either convicted at trial, acquitted at trial, or pled guilty.*

8. $C'$

*The set of people who were charged with a felony and are either in prison, or were never sentenced to jail time.*

9. $B \cap C$

*The set of people who have been convicted of a felony and have been released from prison.*

## 6-2 Applications

Name _____

**10.** $C \cap B'$

This set is empty; to be in set $B'$, you need to have never been convicted of a felony, but everyone in $C$ has been.

**11.** $(A \cup B)'$

This is the set of people who have been charged with a felony, and their case has either been dismissed, or they were acquitted.

**12.** $B \cap D$

It's tempting to say the set is empty, but people that were found not guilty of one felony but convicted of another make up the set.

**13.** $A - (B \cap C)$

This is the set of people who are on trial or awaiting trial on a felony charge that have never been convicted of another felony.

In Questions 14–17, decide if the statement is true or false. You may have to do some poking around on the Internet for information.

**14.** $\varnothing \subseteq A$, where $A$ is the set of four-leaf clovers.

True. The empty set is a subset of every set.

**15.** $\varnothing \subset B$, where $B$ is the set of living unicorns.

False. Both sets are empty, and a set can't be a proper subset of itself.

## 6-2 Applications

Name _____

**16.** {Elvis Presley, Elvis Costello} ⊂ {*x* | *x* is a member of the rock and roll hall of fame}

*True: both Elvises (Elvi?) are members of the hall of fame, and they're not the only two people in it.*

**17.** {Neil Armstrong, John Glenn, Alan Shepard, Buzz Aldrin} ⊄ {*y* | *y* is a person that has landed on the moon}

*True. John Glenn never went to the moon.*

# Lesson 6-3 Prep Skills

This is a short review of skills that will come in handy in the next lesson. In each case, answer the question, then rate your confidence level by checking one of the boxes. If you feel like you're struggling with these skills, consult the online resources provided by your instructor for extra practice.

### SKILL 1: INTERPRET A VENN DIAGRAM

1. Based on the Venn diagram below, write sets *A, B,* and *A'* using the roster method.

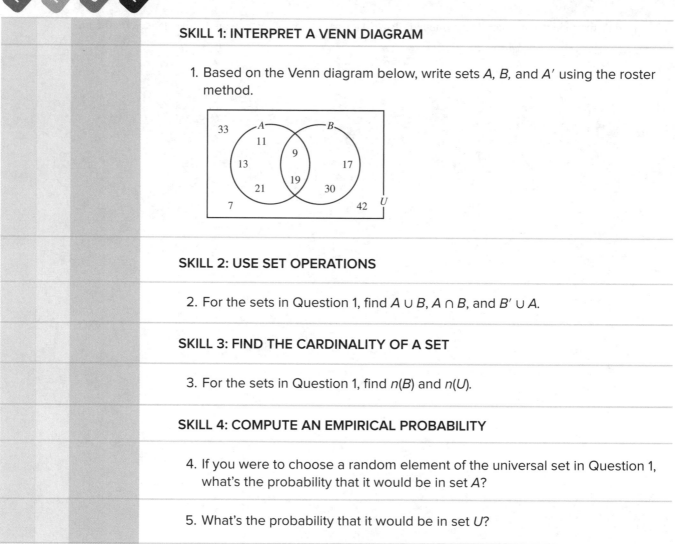

### SKILL 2: USE SET OPERATIONS

2. For the sets in Question 1, find $A \cup B$, $A \cap B$, and $B' \cup A$.

### SKILL 3: FIND THE CARDINALITY OF A SET

3. For the sets in Question 1, find $n(B)$ and $n(U)$.

### SKILL 4: COMPUTE AN EMPIRICAL PROBABILITY

4. If you were to choose a random element of the universal set in Question 1, what's the probability that it would be in set *A*?

5. What's the probability that it would be in set *U*?

# Lesson 6-3 **Worlds Collide** (Studying Sets with Two-Circle Venn Diagrams)

## LEARNING OBJECTIVES

☐ 1. Illustrate sets with two-circle Venn diagrams.

☐ 2. Develop and use De Morgan's laws.

☐ 3. Use Venn diagrams to decide if two sets are equal.

☐ 4. Review how Venn diagrams can be used in probability.

Source: Facebook; courtesy David Sobecki

*The interesting thing about the Internet is that it has created a kind of alternative circle of friends for people.*
　　　　　　　　　　—Joanne Harris

Have you ever wanted to post something on Facebook or Instagram, then decided not to because it may not be something you want everyone you know to see? Some people are social media friends only with their closest buddies: more people are friends with hundreds of people, from their Mom to casual work acquaintances. My closest friends and I have a secret private group on Facebook for exactly this reason: the set of things I feel comfortable saying to my college buddies is most definitely not equal, or even equivalent, to the set of things I feel comfortable saying to my Mom and my golf pro. Most of us have many distinct circles of friends and contacts, and when those worlds collide the results can be unpredictable, and maybe unintentionally hilarious.

　　One good way to get a handle on complicated interplay between varying groups is with diagrams. And can you guess what kind of diagrams we'll choose to accomplish this? If you didn't say "Venn," please go back and rework the previous lesson. We'll wait here for you.

**0.** After reading the opening paragraphs, what do you think the main topic of this lesson will be?

## 6-3 Class

Notice that there are four distinct regions in a Venn diagram illustrating two sets $A$ and $B$. We'll want to number the regions for reference; we use Roman numerals so that we don't confuse the number of the region with elements in the set or the cardinality of the set.

**1.** Write the appropriate description next to each region. Pick your answer from the following list.

the elements in set $B$ that are not in set $A$
the elements in both sets $A$ and $B$
the elements in the universal set that are in neither set $A$ nor set $B$
the elements in set $A$ that are not in set $B$

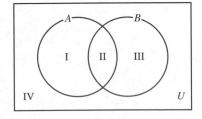

Region I represents *the elements in set A that are not in set B.*

Region II represents *the elements in both sets A and B.*

Region III represents *the elements in set B that are not in set A.*

Region IV represents *the elements in the universal set that are in neither set A nor set B.*

The procedure that we use to illustrate set statements is found in the following box.

### Illustrating a Set Statement with a Venn Diagram

**Step 1.** Draw a diagram for the sets, with Roman numerals in each region.
**Step 2.** Using those Roman numerals, list the regions described by each set.
**Step 3.** Find the set of numerals that correspond to the set given in the set statement.
**Step 4.** Shade the area corresponding to the set of numerals found in Step 3.

**2.** Draw a Venn diagram to illustrate the set $(A \cup B')'$. We've generously completed the first step for you, which is drawing the generic diagram. Feel free to send us a nice gift, or maybe some cash.

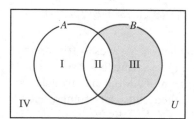

Regions in set $A$: _____I and II_____

Regions in set $B'$: _____I and IV_____

> **Math Note**
>
> In any problem where we're asked to illustrate a set statement involving two sets, Steps 1 and 2 will be exactly the same.

$A \cup B'$ consists of region(s) ____I, II, and IV____.

The complement of $A \cup B'$ consists of region(s) ____III____.

Shade the region(s) corresponding to $(A \cup B')'$.

**3.** Draw a Venn diagram to illustrate the set $A \cap B'$. (This time you're on your own.)

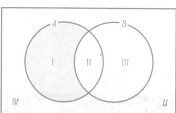

**4.** Based on your Venn diagram, think of another way to write $A \cap B'$ using an operation from Lesson 6-2. (This is one of the big things we'll use Venn diagrams for: to identify when two sets that are written differently are actually the same.)

$A - B$

### Did You Get It?

Try these problems to see if you understand the concepts we just studied. The answers can be found at the bottom of the portfolio page.

1. Draw a Venn diagram to illustrate the set $A' \cap B$.
2. Draw a Venn diagram to illustrate the set $A' \cup B$.

## De Morgan's Laws

There are two very well-known formulas that are useful in simplifying some set operations. They're named in honor of a 19th-century mathematician named Augustus De Morgan. First, we'll write the first of the formulas and illustrate it with an example. Then we'll see how Venn diagrams can be used to prove the formula.

### De Morgan's First Law

For any two sets $A$ and $B$,

$$(A \cup B)' = A' \cap B'$$

5. The first law states that the complement of the _____union_____ of two sets will always be equal to the _____intersection_____ of the complements of each set.

6. If $U = \{a, b, c, d, e, f, g, h\}$, $A = \{a, c, e, g\}$, and $B = \{b, c, d, e\}$, find $(A \cup B)'$ and $A' \cap B'$.

   $A \cup B = \{a, b, c, d, e, g\}$, so $(A \cup B)' = \{f, h\}$

   $A' = \{b, d, f, h\}$ and $B' = \{a, f, g, h\}$, so $A' \cap B' = \{f, h\}$

7. If we use the result of Question 6 to conclude that De Morgan's first law is likely to be true, we're using what type of reasoning, inductive or deductive?

   Inductive

8. Explain why this doesn't prove that the law is true.

   All we know for sure is that it works for those specific sets. That doesn't tell us anything about whether it will work for ANY other sets, let alone EVERY pair of sets.

Now we'll prove that the law is true. The plan is to use Venn diagrams to show that $(A \cup B)'$ and $A' \cap B'$ are the same set.

9. In the Venn diagrams below, set $U$ contains which regions?

I, II, III, and IV

10. Set $A$ contains which regions?

I and II

11. Set $B$ contains which regions?

II and III

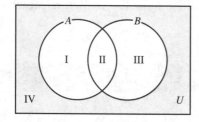 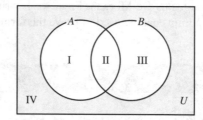

Fill in numbers of the regions in the above Venn diagram to answer Questions 12, 13, 15, and 16. Write as sets using the roster method.

12. $A \cup B = \{I, II, III\}$            14. Shade the region to illustrate $(A \cup B)'$.

13. So $(A \cup B)' = \{IV\}$            15. $A' = \{III, IV\}$

16. $B' = \{I, IV\}$

17. So $A' \cap B' = \{IV\}$

18. Shade the region to illustrate $A' \cap B'$.

19. Since the diagrams for each side of the equation are identical, we use deductive reasoning to conclude that

     $(A \cup B)' = A' \cap B'$      .

20. The second of De Morgan's laws involves an alternate form for the set $(A \cap B)'$. Based on the first law, make a conjecture as to what you think the alternate form for that set is.

The reasonable conjecture is $A' \cup B'$.

**21.** Draw two Venn diagrams: one for $(A \cap B)'$, and one for the set that you believe it's equal to (from the previous question). Does this confirm your conjecture? If yes, great job. If not, revise your conjecture and try again.

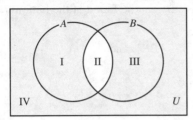 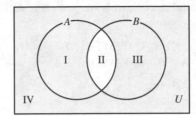

*It does confirm the conjecture.*

**22.** Fill in your result in the box below, then congratulate yourselves on being real mathematicians, because you just discovered AND proved a result.

## De Morgan's Second Law

For any two sets *A* and *B*,

$(A \cap B)' = \underline{A' \cup B'}$

**23.** Even after proving a result, it's a good idea to use it in a specific example to make sure that it appears to be working correctly. For the sets $U = \{10, 11, 12, 13, 14, 15, 16\}$, $A = \{10, 11, 12, 13\}$, and $B = \{12, 13, 14, 15\}$, find $(A \cap B)'$ and $A' \cup B'$. Does the result confirm your version of De Morgan's second law? Does your result prove it?

*$A \cap B = \{12, 13\}$, so $(A \cap B)' = \{10, 11, 14, 15, 16\}$*

*$A' = \{14, 15, 16\}$ and $B' = \{10, 11, 16\}$, so $A' \cup B' = \{10, 11, 14, 15, 16\}$*

*The result confirms the law, but certainly does not prove it.*

---

### Did You Get It?

Try these problems to see if you understand the concepts we just studied. The answers can be found at the bottom of the portfolio page.

3. If $U = \{$ABC, NBC, CBS, Fox, USA, TBS, TNT, MTV$\}$, $A = \{$NBC, Fox, USA, TBS$\}$, and $B = \{$ABC, NBC, CBS, Fox$\}$, find $(A \cap B)'$ and $A' \cup B'$.

4. Use Venn diagrams to show that $B' \cap A = A - B$.

---

## 6-3 Group

### The Cardinal Number of a Union

If 10 of your friends belong to the set of students taking a math class, and 14 belong to the set of students taking an English class, how many are in the union of those two sets? If your first instinct is 24, you're not alone—that's sort of the standard guess. And it might actually be right, but only if none of your friends are taking both a math and an English class. If any of them are in both classes, you'd be counting them twice by just adding the number of friends in each set. Venn diagrams can be used to analyze this situation.

As you can see in the figure below, if we start with the number of elements in *A*, we're counting all the members in regions I and II. When we add the number of elements in *B*, we're counting all the members in regions II and III. Do you see the issue? The elements in region II get counted twice.

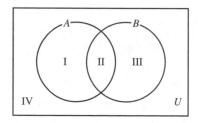

1. After adding the number of elements in sets *A* and *B*, what can we do to turn the result into the correct cardinality of the set $A \cup B$?

   *Subtract the number of elements in both sets.*

2. Use your answer to Question 1 to fill in the blank in the following box. Then congratulate yourselves again, because you've developed another formula! (Check with your instructor to make sure you have the right formula before moving on.)

---

 ### The Cardinality of a Union

If $n(A)$ represents the cardinality of set *A*, then for any two finite sets *A* and *B*,

$$n(A \cup B) = n(A) + n(B) \underline{\quad - n(A \cap B) \quad}$$

---

Next, we'll use your shiny new formula to solve a problem.

3. In a survey of 100 randomly selected freshmen walking across campus, it turns out that 42 are taking a math class, 51 are taking an English class, and 12 are taking both. How many students are taking either a math class or an English class?

$42 + 51 - 12 = 81$

© Digital Vision/Getty Images RF

4. What's the probability that one of those freshmen is taking either a math class or an English class?

$81/100 = 0.81$

5. Explain how the procedure you developed for finding the cardinality of a union is used in developing the second addition rule for probability: $P(A \text{ or } B) = P(A) + P(B) - P(A \text{ and } B)$.

All of the probabilities on the right side are fractions with the same denominator-the size of the sample space-and the numerators will be the number of outcomes in event A plus the number of outcomes in event B minus the number of outcomes in the intersection. That's exactly what we figured out in terms of cardinality.

## Did You Get It?

Try this problem to see if you understand the concepts we just studied. The answer can be found at the bottom of the portfolio page.

5. A poll of 200 doctors across the nation found that 112 were assisted in their office by registered nurses, 83 were assisted by licensed practical nurses, and 21 were assisted by both. How many were assisted by at least one type of nurse?

We live in the information age—every time you turn around, somebody somewhere is trying to gather information about you, your opinions, and (most commonly) your spending habits. Surveys are conducted by the thousands every day, and every person, pet, pastime, and product are classified. The things we've learned about sets can be very helpful in interpreting information from surveys and classifications, and that will be the focus of the remainder of this lesson.

The plan is to give you some guidance on the first problem, providing steps that you can use for subsequent problems.

**The problem:** In 2015, there were 40 states that had some form of casino gambling in the state, 44 states that sold lottery tickets of some kind, and 36 states that had both casinos and lotteries. Draw a Venn diagram to represent this data, and find how many states have only casino gambling, how many states have only lotteries, and how many states have neither.

© Digital Vision Ltd./SuperStock RF

6. Draw a Venn diagram with two circles, and label the circles *L* and *C* for lottery and casino respectively.

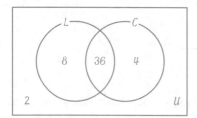

> I can almost guarantee that a majority of students will begin by writing 40 in the part of the diagram that should be 4. I can also guarantee that if you don't address this issue up front, it'll be REALLY hard to get them past it later.

7. How many states have both casinos and a lottery? Put this value in the intersection of *C* and *L*.

8. Since 40 states have casino gambling and 36 have both, how many have casino gambling but not a lottery? Put that number in the portion of the circle labeled *C* that is outside of the intersection of *C* and *L*.

9. Since 44 states have a lottery and 36 have both, how many have a lottery but no casinos? Put that number in the portion of the circle labeled *L* that is outside of the intersection of *C* and *L*.

10. Add up the numbers in your diagram so far. There are fifty states (duh), so you can subtract from 50 to find how many states go inside the universal set but outside both circles. Do that.

11. Now that you have the diagram completed, answer all the questions in the original problem. Make sure you answer ALL of the questions.

Only casino gambling: 4. Only lotteries: 8. Neither: 2.

The key starting point in that problem is knowing the number that goes into the intersection region of the Venn diagram. Once you know that, if you're given the total number that goes inside one of the circles, you can subtract the number in the intersection from that number to find the number that goes in that circle, but outside the intersection. Now you should be able to use the procedure outlined above to solve the next problem.

12. A dietitian studying the nutritional value of food at eight popular fast-food restaurants examines the amount of protein and the amount of fat in all of the breakfast meals available. She finds that out of 93 meals available, 43 have more than 20 grams of protein, 65 have more than 25 grams of fat, and 31 have both more than 20 grams of protein and more than 25 grams of fat. How many meals have more than 20 grams of protein and less than 25 grams of fat? How many have less than 25 grams of fat and less than 20 grams of protein?

*Twelve have more than 20 grams of protein and less than 25 g of fat.*
*Sixteen have less than 25 grams of fat and less than 20 g of protein.*

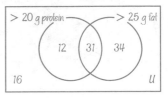

One of the most useful applications of Venn diagrams is for studying the results of surveys. Whether they are for business-related research or just to satisfy curiosity, surveys seem to be everywhere these days, especially online. Many news websites include daily surveys, like this one from cnn.com.

Our last problem, based on survey results, also uses a two-circle Venn diagram, but is just a bit different: we're not given the number that goes in the intersection.

In a survey published in the *Journal of The American Academy of Dermatologists,* 500 people were asked by random telephone dialing whether they have a tattoo and/or a body piercing. Of these, 79 reported having a tattoo only, 31 reported having a piercing only, and 151 reported having at least one of the two. Draw a Venn diagram to represent these results and use your diagram to find the percentage of respondents that have a tattoo, that have a piercing, that have both, and that have neither.

13. Draw a two-circle Venn diagram, with one circle labeled to represent people with tattoos, and the other labeled to represent people with piercings.

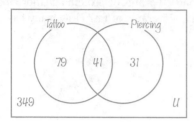

14. The key difference in this problem is that we're given the number of people with tattoos only (79). Does this number get entered into your Venn diagram? Where? Why?

It goes in the portion that's inside the left circle and outside the right one.

15. Use what you discovered in Question 14 to finish the diagram and answer all questions in the problem.

Tattoo: 120/500 = 24%; Piercing: 72/500 = 14.4%;

Both: 41/500 = 8.2%; Neither: 349/500 = 69.8%

---

**Did You Get It?**

Try this problem to see if you understand the concepts we just studied. The answer can be found at the bottom of the portfolio page.

6. According to an online survey on Howstuffworks.com, 12,595 people gave their thoughts on Coke vs. Pepsi. Of these, 5,786 drink only Coke, 3,763 drink only Pepsi, and 11,405 drink at least one. Draw a Venn diagram to represent these results and use your diagram to find the percentage of respondents that drink Coke, that drink Pepsi, that drink both, and that drink neither.

## 6-3  Portfolio

Name _____

Check each box when you've completed the task. Remember that your instructor will want you to turn in the portfolio pages you create.

### Technology

1. ☐  Back to the Internet! Find a survey online that you can represent with a two-circle Venn diagram. Provide a URL to where you found the survey, then draw a Venn diagram based on the survey, and use it to discuss all of the information you can get about the survey results.

### Online Practice

1. ☐  Include any written work from the online assignment along with any notes or questions about this lesson's content.

### Applications

1. ☐  Complete the applications problems.

### Reflections

Type a short answer to each question.

1. ☐  Describe the process of using a Venn diagram to decide if two sets that are written differently are actually the same.
2. ☐  Explain what type of surveys lend themselves to being analyzed with Venn diagrams.
3. ☐  Take another look at your answer to Question 0 at the beginning of this lesson. Would you revise your answer now that you've completed the lesson? How would you summarize the topic of this lesson now?
4. ☐  What questions do you have about this lesson?

### Looking Ahead

1. ☐  Complete the Lesson 6-4 Prep Skills and read the opening paragraph in Lesson 6-4 carefully, then answer Question 0 in preparation for that lesson.

### Answers to "Did You Get It?"

1.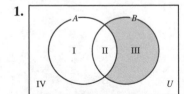
2. 
3. Both are {ABC, CBS, USA, TBS, TNT, MTV}

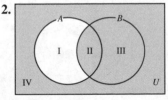

4. Both diagrams are

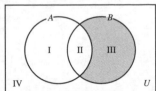

5. 174    6. Coke: 60.7%; Pepsi: 44.6%; both: 14.7%; neither: 9.4%

**6-3**   Applications

Name _____

1. Draw a Venn diagram for each set described, and use your diagrams to decide if the two sets are equal or not.
   $A \cup B'$  and  $A' \cap B$

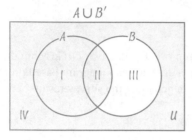

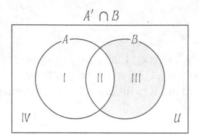

The sets are not equal.

In Questions 2 and 3, $A$ = {People majoring in a science} and $B$ = {People majoring in Botany, Zoology, or Biochemistry}. Draw a Venn diagram that represents each set, and write a sentence describing what the set represents. Think carefully about the relationship between these sets before you draw your diagram.

2. $A \cup B$

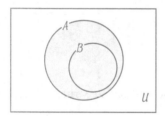

This is the set of people majoring in a science.

> **Math Note**
>
> Contrary to popular belief, "zoology" is pronounce "ZO - ology", not "ZOO-ology". It is NOT the study of zoos.

3. $A \cap B$

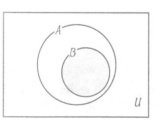

This is the set of people majoring in Botany, Zoology, or Biochemistry.

# 6-3 Applications

Name _____

The table and Venn diagram below are for Questions 4–7. The table shows the ten states that had the highest percentage of people voting Republican in the 2008 and 2012 presidential elections. For each question, write which region of the Venn diagram would include the state listed. Set *A* represents states in the top ten in 2008, and set *B* the top ten in 2012.

| Year | 2008 | 2012 |
|---|---|---|
| States | Oklahoma | Utah |
| | Wyoming | Wyoming |
| | Utah | Oklahoma |
| | Idaho | Idaho |
| | Alabama | West Virginia |
| | Alaska | Alabama |
| | Arkansas | Arkansas |
| | Louisiana | Kentucky |
| | Nebraska | Nebraska |
| | Tennessee | Kansas |

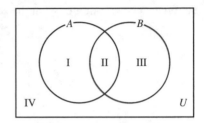

**4.** Utah

*Region II*

**5.** Kansas

*Region III*

**6.** Alaska

*Region I*

**7.** Arizona

*Region IV*

**8.** The economic downturn in the mid-2000s had a devastating effect on the automobile industry: more people than ever were hanging onto used cars as long as they could, and safety was affected. According to a survey conducted in 2012, out of 400 cars that were given inspections while getting an oil change, 138 were in need of brake repair, 94 needed new tires, and 78 needed both. Use a Venn diagram to find the number of cars that didn't need either repair, and the number with good tires that needed new brakes.

*There were 246 that needed neither repair, and 60 that had good tires but needed new brakes.*

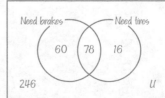

## 6-3   Applications

Name _____

Use this information for Questions 9–14. Five hundred people are involved in a drug trial, testing two new acne medications. The two drugs involved are called Felafin and Gantex, and participants could have been given either, both, or neither medication. Let's call the set of people who were given Felafin *F,* and the set who were given Gantex *G.* (Pretty original, right?)

**9.** Write a description of what the set $F \cup G$ represents.

This is the set of people that were given at least one of Felafin or Gantex.

**10.** Using your answer to Question 9, what does set $(F \cup G)'$ represent?

These are the people that were given neither Felafin nor Gantex.

**11.** Draw a Venn diagram illustrating the set $(F \cup G)'$.

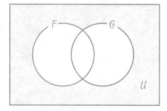

**12.** Write descriptions of what the sets $F'$ and $G'$ represent.

$F'$ is the people that were not given Felafin, and $G'$ is the people that were not given Gantex.

**13.** Using your answer to Question 12, what does the set $F' \cap G'$ represent?

This is the set of people who were not given Felafin AND were not given Gantex. In other words, the set of people who were given neither.

## 6-3 Applications

Name _____

14. Compare your responses to Questions 10 and 13. Are they the same? Explain why they should be the same.

They are the same, and they should be: We know from DeMorgan's laws that $(F \cup G)' = F' \cap G'$.

15. Based on an online poll of 70,000 people in February 2016, 49% had eaten at McDonald's at least once in the previous month, 26% had eaten at Burger King in the last month, and 41% had eaten at neither restaurant. Draw a Venn diagram with the NUMBER of people who ate at these restaurants, and use it to answer Questions 16–18.

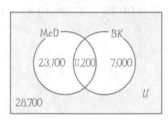

16. How many of the people polled ate at both restaurants at least once in the last month?

11,200

17. How many had eaten at McDonald's but not Burger King?

23,100

18. What percentage of those polled had visited at least one of the two restaurants?

59%

## Lesson 6-4   Prep Skills

This is a short review of skills that will come in handy in the next lesson. In each case, answer the question, then rate your confidence level by checking one of the boxes. If you feel like you're struggling with these skills, consult the online resources provided by your instructor for extra practice.

### SKILL 1: FILLING IN A VENN DIAGRAM

1. From a universal set with 90 elements, there are 8 elements that are in both sets *A* and *B*, 24 in set *A*, and 50 in set *B*. Fill in the number of elements in each region of the Venn diagram provided.

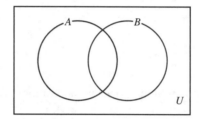

### SKILL 2: INTERPRETING A SHADED PORTION OF A VENN DIAGRAM

2. Write the set that is represented by the shaded portion of the Venn diagram.

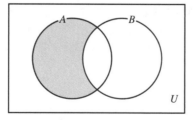

3. Write the set that is represented by the shaded portion of the Venn diagram.

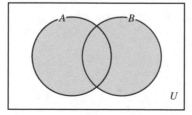

# Lesson 6-4 A Dollar for Your Thoughts (Using Sets to Solve Problems)

## LEARNING OBJECTIVES

☐ 1. Illustrate sets with three-circle Venn diagrams.

☐ 2. Decide if two sets are equal using three-circle Venn diagrams.

☐ 3. Solve a variety of applied problems using Venn diagrams.

*Prejudice is a great time saver. You can form opinions without having to get the facts.*
*—E.B. White*

© BananaStock Ltd. RF

Communication in our society is becoming cheaper, easier, and more effective all the time. In the age of smart phones and online communication, businesses are finding it simpler than ever to contact people for their opinions, and more and more people are finding out that companies are willing to pay to hear what they have to say. There are literally hundreds of companies in the United States today whose main function is to gather opinions on everything from political candidates to potato chips. In fact, over $6 *billion* is spent on market research in the United States each year. Maybe you'll think twice the next time somebody asks you for your opinion for free.

   With all the money at stake, not surprisingly it's important to organize all of the information that gets gathered. That sure sounds a lot like what we've been using set theory for! When the interplay between sets becomes more complicated, a more flexible tool is needed, and so we bring you the three-circle Venn diagram. In my opinion, it's a great way to organize information gathered from surveys and other sources. (Oh, and no charge—you can have that opinion for free.)

   **0.** After reading the opening paragraphs, what do you think the main topic of this lesson will be?

> Here's a shocking observation: 3-circle Venn diagrams are more complicated than 2-circle Venn diagrams. While students can get a little overwhelmed with all the information, use that to your advantage! Point out that if it's hard to organize and interpret all that information with a diagram, imagine how hard it would be without one!

## 6-4 Class

Here's some good news: the procedures we used for organizing and evaluating data in the last lesson work just fine for situations involving three sets: you just get a more complicated diagram.

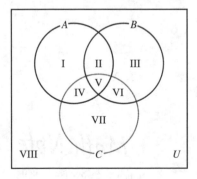

For Questions 1–8, fill in the blanks to describe each region in the diagram.

**1.** Region I represents the elements in set __A__ but not in set __B__ or set __C__.

**2.** Region II represents the elements in set __A__ and set __B__ but not in set __C__.

**3.** Region III represents the elements in set __B__ but not in set __A__ or set __C__.

**4.** Region IV represents the elements in sets __A__ and __C__ but not in set __B__.

**5.** Region V represents the elements in sets __A__, __B__, and __C__.

**6.** Region VI represents the elements in sets __B__ and __C__ but not in set __A__.

**7.** Region VII represents the elements in set __C__ but not in set __A__ or set __B__.

**8.** Region VIII represents the elements in the universal set __U__, but not in set __A__, __B__, or __C__.

<table>
<tr><td>Do not let students move on until you're sure they understand all of Questions 1–8. Without a comfort level there, they have no chance of working with these diagrams successfully.</td></tr>
</table>

A survey is conducted about the radio listening habits of adults in the 18–45 age bracket. Specifically, those surveyed were asked whether they listen to terrestrial radio over the airwaves, Internet radio, or satellite radio. To organize the results, the marketing group conducting the survey defines sets as follows:

$A$ = people that listen to terrestrial radio
$B$ = people that listen to Internet radio
$C$ = people that listen to satellite radio

The goal of Questions 9–14 will be to study the set $A \cap (B \cap C)'$.

**9.** What do you think this set represents in the context of this problem? (Not so easy, is it? If you can't decide, that's fine. The point is to try quickly.)

*This is the set of people that listen to terrestrial radio and either Internet or satellite radio, but not both. I think.*

**10.** We're going to use a Venn diagram to see if we can more easily decide what this set represents. We've helpfully supplied a diagram for reference. First, set $B \cap C$ contains which regions?

*V and VI*

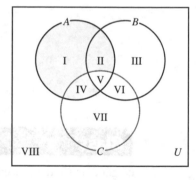

**11.** Based on your previous answer, set $(B \cap C)'$ contains which regions?

*I, II, III, IV, VII, and VIII*

**12.** Set $A$ contains which regions?

*I, II, IV, and V*

**13.** Now you are ready to shade the region to illustrate $A \cap (B \cap C)'$. It's the regions that are common to your answers from Questions 11 and 12.

**14.** Now describe what this set represents in the context of the problem.

*Now I'm sure that this is the set of people that listen to terrestrial radio only, or terrestrial and either Internet or satellite radio, but not both.*

## Math Note

Notice that when illustrating complicated sets like $A \cap (B \cap C)'$, we find the set in parentheses first. That's why the parentheses are there!

**Did You Get It?**

Try this problem to see if you understand the concepts we just studied. The answer can be found at the bottom of the portfolio page.

1.  Draw a Venn diagram to illustrate the set $(A \cap B') \cup C$.

To get even better at working with Venn diagrams, it's helpful to turn the process around, starting with a shaded diagram and figuring out what set it represents.

15.  Write the set illustrated by the Venn diagram. Your answer should use set operation symbols, not words. There may be more than one way to do so.

     *One way is $B - (A \cup C)$. Another is $B \cap (A \cup C)'$.*

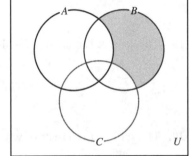

16.  Give a verbal description of your answer to Question 15. Then explain where in this lesson you've already answered this question.

     *This is the set of elements that are in set B, but not sets A or C. This is the region that was labeled III in the first diagram, making this the answer to Question 3.*

**Did You Get It?**

Try this problem to see if you understand the concepts we just studied. The answer can be found at the bottom of the portfolio page.

2.  Write the set illustrated by the Venn diagram to the right. Your answer should use set operation symbols, not words. There may be more than one way to do so.

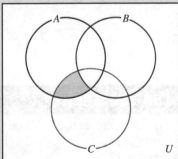

In Questions 17–22, the goal is to decide if the two sets are equal using Venn diagrams:

$(A \cup B) \cap C$ and $(A \cap C) \cup (B \cap C)$.

**17.** The set $A \cup B$ consists of which regions?

I, II, III, IV, V, VI

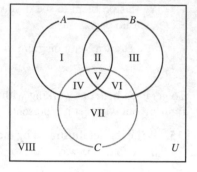

**18.** So $(A \cup B) \cap C$ consists of which regions?

IV, V, VI

**19.** The set $A \cap C$ consists of which regions?

IV, V

**20.** The set $B \cap C$ consists of which regions?

V, VI

**21.** So $(A \cap C) \cup (B \cap C)$ consists of which regions?

IV, V, VI

**22.** True or false: $(A \cup B) \cap C = (A \cap C) \cup (B \cap C)$. Describe how you decided on your answer.

True. The answers to Questions 18 and 21 are the same.

---

## Did You Get It?

Try this problem to see if you understand the concepts we just studied. The answer can be found at the bottom of the portfolio page.

   3.  Decide if the two sets are equal using Venn diagrams: $B \cup (A \cap C)$ and $(A \cup B) \cap (B \cup C)$.

# 6-4   Group

A criminal justice major is studying the frequency of certain types of crimes in a nearby county. He studies the arrest records of 300 inmates at the county jail, specifically asking about drug-related offenses, domestic violence, and theft of some sort. He finds that 194 had been arrested for theft, 210 for drug offenses, and 170 for domestic violence. In addition, 142 had arrests for both theft and drugs, 111 for both drugs and domestic violence, 91 for both theft and domestic violence, and 45 had been arrested for all three. Our goal will be to draw a Venn diagram to represent these results. Once we've done so, we'll be able to use it to get a wealth of information about this study.

The first diagram is for reference, with the regions numbered as usual. The second diagram is the one we'll fill in with information specific to this study.

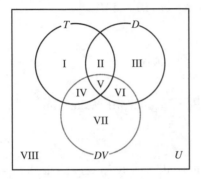
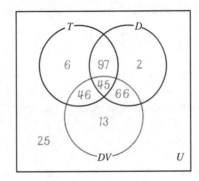

> Don't let the students revert to the bad habit of automatically putting the number arrested for theft (194) somewhere in the diagram. Even if they got past that in the last lesson, when the diagrams get more complicated, they may panic and stop thinking.

1. The only region we know for sure from the given information is region V—the number of inmates arrested for all three offenses. So we begin by putting _45_ in region V.

2. There are _142_ inmates with arrests for both theft and drugs, but we have to subtract the number arrested for all three offenses to find the number in region II: _142_ – _45_ = _97_. Make sure you write this number into your diagram.

3. In the same way, find (and write in) the values in regions IV and VI.

   The number in region IV = $91 - 45 = 46$

   The number in region VI = $111 - 45 = 66$

## Math Note

An important observation: we started with the number of elements in the innermost region and worked our way outward.

4. Now we're almost ready to find the number of elements in regions I, III, and VII. There were __194__ inmates arrested for theft, but the values in regions II, IV, and V are already accounted for in the diagram.

5. Add the values for II, IV, and V here:

   $97 + 46 + 45 = 188$

6. Subtract the value from Question 5 from the total number of inmates arrested for theft. That leaves __6__ in region I. Write it into your diagram.

7. Using the steps in Questions 5 and 6 as a model, find and write in the values in regions III and VII.

   The number in region III = $210 - (97 + 45 + 66) = 2$

   The number in region VII = $170 - (45 + 46 + 66) = 13$

8. Adding up all the numbers in the diagram so far, we get __275__. That leaves __25__ in region VIII. Write it in.

Now that we have the diagram completed, we're ready to answer some questions that would have been very difficult to answer (to say the least) without first organizing/understanding the data in a Venn diagram.

9. Find the number of inmates that had been arrested for only drug-related offenses.

   Two

10. What percentage of inmates arrested for theft were also arrested for drug-related offenses?

    $(97 + 45)/194 \approx 0.732$: About 73.2%.

**11.** Find the number of inmates that had been arrested for theft and domestic violence but not drugs.

46

**12.** Find the number of inmates that had been arrested for theft or drugs.

$300 - (25 + 13) = 262$

**13.** Find the number of inmates that had been arrested for none of these offenses.

25

Encourage students to use the stepped-out sample problems in this lesson as a model when working on homework.

When solving problems with Venn diagrams, the key is to write in the given information that applies exactly to certain regions, then use subtraction to find other regions one-by-one.

## Did You Get It?

Try this problem to see if you understand the concepts we just studied. The answer can be found at the bottom of the portfolio page.

4. Follow the steps laid out in Questions 1–8 to draw a Venn diagram for the following survey, then use it to answer the questions.

An online music service surveyed 500 customers and found that 270 listen to hip-hop music, 320 listen to rock, and 160 listen to country. In addition, 140 listen to both rock and hip-hop, 120 listen to rock and country, and 80 listen to hip-hop and country. Finally, 50 listen to all three. Draw a Venn diagram to represent the results of the survey and find the number of customers who

a. Listen to only hip-hop.
b. Listen to rock and country but not hip-hop.
c. Don't listen to any of these three types of music.
d. Don't listen to country music.

In this example, rather than walking you through the steps, we're going to just provide the problem, a blank diagram and let you and your group mates work it out. The key difference here is that you won't be provided with the number of elements in the intersection of all three sets, so you'll have to read the information very carefully, and work from "out to in," rather than from the innermost region outward, like in the last example. Subtraction is still your friend.

Three of the most dangerous risk factors for heart attack are high blood pressure, high cholesterol, and smoking. In a survey of 690 heart attack survivors, 62 had only high cholesterol among those three risk factors; 36 had only smoking; and 93 had only high blood pressure. There were 370 total with high cholesterol, 159 with high blood pressure and cholesterol that didn't smoke, and 23 that smoked and had high cholesterol but not high blood pressure. Finally, 585 had at least one risk factor.

**14.** Draw a Venn diagram representing this information and use it to answer the following questions.

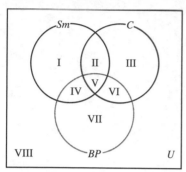  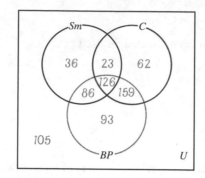

**15.** How many survivors had all three risk factors?

*126*

**16.** How many had exactly two of the three risk factors?

*23 + 86 + 159 = 268*

**17.** How many had none?

*105*

**18.** What percentage were smokers?

*(36 + 23 + 86 + 126)/690 = 0.393,*
*about 39.3% were smokers*

---

## Did You Get It?

Try this problem to see if you understand the concepts we just studied. The answer can be found at the bottom of the portfolio page.

5. Three other risk factors are obesity, family history of heart disease, and stress. Of the group of heart attack patients in Questions 14–18, 213 had a family history of heart disease; 47 of those with family history also suffered from stress but not obesity, 60 were obese but had no stress issues, and 12 were neither stressed nor obese. Stress was a factor for 170 total, 8 of whom had no family history of heart disease and weren't obese. There were 396 patients with none of these three risk factors.
   a. How many of the patients were obese?
   b. What percentage had all three of these risk factors?
   c. How many were not obese and did not have a family history of heart disease?

# 6-4  Portfolio

Name _____

Check each box when you've completed the task. Remember that your instructor will want you to turn in the portfolio pages you create.

### Technology

1. ☐ Refer to the technology assignment for Lesson 6-3: repeat it, but this time find results that you can represent with a three-circle Venn diagram.

### Online Practice

1. ☐ Include any written work from the online assignment along with any notes or questions about this lesson's content.

### Applications

1. ☐ Complete the applications problems.

### Reflections

Type a short answer to each question.

1. ☐ Explain why Venn diagrams are so useful in organizing survey information with three responses.
2. ☐ Describe one thing you learned in this lesson that you found interesting. It doesn't have to be a math topic. Look at the context of the problems we've worked.
3. ☐ Take another look at your answer to Question 0 at the beginning of this lesson. Would you revise your answer now that you've completed the lesson? How would you summarize the topic of this lesson now?
4. ☐ What questions do you have about this lesson?

### Looking Ahead

1. ☐ Complete the Lesson 7-1 Prep Skills and read the opening paragraph in Lesson 7-1 carefully, then answer Question 0 in preparation for that lesson.

### Answers to "Did You Get It?"

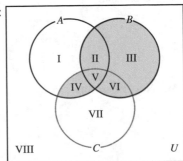

**1.**

**3.** Both diagrams are:

**2.** $(A \cap C) - B$ or $(A \cap C) \cap B'$     **4. a.** 100     **b.** 70     **c.** 40     **d.** 340

**5. a.** 227     **b.** 13.6%     **c.** 404

## 6-4   Applications

Name _____

1. Draw a Venn diagram for each set described, and use your diagrams to decide if the two sets are equal or not.

$(A \cup B) \cup C'$   and   $A \cup (B \cap C)$

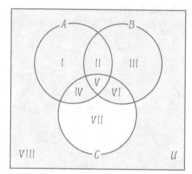

$(A \cup B) \cup C'$

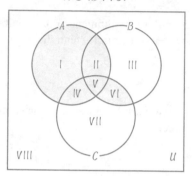

$A \cup (B \cap C)$

*The sets are not equal.*

The table and Venn diagram below are for Questions 2–7. The table shows the five states that had the highest percentage of people living in poverty for the years 2008, 2011, and 2014. For each question, write which region of the Venn diagram would include the state listed. Set *A* represents states in the top five in 2008, set *B* in 2011, and set *C* in 2014.

| Year States | 2008 | 2011 | 2014 |
|---|---|---|---|
| | Mississippi Louisiana Kentucky Arizona West Virginia | New Mexico Louisiana South Carolina Arkansas Georgia | Mississippi Louisiana New Mexico Arizona Texas |

*Source: U.S. Census Bureau*

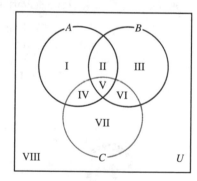

2. Arizona

   IV

3. Louisiana

   V

4. North Carolina

   VIII

## 6-4 Applications

Name _____

**5.** South Carolina

III

**6.** New Mexico

VI

**7.** Texas

VII

In Questions 8 and 9, $S$ = {United States Senators}, $D$ = {Elected officials who are Democrats}, and $R$ = {Elected officials who are Republicans}. Draw a Venn diagram that represents each set, and write a sentence describing what the set represents.

**8.** $D \cup (R \cap S)$

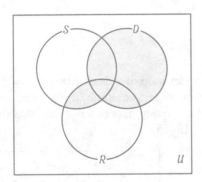

This is the set consisting of Democratic elected officials and Republican senators.

**9.** $S - (D \cup R)$

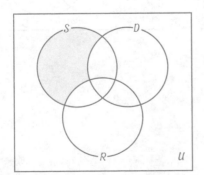

This is the set of senators who are independent.

# 6-4  Applications

Name _____

A large inpatient addiction treatment facility currently houses 80 patients. Thirty-two of them have an addiction to alcohol, 25 have an addiction to narcotics, and 4 are addicted to both. Fill in the Venn diagram and use it to answer Questions 10–12.

**10.** How many patients are addicted only to narcotics?

21

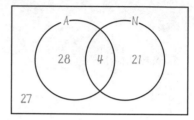

**11.** How many aren't addicted to narcotics?

55

**12.** How many are addicted to something other than alcohol or narcotics?

27

There's no official definition of a mountain, but one generally accepted standard is an elevation of at least 1,000 feet over the surrounding terrain. By that definition, there are 18 states that have at least one mountain, but no coastline (if we define coastline to mean areas where the land meets an ocean). There are 7 states that have coastline, but no mountains. Nine states have neither a mountain nor coastline. Draw a Venn diagram and use it to answer Questions 13–15.

**13.** How many states have at least one mountain?

34

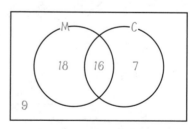

**14.** How many have coastline?

23

**15.** How many states have both?

16

## 6-4 Applications

Name _____

The arts communities in 230 cities across the country were rated according to whether or not they have an art museum, a symphony orchestra, and a ballet company. There are 119 cities with an art museum; 20 of those also have ballet but no orchestra, and 41 have an orchestra but no ballet; 30 have neither. Of the 75 cities with a ballet company, 10 have an orchestra as well, but lack an art museum. Twenty-two cities have only an orchestra. Fill in the Venn diagram and use it to answer Questions 16–18.

**16.** What percentage of the cities have an art museum?

$(30 + 41 + 28 + 20)/230 \approx 0.517$

About 51.7% have an art museum.

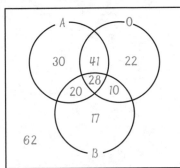

**17.** How many more cities are there with none of these three than with all of them?

$62 - 28 = 34$

**18.** If you pick a city at random from this list to travel to and really want to go either to an art museum or an orchestral concert, what is the percent chance that you'll end up disappointed?

All but 79 have one or the other, so we get $79/230 \approx 0.343$. There's about a 34.3% chance that you'll be disappointed.

# Unit 7
# Uncommon Sense

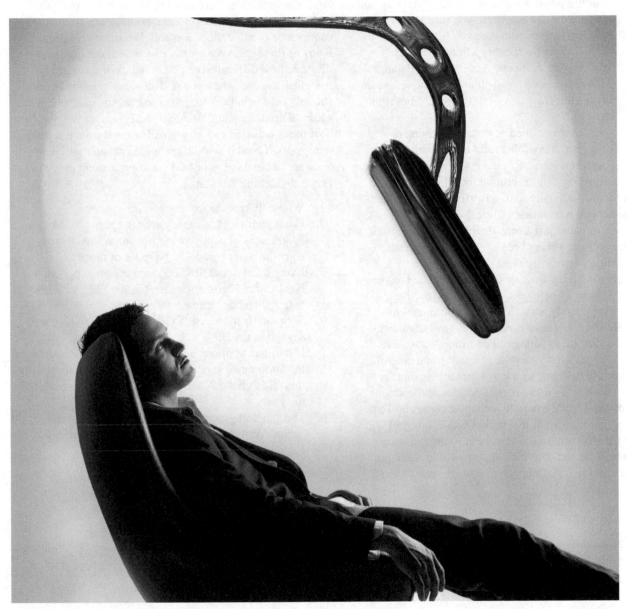

© Colin Anderson/Blend Images LLC RF

## Outline

# Math In     Mind Control

The term mind control is an absolute favorite of conspiracy theorists and science fiction writers, but is it real? That largely depends on what you mean by the term, but I can guarantee you one thing: there are a LOT of people and organizations out there that are trying to control the way you think each and every day. Everywhere you turn in modern society, someone is trying to convince you of something. "Buy my product!" "Vote for the guy I like!" "You can't afford NOT to lease a car from our dealership!" "Bailing out banks is a horrible idea!" "You should go out with me, and soon!" "Pledge our fraternity—all the other ones stink!" Should I go on?

Logic is sometimes defined as correct thinking or correct reasoning, but many folks refer to logic by a more casual name: common sense. Regardless of what you call it, the ability to think logically is crucial for all of us because our lives are inundated daily with advertisements, contracts, product and service warranties, political debates, and news commentaries, to name just a few. People often have problems processing these things because of misinterpretation, misunderstanding, and faulty logic.

You can look up the truth or falseness of a fact on the Internet, but that won't help you in analyzing whether a certain claim is logically valid. The term common sense is really misleading, because evaluating logical arguments involves skills that are anything but common—but we're here to help! Forget what you've seen about mind control in the movies: the best way to control someone's mind is to bias their thinking by using their emotions and opinions against them. And that's where this chapter comes in. To decide whether or not an argument makes sense, our goal will be to study the structure of the argument without thinking about the particular topic: to make that possible, we'll use variables to stand in for sentences so that we won't know what the exact topic is. This enables us to focus simply on whether you can logically draw a conclusion based on certain types of statements.

To that end, we've written some claims below. To be honest, some of them are a little controversial, touching on hot-button issues like religion, politics, and, the most contentious of all, college football. We sincerely apologize if any of these statements offends you, but our aim is to illustrate how difficult it can be to decide if an argument is logically sound when you're distracted by emotion and strongly held beliefs. Your job is to evaluate each claim as a logical argument, and decide if the argument is valid: that is, if the conclusion can be logically drawn from a set of statements. The skills you learn in this chapter will help you to do so, but making your best guess now might prove to be very enlightening later on.

1. Where there's smoke, there's fire.
2. People with lots of money are always happy. My neighbor is so happy you just want to smack him sometimes, so I guess he has a lot of money.
3. Every team in the SEC is good enough to play in a bowl game. Florida State isn't in the SEC, so it doesn't belong in a bowl game.
4. Scripture is the word of God. I know this because it says so in the Bible.
5. If Iraq has weapons of mass destruction, we should go to war to make sure they never use them. It turned out they didn't have WMDs, so we shouldn't have started the war.
6. The sun will go out before Kansas City wins the World Series. Wait, what? They won in 2015? I better buy some heat lamps.

# Lesson 7-1 Prep Skills

This is a short review of skills that will come in handy in the next lesson. In each case, answer the question, then rate your confidence level by checking one of the boxes. If you feel like you're struggling with these skills, consult the online resources provided by your instructor for extra practice.

### SKILL 1: RECOGNIZE SENTENCES THAT CAN BE TRUE OR FALSE

For each sentence below, decide if it's possible to objectively classify the statement as either true or false.

1. Seventy percent of voters believe that Congress is ineffective.

2. Congress is ineffective.

3. Where did you get those shoes?

4. I'm going to work or to sleep after class.

5. Bring me my brown pants.

6. If we don't get this patient to surgery stat, she won't survive.

7. Nobody can beat me at *Call of Duty*.

## Lesson 7-1 **Opening Statements** (Statements and Quantifiers)

**LEARNING OBJECTIVES**

☐ 1. Define and identify statements.

☐ 2. Define the logical connectives and identify their use.

☐ 3. Recognize and write negations of statements.

☐ 4. Write statements symbolically, and translate symbolic statements back to verbal.

*You can get along very well in this world by simply coming up with a quantity of reasonably valid statements.*

—B. F. Skinner

© McGraw-Hill Education/Jill Braaten, photographer

For dozens of years, surveys done by marketing companies have shown that the primary concern for a majority of American women is taking care of their families. So it's no coincidence that a lot of the household products that are traditionally bought by women are advertised in a way that plays on that concern. The implication, sometimes overt and sometimes subconscious, is that if you're a good mom that cares about your family, you'll buy this particular product. It's easy to say that people can't possibly fall for stunts that blatant, but here's all the evidence you need that it works: advertisers keep doing it.

This is exactly the sort of mind control we talked about in the unit opener: the advertiser doesn't want you to think about the fact that their actual argument is silly, so they try to tug at your heart strings. But today, you begin to fight back by beginning your study of symbolic logic, which uses letters to represent statements and special symbols to represent words like and, or, and not. This will enable us to remove our emotional bias from an argument so that we can analytically evaluate the logic behind it. It begins with studying what exactly can be evaluated for logical correctness.

**0.** After reading the opening paragraph, what do you think the main topic of this lesson will be?

> The best way to keep students from totally freaking out about evaluating statements like *p* implies *q* is to do a lot of ground work on what the study of formal logic is about: studying logical structure outside of the actual topics in an argument.

## 7-1 | Class

### Statements

In the English language there are many types of sentences; a few of the types are

- Factual statements (You have to pass the bar exam to practice law.)
- Commands (Get out of my face!)
- Opinions (Chocolate cake with cream cheese icing is the best dessert EVER.)
- Questions ('Sup with you?)
- Exclamations (Holy cow!)

In the objective study of logic, we will use only factual statements—it's pretty hard to decide if "Get out of my face" is true or false. And by "pretty hard" I mean "completely impossible."

A **statement** is a declarative sentence that can be objectively determined to be either true or false, but not both.

1. Decide whether or not each sentence is a statement. If it is a statement, decide whether it's true or false. If not, describe what type of sentence it is.

| Sentence | Statement? Yes or no | If statement, true or false? | If not, what type of sentence? |
|---|---|---|---|
| Where in the world did you find gold suede sneakers? | No | | Question |
| Moose are the largest members of the horse family. | Yes | True | |
| Give me a bottle of anything and a glazed donut—to go. | No | | Command |
| Radioactive spiders can make you a superhero. | Yes | False | |
| 2 + 10 = 12 | Yes | True | |
| Dude, that is awesome! | No | | Exclamation |
| 10 − 6 = 143 | Yes | False | |
| The guy sitting next to me smells funny. | No | | Opinion |

Decide which of the following are statements and which are not. If a sentence is not a statement, explain why not.

2. Most scientists agree that global warming is a threat to the environment.

   Statement

3. Is that your laptop?

   This is a question, not a statement.

4. Man, that hurts!

   This is an exclamation, not a statement.

**5.** $432 + 8 \div 1.3 = \sqrt{115{,}000}$

*Statement.*

**6.** This book is about database management.

*Statement*

**7.** Watching reality shows turns your brain to mush.

*This is an opinion, not a statement.*

---

## Did You Get It?

Try this problem to see if you understand the concepts we just studied. The answer can be found at the bottom of the portfolio page.

1. Decide which of the following are statements and which are not.
   a. Dude, those pants rock!
   b. $12 - 8 = 5$
   c. Jimmy Kimmel is the host of the *Daily Show*.
   d. Cat can shoot slow motion video with her phone.
   e. When does the party start?
   f. History is interesting.

---

## Simple and Compound Statements

Statements can be classified as simple or compound. A simple statement contains only one idea. Each of these statements is an example of a simple statement.

- Your jeans are torn.
- My dorm room has a pile of dirty socks in it.
- Daytona Beach is in Florida.

A statement like "I'm taking chemistry this semester and I'm going to get an A" is called a *compound statement* because it's formed from more than one simple statement.

---

A **compound statement** is a statement formed by joining two or more simple statements with a **connective**. There are four basic connectives used in logic: and (the **conjunction**), or (**disjunction**), if . . . then (**conditional**), and if and only if (**biconditional**).

Here are some examples of compound statements using connectives. For each compound statement, state the connective used.

**8.** We will win the game if and only if we score more points than the other team.

*Biconditional*

**9.** John studied for 5 hours, and he got an A.

*Conjunction*

**10.** If I get 80% of the questions on the LSAT right, then I will get into law school.

*Conditional*

> **Math Note**
>
> In standard usage, the word "then" is often omitted from a conditional statement; instead of "If it snows, then I will go skiing," you'd probably just say, "If it snows, I'll go skiing."

**11.** Luisa will run in a mini triathlon or she will play in the campus tennis tournament.

*Disjunction*

Now let's compare the two main types of statements we've learned about. Classify each statement as simple or compound. If it is compound, state the name of the connective used.

**12.** Our school mascot is a moose.

*Simple*

> **Math Note**
>
> Technically, we've given the names conjunction, disjunction, conditional, and biconditional to the connectives themselves, but from now on, we'll refer to whole statements using these connectives by those names. For example, we would call the compound statement in Question 15 a disjunction.

**13.** If you register for WiFi service, you will get 3 days of free access.

*Compound, conditional*

**14.** Tomorrow is the last day to register for classes.

*Simple*

**15.** In the interest of saving the planet, I plan to buy either a hybrid or a motorcycle.

*Compound, disjunction*

We'll worry later about determining whether statements involving quantifiers and connectives are true or false. For now, focus on learning and understanding the terms.

## Did You Get It?

Try this problem to see if you understand the concepts we just studied. The answer can be found at the bottom of the portfolio page.

2. Classify each statement as simple or compound. If it is compound, state the name of the connective used.
   a. My jacket is both warm and light.
   b. This is an informative website on STDs.
   c. If it doesn't rain tomorrow, I'm going windsurfing.
   d. I'm going to eat at Taco Bell or Wendy's today.
   e. Yesterday was the deadline to withdraw from a class.

## Quantified Statements

**Quantified statements** involve terms like *all, each, every, no, none, some, there exists,* and *at least one.* The first five *(all, each, every, no, none)* are called **universal quantifiers** because they either include or exclude every element of the universal set. The latter three *(some, there exists, at least one)* are called **existential quantifiers** because they show the existence of something, but do not include the entire universal set. Here are some examples of quantified statements:

- Every student that comes to class and studies will pass.
- No nursing student is also majoring in criminal justice.
- Some people who are Miami Hurricane fans are also Miami Dolphin fans.
- There is at least one professor in this school who does not have brown eyes.

The first two statements use universal quantifiers, while the third and fourth use existential quantifiers. Note that the statements using existential quantifiers are not "all inclusive" (or all exclusive) as the other two are.

**16.** Write an example of a statement using a universal quantifier about college courses.

*Sample answer: Every college course is taught by someone with a degree.*

**17.** Write an example of a statement using an existential quantifier about pizza. (Note: Mmmmm, pizza! is not a statement.)

*Sample answer: Some pizzas are delivered.*

### Math Note

The words "each," "every," and "all" mean the same thing, so what we say about all in this lesson applies to the others as well. Likewise, "some," "there exists," and "at least one" are considered to be the same and are treated that way as well.

## 7-1 Group

### Negations

The negation of a statement is a corresponding statement with the opposite truth value. This means that if a statement is true its negation is false, and if a statement is false its negation is true.

Consider the statement "My dorm room is blue."

**1.** Can the statement "My dorm room is white" represent the negation of the first statement?

*No.*

© Fuse/Getty Images RF

**2.** Could both statements be true? Explain how.

*Yes. It's possible to paint walls more than one color.*

**3.** Could both statements be false? Explain how.

*Easily: if the dorm room is neither of those colors.*

**4.** Can the statement "My dorm room is not blue" represent the negation of the statement "My dorm room is blue?"

*Yes.*

**5.** Could both statements be true? Explain.

*No. If the room is blue, then the second statement is true and the first is not. If it's not blue, then the first is true and the second is not.*

**6.** Could both statements be false? Explain.

*No. Same explanation as Question 5.*

7. Explain how the previous two questions agree with the definition of negation.

*It's not possible for the two statements to have the same truth value, so if one is true the other is false, and vice versa.*

To make sure that you have a correct negation, check that if one of the statements is true, the other must be false, and vice versa. The simplest way to negate a simple statement is by adding the word not. Write the negation of each statement.

8. Auburn will win their game this Saturday.

*Auburn will not win their game this Saturday.*

9. I took a shower today.

*I did not take a shower today.*

10. My car is clean.

*My car is not clean.*

11. We said that adding "not" is the *simplest* way to negate a statement. That doesn't mean it's the *only* way, or even necessarily the best way. Rewrite each of the negations in Questions 8–10 in a more natural, conversational way.

*Auburn will lose their game this Saturday.*

*I didn't take a shower today.*

*My car is dirty.*

12. Negations are a little more complicated for quantified statements. Consider the statements "All dogs are fuzzy" and "All dogs are not fuzzy." Explain how these do NOT fit the definition of a negation.

*If there's at least one dog that is fuzzy and one that isn't, both statements are false.*

13. What would it take for the statement "All dogs are fuzzy" to be false?

*One dog that is not fuzzy.*

**14.** Write the negation of "All dogs are fuzzy." (Hint: In this setting, we define the word *some* to mean "at least one.")

*Some dogs are not fuzzy. (For the record, they're probably still awesome.)*

The negations of quantified statements are summarized in the table below.

| Statement contains . . . | Example | Negation | Example |
|---|---|---|---|
| All do | All of my meals are low in fat. | Some do not, or not all do | Some of my meals are not low in fat. |
| Some do | Some majors require 5 years of study. | None do, or all do not | There are no majors that require 5 years of study. |
| Some do not | Some people don't go to football games. | All do | Everyone goes to football games. |
| None do | No airlines include checked bags for free. | Some do | At least one airline allows a checked bag for free. |

You should be especially careful when negating statements. It's tempting to say that the negation of a statement like "Every student will pass" is "Every student will fail," but it isn't. Not only is it possible that both statements are false, in most classes it's *likely* that both are false. Think about it for a second.

In Questions 15–18, write the negation of each of the following quantified statements.

**15.** Every student taking Quantitative Reasoning this semester will pass.

*Some students taking quantitative reasoning this semester won't pass.*

**16.** Some people who are Miami Hurricane fans are also Miami Dolphin fans.

*No Miami Hurricane fans are also Miami Dolphin fans.*

**17.** There is at least one professor in this school who does not have brown eyes.

*Every professor in this school has brown eyes.*

> A nice point of emphasis here is that, outside of formally evaluating arguments, the study of logic is still really great exercise in THINKING. Questions like these absolutely require clear and logical thinking, and nobody can say that's not a valuable skill to practice.

**18.** No nursing student is also majoring in criminal justice.

*Some nursing students are also majoring in criminal justice.*

## Did You Get It?

Try this problem to see if you understand the concepts we just studied. The answer can be found at the bottom of the portfolio page.

3. Write the negation of each of the following quantified statements.
   a. All cell phones have cameras.
   b. No woman can win the lottery.
   c. Some professors have PhDs.
   d. Someone in this class will get a B.

## Symbolic Notation

Recall that one of our goals in this lesson is to write statements in symbolic form to help us evaluate logical arguments objectively. Now we'll introduce the symbols and methods that will be used. The symbols for the connectives and, or, if . . . then, and if and only if are shown in the table below.

| Connective | Symbol | Name |
|---|---|---|
| and | $\wedge$ | Conjunction |
| or | $\vee$ | Disjunction |
| if . . . then | $\rightarrow$ | Conditional |
| if and only if | $\leftrightarrow$ | Biconditional |

Simple statements in logic are usually denoted with lowercase letters like $p$, $q$, and $r$.

19. Suppose we use $p$ to represent the statement "I get paid Friday" and $q$ to represent the statement "I will go out this weekend." Then the conditional statement "If I get paid Friday, then I will go out this weekend" can be written in symbols as _____$p \rightarrow q$_____.

We have symbols for the connectives, but what about negations? The symbol ~ (tilde) represents a negation.

20. If $p$ still represents "I get paid Friday," then $\sim p$ represents the statement

"_____I don't get paid on Friday_____."

When writing more complicated statements in symbols, we'll make use of parentheses often to specify an order. (We'll deal with this issue more in the next lesson.) To begin studying the use of parentheses, we'll study these two statements: $\sim p \wedge q$ and $\sim(p \wedge q)$. Both could be read as "Not $p$ and $q$" or "The negation of $p$ and $q$." But are they the same?

21. The statement $\sim p \wedge q$ means "First negate the statement $p$, then use that negation in a conjunction with statement $q$." If $p$ is the statement "Large Coney is a dog" and $q$ is the statement "Guinness is a cat," describe what the statement $\sim p \wedge q$ means.

Large Coney is not a dog and Guinness is a cat.

**22.** The statement ~(p ∧ q) means "Negate the conjunction of the statement p and the statement q." If p is once again "Large Coney is a dog" and q is once again "Guinness is a cat," what does the statement ~(p ∧ q) mean? Is this the same meaning as the statement in Question 21? (By the way, Large Coney is in fact a dog. See page 5.)

*It is not the case that Large Coney is a dog and Guinness is a cat. This doesn't mean quite the same thing as the statement in Question 21, because the second statement could be true if Large Coney is a dog and Guinness is not a cat.*

The same line of reasoning applies when the negation is used with other connectives. For example, ~p → q means (~p) → q, which is not the same thing as ~(p → q).

For Questions 23–26, let p represent the statement "It is cloudy" and q represent the statement "I will go to the beach." Write each statement in symbols.

**23.** I will not go to the beach.

*~q*

**24.** It is cloudy, and I will go to the beach.

*p ∧ q*

> Make sure students take these questions very seriously. This is the first core skill that's necessary in evaluating logical arguments.

**25.** If it is cloudy, then I will not go to the beach.

*p → ~q*

**26.** I will go to the beach if and only if it is not cloudy.

*q ↔ ~p*

© John Dakers/Life File/Getty Images RF

## Did You Get It?

Try this problem to see if you understand the concepts we just studied. The answer can be found at the bottom of the portfolio page.

4. Let p represent the statement "I will buy a Coke" and q represent the statement "I will buy some popcorn." Write each statement in symbols.
   a. I will buy a Coke, and I will buy some popcorn.
   b. I will not buy a Coke.
   c. If I buy some popcorn, then I will buy a Coke.
   d. I will not buy a Coke, or I will buy some popcorn.

You probably noticed that some of the compound statements we've written sound a little awkward. It isn't always necessary to repeat the subject and verb in a compound statement using *and* or *or*. Here are some examples of statements written formally, then rewritten in a more natural way.

> **Formal:** "It is cold, and it is snowing"
> **More natural:** "It's cold and snowing."
>
> **Formal:** "I will go to a movie, or I will go to a play"
> **More natural:** "I'll go to a movie or a play."

Also the words *but* and *although* can be used in place of *and*.

> **Formal:** "I will not buy a DVD player, and I will buy a video streaming device."
> **More natural:** "I won't buy a DVD player, but I will buy a video streaming device."

Now that we've practiced writing verbal statements in symbols, it's a good time to practice the opposite skill: translating from symbolic to verbal form. In Questions 27–31, write each statement in words. Let *p* = "My dog is a golden retriever" and *q* = "My dog is fuzzy." First, write in formal language. Then try to write in a more natural, conversational way.

**27.** $\sim p$

**Formal:** My dog is not a golden retriever.

**More natural:** My dog isn't a golden retriever.

**28.** $p \vee q$

**Formal:** My dog is a golden retriever or my dog is fuzzy.

**More natural:** My dog is a golden retriever or fuzzy.

If this is your dog (which it's not, because it's mine), the statement in Question 30 describes it pretty well.

Courtesy of David Sobecki

**29.** $\sim p \rightarrow q$

**Formal:** If my dog is not a golden retriever, then my dog is fuzzy.

**More natural:** If my dog isn't a golden retriever, it's fuzzy.

**30.** $q \wedge p$

**Formal:** My dog is fuzzy and my dog is a golden retriever.

**More natural:** My dog is a fuzzy golden retriever.

> It's a lot easier for students to see logic as abstract and inapplicable if all of the statements they work with are overly formal and awkward. Emphasize that statements in plain English can be studied in logic, but that the more formal statements are easier to write in symbols.

**31.** $q \leftrightarrow p$

**Formal:** My dog is fuzzy if and only if my dog is a golden retriever.

**More natural:** My dog is fuzzy if and only if it's a golden retriever.

---

## Did You Get It?

Try this problem to see if you understand the concepts we just studied. The answer can be found at the bottom of the portfolio page.

5. Write each statement in words. Let $p$ = "My friend is a football player" and $q$ = "My friend is smart."
   a. $\sim p$          b. $p \vee q$          c. $\sim p \rightarrow q$
   d. $p \leftrightarrow q$          e. $p \wedge q$

---

## Using Technology: Logical Tests and Excel

Excel has logical functions built into it that enable you to test the truth value of a statement. We'll make use of these throughout this unit. For now, we'll just learn how to do a basic logical test based on the size of the output for a given function.

In this case, the question is to find whether or not the outputs for the function $y = -2x^2 + 30x + 100$ are more or less than 150 for whole number inputs. In the first column of the sheet below, whole numbers are entered, starting with 1. In the second column, we have the outputs for the above function. To get these, we entered into cell B2: "=−2*A2^2+30*A2+100," then copied down to the cells underneath. Then the key cell is D2: look carefully at the formula entered in that cell. The IF command is used to test the truth value of the statement "The output of the function is less than 150." So we began with "=IF(B2<150." After that, we had to tell Excel what to enter in the cell depending on whether the statement B2<150 is true or false. You can enter numbers if you like (It's common in computer science to enter 1 for true and 0 for false), but we chose the truth values TRUE and FALSE. When entered in all capitals, Excel recognizes these are truth values: we'll need that later in the unit.

| D2 | | | | $fx$ | =IF(B2<150,TRUE,FALSE) | |
|---|---|---|---|---|---|---|
| | A | B | C | D | E | F |
| 1 | Input (x) | Output | | Test | | |
| 2 | 1 | 128 | | TRUE | | |
| 3 | 2 | 152 | | FALSE | | |
| 4 | 3 | 172 | | FALSE | | |
| 5 | 4 | 188 | | FALSE | | |

*See the Lesson 7-1 Using Tech video in class resources for further information.*

# 7-1 Portfolio

Name _____

Check each box when you've completed the task. Remember that your instructor will want you to turn in the portfolio pages you create.

## Technology

1. ☐ Symbolic logic is hugely important in computer programming. Not surprisingly, then, there are logic functions built into Excel, which we'll use throughout this unit. Read the technology box on the previous page, then set up a spreadsheet that tests the truth value of the statement "The output of the function $y = 4x^2 - 80x + 300$ is positive" for whole number inputs ranging from 1 to 25. Your spreadsheet will be very similar to the one at the bottom of the technology box, and a template is included in the online resources for this lesson to help you get started.

## Online Practice

1. ☐ Include any written work from the online assignment along with any notes or questions about this lesson's content.

## Applications

1. ☐ Complete the applications problems.

## Reflections

Type a short answer to each question.

1. ☐ Describe the difference between a sentence and a statement.
2. ☐ List the logical connectives and give an example of at least one statement that uses each.
3. ☐ Take another look at your answer to Question 0 at the beginning of this lesson. Would you revise your answer now that you've completed the lesson? How would you summarize the topic of this lesson now?
4. ☐ What questions do you have about this lesson?

## Looking Ahead

1. ☐ Complete the Lesson 7-2 Prep Skills and read the opening paragraph in Lesson 7-2 carefully, then answer Question 0 in preparation for that lesson.

## Answers to "Did You Get It?"

1. b, c, and d are statements.　　2. a. Compound, conjunction　　b. Simple
c. Compound, conditional　　d. Compound, disjunction　　e. Simple
3. a. No cell phones have cameras.　　b. All women can win the lottery.
c. No professors have PhDs.　　d. No one in this class will get a B.
4. a. $p \wedge q$　　b. $\sim p$　　c. $q \rightarrow p$　　d. $\sim p \vee q$
5. a. My friend is not a football player.　　b. My friend is a football player or my friend is smart.　　c. If my friend is not a football player, then my friend is smart.
d. My friend is a football player if and only if my friend is smart.
e. My friend is a football player and my friend is smart.

**7-1**    **Applications**

Name _____

In Questions 1–9, a boatload of sentences are provided. (Well, nine actually.) First, decide if each sentence is or is not a statement. If it's not, explain why and move on. If it is, classify the statement as simple or compound. Finally, if the statement is compound, identify the type of compound statement that it is.

**1.** Porsche now makes coupes and sedans.

*Compound statement; conjunction*

**2.** Please close the door on the way out.

*Not a statement because it's a command.*

**3.** Anyone that votes for that guy for president is either drunk or stupid.

*Not a statement because it's an opinion.*

**4.** If 1,200 more people sign this petition, a ballot initiative to legalize marijuana will be voted on in November.

*Compound statement; conditional*

**5.** Holy cow, a UFO!

*Not a statement because it's an exclamation.*

**6.** The two square roots of 49 are 7 and 11.

*Compound statement; conjunction*

© Brand X/Superstock RF

**7.** I'm going to quit my job if and only if I get a huge inheritance when my aunt passes.

*Compound statement; biconditional*

**8.** Who do you think I am, Bill Gates?

*Not a statement because it's a question.*

## 7-1   Applications

Name _____

9. For the last 7 years, the champion of the American Football Conference west division has been either Denver or Kansas City.

   *Compound statement: disjunction*

In Questions 10–13, write the negation of the statement.

10. I've been running miles each morning before work for the last 6 weeks.

    *I haven't been running miles each morning before work for the last 6 weeks.*

11. Everyone I hang out with regularly has a smartphone.

    *Some of the people I hang out with regularly don't have smartphones.*

12. Some of the new shows that premiered last week will be canceled before their fifth episode airs.

    *Every new show that premiered last week will last longer than five episodes.*

13. Nobody puts guacamole on a hot dog.

    *Some people put guacamole on a hot dog. That doesn't make it right, mind you, but some people do it.*

For Questions 14–17, let $p$ = "Bob sees a physical therapist" and $q$ = "Bob is prescribed a narcotic pain reliever." Write each statement in symbols.

14. Bob is prescribed a narcotic pain reliever or he's seeing a physical therapist.

    *$q \lor p$*

15. Bob is seeing a physical therapist and he hasn't been prescribed a narcotic pain reliever.

    *$p \land \sim q$*

16. If Bob sees a physical therapist, then he won't be prescribed a narcotic pain reliever.

    *$p \rightarrow \sim q$*

**7-1**  **Applications**

Name _____

17. Bob isn't prescribed a narcotic pain reliever if and only if he isn't going to physical therapy.

   $\sim q \leftrightarrow \sim p$

In Questions 18–22, let $r$ = "A suspect in the case has been arrested" and $s$ = "Our investigation has been concluded." For each compound statement in symbols, first write a formal translation using the simple statements above. Then write the same statement in a more natural, conversational way.

18. $\sim s$

   Formal: Our investigation has not been concluded.

   Natural: Our investigation is still going on.

© moodboard/123RF

19. $r \wedge s$

   Formal: A suspect in the case has been arrested and our investigation has been concluded.

   Natural: We've concluded our investigation and arrested a suspect.

20. $\sim r \vee s$

   Formal: A suspect in the case has not been arrested or our investigation has been concluded.

   Natural: A suspect hasn't been arrested or we've finished the investigation.

21. $s \rightarrow r$

   Formal: If our investigation has been concluded, then a suspect in our case has been arrested.

   Natural: If we've concluded our investigation, a suspect has been arrested.

22. $\sim s \leftrightarrow \sim r$

   Formal: Our investigation has not been concluded if and only if a suspect in our case has not been arrested.

   Natural: We haven't concluded our investigation if and only if we haven't arrested a suspect.

# Lesson 7-2  **Prep Skills**

This is a short review of skills that will come in handy in the next lesson. In each case, answer the question, then rate your confidence level by checking one of the boxes. If you feel like you're struggling with these skills, consult the online resources provided by your instructor for extra practice.

**SKILL 1: RECOGNIZE TYPES OF COMPOUND STATEMENTS**

Identify the type of each compound statement.

1. This is my birthday, and I'm planning to bury my face in cake.

2. If my party is canceled I'm going to hit the roof.

3. I'll go to bed tonight if and only if I run out of cash.

4. I won't open all my gifts at dinner.

5. I plan to have pasta or steak for dinner.

**SKILL 2: TRANSLATE SYMBOLIC STATEMENTS INTO WORDS**

Let $p$ = "The patient is in critical condition" and $q$ = "A surgery room is being prepped." Write a verbal translation of each statement.

6. $p \rightarrow q$

7. $\sim p \vee q$

8. $\sim(q \wedge p)$

9. $q \leftrightarrow p$

# Lesson 7-2   **Finding the Truth**   (Truth Tables)

## LEARNING OBJECTIVES

☐  1. Build truth tables for negations, disjunctions, and conjunctions.

☐  2. Build truth tables for conditional and biconditional statements.

☐  3. Build truth tables for compound statements.

☐  4. Use the hierarchy of connectives, and compare it to order of operations.

*Three things cannot be long hidden: the sun, the moon, and the truth.*
—Buddha

© Columbia/courtesy Everett Collection

"You can't believe everything you hear." Chances are you were taught this when you were younger, and it's pretty good advice. In an ideal world, everyone would tell the truth all the time, but in this world, it is extremely important to be able to separate fact from fiction. When someone is trying to convince you of some point of view, the ability to logically evaluate the validity of an argument can be the difference between being informed and being deceived—and maybe between keeping and being separated from your hard-earned money! (Perhaps by someone like the dude in the picture.)

This lesson is all about deciding when a compound statement is or is not true, based not on the topic of that statement, but simply on the structure of the statement and the truth of the underlying components. We learned about logical connectives in Lesson 7-1. In this lesson, we'll analyze these connectives using *truth tables*. A **truth table** is a diagram in table form that is used to show when a compound statement is true or false based on the truth values of the simple statements that make up that compound statement. This will allow us to analyze arguments objectively.

**0.** After reading the opening paragraphs, what do you think the main topic of this lesson will be?

> To help students work with truth tables, you'll need to do some physical preparation for this lesson. We've volunteered you to prepare some strips that students can use to cover up intermediate columns: see the paragraph above the truth table on page 640.

## 7-2   Class

### Negation

According to our definition of statement, a statement is either true or false, but never both. Consider the simple statement $p$ = "Today is Tuesday."

**1.** If it is in fact Tuesday, then $p$ is _____*true*_____, and its negation ($\sim p$), which is "Today is not Tuesday" is _____*false*_____.

**2.** If it's not Tuesday, then $p$ is _____*false*_____ and $\sim p$ is _____*true*_____.

**3.** A truth table is a table used to summarize the possible truth values for statements. When a statement is true, we put a T in the table to represent that. When false, we put an F in the table. Use your answers from Questions 1 and 2 to build a truth table for the negation. The first column indicates that there are two possible truth values for any statement $p$.

| $p$ | $\sim p$ |
|-----|----------|
| T | F |
| F | T |

> The best way to get students to understand and appreciate truth tables is to start out with having them build truth tables for all the connectives. Provide guidance, not answers in this Class activity.

**4.** For each condition for the statement $p$—true or false—the table tells us that the negation $\sim p$ has the

_____opposite_____ truth value.

## Conjunction

If we have a compound statement with two component statements $p$ and $q$, there are four possible combinations of truth values for these two statements.

**5.** Complete the symbolic values for each of $p$ and $q$ in the table below.

**Possibilities**

Both $p$ and $q$ are true.

$p$ is true and $q$ is false.

$p$ is false and $q$ is true.

Both $p$ and $q$ are false.

**Truth Value for Each**

| $p$ | $q$ |
|-----|-----|
| T | T |
| T | F |
| F | T |
| F | F |

So when setting up a truth table for a compound statement with two component statements, we'll need a row for each of the four possibilities.

Now we're ready to analyze conjunctions. Recall that a conjunction is a compound statement involving the word "and." Suppose a friend who's prone to exaggeration tells you, "I bought a new laptop and a new iPad."

**6.** This compound statement can be symbolically represented by ___$p \wedge q$___, where $p =$ "I bought a new laptop" and $q =$ "I bought a new iPad."

© McGraw-Hill Education/Mark Dierker, photographer

7. Under what circumstances would that conjunctive statement be true? When would it be false? Explain in as much detail as you can.

   *It's only true if the friend bought BOTH of those items. If they bought only one, or neither, the statement is false.*

The best way to describe the purpose of a truth table is to put some organization to that stuff you just wrote. Let's do that here.

8. If your friend actually had made both purchases, then of course the statement "I bought a new laptop and a new iPad" would be ___*true*___. In terms of a truth table, that tells us that if $p$ and $q$ are both true, then the conjunction $p \wedge q$ is ___*true*___ as well. Complete the first row of the truth table.

9. On the other hand, suppose your friend bought only a new laptop or only a new iPad, or maybe neither of those things. Then the statement "I bought a new laptop and a new iPad" would be ___*false*___. In other words, if either or both of $p$ and $q$ are false, then the compound statement $p \wedge q$ is ___*false*___ as well. With this information, complete the second, third, and fourth rows of the truth table for a basic conjunction.

| $p$ | $q$ | $p \wedge q$ |
|---|---|---|
| T | T | *T* |
| T | F | *F* |
| F | T | *F* |
| F | F | *F* |

## Truth Values for a Conjunction

The conjunction $p \wedge q$ is true only when both $p$ and $q$ are true.

## Did You Get It

Try this problem to see if you understand the concepts we just studied. The answer can be found at the bottom of the portfolio page.

1. Let $p$ = "My pants were designed by Michael Kors" and $q$ = "My pants cost more than an average citizen of Jamaica makes in a week." Under what circumstances would the conjunction $p \wedge q$ be true?

## Disjunction

Next, we'll look at truth tables for or statements. Suppose your friend from the previous example made the statement, "I bought a new laptop or a new iPad" (as opposed to "and").

10. If your friend actually did buy both, then this statement would be ___true___. Complete the first row of the truth table.

11. If your friend actually did buy one or the other, then this statement would be ___true___. Complete rows 2 and 3 of the truth table.

12. And if he or she bought neither, then the statement would be ___false___. Complete the last row of the truth table.

| p | q | p ∨ q |
|---|---|---|
| T | T | T |
| T | F | T |
| F | T | T |
| F | F | F |

Important note: In the study of logic, we use what's known as the *inclusive or*. That means that we'll consider a disjunction, like "I bought a new laptop or a new iPad" to be true if both of the component statements are true. In short, we're interpreting "or" to mean "one or the other, or both."

## Truth Values for a Disjunction

The disjunction p ∨ q is true unless both p and q are false.

## Did You Get It

Try this problem to see if you understand the concepts we just studied. The answer can be found at the bottom of the portfolio page.

2. Let p = "Global temperatures have been rising for the last 50 years" and q = "Climate change poses a threat to human survival." Under what circumstances would the disjunction p ∨ q be true?

## Conditional Statement

Quick review: A conditional statement, which is sometimes called an *implication,* consists of two simple statements using the connective if . . . then. For example, the statement "If I bought a ticket, then I can go to the concert" is a conditional statement. The first component, in this case "I bought a ticket," is called the **antecedent.** The second component, in this case "I can go to the concert," is called the **consequent.**

Conditional statements are used all the time in math, not just in logic. "If an element is in both set A and set B, then it's in the intersection of A and B" is one of MANY examples from earlier in the book. To build the truth table for the conditional statement, we'll think about the following example:

If the Cubs win tomorrow, they make the playoffs.

**13.** We'll use $p$ = "the Cubs win tomorrow" and $q$ = "they make the playoffs." This makes our conditional
statement ___$p \rightarrow q$___.

**14.** We'll be considering four cases to fill out the truth table. Describe the four cases verbally.

*The Cubs win and make the playoffs, the Cubs win and don't make the playoffs, the Cubs lose and make the playoffs,*
*the Cubs lose and don't make the playoffs.*

> The conditional is the hardest part to understand in terms of truth tables. Direct students' attention to the paragraph just above the colored box below.

For Questions 15–18, fill in the blanks for each case. Then use that information to complete the truth table.

**15.** Case 1: The Cubs win tomorrow, and they make the playoffs (both $p$ and $q$ are true). The
statement was that if the Cubs won, they would make the playoffs, so if they win and make the
playoffs, the statement was definitely ___*true*___.

| $p$ | $q$ | $p \rightarrow q$ |
|-----|-----|-------------------|
| T | T | T |
| T | F | F |
| F | T | T |
| F | F | T |

**16.** Case 2: The Cubs win tomorrow, but don't make the playoffs ($p$ is true, but $q$ is false). I told
you that if the Cubs won, they'd make the playoffs; if they won and didn't make the playoffs,
I'm a liar liar pants on fire, and the conditional statement is ___*false*___.

**17.** Case 3: The Cubs lose tomorrow and still make the playoffs ($p$ is false and $q$ is true). This
requires some serious thought. My claim was that if the Cubs won, they'd make the playoffs.
In order for that claim to be false, the Cubs would have to win and not make the playoffs.
That's not the case if they didn't win, so the statement is not false. And we know that if a
statement isn't false, it's ___*true*___! That makes the conditional statement ___*true*___.

**18.** Case 4: The Cubs lose tomorrow and don't make the playoffs ($p$ and $q$ are both false). This is pretty much the same as
Case 3: the statement is only false if the Cubs win and don't make the playoffs, so again if the Cubs lose, the statement
isn't false, making it ___*true*___.

For Cases 3 and 4, it might help to think of it this way: we'll be optimists and consider a statement to be true unless we have
absolute proof that it's false. If you're totally unconvinced by the discussions in Cases 3 and 4, hang in there. . . . In the applications for this lesson, we'll develop a way to rewrite a conditional statement as a disjunction, in which case we can use what we
already know about disjunctions to study truth values.

## Truth Values for a Conditional

The conditional statement $p \rightarrow q$ is false only when the antecedent $p$ is true and the consequent $q$ is false.

## Did You Get It

Try this problem to see if you understand the concepts we just studied. The answer can be found at the bottom of the
portfolio page.

3. Let $p$ = "Ebola outbreaks are becoming more frequent" and $q$ = "The CDC infectious disease team is traveling
more than in previous years." Under what circumstances would the conditional $p \rightarrow q$ be true?

## Biconditional Statement

A biconditional statement is really two statements; it's the conjunction of two conditional statements. For example, the statement "I will stay in and study Friday if and only if I don't have any money" is the same as "If I don't have any money, then I will stay in and study Friday and if I stay in and study Friday, then I don't have any money." In symbols, we can write either $p \leftrightarrow q$ or $(p \rightarrow q) \wedge (q \rightarrow p)$. Since the biconditional is a conjunction, for it to be true, both of the statements $p \rightarrow q$ and $q \rightarrow p$ must be true. We will once again look at cases to build the truth table. Don't forget to fill in the truth table.

**Case 1:** Both $p$ and $q$ are true.

19. What are the truth values for $p \rightarrow q$, and for $q \rightarrow p$? (Two questions here.)

    *Both are true.*

| $p$ | $q$ | $p \leftrightarrow q$ |
|---|---|---|
| T | T | T |
| T | F | F |
| F | T | F |
| F | F | T |

20. What is the truth value of $(p \rightarrow q) \wedge (q \rightarrow p)$ (which is also $p \leftrightarrow q$)?

    *It's true because both of the two statements in the conjunction are true.*

**Case 2:** $p$ is true and $q$ is false.

21. What are the truth values for $p \rightarrow q$, and for $q \rightarrow p$?

    *$p \rightarrow q$ is false, $q \rightarrow p$ is true.*

22. What is the truth value of $(p \rightarrow q) \wedge (q \rightarrow p)$, which is also $p \leftrightarrow q$?

    *It's false because only one of the two statements in the conjunction is true.*

**Case 3:** $p$ is false and $q$ is true.

23. What are the truth values for $p \rightarrow q$, and for $q \rightarrow p$?

    *$p \rightarrow q$ is true, $q \rightarrow p$ is false.*

24. What is the truth value of $(p \rightarrow q) \wedge (q \rightarrow p)$, which is also $p \leftrightarrow q$?

    *It's false because only one of the two statements in the conjunction is true.*

**Case 4:** $p$ is false and $q$ is false.

25. What are the truth values for $p \rightarrow q$ and $q \rightarrow p$?

    *Both are true.*

26. What is the truth value of $(p \rightarrow q) \wedge (q \rightarrow p)$, which is also $p \leftrightarrow q$?

    *It's true because both of the two statements in the conjunction are true.*

## Truth Values for a Biconditional

The biconditional statement $p \leftrightarrow q$ is true when $p$ and $q$ have the same truth value and false when they have opposite truth values.

**27.** A technician who designs an automated irrigation system needs to decide whether the system should turn on if the water in the soil falls below a certain level or if and only if the water in the soil falls below a certain level. Describe what the difference would be. Don't think in terms of logic vocabulary: describe in terms of how this would affect the operation of the system.

*As an if statement, the system could still turn on even if the water level in the soil doesn't fall below that level. For example, it could turn on at least once a week. But with the if and only if statement, the system would turn on ONLY when the water level in the soil gets low.*

Here's a quick summary of all the truth tables you've built so far in this lesson. DO NOT TRY TO MEMORIZE THESE TABLES! There's just too much there, and the Ts and Fs start to all look the same. The reason we built the tables from scratch is to help you *understand* them so that you don't need to rely on memorization.

## Summary of Truth Values

| Negation (not) | | | Conjunction (and) | | | Disjunction (or) | | | Conditional (if . . . then) | | | Biconditional (if and only if) | | |
|:---:|:---:|:---:|:---:|:---:|:---:|:---:|:---:|:---:|:---:|:---:|:---:|:---:|:---:|:---:|
| $p$ | $\sim p$ | | $p$ | $q$ | $p \wedge q$ | $p$ | $q$ | $p \vee q$ | $p$ | $q$ | $p \rightarrow q$ | $p$ | $q$ | $p \leftrightarrow q$ |
| T | F | | T | T | T | T | T | T | T | T | T | T | T | T |
| F | T | | T | F | F | T | F | T | T | F | F | T | F | F |
| | | | F | T | F | F | T | T | F | T | T | F | T | F |
| | | | F | F | F | F | F | F | F | F | T | F | F | T |

# 7-2 Group

## Truth Tables for Compound Statements

Once we know truth values for the basic connectives, we can use truth tables to find the truth values for any logical statement. The key to the procedure is to take it step by step, so that in every case, you're deciding on truth values based on one of the truth tables in the colored box at the end of the Class portion of this lesson.

"My leg isn't better, or I'm taking a break" is an example of a statement that can be written as $\sim p \lor q$.

1. Think about the situations that would make this statement true. Can you describe them all?

   *I guess I probably could, but it's not easy. That's the point of this question.*

© Photodisc Inc/Getty Images RF

Completing a truth table can help organize your thoughts, and this is the real value of truth tables. Your instructor should have given you thin strips of paper or card stock: you'll use those in the remainder of the lesson.

2. To fill in the truth values for the $\sim p$ column, all you need to focus on is the values in the $p$ column: what's in the $q$ column is irrelevant. So use one of your strips to cover the $q$ column, since all it can do is distract you. Then use what you learned about truth values for negations to fill in the $\sim p$ column.

| $p$ | $q$ | $\sim p$ | $\sim p \lor q$ |
|-----|-----|----------|-----------------|
| T   | T   | F        | T               |
| T   | F   | F        | F               |
| F   | T   | T        | T               |
| F   | F   | T        | T               |

3. To fill in truth values for the $\sim p$ or $q$ column, you need to focus on the existing columns for $\sim p$ and for $q$, so use a strip to cover up the $p$ column. Then use what you learned about truth values for disjunctions to fill in the $\sim p$ or $q$ column.

4. Use the results from your truth table to describe situations when the statement "My leg isn't better, or I'm taking a break" is true. Then explain why using a truth table here was useful.

   *The statement is true unless your leg is better and you're taking a break. It would be awful difficult to just puzzle that out based on the description of the statement.*

> Emphasize the importance of Questions 4, 10, and 13. A truth table makes it WAY easier to decide when a statement is true compared to just trying to figure it out.

When a compound statement has multiple connectives, it will sometimes have parentheses to indicate the order in which we should work with those connectives. It is important to follow the order of operations—specifically, find the truth value of statements in parentheses first. (If this doesn't remind you of the order of operations for arithmetic and algebra, you're just not paying attention.)

"It is not true that if it rains, then we can't go out" is an example of a statement that can be written as $\sim(p \to \sim q)$. In order to build a truth table for this statement, we'll need to have a column for the conditional statement $p \to \sim q$, and then find the negation of that statement.

5. This means we'll need columns for $p$ and $q$ (as usual), and also columns for
   $\underline{\sim q}$, $\underline{p \to \sim q}$, and $\underline{\sim(p \to \sim q)}$.

6. Fill in the column headers in the truth table below using your answers to Question 5.

| $p$ | $q$ | $\sim q$ | $p \to \sim q$ | $\sim(p \to \sim q)$ |
|---|---|---|---|---|
| T | T | F | F | T |
| T | F | T | T | F |
| F | T | F | T | F |
| F | F | T | T | F |

© Creatas/PictureQuest RF

7. The only information needed to fill in the $\sim q$ column is the $q$ column, so cover up the $p$ column, then use what you learned about truth values for negations to fill in the $\sim q$ column.

8. Which columns will you cover up to help decide on truth values for the next column in the table?

   *Just the q column.*

9. Cover up the column or columns listed in Question 8, then fill in the second last column in the truth table.

10. Finish the truth table by finding the negations of the values in the second last column. Then describe under what circumstances the statement "It is not true that if it rains, then we can't go out" is true.

   *It's true only if it rains and we still go out.*

## Did You Get It

Try this problem to see if you understand the concepts we just studied. The answer can be found at the bottom of the portfolio page.

4. Using the technique from Questions 2 and 3, build a truth table for the statement $p \leftrightarrow (p \wedge q)$.

We can also construct truth tables for compound statements that involve three or more components. For a compound statement with three simple statements $p$, $q$, and $r$, there are eight possible combinations of Ts and Fs to consider. These are listed out in the truth table we'll use next. The order of the Ts and Fs doesn't matter as long as all the possible combinations are listed. Whenever there are three letters in the statement, we suggest using the order shown below for consistency.

| $p$ | $q$ | $r$ | $q \rightarrow r$ | $p \vee (q \rightarrow r)$ |
|---|---|---|---|---|
| T | T | T | T | T |
| T | T | F | F | T |
| T | F | T | T | T |
| T | F | F | T | T |
| F | T | T | T | T |
| F | T | F | F | F |
| F | F | T | T | T |
| F | F | F | T | T |

"I'll do my math assignment, or if I think of a good topic, then I'll start my English essay" is an example of a statement that can be written as $p \vee (q \rightarrow r)$.

© Getty Images RF

11. Cover up the $p$ column so that you can focus strictly on $q$ and $r$, then use what you learned about truth values for conditionals to fill in the $q \rightarrow r$ column.

12. Now cover up every column except the $p$ column and the $q \rightarrow r$ column, then use those and what you learned about truth values for disjunctions to finish the truth table.

13. Describe situations under which the statement "I'll do my math assignment, or if I think of a good topic, then I'll start my English essay" is true.

*It's always true unless you thought of a good topic but didn't either do your math assignment or start your English essay.*

In the statement $p \vee (q \rightarrow r)$, the parentheses are significant: they tell us to first find truth values for $q \rightarrow r$, then form a disjunction with $p$. This doesn't necessarily have the same meaning, or truth values, as $(p \vee q) \rightarrow r$. One way to make sure the intended groupings are always clear would be to include parentheses 100% of the time. Once again, this sounds an awful lot like the order of operations for arithmetic: in order to avoid *always* having to use parentheses, we agree on a standard order for multiple operations, using parentheses only when the intent is to violate that order.

To accomplish the same thing in dealing with statements in logic, a **hierarchy of connectives** has been agreed upon some-where along the line. This hierarchy tells us which connectives should be done first when there are no parentheses to guide us:

1. Negation ($\sim$)
2. Conjunction ($\wedge$) or disjunction ($\vee$)
3. Conditional ($\rightarrow$)
4. Biconditional ($\leftrightarrow$)

The connectives higher on the list are done first. The connective that's lowest on the list is done last, so it describes the type of statement overall.

**14.** For example, $p \vee q \rightarrow r$ is a conditional statement; the hierarchy tells us to first find the _____*disjunction*_____, which means we could use parentheses to write the compound statement as _____*$(p \vee q) \rightarrow r$*_____. That shows that the state-ment is a conditional: if $p$ or $q$, then $r$.

When a compound statement has both a conjunction and a disjunction, we'll need to use parentheses to indicate which should be considered first.

**15.** A statement like $p \wedge q \vee r$ is ambiguous without parentheses: $(p \wedge q) \vee r$ is a _____*disjunction*_____, and $p \wedge (q \vee r)$ is a _____*conjunction*_____.

If we decide to use parentheses to make a statement clearer, the parentheses go around the connectives that would be done first. So we'd write $p \leftrightarrow q \rightarrow r$ as $p \leftrightarrow (q \rightarrow r)$ since the conditional comes before the biconditional in the hierarchy of connectives.

For each statement in Questions 16–19, identify the type of statement using the hierarchy of connectives, and rewrite using parentheses to indicate order.

**16.** $\sim p \vee \sim q$

Disjunction: $(\sim p) \vee (\sim q)$

**17.** $p \rightarrow \sim q \wedge r$

Conditional: $p \rightarrow ((\sim q) \wedge r)$

**18.** $p \vee q \leftrightarrow q \vee r$

Biconditional: $(p \vee q) \leftrightarrow (q \vee r)$

**19.** $p \to q \leftrightarrow r$

Biconditional: $(p \to q) \leftrightarrow r$

---

## Did You Get It

Try this problem to see if you understand the concepts we just studied. The answer can be found at the bottom of the portfolio page.

5. For each, identify the type of statement using the hierarchy of connectives, and rewrite using parentheses to indicate order.
   a. $\sim p \lor q$
   b. $p \lor \sim q \to r$
   c. $p \lor \sim q \leftrightarrow \sim p \lor \sim q$
   d. $p \land \sim q$
   e. $p \leftrightarrow q \to r$

---

**20.** Use the truth value of each simple statement to determine the truth value of the compound statement. If you need help finding the truth value for the simple statements, either use the Internet as a resource, or ask your professor very, very nicely for help.

   *p:* Kate Middleton married Prince William in 2011.
   *q:* Prince William's mother was the Queen of England.
   *r:* Barring death or divorce, Kate Middleton will become queen one day.

Statement: $p \lor q \to r$

*p and r are true, q is not. So p ∨ q is true, and true → true is true, so the statement is true.*

---

## Did You Get It

Try this problem to see if you understand the concepts we just studied. The answer can be found at the bottom of the portfolio page.

6. Using the simple statements in Question 20, find the truth value of the statement $(\sim p \land \sim q) \to r$.

# 7-2 Portfolio

Name _____

Check each box when you've completed the task. Remember that your instructor will want you to turn in the portfolio pages you create.

## Technology

1. ☐ There are commands built into spreadsheets that enable us to construct truth tables. Download the technology template for this lesson and study the commands that have been entered into cells C2 through G2. These demonstrate the commands needed to test truth values for the negation and four basic connectives. Then use similar commands to build truth tables for the compound statements in columns L and M.

## Online Practice

1. ☐ Include any written work from the online assignment along with any notes or questions about this lesson's content.

## Applications

1. ☐ Complete the applications problems.

## Reflections

Type a short answer to each question.

1. ☐ Explain when a conjunction is true, and when a disjunction is true, and why that makes sense.
2. ☐ If you had to describe to someone not in this class what we used truth tables for in this lesson, what would you say?
3. ☐ Take another look at your answer to Question 0 at the beginning of this lesson. Would you revise your answer now that you've completed the lesson? How would you summarize the topic of this lesson now?
4. ☐ What questions do you have about this lesson?

## Looking Ahead

1. ☐ Complete the Lesson 7-3 Prep Skills and read the opening paragraph in Lesson 7-3 carefully, then answer Question 0 in preparation for that lesson.

## Answers to "Did You Get It?"

**1.** If your pants were both designed by Michael Kors and cost more than the average Jamaican citizen makes in a week. **2.** If global temperatures actually have been rising for the last 50 years or climate change poses a threat to human survival, or both. **3.** It's always true unless Ebola outbreaks are becoming more frequent and the CDC infectious disease team is not traveling more than in previous years. **4.** See truth table at the bottom of the last applications page. **5. a.** Disjunction; $(\sim p) \vee q$ **b.** Conditional: $(p \vee \sim q) \to r$ **c.** Biconditional: $(p \vee \sim q) \leftrightarrow (\sim p \vee \sim q)$ **d.** Conjunction: $p \wedge (\sim q)$ **e.** Biconditional: $p \leftrightarrow (q \to r)$ **6.** The statement is true.

## 7-2 Applications

Name _____

For each compound statement in Questions 1–4, identify the truth value for each simple statement, then use that and the basic truth tables we built in this lesson to decide if the compound statement is true or false.

1. $p$ = Ebola is highly contagious, $q$ = There is a vaccine that protects against Ebola infection; $p \lor q$

   *p is true, q is not, so the disjunction is true.*

2. Same $p$ and $q$: $p \rightarrow q$

   *The conditional is false.*

3. $p$ = Recreational marijuana is legal in every state, $q$ = Millions of people have been arrested for possessing marijuana; $p \land q$

   *p is false and q is true, so the conjunction is not true.*

4. Same $p$ and $q$: $p \leftrightarrow q$

   *The biconditional is false.*

The manager of a resort tells his staff "You will be receiving holiday bonuses and an extra day off next year."

5. This compound statement is made up of two simple statements. Identify the statements and assign a letter to each.

   *p = you will be receiving holiday bonuses, q = you will be receiving an extra day off next year.*

6. Write the compound statement in symbols using a connective.

   *p ∧ q*

7. Build a truth table for the compound statement, then describe under what conditions the manager's claim is not true.

   *Truth table can be found within the lesson. The claim is true only if everyone on the staff gets a holiday bonus and gets an extra day off next year.*

## 7-2 Applications

Name _____

An advertiser is claiming that if you buy their foreign language system and use it for at least an hour every single day, you'll be able to speak a new language conversationally in 6 weeks.

**8.** This compound statement is made up of three simple statements. Identify them and assign a letter to each.

*p* = You buy their foreign language system, *q* = you use that system for at least an hour every day,

*r* = you'll be able to speak a new language conversationally in 6 weeks.

**9.** Write the compound statement in symbols using connectives.

$(p \wedge q) \rightarrow r$

**10.** Build a truth table for the compound statement.

| *p* | *q* | *r* | $p \wedge q$ | $(p \wedge q) \rightarrow r$ |
|---|---|---|---|---|
| T | T | T | T | T |
| T | T | F | T | F |
| T | F | T | F | T |
| T | F | F | F | T |
| F | T | T | F | T |
| F | T | F | F | T |
| F | F | T | F | T |
| F | F | F | F | T |

**11.** If you buy their Spanish language product and use it only for a half hour a day, then can't speak conversational Spanish in 6 weeks, is the claim made by the advertiser true or false?

True

**12.** If you buy their French language product and use it for an hour 5 days a week, and can speak conversational French in 6 weeks, is their claim true or false?

True

**13.** If you buy and use their Chinese language product for 75 minutes every day and can speak just a little bit of Chinese 6 weeks later, is their claim true or false?

False

## 7-2   Applications

Name _____

**14.** If you can speak conversational German in 6 weeks, are there any circumstances under which their claim can be considered false? Explain.

*No. The result of the truth table is true in every row that has true in the r column.*

In a nationally televised debate, a politician claimed that if he was elected, he would build a wall between the United States and Mexico, and force the Mexican government to pay for it.

**15.** This compound statement is made up of three simple statements. Identify them and assign a letter to each.

*p = he is elected, q = he builds a wall between the United States and Mexico, r = he forces the Mexican government to pay for it.*

**16.** Write the compound statement in symbols using a connective.

*p → (q ∧ r)*

**17.** Build a truth table for the compound statement, then describe under what conditions the politician's claim is true.

| p | q | r | q ∧ r | p → (q ∧ r) |
|---|---|---|-------|-------------|
| T | T | T | T | T |
| T | T | F | F | F |
| T | F | T | F | F |
| T | F | F | F | F |
| F | T | T | T | T |
| F | T | F | F | T |
| F | F | T | F | T |
| F | F | F | F | T |

*The claim is true if he doesn't get elected. If he does get elected, it's true only if the Mexican government pays to build a wall between the United States and Mexico.*

## 7-2  Applications

Name _____

**18.** Let $p$ = "My favorite band is dropping a new album next Tuesday" and $q$ = "I'm going to order the album from Amazon." Build a truth table for the statement $p \rightarrow q$ and describe the circumstances under which the statement is true.

| $p$ | $q$ | $p \rightarrow q$ |
|---|---|---|
| T | T | T |
| T | F | F |
| F | T | T |
| F | F | T |

The statement is true unless the album drops on Tuesday and you don't order it from Amazon.

**19.** For the same two statements $p$ and $q$, build a truth table for the statement $\sim p \lor q$, then describe the circumstances under which the statement is true. What do you notice?

| $p$ | $q$ | $\sim p$ | $\sim p \lor q$ |
|---|---|---|---|
| T | T | F | T |
| T | F | F | F |
| F | T | T | T |
| F | F | T | T |

This is true under the exact same circumstances as $p \rightarrow q$.

## Answers to "Did You Get It?"

Answer to Did You Get It 4

| $p$ | $q$ | $p \land q$ | $p \leftrightarrow p \land q$ |
|---|---|---|---|
| T | T | T | T |
| T | F | F | F |
| F | T | F | T |
| F | F | F | T |

# Lesson 7-3    Prep Skills

This is a short review of skills that will come in handy in the next lesson. In each case, answer the question, then rate your confidence level by checking one of the boxes. If you feel like you're struggling with these skills, consult the online resources provided by your instructor for extra practice.

### SKILL 1: IDENTIFY TRUTH VALUES FOR THE CONNECTIVES

1. Under what circumstances is the negation ~$p$ true?

2. Under what circumstances is the conjunction $p \wedge q$ false?

3. Under what circumstances is the disjunction $r \vee s$ true?

4. Under what circumstances is the conditional $r \rightarrow p$ true?

5. Under what circumstances is the biconditional $q \leftrightarrow p$ false?

### SKILL 2: COMPLETE A TRUTH TABLE FOR A COMPOUND STATEMENT

6. Complete a truth table for the statement $q \vee \sim p \rightarrow r$. Draw in columns as necessary.

| $p$ | $q$ | $r$ | |
|---|---|---|---|
| T | T | T | |
| T | T | F | |
| T | F | T | |
| T | F | F | |
| F | T | T | |
| F | T | F | |
| F | F | T | |
| F | F | F | |

# Lesson 7-3   To Be and Not to Be   (Types of Statements in Logic)

## LEARNING OBJECTIVES

☐ 1. Classify a statement as a tautology, a self-contradiction, or neither.

☐ 2. Identify statements that are logically equivalent.

☐ 3. Write and recognize negations of compound statements.

☐ 4. Write and recognize the converse, inverse, and contrapositive of a statement.

☐ 5. Evaluate logical connections between a statement and its converse, inverse, and contrapositive.

*"Good morning" is a contradiction of terms.*
—Jim Davis

© McGraw-Hill Education/Jill Braaten, photographer

It's no secret that weight loss has become big business in the United States. It seems like almost every week, a new company pops into existence with the latest miracle pill to turn you into a supermodel. A typical advertisement will say something like "Use of our product may result in significant weight loss." That sounds great, but think about what that statement really means. If use of the product "may" result in significant weight loss, it also may not result in any weight loss at all, it may result in weight gain, or it may result in you turning into a pumpkin. In fact, the statement could be translated into "You will lose weight or you will not lose weight." Of course, this statement is always true. In this lesson, we'll study statements of this type (and others).

   **0.** After reading the opening paragraph, what do you think the main topic of this lesson will be?

## 7-3   Class

### Tautologies and Self-Contradictions

In our study of truth tables in Lesson 7-2, we saw that most compound statements are true in some cases and false in others. What we haven't done is think about whether that's how it works for every compound statement. Some simple examples should be enough to convince you that this is most definitely not the case.

   Consider the simple statement "I'm going to Cancun for spring break this year."

   **1.** Describe what would make this statement true.

   *Going to Cancun for spring break this year!*

   **2.** Describe what would make this statement false.

   *Not going to Cancun for spring break this year. This could mean going somewhere else, going nowhere, going next year . . .*

The negation of that statement is "I'm not going to Cancun for spring break this year."

**3.** Describe what would make this statement true.

Not going to Cancun for spring break this year.

**4.** Describe what would make this statement false.

Going to Cancun for spring break this year.

Now think about this compound statement: "I'm going to Cancun for spring break this year, or I'm not going to Cancun for spring break this year."

**5.** Describe what would make this statement true.

Everything.

**6.** Describe what would make this statement false.

Nothing.

Since it is always true, this statement is an example of a *tautology*.

Next, think about this compound statement: "I'm going to Cancun for spring break this year, and I'm not going to Cancun for spring break this year."

**7.** Describe what would make this statement true.

Nothing short of becoming two people.

**8.** Describe what would make this statement false.

Everything.

Since it is always false, this statement is an example of a *self-contradiction*.

A **tautology** is a compound statement that's always true, regardless of the truth values of the simple statements that make it up.
A **self-contradiction** is a compound statement that is always false.

**9.** Is every compound statement either a tautology or a self-contradiction? Discuss.

*Absolutely not. Most compound statements, in fact, are true sometimes and not true others.*

---

## Did You Get It

Try this problem to see if you understand the concepts we just studied. The answer can be found at the bottom of the portfolio page.

1. Describe each statement as tautology, self-contradiction, or neither.
   a. Mornings are great and mornings aren't great.
   b. Mornings are great and waffles aren't great.
   c. Mornings are great or mornings aren't great.

---

The sample statements above are simple enough that it's easy to tell that they are always true or always false based on common sense (or uncommon sense, if you like the title of this unit). But for more complicated statements, we'll need to construct a truth table to decide if a statement is a tautology, a self-contradiction, or neither. And this is when we really start to get into the value of formal logic. There are many ways to state things in confusing manner that make it hard to decide whether it actually makes sense or not.

Courtesy of David Sobecki

Consider the statements $p$ = "I am going to a concert" and $q$ = "I will wear black." Translate each statement in Questions 10–12 into a word statement using this choice of $p$ and $q$.

**10.** $(p \wedge q) \to p$

*If I go to a concert and wear black, then I go to a concert.*

**11.** $(p \vee q) \to q$

*If I go to a concert or wear black, then I wear black.*

**12.** $(p \wedge q) \wedge (\sim p \wedge \sim q)$

*I'm going to a concert and wearing black, and I'm not going to a concert and I'm not wearing black.*

13. Can you predict which statements are tautologies, self-contradictions, or neither? Give it a shot.

*Ten seems like a tautology, and 12 sounds like a self-contradiction.*

> This is an instance where it's a good thing if students are confused. The point is that it can be hard to recognize a tautology or self-contradiction without a truth table. Don't let them spend too much time trying to figure these out.

In Questions 14–16, make a truth table to decide if each of the statements in Questions 10–12 is a tautology, a self-contradiction, or neither. Make sure you answer the question after completing each table!

14. $(p \land q) \to p$

| $p$ | $q$ | $p \land q$ | $(p \land q) \to p$ |
|-----|-----|-------------|---------------------|
| T | T | T | T |
| T | F | F | T |
| F | T | F | T |
| F | F | F | T |

*Tautology*

15. $(p \lor q) \to q$

| $p$ | $q$ | $p \lor q$ | $(p \lor q) \to p$ |
|-----|-----|------------|--------------------|
| T | T | T | T |
| T | F | T | F |
| F | T | T | T |
| F | F | F | T |

*Neither*

16. $(p \land q) \land (\sim p \land \sim q)$

| $p$ | $q$ | $\sim p$ | $\sim q$ | $p \land q$ | $\sim p \land \sim q$ | $(p \land q) \land (\sim p \land \sim q)$ |
|-----|-----|----------|----------|-------------|-----------------------|-------------------------------------------|
| T | T | F | F | T | F | F |
| T | F | F | T | F | F | F |
| F | T | T | F | F | F | F |
| F | F | T | T | F | T | F |

*Self-contradiction*

17. How do you feel about your answers to Question 13 now? Did the truth tables make it easier to recognize tautologies or self-contradictions?

*Hey, I was right! Yay me. It sure made it easier to use the truth tables though.*

## Did You Get It

Try this problem to see if you understand the concepts we just studied. The answer can be found at the bottom of the portfolio page.

2. Decide if each statement is a tautology, a self-contradiction, or neither.
   a. $(p \vee q) \wedge (\sim p \rightarrow q)$
   b. $(p \wedge \sim q) \wedge \sim p$
   c. $(p \rightarrow q) \vee \sim q$

## Logically Equivalent Statements

In Applications 18 and 19 of Lesson 7-2, we studied the two logical statements $p \rightarrow q$ and $\sim p \vee q$. The truth tables for the two statements are combined into one here:

| $p$ | $q$ | $\sim p$ | $p \rightarrow q$ | $\sim p \vee q$ |
|-----|-----|----------|-------------------|-----------------|
| T | T | F | T | T |
| T | F | F | F | F |
| F | T | T | T | T |
| F | F | T | T | T |

Notice that the truth values for both statements are *identical:* TFTT. When this occurs, the statements are said to be *logically equivalent*; this means that if we start with the same simple statements, then $p \rightarrow q$ and $\sim p \vee q$ will always have the same truth value. Let's look at a specific example.

If $p =$ "it snows" and $q =$ "I will go skiing":

18. The word statement for $p \rightarrow q$ is _____If it snows, then I will go skiing._____

   _____.

19. It is logically equivalent to the word statement for $\sim p \vee q$, which is: _____It doesn't snow, or I'll go skiing._____

   _____.

Two compound statements are **logically equivalent** if and only if they have the same truth values for all possible combinations of truth values for the simple statements that compose them. The symbol for logically equivalent statements is ≡, but the symbol ⇔ is often used as well.

Let $p =$ "Erin earns at least an 80% on her final exam" and $q =$ "She passes her math class."

**20.** Write the word statement for $p \rightarrow q$.

*If Erin earns at least 80% on her final exam, then she passes her math class.*

**21.** Write the word statement for $\sim q \rightarrow \sim p$.

*If Erin doesn't pass her math class, then she doesn't earn at least 80% on her final exam.*

**22.** Complete the truth table to decide if the two statements $p \rightarrow q$ and $\sim q \rightarrow \sim p$ are logically equivalent.

| $p$ | $q$ | $\sim p$ | $\sim q$ | $p \rightarrow q$ | $\sim q \rightarrow \sim p$ |
|---|---|---|---|---|---|
| T | T | F | F | T | T |
| T | F | F | T | F | F |
| F | T | T | F | T | T |
| F | F | T | T | T | T |

*They are logically equivalent.*

---

## Did You Get It

Try this problem to see if you understand the concepts we just studied. The answer can be found at the bottom of the portfolio page.

3. Decide which two statements are logically equivalent. Then write examples of simple statements $p$ and $q$ and write each compound statement verbally.
   a. $\sim(p \wedge \sim q)$
   b. $\sim p \wedge q$
   c. $\sim p \vee q$

---

 **7-3**  **Group**

We've seen that being able to recognize when two statements are logically equivalent can be helpful in getting to the real meaning of statements that may be confusing, either intentionally or not. De Morgan's laws for logic are a commonly used tool for recognizing logically equivalent statements.

### De Morgan's Laws for Logic

For any two statements $p$ and $q$:

- The statement $p \vee q$ is logically equivalent to $\sim p \wedge \sim q$.
- The statement $p \wedge q$ is logically equivalent to $\sim p \vee \sim q$.

If you don't remember De Morgan's laws for sets, now would be a good time to look back at Lesson 6-3 for a review. We'll wait here for you.

Do you see the similarities between De Morgan's laws for logic and the ones for sets? We're exchanging sets like *A* and *B* for statements *p* and *q,* and exchanging intersection and union for "and" and "or." (It's not a coincidence that the symbols for "and" and "or" look suspiciously like the symbols for intersection and union.) We can prove De Morgan's laws using truth tables, but it's more fun to make you do it in the applications, so that's what we did.

De Morgan's laws are most often used to write the negation of conjunctions and disjunctions. For example, the negation of the statement "I will go to work or I will go to the beach" is "I will not go to work and I will not go to the beach." Notice that when you negate a conjunction, it becomes a disjunction; and when you negate a disjunction, it becomes a conjunction—that is, the *and* becomes an *or,* and the *or* becomes an *and.*

In Questions 1–4, write the negations of the following statements, using De Morgan's laws.

1. Studying is necessary and I am a hard worker.

    Studying is not necessary or I am not a hard worker.

> Here's a good place to observe that without using De Morgan's laws, it's not at all easy to identify negations for conjunctions and disjunctions. You might consider asking students to try to write negations first without using De Morgan's laws.

2. Shoplifting is a felony or a misdemeanor.

    Shoplifting is not a felony and it's not a misdemeanor.

3. I will pass this test or I will drop this class.

    I will not pass this test and I will not drop this class.

4. The patient needs an RN or an LPN, and she's very sick. (This one requires two applications of De Morgan.)

    The patient doesn't need an RN and doesn't need an LPN or she is not very sick.

## Did You Get It

Try this problem to see if you understand the concepts we just studied. The answer can be found at the bottom of the portfolio page.

4. Write the negations of the following statements, using De Morgan's laws.
    a. I will study for this class or I will fail.
    b. I will go to the dance club and the restaurant.
    c. The movie is a comedy or a thriller, and it is awesome.

Earlier in this lesson, we saw that the two statements $p \to q$ and $\sim p \vee q$ are logically equivalent. Now that we know De Morgan's laws, we can use this fact to find the negation of the conditional statement $p \to q$.

**5.** The first step in finding the negation is to replace $p \to q$ with its equivalent form from the paragraph above. Do this to fill in the blank:

$$\sim(p \to q) \equiv \sim(\underline{\quad \sim p \vee q \quad})$$

**6.** Now the right side is the negation of a disjunction, so you can use De Morgan's law for the disjunction to rewrite it. Then you can simplify, removing any parentheses. (Hint: What is the negation of a negation?)

$$\sim(\sim p \vee q) \equiv \sim(\sim p) \wedge \sim q \equiv p \wedge \sim q$$

**7.** Complete the truth table below to verify the formula you developed for the negation of an implication. First you'll need to fill in your formula at the top of the last column.

| $p$ | $q$ | $\sim q$ | $p \to q$ | $\sim(p \to q)$ | $p \wedge \sim q$ |
|---|---|---|---|---|---|
| T | T | F | T | F | F |
| T | F | T | F | T | T |
| F | T | F | T | F | F |
| F | F | T | T | F | F |

**8.** Do the last two columns confirm your formula for the negation of a conditional? If not, go back and try Questions 5–7 again. If yes, write your formula below:

The negation of $p \to q$ is $p \wedge \sim q$

Let's try our shiny new formula in an example. If you say "It is not the case that if I get a biology degree then I'll be guaranteed a good job," that's the same thing as saying "I got a biology degree and wasn't guaranteed a good job."

In Questions 9 and 10, we'll use our formula to write the negation of the statement "If you agree to go out with me, I'll buy you a late-model vehicle."

**9.** If we want to write that statement as $p \to q$, identify the statements $p$ and $q$.

$p =$ " You go out with me
_____ "

and $q =$ " I buy you a late-model vehicle
_____ "

Courtesy of David Sobecki

**10.** Now use your formula to write the negation of the statement "If you agree to go out with me, I'll buy you a late-model vehicle."

"*You went out with me and I don't buy you a late-model vehicle.* "

---

## Did You Get It

Try this problem to see if you understand the concepts we just studied. The answer can be found at the bottom of the portfolio page.

5. Write the negation of the statement "If the video I made goes viral, it will be on Tosh.0."

---

## Variations of the Conditional Statement

In addition to their obvious importance in logic, conditional statements play a huge role in math in general. Many of the most important results in the history of math are if . . . then statements. Consider the famous Pythagorean theorem, which almost everyone remembers as simply $a^2 + b^2 = c^2$. But with no context, and especially without describing what quantities $a$, $b$, and $c$ represent, that equation is completely meaningless.

So here's the context. First, we need to know that those variables represent the lengths of sides in a right triangle. Second, we get more specific: $a$ and $b$ are the lengths of the legs (the two shorter sides), and $c$ is the length of the hypotenuse, which sounds a lot like a Muppet, but is actually the side across from the right angle. If all of those conditions are met, we can conclude that the famous equation is a true statement.

**11.** Write the Pythagorean theorem as a conditional statement. All the information you need is in the above paragraph.

*If $a$ and $b$ are lengths of the legs of a right triangle, and $c$ is the length of the hypotenuse, then $a^2 + b^2 = c^2$.*

> You might remind students of some other results they probably remember from other math courses, showing how they're conditional statements as well.

One of the ways we can learn more about conditional statements is to study three related statements, the *converse,* the *inverse,* and the *contrapositive.*

## Variations of a Conditional Statement

| Name | In Symbols | In Words |
|------|------------|----------|
| Conditional | $p \rightarrow q$ | If $p$, then $q$. |
| Converse | $q \rightarrow p$ | If $q$, then $p$. |
| Inverse | $\sim p \rightarrow \sim q$ | If not $p$, then not $q$. |
| Contrapositive | $\sim q \rightarrow \sim p$ | If not $q$, then not $p$. |

12. Discuss this among your group, and write any conclusions you agree on: which, if any, of the three variations on a conditional do you think have the same meaning as $p \rightarrow q$?

*Answers vary.*

> This can be one of the better group discussions in the course. There's nothing wrong with some intra-group arguing as long as it's civil and backed up with reasoning.

Courtesy of David Sobecki

Now let's see how you did, with the help of a nice doggie named Bear. (Her real name is Tessa, but everyone calls her Bear.)

We'll use the statement "If Bear is a chocolate Lab, then Bear is brown" to illustrate the variations of a conditional, and to decide if each is logically equivalent to the original conditional statement. Note that the original conditional statement is true—the thing that makes a Labrador retriever a chocolate Lab is brown fur.

13. The converse is "If Bear is brown, then Bear is a chocolate Lab." Is this true? Discuss.

*It is not. There are plenty of animals that are brown but are not Labrador retrievers, so obviously they're not chocolate Labs. Brown bears, for example.*

14. The inverse is "If Bear isn't a chocolate Lab, then Bear isn't brown." True or false? Discuss.

*False again, for the same reason. Bear could still be brown even if she's not a chocolate Lab.*

15. The contrapositive is "If Bear isn't brown, then Bear isn't a chocolate Lab." True or false? Discuss.

*This one is true. If Bear's not brown, she definitely cannot be a chocolate Lab because all chocolate Labs are brown.*

16. Based on the above examples, only one of the three variations on $p \rightarrow q$ can possibly be logically equivalent to the original conditional. Which one, and how do we know that? (Hint: Questions 13–15 deal with a *specific example*.)

*The contrapositive. We have at least one example for which the converse and inverse are not equivalent to the original statement, so they can't ALWAYS be equivalent. For the contrapositive, we know for this example that it is equivalent to the original statement, which means it COULD always be equivalent.*

17. If only we had a way to check your conclusion from Question 16 . . . oh wait, there is: a truth table! This time, you're on your own: set up and complete a truth table comparing truth values for a conditional $p \rightarrow q$ and the variation that you chose in Question 16. If they're logically equivalent, then your conjecture was correct and you win! If not, reevaluate your answer to Question 16 and try again.

| $p$ | $q$ | $\sim q$ | $\sim p$ | $p \rightarrow q$ | $\sim q \rightarrow \sim p$ |
|---|---|---|---|---|---|
| T | T | F | F | T | T |
| T | F | T | F | F | F |
| F | T | F | T | T | T |
| F | F | T | T | T | T |

Next, consider the conditional "If you earned a bachelor's degree, then you got a high-paying job."

18. Write the converse, and discuss if it does or does not have the same meaning as the original statement.

    *If you got a high-paying job, then you earned a bachelor's degree. This doesn't mean the same thing as the original. There are high-paying jobs that don't require a degree.*

19. Write the inverse, and discuss if it does or does not have the same meaning as the original statement.

    *If you didn't get a bachelor's degree, then you didn't get a high paying job. This means the same thing as the converse, but not the original statement.*

20. Write the contrapositive, and discuss if it does or does not have the same meaning as the original statement.

    *If you didn't get a high-paying job, then you didn't earn a bachelor's degree. This says the same thing as the original statement.*

You now know that the converse of a conditional is NOT logically equivalent to the original conditional. That's a good thing, because maybe the most common flaw in logic is thinking that they *are* equivalent. If you watch out for it, you can see people making this mistake all over the place, from daily conversation all the way up to presidential debates.

## Did You Get It

Try this problem to see if you understand the concepts we just studied. The answer can be found at the bottom of the portfolio page.

6. Write the three variations of the statement "If the video I made goes viral, it will be on Tosh.0." and classify each one as equivalent or not equivalent to the original statement.

Earlier in this unit, we pointed out that in the study of formal logic, we tend to use very formal wording for statements, which often sounds kind of stiff and unnatural. There are other wordings that can be used for conditional statements aside from the standard "if . . . then" connective. To close the lesson, we're going to ask you to think about some alternative words that are used, and decide how to use them in statements.

Our base statement will be "If you are convicted of a felony, you will serve time in jail." Listed below are alternative wordings for a conditional.

$p$ implies $q$
$q$ if $p$
$p$ only if $q$
$p$ is sufficient for $q$
$q$ is necessary for $p$
All $p$ are $q$

21. Your job is to figure out how to write a statement using each of those wordings that has the same meaning as the original statement. Go.

Being convicted of a felony implies that you will serve time in jail.

You will serve time in jail if you're convicted of a felony.

You were convicted of a felony only if you served time in jail.

Being convicted of a felony is sufficient for serving time in jail.

Serving time in jail is necessary for having committed a felony.

All people who were convicted of a felony are people that served time in jail.

# 7-3 Portfolio

Name _____

Check each box when you've completed the task. Remember that your instructor will want you to turn in the portfolio pages you create.

### Technology

1. ☐ You might remember that the Excel formula we used for conditional statements in Lesson 7-2 Technology was . . . well, let's be polite and just say it was cumbersome. But all of negation, conjunction, and disjunction were pretty straightforward. Now that we have a logically equivalent form for conditions in terms of negation and disjunction, we can fix that! The template in the online resources for this lesson is similar to the one from the last lesson, but this time your job is to rewrite the commands in the conditional column using the equivalent form we used in this lesson. Then build a truth table for the statement $(p \wedge q) \rightarrow (p \vee q)$ to see if it's a tautology, self-contradiction, or neither.

### Online Practice

1. ☐ Include any written work from the online assignment along with any notes or questions about this lesson's content.

### Applications

1. ☐ Complete the applications problems.

### Reflections

Type a short answer to each question.

1. ☐ Explain what it means for two statements to be logically equivalent.
2. ☐ What is a tautology? What is a self-contradiction?
3. ☐ Describe the process of using truth tables to decide if two statements are logically equivalent.
4. ☐ Take another look at your answer to Question 0 at the beginning of this lesson. Would you revise your answer now that you've completed the lesson? How would you summarize the topic of this lesson now?
5. ☐ What questions do you have about this lesson?

### Looking Ahead

1. ☐ Complete the Lesson 7-4 Prep Skills and read the opening paragraph in Lesson 7-4 carefully, then answer Question 0 in preparation for that lesson.

### Answers to "Did You Get It?"

1. **a.** Self-contradiction **b.** Neither **c.** Tautology **2. a.** Neither
**b.** Self-contradiction **c.** Tautology **3.** a and c are equivalent; answers vary on second part. **4. a.** I will not study for this class and I will not fail.
**b.** I will not go to the dance club or the restaurant.
**c.** The movie is not a comedy and it is not a thriller, or it is not awesome.
**5.** The video I made went viral and it was not on Tosh.0.
**6.** Converse: "If my video is on Tosh.0, then it went viral." Inverse: "If my video doesn't go viral, then it won't be on Tosh.0." Contrapositive: "If my video isn't on Tosh.0, then it didn't go viral." Only the contrapositive is equivalent to the original statement.

## 7-3 Applications

Name _____

In Questions 1–4, use De Morgan's laws to write the negation of each statement.

1. I'm flying to Houston tomorrow and staying at the Westin.

   *I'm not flying to Houston tomorrow or I'm not staying at the Westin.*

2. I'll pick up a sandwich on the way or eat dinner at the airport on the way out.

   *I won't pick up a sandwich on the way and I won't eat dinner at the airport on the way out.*

3. I'm going through the TSA precheck lane and I won't remove my shoes while going through security.

   *I'm not going through the TSA precheck lane or I will remove my shoes while going through security.*

4. I won't fall asleep during the flight or I won't have a complementary beverage.

   *I will fall asleep during the flight and I will have a complementary beverage.*

In Questions 5–7, decide if the two statements are negations. If you can, use De Morgan's laws. If not, write each statement in symbols and use truth tables.

5. 1: A majority of drivers stopped by police in this jurisdiction are black and the police department is under federal investigation.
   2: The police department in this jurisdiction is not under federal investigation or a majority of drivers stopped by police are not black.

   *They are negations: if the first statement is written as p and q, the second is not q or not p.*

# 7-3 Applications

Name _____

**6.** 1: If social workers get a pay raise, then children in our community will be at less risk.
   2: It's not the case that if children in our community will be at less risk, then social workers get a pay raise.

| $p$ | $q$ | $p \rightarrow q$ | $q \rightarrow p$ | $\sim(q \rightarrow p)$ |
|---|---|---|---|---|
| T | T | T | T | F |
| T | F | F | T | F |
| F | T | T | F | T |
| F | F | T | T | F |

*The two statements don't have opposite truth values, so they are not negations.*

**7.** 1: You won't get a good job with a major in medieval history, and you will regret that major.
   2: You won't regret majoring in medieval history or you will get a good job.

| $p$ | $q$ | $\sim p$ | $\sim q$ | $\sim p \wedge q$ | $\sim q \vee p$ |
|---|---|---|---|---|---|
| T | T | F | F | F | T |
| T | F | F | T | F | T |
| F | T | T | F | T | F |
| F | F | T | T | F | T |

*The two statements have opposite truth values, so they are negations. De Morgan's laws can be used as well.*

Let $p$ = "Lobbyists play a key role in shaping public policy" and $q$ = "Campaign donations influence politicians' positions on issues." In Questions 8–10, translate each symbolic statement into words, then use truth tables to decide if each is a tautology, a self-contradiction, or neither.

**8.** $(p \vee q) \vee (\sim p \wedge \sim q)$

*Lobbyists play a key role in shaping public policy or campaign donations influence politicians' positions on issues, or lobbyists don't play a key role in shaping public policy and campaign donations don't influence politicians' positions on issues.*

| $p$ | $q$ | $\sim p$ | $\sim q$ | $p \vee q$ | $\sim p \wedge \sim q$ | $(p \vee q) \vee (\sim p \wedge \sim q)$ | |
|---|---|---|---|---|---|---|---|
| T | T | F | F | T | F | T | *Tautology* |
| T | F | F | T | T | F | T | |
| F | T | T | F | T | F | T | |
| F | F | T | T | F | T | T | |

## 7-3 | Applications

Name _____

**9.** $(p \wedge q) \wedge (\sim p \vee \sim q)$

Lobbyists play a key role in shaping public policy and campaign donations influence politicians' positions on issues, and lobbyists don't play a key role in shaping public policy or campaign donations don't influence politicians' positions on issues.

| $p$ | $q$ | $\sim p$ | $\sim q$ | $p \wedge q$ | $\sim p \vee \sim q$ | $(p \wedge q) \wedge (\sim p \vee \sim q)$ |
|---|---|---|---|---|---|---|
| T | T | F | F | T | F | F |
| T | F | F | T | F | T | F |
| F | T | T | F | F | T | F |
| F | F | T | T | F | T | F |

Self-contradiction

**10.** $(p \leftrightarrow q) \wedge (\sim p \leftrightarrow \sim q)$

Lobbyists play a key role in shaping public policy if and only if campaign donations influence politicians' positions on issues, and lobbyists don't play a key role in shaping public policy if and only if campaign donations don't influence politicians' positions on issues.

| $p$ | $q$ | $\sim p$ | $\sim q$ | $p \leftrightarrow q$ | $\sim p \leftrightarrow \sim q$ | $(p \leftrightarrow q) \wedge (\sim p \leftrightarrow \sim q)$ |
|---|---|---|---|---|---|---|
| T | T | F | F | T | T | T |
| T | F | F | T | F | F | F |
| F | T | T | F | F | F | F |
| F | F | T | T | T | T | T |

Neither

For each statement in Questions 11–13, write the negation, converse, inverse, and contrapositive. Then explain why the contrapositive says the same thing as the original statement.

**11.** If work calls, you should tell them I have Legionnaire's disease.

Negation: Work calls and you shouldn't tell them that I have Legionnaire's disease.

Converse: If you should tell them I have Legionnaire's disease, then work calls.

Inverse: If work doesn't call, you shouldn't tell them I have Legionnaire's disease.

Contrapositive: If you don't tell them I have Legionnaire's disease, then work didn't call.

Explanations vary.

## 7-3   Applications

Name _____

**12.** Getting no raise this year implies that my boss thinks I'm doing a rotten job.

Negation: I got no raise this year and my boss doesn't think I'm doing a rotten job.

Converse: If my boss thinks I'm doing a rotten job, then I'm not getting a raise this year.

Inverse: If I get a raise this year, then my boss doesn't think I'm doing a rotten job.

Contrapositive: If my boss doesn't think I'm doing a rotten job, then I'll get a raise this year.

Explanations vary.

**13.** Signing a waiver is necessary for participating in the drug trial.

This statement can be translated as "If you participate in the drug trial, then you sign a waiver."

Negation: You participated in the drug trial and didn't sign a waiver.

Converse: If you sign a waiver, then you participate in the drug trial.

Inverse: If you don't participate in the drug trial, then you don't sign a waiver.

Contrapositive: If you don't sign a waiver, then you don't participate in the drug trial.

Explanations vary.

# Lesson 7-4   Prep Skills

This is a short review of skills that will come in handy in the next lesson. In each case, answer the question, then rate your confidence level by checking one of the boxes. If you feel like you're struggling with these skills, consult the online resources provided by your instructor for extra practice.

### SKILL 1: WRITE STATEMENTS IN SYMBOLS

Write each statement in symbols. Identify what the letters in your symbolic statement represent.

1. I ate an entire side of beef for lunch and my stomach does NOT feel good.

2. If I don't take some medicine soon, I might pass out.

3. I'm going to work tomorrow if and only if I feel better.

4. Next time I go to that restaurant I won't order the same thing or I'll call an ambulance in advance.

### SKILL 2: BUILD TRUTH TABLES

5. Build a truth table for the statement $p \wedge (\sim q \vee p)$.

6. Build a truth table for the statement $r \rightarrow (p \wedge \sim q)$.

## Lesson 7-4 **Being Argumentative** (Evaluating Logical Arguments)

### LEARNING OBJECTIVES

☐ 1. Identify the difference between a valid argument and a fallacy.

☐ 2. Use truth tables to evaluate validity of arguments.

☐ 3. Determine the validity of common argument forms.

☐ 4. Use common argument forms to decide if arguments are valid.

© J.R. Bale/Alamy RF

*Be able to defend your arguments in a rational way. Otherwise, all you have is an opinion.*

—Marilyn vos Savant

Common sense is a funny thing in our society: we all think we have it, and we also think that most other people don't. This thing that we call common sense is really the ability to think logically, to evaluate an argument or situation and decide what is and is not reasonable. It doesn't take a lot of imagination to picture how valuable it is to be able to think logically. We're pretty well protected by parents for our first few years of life, but after that the main tool we have to guide us through the perils of life is our brain. The more effectively that brain can analyze and evaluate the mass of information we're all exposed to every day, the more successful we're likely to be.

The work we've done in building the basics of symbolic logic in the first three lessons in this chapter has prepared us for the real point: analyzing logical arguments objectively. That's the topic of this important lesson. Remember why we're using letters to represent statements: your goal is to ignore the TOPIC of an argument, and simply focus on whether or not a conclusion can be reasonably drawn from a preliminary set of statements. Check your emotions and opinions at the door, and get ready to be argumentative.

**0.** After reading the opening paragraphs, what do you think the main topic of this lesson will be?

## 7-4 Class

### Valid Arguments and Fallacies

A logical argument consists of two parts: a set of premises and a conclusion based on those premises. Premises are statements that are offered as supporting evidence for the conclusion. Our goal is to decide whether an argument is *valid* or *invalid.*

> An argument is **valid** if the conclusion necessarily follows from the premises, and **invalid** if it's not valid. An error in reasoning that leads to an invalid argument is known as a **fallacy.**

Notice that our definition of valid doesn't use the word "true," because *logic is not about deciding if a claim is true: it's about deciding if the claim can be deduced from the premises.* This is a really important idea to keep in mind, or this lesson will really be a struggle for you.

Let's look at an example of a logical argument.

    Premise 1: All students in this class will pass.

    Premise 2: Rachel is a student in this class.

    Conclusion: Rachel will pass this class.

1.  What are we told about who will pass this class in premise 1?

    *All students in the class.*

2.  Is Rachel a student in this class?

    *Based on premise 2, yes.*

3.  What can you say about the validity of the conclusion? Why?

    *It's perfectly valid based on the premises.*

> Questions 4 through 7 are likely to require more in-class discussion and explanation than any other questions in this unit. Understanding them is in some sense the essence of understanding validity, so make sure you devote plenty of effort here.

It's very important at this point to understand the difference between a true statement and a conclusion to a valid argument. A statement that is known to be false can still be a valid conclusion if it follows logically from the given premises.

    Random question: Is Los Angeles in Mexico?

4.  The statement "Los Angeles is in Mexico" is definitely ___*false*___. (Hint: A good answer will end in "alse.")

Consider this argument:

    Premise 1: Los Angeles is in California or Mexico.

    Premise 2: Los Angeles is not in California.

    Conclusion: Therefore, Los Angeles is in Mexico.

### Math Note

Interesting but not particularly relevant note: there are no words in common spoken English that exactly rhyme with "false."

5.  What does the statement "Los Angeles is in California or Mexico" mean?

    *That Los Angeles is in one of those two places.*

6.  What does the statement "Los Angeles is not in California" mean? This one is kind of obvious.

    *That Los Angeles is in some place other than California.*

**7.** If we accept both of the two previous statements (premises), then the statement "Therefore, Los Angeles is in Mexico" must be _____*true*_____. (Hint: Your answer should rhyme with "shrew.")

This is a valid argument: if we accept the two premises, then Los Angeles would in fact be in Mexico. We know, however, that Los Angeles is NOT in Mexico, and there's the tricky part. *To be valid, the conclusion of an argument has to follow from the premises whether they're true or not.* In this case, we're accepting the premise "Los Angeles is not in California" even though we know that it's actually false. We can then deduce that the conclusion (Los Angeles is in Mexico) follows logically from that premise. Again, this emphasizes that the validity of an argument is not about whether or not the conclusion is a true statement.

## Truth Table Method

One way to decide if an argument is valid is based on truth tables. We'll use the following procedure.

---

### Testing the Validity of an Argument

**Step 1.** Write the argument in symbols.

**Step 2.** Write the argument as a conditional statement; use a conjunction between all premises and the implication (⇒) for the conclusion. (Note: the symbol ⇒ means the same as → but will be used to designate an argument.)

**Step 3.** Set up and construct a truth table as follows:

Symbols | Premise ∧ Premise ⇒ Conclusion

**Step 4.** If all truth values under ⇒ are Ts (that is, the statement in the last column is a tautology), then the argument is valid; otherwise, it is invalid.

---

Let's use that procedure to decide if the following argument is valid.

If a figure has three sides, then it is a triangle.

This figure is not a triangle.
_____

Therefore, this figure does not have three sides.

**8. Step 1** *Write the argument in symbols.*

Let $p$ = "___*A figure has three sides*___,"

and let $q$ = "___*A figure is a triangle*___."

> **Math Note**
>
> There can be more than two premises in an argument; in that case, put the conjunction sign between all premises.

**9.** Write the premise "If a figure has three sides, then it is a triangle" in symbols using the statements $p$ and $q$.

$p \rightarrow q$

**10.** Write the premise "This figure is not a triangle" in symbols.

$\sim q$

**11.** Write the conclusion "this figure does not have three sides" in symbols, then use your answers to Questions 8–10 to write the argument in symbols below.

$p \to q$          (Premise)

$\sim q$          (Premise)

∴ $\sim p$          (Conclusion)

Note that a line is used to separate the premises from the conclusion and the three triangular dots ∴ mean "therefore."

**12.** **Step 2** *Write the argument as an implication by connecting the premises with a conjunction and implying the conclusion.*

|  **Premise 1**  |  | **Premise 2** |  | **Conclusion** |
|---|---|---|---|---|
| $p \to q$ | $\wedge$ | $\sim q$ | $\Rightarrow$ | $\sim p$ |

**13.** **Step 3** *Construct a truth table as shown.*

| $p$ | $q$ | $\sim p$ | $\sim q$ | $p \to q$ | $(p \to q) \wedge \sim q$ | $[(p \to q) \wedge \sim q] \Rightarrow \sim p$ |
|---|---|---|---|---|---|---|
| T | T | F | F | T | F | T |
| T | F | F | T | F | F | T |
| F | T | T | F | T | F | T |
| F | F | T | T | T | T | T |

**14.** **Step 4** *Determine the validity of the argument.* Look at all the truth values in the last column of your truth table above. What do you conclude?

*The implication is always true, which tells us that the conclusion follows logically from the premises, and the argument is valid.*

> Refer back to the concept discussed in Questions 4–7 here. For an argument to be valid, it's the IMPLICATION between the premises and the conclusion that has to be true, not any of the premises, or the conclusion itself.

In Questions 15 and 16, we will decide if this argument is valid: Emerging research shows that if cancer patients undergo aromatherapy, depression is lessened. One of my cancer patients is reporting a decrease in depression, so she must have undergone aromatherapy.

15. Let $p$ = "A cancer patient undergoes aromatherapy" and let $q$ = "The patient suffers less from depression." Write the argument in symbols.

$p \to q$
$q$
——————
$\therefore p$

16. Follow the remaining steps in the procedure we've outlined for using a truth table to determine the validity of an argument. A truth table has been provided to help.

| $p$ | $q$ | $p \to q$ | $(p \to q) \wedge q$ | $[(p \to q) \wedge q] \Rightarrow p$ |
|---|---|---|---|---|
| T | T | T | T | T |
| T | F | F | F | T |
| F | T | T | T | F |
| F | F | T | F | T |

The argument is not valid.

© TRBfoto/Getty Images RF

## Did You Get It ❓

Try these problems to see if you understand the concepts we just studied. The answers can be found at the bottom of the portfolio page.

Use the procedure you just practiced to decide if each argument is valid or not.

1. I will run for student government or I will join the athletic boosters.

   I'm not joining the athletic boosters.
   ——————————————————————————
   Therefore, I will run for student government.

2. John's boss warned him that if he blew off work to go to the playoff game, he'd get fired. I heard John got fired, so I guess he must have gone to that playoff game. Cool!

We haven't bugged you for a while about the connection (or lack of connection) between the truth of a conclusion and the validity of an argument, so think about each of these arguments:

Either $2 + 2 \neq 4$ or $2 + 2 = 5$.

$2 + 2 = 4$.
_____

So, $2 + 2 = 5$.

**17.** Is this argument valid?

Yes

**18.** Is this conclusion true?

No

If $2 + 2 \neq 5$, then my feet hurt.

My feet don't hurt.
_____

So, $2 + 2 \neq 5$.

**19.** Is this argument valid?

No

**20.** Is this conclusion true?

Yes

Did we mention that validity of arguments is not about the conclusion being true? In the Applications for this lesson, you'll build truth tables to check the validity of these arguments.

You might be thinking that you could just figure out whether the arguments we've studied are valid or not. You might even be right. But when arguments get more complicated, the value of having a systematic approach becomes more apparent. When an argument has three premises, that's usually the case. In this case, the last column will contain a conjunction of three premises.

In Questions 21–23, we'll decide if this argument is valid:

$p \rightarrow r$

$q \wedge r$

$p$
_____

$\therefore \sim q \rightarrow p$

**21.** *Write the argument as an implication.* Make a conjunction of all three premises and imply the conclusion:

$[(p \rightarrow r) \wedge (q \wedge r) \wedge p] \Rightarrow (\sim q \rightarrow p)$

**22.** *Construct a truth table.* When there are three premises, we will begin by finding the truth values for each premise and then work the conjunction from left to right as shown.

| $p$ | $q$ | $r$ | $\sim q$ | $p \to r$ | $q \wedge r$ | $\sim q \to p$ | $(p \to r) \wedge (q \wedge r) \wedge p$ | $[(p \to r) \wedge (q \wedge r) \wedge p] \Rightarrow (\sim q \to p)$ |
|---|---|---|---|---|---|---|---|---|
| T | T | T | F | T | T | T | T | T |
| T | T | F | F | F | F | T | F | T |
| T | F | T | T | T | F | T | F | T |
| T | F | F | T | F | F | T | F | T |
| F | T | T | F | T | T | T | F | T |
| F | T | F | F | T | F | T | F | T |
| F | F | T | T | T | F | F | F | T |
| F | F | F | T | T | F | F | F | T |

**23.** Is the argument valid? Why or why not?

*The argument is valid: the implication is always true, so the conclusion follows logically from the premises.*

## Did You Get It

Try this problem to see if you understand the concepts we just studied. The answer can be found at the bottom of the portfolio page.

3. Decide if the argument is valid.

$p \vee q$

$\underline{q \vee \sim r}$

$\therefore q$

## 7-4   Group

### Common Valid Argument Forms

We have seen that truth tables can be used to test an argument for validity. But some argument forms are common enough that they are recognized by special names. When an argument fits one of these forms, we can decide if it is valid or not just by knowing the general form, rather than constructing a truth table. We'll start with a description of some commonly used valid arguments.

**Law of Detachment**

$p \rightarrow q$

$p$

$\therefore q$

**Example**

If our team wins Saturday, then they go to a bowl game.

Our team won Saturday.

Therefore, our team goes to a bowl game.

**Law of Contraposition**

$p \rightarrow q$

$\sim q$

$\therefore \sim p$

**Example**

If I try hard, I'll get an A.

I didn't get an A.

Therefore, I didn't try hard.

**Law of Syllogism**

$p \rightarrow q$

$q \rightarrow r$

$\therefore p \rightarrow r$

**Example**

If I make an illegal U-turn, I'll get a ticket.

If I get a ticket, I'll get points on my driving record.

Therefore, if I make an illegal U-turn, I'll get points on my driving record.

**Law of Disjunctive Syllogism**

$p \lor q$

$\sim p$

$\therefore q$

**Example**

My top client demands the penthouse or an executive suite.

He couldn't stay in the penthouse.

Therefore, he stayed in an executive suite.

1. Make up your own example that fits the law of detachment. Compare with others and make sure your examples fit.

Answers vary.

**2.** Make up your own example that fits the law of contraposition. Compare with others and make sure your examples fit.

*Answers vary.*

**3.** Make up your own example that fits the law of syllogism. Compare with others and make sure your examples fit.

*Answers vary.*

> **Math Note**
>
> The law of syllogism is also known as the law of transitivity. This is because it looks just like the transitive property of equality: if $a = b$ and $b = c$, then $a = c$.

**4.** Make up your own example that fits the law of disjunctive syllogism. Compare with others and make sure your examples fit.

*Answers vary.*

## Common Fallacies

Next, we'll study some commonly used arguments that are invalid because they result from a fallacy—that is, an incorrect way of reasoning. Sometimes people use these without realizing they're being illogical. Other times, people use them in a deliberate attempt to confuse or deceive. Beware!

| **Fallacy of the Converse** | **Example** |
|---|---|
| $p \rightarrow q$ | If it's Friday, then I'll go to happy hour. |
| $q$ | I'm at happy hour. |
| $\therefore p$ | Therefore, it must be Friday. |

**5.** Explain why this argument isn't valid.

*Because it's possible to go to happy hour on other days. In fact, I highly recommend doing so.*

> Great opportunity for class discussion here!

| **Fallacy of the Inverse** | **Example** |
|---|---|
| $p \rightarrow q$ | If I exercise every day, then I will lose weight. |
| $\sim p$ | I don't exercise every day. |
| $\therefore \sim q$ | Therefore, I won't lose weight. |

© Comstock Images RF

**6.** Explain why this argument isn't valid.

*You may lose weight if you exercise every day, but you can still lose weight even if you don't exercise every day.*

| **Fallacy of the Inclusive Or** | **Example** |
|---|---|
| $p \vee q$ | I'm going to take chemistry or physics. |
| $p$ | I signed up for chemistry. |
| $\therefore \sim q$ | Therefore, I'm not taking physics. |

**7.** Explain why this argument isn't valid. You might find it helpful to look back at our discussion of truth values for disjunctions back in Lesson 7-2.

*The statement 'I'm going to take chemistry or physics' doesn't mean one or the other but not both. If you take both, the statement is still true.*

In Questions 8–12, use the known valid arguments and fallacies to decide if each argument is valid. Make sure you list the name of the argument form you used.

**8.** If you eat a healthy diet, you'll live past 70.

You've really made an effort to eat healthy foods.

Therefore, you'll live past 70.

*This is valid: it's the law of detachment.*

9. You can access the Web at this hotel if you pay for wifi.

   You're too broke to pay for wifi.
   _____

   So you won't be able to access the web.

   *This is invalid: it's the fallacy of the inverse.*

10. If you watch Big Brother, you watch reality shows.

    If you watch reality shows, you have time to kill.
    _____

    Therefore, if you watch Big Brother, you have time to kill.

    *This is valid: it's the law of syllogism.*

11. You planned to major in criminal justice or pre-law. Since you're majoring in criminal justice, I guess that means you're not majoring in pre-law.

    *This is invalid: it's the fallacy of the inclusive or.*

12. Botany grads work in parks or at research labs. Linh got her degree in botany last year and doesn't work at a park, so she must work at a research lab.

    *This is valid: it's the law of disjunctive syllogism.*

**Bonus Question:** Explain why the law of contraposition, the fallacy of the converse, and the fallacy of the inverse were given the names that they have.

*The law of contraposition essentially says that a conditional and its contrapositive are logically equivalent, which is true. The two fallacies make the same claim for the converse and inverse, and we know that those aren't true.*

To close the lesson, we'll talk about one final common fallacy that doesn't necessarily fit a particular form in terms of letters, like the others. It's known as **circular reasoning.** Think about this little story.

A suspect in a criminal investigation tells the police detective questioning him that his statements can be trusted because his friend Sue can vouch for him. The detective asks the suspect how he knows that Sue can be trusted, and he says "I can assure you of her honesty." Ultimately, the suspect becomes even more suspect because of circular reasoning: his argument boils down to "I am honest because I am honest."

This is the essence of circular reasoning: by making the conclusion one of the premises, you can pretty much guarantee that if the premises are true, so is the conclusion. You might think this example seems blatantly silly, but you'd be surprised at how often people try to get away with this fallacy. A Google search for the string "circular reasoning" brings up hundreds of arguments that are thought to be circular.

**13.** Write an example of an argument that uses circular reasoning.

*Answers vary.*

> Be prepared with some examples of circular reasoning here. That Google search mentioned in the paragraph above is a gold mine.

## Did You Get It

Try these problems to see if you understand the concepts we just studied. The answers can be found at the bottom of the portfolio page.

4. Use the known valid arguments and fallacies to decide if each argument is valid. Make sure you list the name of the argument form you used.

   a. If you do well in hospitality management, you'll get a job at a great resort.

   You graduated with a 3.8 GPA in hospitality management.
   _____
   Therefore, you should get a job at a great resort.

   b. If you work hard, you will be a success.

   You are not a success.
   _____
   I guess you don't work hard.

   c. Jon is either really cheap, or flat broke. I got a look at his checking account statement and he's not broke, so he must just be cheap.

   d. If my lab rats don't die, I'll get a passing lab grade. Since I passed bio lab, that means the rats didn't die.

## 7-4 | Portfolio

Name _____

Check each box when you've completed the task. Remember that your instructor will want you to turn in the portfolio pages you create.

### Technology

1. ☐ This is where we bring it all home! Over the last three tech assignments, we learned how to use logic functions and build truth tables for connectives. The real goal was to be able to build a spreadsheet that will evaluate logical arguments, so that's what we're going to do here. In the template provided in online resources, we've set up truth tables to evaluate all of the common argument forms and common fallacies within this lesson. Your job is to use the formulas we practiced in the earlier tech assignments to fill in the truth tables, confirming that these arguments are or are not valid. Good luck!

### Online Practice

1. ☐ Include any written work from the online assignment along with any notes or questions about this lesson's content.

### Applications

1. ☐ Complete the applications problems.

### Reflections

Type a short answer to each question.

1. ☐ Looking back over this unit, what is the point of studying logical arguments using symbols rather than the original words they're stated in?
2. ☐ Describe the process of using truth tables to evaluate a logical argument.
3. ☐ Why is the last column of a truth table used to evaluate the validity of an argument always an implication?
4. ☐ Take another look at your answer to Question 0 at the beginning of this lesson. Would you revise your answer now that you've completed the lesson? How would you summarize the topic of this lesson now?
5. ☐ What questions do you have about this lesson?

### Looking Ahead

1. ☐ Complete the Lesson 8-1 Prep Skills and read the opening paragraph in Lesson 8-1 carefully, then answer Question 0 in preparation for that lesson.

### Answers to "Did You Get It?"

1. Valid     2. Invalid     3. Invalid     4. a. Valid: law of detachment
b. Valid: law of contraposition     c. Valid: law of disjunctive syllogism
d. Invalid: fallacy of the converse

## 7-4 Applications

Name _____

1. For the two arguments in Questions 17–20 of the Class portion of this lesson, write each argument in symbols then use truth tables to decide which (if either) is valid. Then talk about the relationship between an argument being valid and the conclusion being true.

Argument 1: $\sim p \lor q$
$$\frac{p}{\therefore q}$$

Argument 2: $\sim p \to q$
$$\frac{\sim q}{\therefore \sim p}$$

| $p$ | $q$ | $\sim p$ | $\sim q$ | $\sim p \lor q$ | $(\sim p \lor q) \land p$ | $[(\sim p \lor q) \land p] \Rightarrow q$ | $\sim p \to q$ | $(\sim p \to q) \land \sim q$ | $[(\sim p \to q) \land \sim q] \Rightarrow \sim p$ |
|---|---|---|---|---|---|---|---|---|---|
| T | T | F | F | T | T | T | T | F | T |
| T | F | F | T | F | F | T | T | T | F |
| F | T | T | F | T | F | T | T | F | T |
| F | F | T | T | T | F | T | F | F | T |

*Argument 1 is valid and argument 2 is not. This illustrates that validity of an argument is in no way connected to whether the conclusion is a true statement.*

2. A logical argument is written below. Just based on reading it, do you think this argument is valid?

The play opens tonight and I won't be in attendance.    *Answers vary.*

If I didn't have to work, I'd attend.
_____
∴ I'll be attending.

3. Assign letters to each of the simple statements involved in this argument.

   $p =$ the play opens tonight, $q =$ I attend the play, $r =$ I have to work

4. Write the argument in symbols.

   $p \land \sim q$          Premise 1

   $\dfrac{\sim r \to q}{\therefore q}$          Premise 2

   ∴ $q$          Conclusion

5. Write the argument as a conditional statement by connecting the premises with a conjunction.

   $(p \land \sim q) \land (\sim r \to q) \Rightarrow q$

# 7-4 Applications

Name _____

**6.** Build a truth table for this argument, then state whether the argument is valid or invalid.

| p | q | r | ~q | ~r | p∧~q | ~r→q | (p∧~q)∧(~r→q) | [(p∧~q)∧(~r→q)]⇒q |
|---|---|---|---|---|---|---|---|---|
| T | T | T | F | F | F | T | F | T |
| T | T | F | F | T | F | T | F | T |
| T | F | T | T | F | T | T | T | F |
| T | F | F | T | T | T | F | F | T |
| F | T | T | F | F | F | T | F | T |
| F | T | F | F | T | F | T | F | T |
| F | F | T | T | F | F | T | F | T |
| F | F | F | T | T | F | F | F | T |

*The argument is not valid.*

In Questions 7–9, an argument is given. Using Questions 2–6 as a model, assign letters to each of the simple statements in the argument, write the argument in symbols, then use a truth table to decide if it's valid.

**7.** I'll take the job if it meets my salary requirements or offers rapid advancement.

The salary they're offering is way too low.

So, I'm not taking the job.

*p = I'll take the job, q = salary meets my requirements, r = job offers rapid advancement*

*(q ∨ r) → p; ~q; ∴ ~p*

| p | q | r | ~p | ~q | q∨r | (q∨r)→p | [(q∨r)→p]∧~q | [((q∨r)→p)∧(~q)]⇒~p |
|---|---|---|---|---|---|---|---|---|
| T | T | T | F | F | T | T | F | T |
| T | T | F | F | F | F | F | F | T |
| T | F | T | F | T | F | T | T | F |
| T | F | F | F | T | F | T | T | F |
| F | T | T | T | F | T | F | F | T |
| F | T | F | T | F | F | T | F | T |
| F | F | T | T | T | F | T | T | T |
| F | F | F | T | T | F | T | T | T |

*The argument is not valid.*

## 7-4  Applications

Name _____

8. If you text while driving, you're endangering other drivers. Either you endanger other drivers, or you think you're invincible. That means that if you think you're invincible, you won't text and drive.

$p =$ you text while driving, $q =$ you endanger other drivers, $r =$ you think you're invincible

$p \rightarrow q$;   $q \vee r$;   $\therefore r \rightarrow \sim p$

| $p$ | $q$ | $r$ | $\sim p$ | $p \rightarrow q$ | $q \vee r$ | $r \rightarrow \sim p$ | $(p \rightarrow q) \wedge (q \vee r)$ | $[(p \rightarrow q) \wedge (q \vee r)] \Rightarrow (r \rightarrow \sim p)$ |
|---|---|---|---|---|---|---|---|---|
| T | T | T | F | T | T | F | T | F |
| T | T | F | F | T | T | T | T | T |
| T | F | T | F | F | T | F | F | T |
| T | F | F | F | F | F | T | F | T |
| F | T | T | T | T | T | T | T | T |
| F | T | F | T | T | T | T | T | T |
| F | F | T | T | T | T | T | T | T |
| F | F | F | T | T | F | T | F | T |

The argument is not valid.

9. I'm changing my major if and only if I get an A in biology this semester. I'll pass that class, or I won't change my major. Therefore, if I changed my major, then I passed the class.

$p =$ I change my major, $q =$ I get an A in biology this semester, $r =$ I pass biology this semester

$p \leftrightarrow q$;   $r \vee \sim p$;   $p \rightarrow r$

| $p$ | $q$ | $r$ | $\sim p$ | $p \leftrightarrow q$ | $r \vee \sim p$ | $p \rightarrow r$ | $(p \leftrightarrow q) \wedge (r \vee \sim p)$ | $[(p \leftrightarrow q) \wedge (r \vee \sim p)] \Rightarrow (p \rightarrow r)$ |
|---|---|---|---|---|---|---|---|---|
| T | T | T | F | T | T | T | T | T |
| T | T | F | F | T | F | F | F | T |
| T | F | T | F | F | T | T | F | T |
| T | F | F | F | F | F | F | F | T |
| F | T | T | T | F | T | T | F | T |
| F | T | F | T | F | T | T | F | T |
| F | F | T | T | T | T | T | T | T |
| F | F | F | T | T | T | T | T | T |

The argument is valid.

## 7-4 Applications

Name _____

In Questions 10–13, an argument is given. Write the argument in symbols, then decide whether the argument is valid by using the common forms of valid arguments and fallacies.

**10.** If background checks for buying guns are expanded, it will be harder for felons to obtain guns. It won't be harder for felons to obtain guns. Therefore, background checks won't be expanded.

$p =$ background checks are expanded, $q =$ it will be harder for felons to obtain guns

$p \rightarrow q; \sim q; \therefore \sim p$

This is the law of contraposition and is valid.

**11.** If the interest rate goes any lower, I'll pull my money out of savings and bury it in my backyard. The interest rate didn't go lower, so I won't pull my money out of savings and bury it in the backyard.

$p =$ interest rate goes lower, $q =$ bury money in backyard

$p \rightarrow q; \sim p; \therefore \sim q$

This is the fallacy of the inverse and is not valid.

**12.** I majored in culinary arts or I got a job working in an art gallery after graduation. I didn't get a job working in an art gallery, so I majored in culinary arts.

$p =$ majored in culinary arts, $q =$ got job working in art gallery

$p \vee q; \sim q; \therefore p$

This is the law of disjunctive syllogism, and is valid.

**13.** If the climate continues to warm, the polar ice caps will melt. If the polar ice caps melt, New Orleans will be under water. So if the climate continues to warm, New Orleans will be under water.

$p =$ climate continues to warm, $q =$ polar ice caps melt, $r =$ New Orleans under water

$p \rightarrow q; q \rightarrow r; \therefore p \rightarrow r$

This is the law of syllogism and is valid.

# Unit 8
# How Do You Measure Up?

© Panoramic Images/Getty Images

## Outline

Lesson 1: Going to Great Lengths (Unit Conversion, Length, and the Metric System)

Lesson 2: New Dimensions (Measuring Area, Volume, and Capacity)

Lesson 3: Weighty Matters (Units of Weight and Temperature)

Lesson 4: Stocking the Shelves (Evaluating Efficiency in Packaging)

# Math In    Travel

I love my house, I love my yard, I love my neighborhood, and I REALLY love my dogs. But I still get the urge to travel—a lot. Traveling to new cities, basking in new surroundings, experiences, cultures—there's just something magical about travel that makes you want to do it more and more once you catch the bug. When you start to travel outside of the States, you realize that a lot of things are different, among them the way that many things are measured.

To measure something means to assign a number that represents its size. In fact, measurement might be the most common use of numbers in everyday life. Numbers are used to measure heights, weights, distances, grades, weather, sizes of homes, capacities of bottles and cans, and much more. Even in our monetary system, we're using numbers to measure sizes: little ones, like the cost of a candy bar, and big ones, like an annual salary.

The one thing that every measurement has in common is that it's good for absolutely nothing unless there are units attached to the number. If a friend asks you how far you live from campus and you answer "three," at best they'll look at you funny and cautiously back away. An answer like that is meaningless because without units, there's no context to describe what the number represents. And that's entirely because there are many different units that can be used to describe similar measurements. That number 3 could mean 3 miles, kilometers, blocks, houses, even parsecs if you come from a galaxy far, far away.

In this unit, we'll study the different ways that things are measured in our world, with a special focus on the different units that are used. You probably have at least a passing familiarity with the metric system, since measurements in units like liters and kilometers are becoming more common. When you gather information of interest to you, you don't always get to choose the units that the information is provided in, so the ability to convert measurements from one unit to another is a particularly useful skill in the information age.

One obvious application of this skill comes into play when traveling outside the United States. Most countries use the metric system almost exclusively, meaning that to understand various bits of information, you need to be able to interpret measurements in an unfamiliar system. Suppose that you and your sweetie are planning a dream vacation to Australia. Who wouldn't want to go to a place where you might see a kangaroo hop across the road in front of you? Seriously, it happens all the time. The little guys are like squirrels over there. The following questions might be of interest to you on the trip. By the time you finish this unit, you'll be able to answer these and other questions, making you a more well-informed traveler.

1. A check of a tourist website informs you that the temperature is expected to range from 24° to 32° Celsius. How should you pack?

2. The airline that will fly you down under allows a maximum of 30 kilograms for each piece of luggage. If your empty suitcase weighs 4 pounds, how many pounds can you pack into it?

3. The resort you will be staying at is 4.2 kilometers from the airport and 0.6 kilometers from downtown. Can you walk downtown? And how long will it take to drive your rental car from the airport at 35 miles per hour?

4. The gas station closest to the airport caters to many tourists, so it has prices listed in both Australian and American dollars. Gas costs $1.43 per liter (in U.S. dollars). If you use the car's entire 16-gallon tank, how much will it cost to refill?

5. At the time of this writing, one Australian dollar is worth 0.72 U.S. dollars. If the resort quotes you a price of 289 dollars per night Australian, how much are you paying in American dollars?

# Lesson 8-1  Prep Skills

This is a short review of skills that will come in handy in the next lesson. In each case, answer the question, then rate your confidence level by checking one of the boxes. If you feel like you're struggling with these skills, consult the online resources provided by your instructor for extra practice.

### SKILL 1: PERFORM BASIC UNIT CONVERSIONS

Convert each measurement below to the new unit requested.

1. 27 hours to minutes

2. 410 minutes to hours

3. 97 inches to feet

4. 12.3 feet to inches

5. 87 dollars to cents

6. 1,493 cents to dollars

### SKILL 2: DIVIDE OUT COMMON FACTORS

Simplify each fraction by dividing out common factors.

7. $\dfrac{4x}{x}$

8. $\dfrac{2y}{12y}$

9. $\dfrac{40xyz}{8xy}$

# Lesson 8-1   **Going to Great Lengths** (Unit Conversion, Length, and the Metric System)

**LEARNING OBJECTIVES**

☐ 1. Understand the importance of units in measurement.

☐ 2. Understand how dimensional analysis makes converting units easy.

☐ 3. Identify the key components of the metric system.

☐ 4. Convert between U.S. and metric units of length, and describe perspective on the size of these measurements.

*There is nothing more tragic than to find an individual bogged down in the length of life, devoid of breadth.*

—Martin Luther King, Jr.

© JGI/Jamie Grill/Blend Images LLC RF

As I reflect back on the history of numeracy in my family (the human family, that is), counting up objects certainly came first. But I bet that second place goes to measuring the lengths of objects. In studying length, we're looking back into our distant past—the earliest units of measure. The fact that lengths can vary so widely describes why different units of measurement are necessary: while inches are perfectly good for measuring your waistline, the Earth is about 5,892,000,000,000 inches from the Sun. Clearly, a larger unit of measure would be a better idea for such a huge distance. In learning how to convert distances from one unit to another, you'll actually learn something much more valuable: a basic approach that can be used to convert any units of measure. Of course, it wouldn't be quantitative reasoning in our world if we didn't also study a variety of situations where this skill comes in handy.

**0.** After reading the opening paragraph, what do you think the main topic of this lesson will be?

## 8-1   Class

The units of length that are commonly used in the United States are the inch, foot, yard, and mile. These are part of the **English system of measurement,** which has been in use for a very, very long time. A list of basic conversion factors between these units of measure is provided in the table below.

### Units of Length in the English System

12 inches (in.) = 1 foot (ft)

3 ft = 1 yard (yd)

5,280 ft = 1 mile (mi)

One way to use this information to convert between different units is multiplication or division.

**1.** To convert 8 yards to feet, we could use the fact that there are 3 feet in 1 yard and ____multiply____ 8 by 3 to get ____24____ feet.

**2.** To convert 564 inches to feet, we could use the fact that there are 12 inches in a foot and _____*divide*_____ by 12 to

get _____47_____ feet.

This works okay, but has one major drawback: it requires some careful thought to make sure you're not multiplying when you should divide or vice versa. You might not think that's a big deal when converting feet to yards, but how about inches to miles? When conversions get more complicated, a systematic approach really comes in handy.

That approach is provided by **dimensional analysis,** which is based on a fiendishly simple idea: if measurements in two different units represent the same actual length, like 1 yard and 3 feet, then a fraction formed from dividing those units is just a fancy way to say 1.

**3.** Start with the fact that 1 yd = 3 ft. Divide both sides of this equation by 3 ft and write the equivalent equation you have remaining. Think about what happens to the units.

$$\frac{1 \, yd}{3 \, ft} = \frac{3 \, ft}{3 \, ft} \Rightarrow \frac{1 \, yd}{3 \, ft} = 1$$

**4.** Start with the fact that 1 yd = 3 ft. Divide both sides of this equation by 1 yd and write the equivalent equation you have remaining.

$$\frac{1 \, yd}{1 \, yd} = \frac{3 \, ft}{1 \, yd} \Rightarrow \frac{3 \, ft}{1 \, yd} = 1$$

If all went well, you've proved that two different fractions involving feet and yards are both equal to 1. We call a fraction of this type a **conversion factor;** multiplying any measurement by a conversion factor won't change the size of the measurement because we're just multiplying by one. Our clever procedure for converting units will be to multiply by one or more conversion factors in a way that the units we don't want will divide out and leave behind the units we do want. Dimensional analysis is emphasized in the next several questions, but it will be useful in most of the problems in this entire unit. In case you didn't catch the significance: *Understanding dimensional analysis is essential for success in this unit.*

**5.** The height of Mount Everest is 29,035 feet. Write two conversion factors that compare feet and miles. Once you have one, the other will be its reciprocal.

$$\frac{5,280 \, ft}{1 \, mi} \quad and \quad \frac{1 \, mi}{5,280 \, ft}$$

**6.** Multiply the measurement 29,035 feet by EACH of the conversion factors from Question 5, and look carefully at the units. Which of the multiplications will divide out feet and leave behind miles?

$$29,035 \, ft \times \frac{5,280 \, ft}{1 \, mi} \qquad 29,035 \, ft \times \frac{1 \, mi}{5,280 \, ft}$$

The second one divides out feet and leaves behind miles.

© Pixtal/SuperStock RF

7. Complete the multiplication that converts 29,035 feet into miles, then congratulate yourself for successfully using dimensional analysis.

    *The height is almost exactly five and a half miles.*

> When students struggle with dimensional analysis, I often find that writing the original measurement as a fraction with denominator 1 helps. Try this with students who aren't getting it. That makes it look more like multiplying fractions.

## Did You Get It

Try this problem to see if you understand the concepts we just studied. The answer can be found at the bottom of the portfolio page.

1. Absolutely true story: I'm writing this question on an airplane on the way to Charlotte, NC, and according to the flight tracker on my American Airlines app, right now we're about 5.1 miles above the ground. Use dimensional analysis to find how many feet above ground we are. (I said it was a true story, not a good one.)

Sometimes we'll need to multiply by more than one conversion factor to complete a conversion. The distance by air from JFK airport to LaGuardia airport in New York is about 11 miles. How many inches is that?

8. Write a conversion factor that will convert from miles to feet. Think carefully about where to put the units you're trying to get rid of.

    $$\frac{5{,}280 \ ft}{1 \ mi}$$

9. Write a conversion factor that will convert from feet to inches.

    $$\frac{12 \ in.}{1 \ ft}$$

**Math Note**

Notice that we put the units we want to eliminate in the denominator, and the units we want to keep in the numerator. If you understand this simple idea, dimensional analysis will be a snap for you no matter how complicated the conversions might look.

10. Use the conversion factors from Questions 8 and 9, and show the work of dimensional analysis (including dividing away units) to find the distance from JFK airport to LaGuardia airport in inches.

    $$11 \ mi \times \frac{5{,}280 \ ft}{1 \ mi} \times \frac{12 \ in.}{1 \ ft} = 696{,}960 \ in.$$

We interrupt this lesson for a history lesson on measuring length. Why? Because it's kind of interesting, and there's nothing wrong with learning some of the history of a subject you're studying.

### A Brief History of Measuring Lengths

Nobody knows how and when human beings started measuring physical objects, but historians seem to be in general agreement that the earliest recorded measurements were lengths. In particular, they were based on parts of the human body. If you search the Internet for early units of measurement, the most common one you will find is the **cubit,** first used by the Egyptians around 5,000 years ago. The cubit was equal to the distance from a person's elbow to the outstretched middle finger. (If you try to measure something that way, make sure to stretch out your other fingers as well. That's funny if you think about it.) Other early units were the **palm** (the distance across the base of a person's four fingers) and the **digit** (the thickness of a person's middle finger).

The fact that these measurements were based on body parts leads us to believe that one of two things was true: either everyone was exactly the same size in ancient Egypt, or their units of measurement were pretty darn imprecise. Things got a little more specific sometime around the year 1100, when King Henry I of England declared that the distance from the tip of his nose to the end of his thumb would be known as a **yard.** (At least this distance was based on one specific person's physical size.) The oldest known yardstick still in existence, believed to have been made in 1445, is accurate to a modern yard within about one three-hundredths of an inch.

A couple hundred years later, King Edward I declared that one third of a yard should be called a **foot.** In 1595, Queen Elizabeth changed the length of a **mile** from the Roman tradition of 5,000 feet to the current 5,280 feet so that it was exactly 8 **furlongs.** (Perhaps she was a big fan of horse racing, which still uses furlongs.) Eventually, the English system of measurement became standard throughout the world. Of course, these units are still used in the United States today. The real irony? England has been officially using the metric system since 1965, which would be sort of like England deciding not to speak English anymore. Go figure. In fact, only three countries in the world have not officially adopted the metric system, which we'll study later in this lesson: The United States, Liberia, and Myanmar.

Now back to unit conversions. Dimensional analysis can also be used to convert more complicated units, like those for speed. This one you'll do with a little less guidance. Be sure to show the multiplication of conversion factors and dividing away of units.

© PhotoLink/Getty Images RF

11. A decent major league pitcher can throw a baseball 90 miles per hour. How fast is that in feet per second? (Hint: First use a conversion factor to eliminate miles from the numerator, then use another conversion factor or two to eliminate hours from the denominator.)

$$\frac{90\ mi}{hr} \times \frac{5{,}280\ ft}{1\ mi} \times \frac{1\ hr}{60\ min} \times \frac{1\ min}{60\ sec} = 132\frac{ft}{sec}$$

> Help students get started here by showing them how to write 90 mph as a fraction in this form.

### Did You Get It

Try this problem to see if you understand the concepts we just studied. The answer can be found at the bottom of the portfolio page.

2. Still on the plane, and it's NOT going the speed of sound. I'm a professor, not a test pilot. However, the speed of sound at sea level and room temperature is about 1,126 feet per second. How fast is that in miles per hour?

## 8-1 | Group

### The Metric System

If you grew up in the United States, you're probably perfectly happy with the English system of measurement. You've been using it your whole life, after all. But the truth is that it's not that great of a system because there's no rhyme or reason to it. Why is 12 inches a foot? Why is 5,280 feet a mile? They just are. Somebody decided, and that was that. The metric system, on the other hand, makes a bit more sense because the different units of measure are all related by powers of 10. We'll see exactly what that means after introducing the base units. The metric system uses three basic units of measure: the *meter*, the *liter*, and the *gram.*

   In this lesson, we'll study the **meter,** since it's the standard metric unit of length. One meter is a bit more than a yard, about 39.4 inches. The symbol for meter is "m." The basic unit for capacity (or volume) in the metric system is the **liter,** which is a little bit more than a quart. (You're probably familiar with 2-liter bottles of soda—that's close to a half gallon.) The symbol for liter is "L." The basic unit for measuring weight in the metric system is the **gram.** This is a very small unit—a nickel weighs about 5 grams. The symbol for gram is "g."

   Now back to other units in the metric system. All units other than the three basic units are based on multiples of the basic units, with those multiples all being powers of 10. For example, a standard unit of weight for people in the metric system is the kilogram: this is equal to 1,000 grams, and 1,000 is 10 raised to the third power. A commonly used unit of length for smaller measurements is the centimeter, which is one-hundredth of a meter. This is the key idea in understanding the metric system: *It's the prefix in front of the basic unit that determines the size.*

   The most common metric prefixes are listed in the table below.

| Prefix | Symbol | Meaning | |
|--------|--------|---------|---|
| kilo | k | 1,000 units | ⎫ |
| hecto | h | 100 units | ⎬ Bigger than the basic unit |
| deka | da | 10 units | ⎭ |
| | m, L, g | 1 unit | |
| deci | d | $\frac{1}{10}$ of a unit | ⎫ |
| centi | c | $\frac{1}{100}$ of a unit | ⎬ Smaller than the basic unit |
| milli | m | $\frac{1}{1,000}$ of a unit | ⎭ |

> **Math Note**
>
> Notice that the prefixes for each of the three most common metric units that are smaller than the basic unit all end in the letter i: deci-, centi-, and milli-.

The relationship between units in the metric system is a lot like the units used in our monetary system.

**1.** Complete the table to demonstrate this comparison for the base unit of meter.

| Metric Unit | kilometer | hectometer | dekameter | meter (base unit) | decimeter | centimeter | millimeter |
|-------------|-----------|------------|-----------|-------------------|-----------|------------|------------|
| **Meaning** | 1,000 meters | 100 meters | 10 meters | 1 meter | $\frac{1}{10}$ meter | $\frac{1}{100}$ meter | $\frac{1}{1,000}$ meter |
| **Monetary Comparison** | $1,000 | $100 | $10 | $1 | 10 cents | 1 cent | Doh! |

There are several ways to do conversions in the metric system. The easiest of them is to multiply or divide by powers of 10. As a review of why this is the easiest way (and for more practice on dimensional analysis), complete the conversions on this page using dimensional analysis without using a calculator. Use the fact that 1 m = 100 cm and 1 cm = 10 mm.

**2.** Find the length of a book in mm that is 25.4 cm long.

$$25.4 \text{ cm} \times \frac{10 \text{ mm}}{1 \text{ cm}} = \underline{\quad 254 \quad} \text{ mm}$$

**3.** Numerically, what calculation did you perform? What did that do to the decimal point?

*Multiplied by ten; decimal moved one place to the right.*

**4.** Find the diameter of a bolt in cm that is 3.25 mm across.

$$3.25 \text{ mm} \times \frac{1 \text{ cm}}{10 \text{ mm}} = \underline{\quad 0.325 \quad} \text{ cm}$$

**5.** Numerically, what calculation did you perform? What did that do to the decimal point?

*Divided by ten; decimal moved one place to the left.*

**6.** Find the height of a child in m who is 135 cm tall.

$$135 \text{ cm} \times \frac{1 \text{ m}}{100 \text{ cm}} = \underline{\quad 1.35 \quad} \text{ m}$$

**7.** Numerically, what calculation did you perform? What did that do to the decimal point?

*Divide by 100; decimal moved two places to the left.*

**8.** Find wheelbase of a car in cm that is 2.761 m.

$$2.761 \text{ m} \times \frac{100 \text{ cm}}{1 \text{ m}} = \underline{\quad 276.1 \quad} \text{ cm}$$

**9.** Numerically, what calculation did you perform? What did that do to the decimal point?

*Multiplied by 100; decimal moved two places to the right.*

**10.** To recap, each time you multiply by 10 the decimal point moves one place to the ____*right*____, and each time you divide by 10, the decimal point moves one place to the ____*left*____.

Rather than remembering or looking up a bunch of different conversion factors for all of the different metric prefixes, we simply move the decimal point based on the number of steps you move in the metric unit conversions table. Let's see how that works.

## Conversions Within the Metric System

- To change a larger unit to a smaller unit in the metric system, multiply by $10^n$, where $n$ is the number of steps that you move down in the diagram below.

- To change a smaller unit to a larger unit in the metric system, divide by $10^n$, where $n$ is the number of steps that you move up in the diagram below.

divide    kilo
          hecto
          deka
          base unit    multiply
          deci
          centi
          milli

Now let's put the box above into use. Two rival colleges have campuses that are 16.9 km apart. How far is that in centimeters?

**11.** How many steps apart are km and cm in the diagram?

Five

**12.** Based on their relative positions, should we multiply or divide to convert km into cm?

Multiply

**13.** What power of 10 should we multiply or divide by?

$10^5$

**14.** How many places should we move the decimal place, and in which direction?

Five places to the right.

**15.** So how many cm apart are the campuses?

1,690,000. I think we can all agree that's a whole lotta centimeters.

### Did You Get It

Try this problem to see if you understand the concepts we just studied. The answer can be found at the bottom of the portfolio page.

3. On a different plane now. Not the one I was supposed to be on, mind you, but that's a long story. Anyhow, the width of my seat is 28", which is 711.2 mm. How many dekameters is that?

---

**16.** A French dip sandwich from a certain fast-food chain contains a whopping 3,610 mg of sodium. If you ate that sandwich, you'd be ingesting way more than the recommended daily amount of sodium (2,300 mg) in one sandwich. How many grams over the recommended amount would you ingest if you ate that sandwich? Read the units in that question carefully, please.

*This is 1,310 mg over the allowance, which is 1.31 grams.*

Because most of the world uses the metric system while the United States uses the English system, it's often necessary to convert between the two systems. (This is especially true in the sciences, where the metric system is used almost exclusively.) We'll use dimensional analysis, along with the conversion factors for units of length listed below. Because we know dimensional analysis and how to convert metric units, we don't need an extensive list of conversion factors.

 **English-Metric Equivalents for Length**

1 in. = 2.54 cm

1 mi ≈ 1.61 km

**17.** Many road signs now list mileages in both miles and kilometers. This sign can be found on the way to my brother-in-law's house, just east of Louisville. (Hi Kevin.) How accurate is the conversion?

$$2 \text{ km} \cdot \frac{1 \text{ mi}}{1.61 \text{ km}} \approx 1.24 \text{ mi} \quad \text{Not bad!}$$

Courtesy of David Sobecki

18. On a stretch of highway, the posted speed limit is 70 miles per hour. Find the speed limit in kilometers per minute.

$$\frac{70 \; mi}{1 \; hr} \cdot \frac{1.61 \; km}{1 \; mi} \cdot \frac{1 \; hr}{60 \; min} \approx 1.88 \frac{km}{min}$$

Looking at a ruler that has both inches and centimeters on it is a good way to get a feel for the connection between them.

19. Notice that 2 inches is just about 5 centimeters. Look carefully. Would you say that 2 inches is a little more or a little less than 5 cm?

    It's a bit more than 5 cm.

20. Use dimensional analysis to find more precisely how many centimeter are equal to 2 inches.

$$2 \; in. \cdot \frac{2.54 \; cm}{1 \; in.} = 5.08 \; cm$$

21. A decent-sized praying mantis is 96.3 millimeters long. Convert this length to inches.

$$96.3 \; mm \cdot \frac{1 \; cm}{10 \; mm} \cdot \frac{1 \; in.}{2.54 \; cm} \approx 3.79 \; in.$$

22. I've never driven a Tesla model S, but I sat in one a few minutes ago. And if you haven't, you really should because it's super-cool. It's also 4.98 m long. Convert this length to feet.

$$4.98 \; m \cdot \frac{100 \; cm}{1 \; m} \cdot \frac{1 \; in.}{2.54 \; cm} \cdot \frac{1 \; ft}{12 \; in.} \approx 16.3 \; ft$$

### Did You Get It

Try these problems to see if you understand the concepts we just studied. The answers can be found at the bottom of the portfolio page.

4.  The Airbus A320 that I'm in right now is 123 feet, 3 inches long. How many centimeters is that?

5.  The wingspan is 35.8 meters, which is how many inches?

We began this lesson by explaining that lots of different units of length exist because there are so many different-sized objects in our world. Let's use this concept to close the lesson and see if you have some perspective on lengths in the metric system. In Questions 23–27, decide if millimeters, centimeters, meters, or kilometers would be the most appropriate unit for describing each length.

**23.** The height of an elephant.

*Meters would seem most reasonable.*

**24.** The height of the letters in the Did You Get It header above.

*Millimeters*

**25.** The height reached by a typical hot air balloon flight.

*I'm not an expert on ballooning, but I'd say meters.*

**26.** The height reached by a typical rocket launch.

*Definitely kilometers.*

**27.** The thickness of the heaviest book you own.

*If it's a comic book, millimeters. If it's War and Peace, centimeters.*

## 8-1 Portfolio

Name _____

Check each box when you've completed the task. Remember that your instructor will want you to turn in the portfolio pages you create.

### Technology

1. ☐ We developed a method for converting units within the metric system by multiplying or dividing by an appropriate power of ten. These divisions can be programmed into a spreadsheet that will use formulas to perform the conversions. You should be able to enter any length in meters, and have the sheet automatically convert it to mm, cm, dm, dam, hm, and km. A template to help you get started can be found in the online resources for this lesson.

2. ☐ Actually, why quit there? You can also program in formulas that will convert that length in meters to inches, feet, yards, and miles as well. Same template, more units!

### Online Practice

1. ☐ Include any written work from the online assignment along with any notes or questions about this lesson's content.

### Applications

1. ☐ Complete the applications problems.

### Reflections

Type a short answer to each question.

1. ☐ What is a conversion factor in measurement?
2. ☐ Explain how we use conversion factors in dimensional analysis to convert units.
3. ☐ What role do prefixes play in the metric system?
4. ☐ Take another look at your answer to Question 0 at the beginning of this lesson. Would you revise your answer now that you've completed the lesson? How would you summarize the topic of this lesson now?
5. ☐ What questions do you have about this lesson?

### Looking Ahead

1. ☐ Complete the Lesson 8-2 Prep Skills and read the opening paragraph in Lesson 8-2 carefully, then answer Question 0 in preparation for that lesson.

### Answers to "Did You Get It?"

**1.** 26,928 feet    **2.** 767.7 mi/hr    **3.** 0.07112 dam    **4.** 3,756.66 cm
**5.** 1,409.45 in.

## 8-1   Applications

Name _____

1. A professional basketball court is 94 feet long. Find the length in both inches and meters.

$$94 \text{ ft} \cdot \frac{12 \text{ in.}}{1 \text{ ft}} = 1{,}128 \text{ in.} \qquad 1{,}128 \text{ in.} \cdot \frac{2.54 \text{ cm}}{1 \text{ in.}} \cdot \frac{1 \text{ m}}{100 \text{ cm}} = 28.6512 \text{ m}$$

2. An official Olympic-sized swimming pool is 50 meters long. How many yards long is it? How many feet would you swim in a 20-lap race?

$$50 \text{ m} \cdot \frac{100 \text{ cm}}{1 \text{ m}} \cdot \frac{1 \text{ in}}{2.54 \text{ cm}} \cdot \frac{1 \text{ yd}}{36 \text{ in.}} \approx 54.68 \text{ yd}$$

$$54.68 \text{ yd} \cdot \frac{3 \text{ ft}}{1 \text{ yd}} = 164.04 \text{ ft} \cdot 20 = 3{,}280.8 \text{ ft}$$

The nutrition information label shown is for a generic brand of peanut butter. Use it to answer Questions 3–6.

| Serving Size 32g | | |
| --- | --- | --- |
| **Amount Per Serving** | | |
| **Calories** 188 | Calories from Fat 135 | |
| | | **% Daily Value*** |
| **Total Fat** 16g | | 25% |
| Saturated Fat 3g | | 17% |
| Trans Fat 0g | | |
| **Cholesterol** 0mg | | 0% |
| **Sodium** 147mg | | 6% |
| **Total Carbohydrate** 6g | | 2% |
| Dietary Fiber 2g | | 8% |
| Sugars 3g | | |
| **Protein** 8g | | |
| Vitamin A 0% | • Vitamin C | 0% |
| Calcium 1% | • Iron | 3% |

3. How many milligrams of peanut butter make up one serving?

milli- is 3 steps from base unit, and is a smaller unit, so multiply 32 g by 1,000: 32,000 mg.

4. How many dekagrams of fat are there in one serving?

deka- is 1 step from base unit, and is a bigger unit, so divide 16 g by 10: 1.6 dag.

5. Based on the % daily value listed, how many centigrams of saturated fat are you recommended to ingest per day?

3 g is 17% of recommended, so 3/0.17 ≈ 17.6 grams recommended per day, which is 17,600 cg.

6. How many kilograms of carbohydrates are you recommended to take in per year?

6 g is 2% of daily amount so daily amount is 300 g, which makes the annual amount 365(300 g) = 109,500 g. This is 109.5 kg.

## 8-1 Applications

Name _____

7. The screen dimensions of a 70-inch HDTV are 34.3 in. high and 61.0 inches wide. Find the dimensions in centimeters and feet.

$$34.3 \text{ in.} \cdot \frac{2.54 \text{ cm}}{1 \text{ in.}} \approx 87.122 \text{ cm}; \quad 61.0 \text{ in.} \cdot \frac{2.54 \text{ cm}}{1 \text{ in.}} \approx 154.94 \text{ cm}$$

$$34.3 \text{ in.} \cdot \frac{1 \text{ ft}}{12 \text{ in.}} \approx 2.86 \text{ ft}; \quad 61.0 \text{ in.} \cdot \frac{1 \text{ ft}}{12 \text{ in.}} \approx 5.08 \text{ ft}$$

8. In April of 2015, a magnetic levitation train in Japan broke the speed record for a train, reaching a top speed of 603 kilometers per hour. How many miles can that baby go in an hour? How many feet in a minute?

$$\frac{603 \text{ km}}{1 \text{ hr}} \cdot \frac{1 \text{ mi}}{1.61 \text{ km}} \approx 374.53 \frac{\text{mi}}{\text{hr}}$$

$$\frac{374.53 \text{ mi}}{1 \text{ hr}} \cdot \frac{5,280 \text{ ft}}{1 \text{ mi}} \cdot \frac{1 \text{ hr}}{60 \text{ min}} = 32,958.64 \frac{\text{ft}}{\text{min}}$$

In this lesson, we studied metric prefixes from milli- (one-thousandth) up to kilo- (thousands). There are, however, many other prefixes. For example, mega- refers to millions ($10^6$), giga- is billions ($10^9$), and micro- is one-millionths ($10^{-6}$).

9. In the movie *Back to the Future*, 1.21 gigawatts of power were needed to send the time machine, well, back to the future. How many watts is this?

*1.21 billion, or 1,210,000,000 watts*

10. The average cell in a human body is about 10 micrometers wide. How many millimeters is that?

*mm is one-thousandth of a meter, and micrometer is one-millionth, so 10 micrometers is 0.01 mm.*

11. The current largest cruise ship in the world weighs 205,930 megagrams. How heavy is that in pounds? (One kilogram is 2.2 pounds.)

*To get to kg multiply by $10^3$, so 205,930,000 kg.*

$$205,930,000 \text{ kg} \cdot \frac{2.2 \text{ lb}}{1 \text{ kg}} = 453,046,000 \text{ lb}$$

### Math Note

Interesting fact: anyone familiar with modern computer technology is comfortable with the term gigabytes. But when *Back to the Future* was made (1985), giga- was so uncommon as a prefix that it's consistently mispronounced in the movie (jiga, rather than giga) and NOBODY involved in production of the movie knew to correct the cast.

# Lesson 8-2   Prep Skills

This is a short review of skills that will come in handy in the next lesson. In each case, answer the question, then rate your confidence level by checking one of the boxes. If you feel like you're struggling with these skills, consult the online resources provided by your instructor for extra practice.

### SKILL 1: USE DIMENSIONAL ANALYSIS

1. Use dimensional analysis to convert 4 miles to yards.

2. Use dimensional analysis to convert 25 inches to centimeters.

3. Use dimensional analysis to convert 230 feet per minute into miles per hour.

### SKILL 2: PERFORM METRIC CONVERSIONS

4. How many milliliters are in 27 liters?

5. How many kilometers are in 347 dekameters?

6. How many centimeters are in 9,000 meters?

### SKILL 3: USE AREA AND VOLUME FORMULAS

7. What is the area of a square with sides that are 4 ft long?

8. What is the volume of a cube with sides that are 1.3 in. long?

# Lesson 8-2 **New Dimensions** (Measuring Area, Volume, and Capacity)

## LEARNING OBJECTIVES

☐ 1. Understand the difference between unit conversions for length, and unit conversions for area and volume.

☐ 2. Convert area and volume measurements within the U.S. system, and describe perspective on sizes of these measurements.

☐ 3. Convert area and volume measurements between the U.S. and metric systems, and describe perspective on sizes of these measurements.

*Like gods, we have created a new universe called cyberspace that contains great good and ominous evil. We do not know yet if this new dimension will produce more monsters than marvels, but it is too late to go back.*
—David Horsey

© Trinette Reed/Blend Images LLC RF

It made perfect sense to begin our study of measurement with length, since that's probably the earliest and most basic form of measuring stuff. But units of length have a serious limitation: they can only be used to measure things in one dimension, and this isn't a cartoon: we all live in a three-dimensional world. If you're looking to buy a house, you might be somewhat interested to know that it's 52 feet long, but you'd surely be a lot more interested to know that it has 2,100 square feet of floor space. If you're looking to buy paint for your bedroom, knowing that the walls are eight feet high won't help a whole lot if you don't also know the length, which would then allow you to find area. How much water does a six-foot-deep swimming pool hold? There's no way to tell—to find the capacity, you need a lot more than just the depth. In order to measure things in our three-dimensional world, we'll become experts at working with area (two dimensions), volume, and capacity (both three dimensions.) And not surprisingly, given the name, we'll find dimensional analysis to be particularly helpful. Don't you just love it when things make sense?

**0.** After reading the opening paragraph, what do you think the main topic of this lesson will be?

> In the study of conversion, we've chosen to provide as few conversion factors as possible and use dimensional analysis to create others. We feel like that's really good practice in problem solving. If desired, you can let students know that they can easily look up a more extensive list of conversion factors on the Internet.

## 8-2 Class

### Conversions of Area

Units of length are also called linear units, because they are used to measure along a line. The units used to measure the size of an object in two dimensions are called square units. They are based on a very simple idea: one square unit is defined to be the area of a square that is one unit long on each side. For example, a square inch is the area of a square that is 1 inch on each side, as shown in the really lame figure below.

1 in.
1 in.    1 in.
1 in.

1. Write the formula for the area of a square.

   $A = l^2$, where $l$ is the length of the sides.

   > This is a great place to remind students that it's important to describe what any variables represent when writing a formula.

2. Use this formula to write and simplify the calculation (including units) to find the area of the square on the previous page.

   $A = (1 \text{ in.})^2 = 1 \text{ in.}^2$

3. From algebra, how would we simplify the expression $(1x)(1x)$?

   $x^2$

4. Describe the connection between your answers to Questions 2 and 3.

   When doing an area calculation with inches as units, you can multiply inches times inches to get inches$^2$ just like you multiply variables.

   ## Math Note

   You can write in.$^2$ or sq. in., but in either case we pronounce it "square inches."

Continuing our course-long philosophy that understanding is ALWAYS better than just knowing, the point of Questions 1–4 was giving you a fundamental understanding of why it makes perfect sense to measure area in square units. Once we're comfortable with that idea, we define the area of other figures to be the number of square units that will fit inside the figure.

For example, the rectangle in the next figure is 3 inches by 5 inches, and we can see that ____15____ one-inch by one-inch squares will fit inside. So its area is ____15____ square inches, which we abbreviate as ____15____ in.$^2$

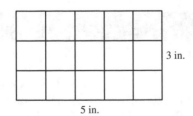

3 in.

5 in.

5. Write the formula for the area of a rectangle.

   $A = lw$, where $l$ is the length and $w$ is the width.

6. Use this formula to write and simplify the calculation (including units) to find the area of this rectangle.

   $A = (3 \text{ in.})(5 \text{ in.}) = 15 \text{ in.}^2$

**7.** From algebra, how would we simplify the expression $(3x)(5x)$? What does this have to do with anything?

*$15x^2$. Same idea again: we can treat the units in a calculation like variables in algebra to decide on the units for the result.*

**8.** At this point you should be pretty darn good at converting units of length. Next we'll turn our attention to units of area. Rather than learning new conversion factors, we'll use ones that we already know and just be clever. For example, we know of course that 1 ft = 12 in. Square both sides of that equation and simplify the result, paying special attention to the units.

*$(1 \text{ ft})^2 = (12 \text{ in.})^2$*

*$1 \text{ ft}^2 = 144 \text{ in.}^2$*

**9.** The figure below illustrates graphically why 1 square foot is ___*144*___ square inches. 1 square foot is made up of ___*144*___ one square inch boxes.

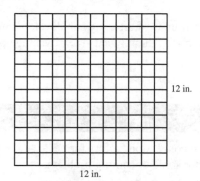

12 in.

12 in.

**10.** A 52-in. wide-screen TV has a screen area of 1,064 in.² How many square feet is that? First, use the fact that 1 ft² = 144 in.² to multiply the area by a conversion factor that will eliminate the inch units. For now, just write the multiplication, don't perform it.

*$1{,}064 \text{ in.}^2 \cdot \dfrac{1 \text{ ft}^2}{144 \text{ in.}^2}$*

**11.** Do the units work out the way they are supposed to? If so, complete the conversion.

*The units work out to be square feet as planned, and the result is 7.39 ft².*

12. A 60-in. wide-screen TV has a screen area of 1,546 in.$^2$ How many square feet is that? Use the fact that 1 ft = 12 in. and write a conversion factor that will eliminate the inch units.

$$1{,}546 \text{ in.}^2 \times \frac{1 \text{ ft}}{12 \text{ in.}}$$

13. The units don't work out quite right, do they? What if we multiply by that same conversion factor again? Give it a try, and if the units work out right, complete the conversion.

$$1{,}546 \text{ in.}^2 \times \frac{1 \text{ ft}}{12 \text{ in.}} \times \frac{1 \text{ ft}}{12 \text{ in.}} \approx 10.74 \text{ ft.}^2$$

---

## Did You Get It

Try this problem to see if you understand the concepts we just studied. The answer can be found at the bottom of the portfolio page.

1. A 32-in. wide-screen TV has screen area 3.05 ft$^2$. How many square inches is that?

---

The point of the last few questions is that there are two ways that we can convert units of area: we can develop new conversion factors, or we can use the ones for length that we already know, and just multiply by them twice. The advantage of the second approach is that it requires remembering less information.

## 8-2 Group

There's one very old measure of area that's still in common use that we'll need conversion factors for because it's not based on squared units of length: the acre. The conversions below will come in handy for some upcoming problems.

 **Conversion Factors for Area**

| 1 acre = 43,560 ft$^2$ | 1 acre ≈ 2.59 km$^2$ |
|---|---|
| 1 mi$^2$ = 640 acres | 1 km$^2$ ≈ 247.1 acres |

1. Find the area of Yellowstone National Park in square miles given that it has an area of 2,219,789 acres.

$$2{,}219{,}789 \text{ acres} \cdot \frac{1 \text{ mi}^2}{640 \text{ acres}} \approx 3{,}468.42 \text{ mi}^2$$

### Math Note

The acre was originally defined to be the size of a field that one man could plow in one day behind one ox.

**2.** An average of 2,191,781 square yards of carpet is discarded into landfills every day in the United States. How many acres would that carpet cover? You'll have to begin by converting square yards into a unit we know how to convert to acres.

$$2,191,781 \text{ yd}^2 \cdot \frac{3 \text{ ft}}{1 \text{ yd}} \cdot \frac{3 \text{ ft}}{1 \text{ yd}} \cdot \frac{1 \text{ acre}}{43,560 \text{ ft}^2} \approx 452.85 \text{ acres}$$

> You should consider demonstrating the multiplication by the repeated conversion factor here as $\frac{(1 \text{ yd})^2}{(3 \text{ ft})^2}$ for convenience. This especially comes in handy when we get to volume.

**3.** It's common to estimate an acre as being about the size of a football field. But how accurate is that comparison? An American football field is 100 yards long (without the end zones) and 160 feet wide. How close is the area to one acre?

$$A = 300 \text{ ft} \cdot 160 \text{ ft} = 48,000 \text{ ft}^2$$

$$48,000 \text{ ft}^2 \cdot \frac{1 \text{ acre}}{43,560 \text{ ft}^2} \approx 1.10 \text{ acres}$$

## Did You Get It

Try these problems to see if you understand the concepts we just studied. The answers can be found at the bottom of the portfolio page.

2.  The state of Delaware has an area of 2,490 square miles. How many acres is that?

3.  Promoters are planning to unfurl a giant flag covering an entire football field at a playoff game, including the end zones. The flag will cover an area of 1.32 acres. How many square yards of fabric will be needed?

**4.** Recall that 1 in. = 2.54 cm. Use this to build two conversion factors between feet and centimeters.

$$\frac{12 \text{ in.}}{12(2.54) \text{ cm}} \Rightarrow \frac{1 \text{ ft}}{30.48 \text{ cm}}, \frac{30.48 \text{ cm}}{1 \text{ ft}}$$

**5.** The plans for building a deck call for 28 square meters of deck boards. If you already have 300 square feet of boards on hand, do you have enough?

$$28 \text{ m}^2 \cdot \frac{100 \text{ cm}}{1 \text{ m}} \cdot \frac{100 \text{ cm}}{1 \text{ m}} \cdot \frac{1 \text{ ft}}{30.48 \text{ cm}} \cdot \frac{1 \text{ ft}}{30.48 \text{ cm}} \approx 301.4 \text{ ft}^2$$

*Bummer. You're a bit short.*

© Wests/iStockphoto.com RF

6. Prince Edward County in Ontario, Canada, has an area of 1,050.1 square kilometers. Is it larger or smaller than Butler County, Ohio, which is 470 square miles?

$$1,050.1 \text{ km}^2 \cdot \frac{1 \text{ mi}}{1.61 \text{ km}} \cdot \frac{1 \text{ mi}}{1.61 \text{ km}} \approx 405.1 \text{ mi}^2$$

It's smaller.

7. Find what percent larger the bigger county is.

$$\frac{470 - 405.1}{405.1} \approx 16\%$$

8. Find what percent smaller the smaller county is. (If you think this is the same question as number 7, think about it more carefully.)

$$\frac{405.1 - 470}{470} \approx -13.8\%$$

## Did You Get It

Try this problem to see if you understand the concepts we just studied. The answer can be found at the bottom of the portfolio page.

4. The campus of the University of Guelph in Ontario has an area of 4.1 km$^2$. How many square miles is that?

The next example shows a very common and very useful application of area conversions for homeowners.

9. Jane plans to have new carpet installed in her living room. She measures and finds that the room is 17 ft wide and 20 ft long. She found a carpet option she likes at two different stores pretty much equally well and decides she'll go with the cheaper one. The carpet she wants sells for $21 per square yard at one store and $2.50 per square foot from another store. Assuming she goes the cheaper route, how much will it cost to have the room carpeted?

The area of the room is 340 ft$^2$. So the second option costs $340 \text{ ft}^2 \cdot \frac{\$2.50}{1 \text{ ft}^2} = \$850$.

Convert to square yards: $340 \text{ ft}^2 \cdot \frac{1 \text{ yd}}{3 \text{ ft}} \cdot \frac{1 \text{ yd}}{3 \text{ ft}} \approx 37.78 \text{ yd}^2$. The first option costs

$37.78 \text{ yd}^2 \cdot \frac{\$21}{1 \text{ yd}^2} = \$793.38$, and that's the cheaper cost.

## Did You Get It

Try this problem to see if you understand the concepts we just studied. The answer can be found at the bottom of the portfolio page.

5. Find the cost of carpeting Jane's basement, which is 520 square feet, with cheaper carpet costing $14.50 per square yard.

## Conversions of Volume and Capacity

Just as the measurements of area are based on the two-dimensional square, measurements of volume are based on the three-dimensional analog, the cube. So volume is measured in cubic units.

In the English system, this is typically cubic inches (in.$^3$), cubic feet (ft$^3$), and cubic yards (yd$^3$). For example, 1 cubic foot consists of a cube whose measure is 12 inches on each side.

10. Write the formula for the volume of a cube.

$V = l^3$, where $l$ is the length of the sides.

11. Use this formula to write and simplify the calculation (including units) to find the volume of both cubes in the figure.

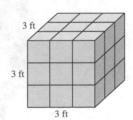

$V = (12 \text{ in.})^3 = 1{,}728 \text{ in.}^3$

$V = (3 \text{ ft})^3 = 27 \text{ ft}^3$

12. From algebra, how would we simplify the expression $(3x)(3x)(3x)$? What's the point?

The expression simplifies to $27x^3$, and one more time we see that we can multiply the numbers and treat the units like a variable.

Measures of volume also include measures of *capacity*. The **capacity** of a container is equal to the amount of fluid the container can hold. In the English system, capacity is measured in fluid ounces, pints, quarts, and gallons. The conversion factors for capacity are shown in the following box.

## Units of Capacity in the English System

1 pint (pt) = 16 fluid ounces (oz)
1 quart (qt) = 2 pints (pt)
1 gallon (gal) = 4 quarts (qt)

Since volume and capacity are both measures of size in three dimensions, we can compare the units. A cubic foot ($\text{ft}^3$) of water is about 7.48 gallons, and a cubic yard of water is about 202 gallons. If a gallon of water is poured into a container, it would take up about 231 cubic inches. Finally, a cubic foot of freshwater weighs about 62.5 pounds and a cubic foot of seawater weighs about 64 pounds. These measures are summarized in the next fancy colored box.

## Conversion Factors for Capacity in the English System

$1 \text{ ft}^3 \approx 7.48 \text{ gal}$

$1 \text{ yd}^3 \approx 202 \text{ gal}$

$1 \text{ gal.} \approx 231 \text{ in.}^3$

$1 \text{ ft}^3 \text{ freshwater} \approx 62.5 \text{ lb}$

$1 \text{ ft}^3 \text{ seawater} \approx 64 \text{ lb}$

**13.** A water tank at an aquarium has a volume of 3,000 cubic feet, and weighs 3,200 pounds empty. How many gallons of water will the tank hold, and now much will it weigh if it's filled with seawater?

$$3{,}000 \text{ ft}^3 \cdot \frac{7.48 \text{ gal}}{1 \text{ ft}^3} = 22{,}400 \text{ gal}; \quad 3{,}000 \text{ ft}^3 \cdot \frac{64 \text{ lb}}{1 \text{ ft}^3} = 192{,}000 \text{ lb}$$

It will hold 22,400 gallons and will weigh 195,200 pounds.

© Erica Simone Leeds RF

## Did You Get It

Try this problem to see if you understand the concepts we just studied. The answer can be found at the bottom of the portfolio page.

6. How many cubic feet of water are in a 100-gallon freshwater tank, and how much does that water weigh?

**14.** The team managers for a college football team carry quart bottles of water for the players to drink during breaks at practice. The bottles are stored in carrying racks that weigh 6 pounds and hold 16 bottles. How heavy (in pounds) is a rack when full? (Ignore the weight of the empty bottles.)

First find the weight of a quart of water (assuming that the team managers aren't giving the players seawater).

$$1 \text{ qt} \cdot \frac{1 \text{ gal}}{4 \text{ qt}} \cdot \frac{1 \text{ ft}^3}{7.48 \text{ gal}} \cdot \frac{62.5 \text{ lb}}{1 \text{ ft}^3} = 2.1 \text{ lb}$$

So 16 bottles will weigh 16(2.1) = 33.6 lb. Adding 6 pounds for the rack, the total weight is 39.6 lb.

In the metric system, a cubic centimeter consists of a cube whose measure is 1 centimeter on each side. Let's build a conversion factor to relate cubic meters and cubic centimeters.

**15.** Begin with the fact that there are ____*100*____ centimeters in 1 meter.

**16.** Write this as an equation.

$100\ cm = 1\ m$

**17.** Raise both sides of that equation to the ____*third*____ power to obtain cubic centimeters and cubic meters as units. Simplify the result.

$(100\ cm)^3 = (1\ m)^3 \Rightarrow 1,000,000\ cm^3 = 1\ m^3$

**18.** Does your answer match what's below the figure?

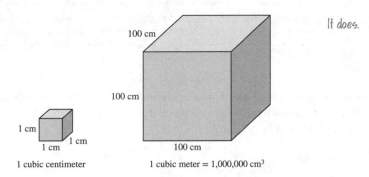

It does.

1 cubic centimeter        1 cubic meter = 1,000,000 cm³

The base unit for volume in the metric system is the liter, defined to be 1,000 cubic centimeters. Cubic centimeters are abbreviated cm³ or cc.

**19.** What are the dimensions of a cube with a volume of 1,000 cubic centimeters? Label those dimensions on the figure below.

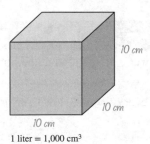

1 liter = 1,000 cm³

**20.** This definition of liter provides a simple and interesting connection between two of the base units in the metric system, meters and liters: 1 cubic centimeter is the same as ____*1*____ milliliter. (Remember what the prefix milli- means!)

**21.** A typical backyard inground pool has a volume of about 82.5 cubic meters. How many milliliters of water are needed to fill such a pool?

$$82.5 \, m^3 \cdot \frac{1,000,000 \, cm^3}{1 \, m^3} \cdot \frac{1 \, mL}{1 \, cm^3} = 82,500,000 \, mL$$

Courtesy of David Sobecki

We really only need one conversion factor for computing units of capacity between the English and metric systems, so that guy will get a colored box all to itself:

## English-Metric Conversion of Capacity

1 Liter ≈ 1.06 quarts

> Explain why we only need one conversion factor between English and metric: because we're so good at converting within each system.

**22.** The owner of a pool the size of the one in Question 21 has an algae problem (which I can assure you is about half as fun as a toothache). He buys a special algaecide, and the directions on the bottle instruct him to apply 16 oz for every 10,000 gallons of water in the pool. How much algaecide should he pour in?

$$82,500,000 \, mL \cdot \frac{1 \, L}{1,000 \, ml} \cdot \frac{1.06 \, qt}{1 \, L} \cdot \frac{1 \, gal}{4 \, qt} \cdot \frac{16 \, oz \, algecide}{10,000 \, gal} = 34.98 \, oz \, algaecide$$

## Did You Get It

Try this problem to see if you understand the concepts we just studied. The answer can be found at the bottom of the portfolio page.

   7. On average, 2,476,000 cubic centimeters of Coke are consumed worldwide every second. How many kiloliters is that? How many gallons?

## 8-2   Portfolio

Name _____

Check each box when you've completed the task. Remember that your instructor will want you to turn in the portfolio pages you create.

### Technology

**1.** ☐ Find a unit conversion website or app and use it to check your applications problems as you go. Don't use it to cheat: use it to CHECK. I can't speak for your professor, but there's a pretty good chance that if you don't show your work using dimensional analysis, you'll get no credit, fail out of school, and resort to a life of crime.

### Online Practice

**1.** ☐ Include any written work from the online assignment along with any notes or questions about this lesson's content.

### Applications

**1.** ☐ Complete the applications problems.

### Reflections

Type a short answer to each question.

**1.** ☐ Explain what "square units" mean. Use examples like "square inches" and "square miles."
**2.** ☐ We know that 1 yd = 3 ft. So how come 1 $yd^2 \neq$ 3 $ft^2$?
**3.** ☐ What's the connection between the base units of length and capacity in the metric system?
**4.** ☐ Describe three things in your house, dorm, or apartment that could be measured using cubic units, and explain why those units would be appropriate.
**5.** ☐ Take another look at your answer to Question 0 at the beginning of this lesson. Would you revise your answer now that you've completed the lesson? How would you summarize the topic of this lesson now?
**6.** ☐ What questions do you have about this lesson?

### Looking Ahead

**1.** ☐ Complete the Lesson 8-3 Prep Skills and read the opening paragraph in Lesson 8-3 carefully, then answer Question 0 in preparation for that lesson.

### Answers to "Did You Get It?"

**1.** 439.2 in.$^2$    **2.** 1,593,600 acres    **3.** 6,388.8 $yd^2$    **4.** 1.58 $mi^2$    **5.** $837.78
**6.** 13.37 $ft^3$, 835.625 lb    **7.** 2.476 kL, 654.09 gal

## 8-2  Applications

Name _____

In Questions 1–6, which unit would be most appropriate: acres, square miles, square feet, liters, milliliters, or kiloliters?

1. The amount of coffee served between noon and 1 P.M. at the nearest Starbucks

   *liters*

© McGraw-Hill Education

2. The average lot size in a middle-class community in Florida

   *square feet*

3. Key West, FL

   *square miles*

4. The daily dosage for an infant pain reliever

   *milliliters*

5. The nearest golf course

   *acres*

6. The amount of gas sold in a year at a fueling station in Toronto.

   *kiloliters*

7. When planning to build a concrete patio in his backyard, KJ lays out the space and finds that the dimensions he wants are 146 inches by 183 inches. First find the area in square inches, then use dimensional analysis to convert that to square feet.

   $146 \text{ in.} \cdot 183 \text{ in.} = 26{,}718 \text{ in.}^2; \ 26{,}718 \text{ in.}^2 \cdot \dfrac{(1 \text{ ft})^2}{(12 \text{ in.})^2} \approx 185.5 \text{ ft}^2$

8. KJ (Question 7) does some online research and finds that 4 inches is the standard thickness for pouring concrete in non-industrial applications. Convert this to feet and multiply by your answer to Question 7 to find the volume of concrete that he needs.

   $185.5 \text{ ft}^2 \cdot \dfrac{1}{3} \text{ ft} \approx 61.83 \text{ ft}^3$

## 8-2   Applications

Name _____

9. Feeling pretty darn proud of himself for doing all the calculations correctly, KJ calls a company that delivers pre-mixed concrete, and is asked how many cubic yards he needs. Rats! The volume he has is in cubic feet. Help this poor sap out, please. How many cubic yards does he need?

$$61.83 \text{ ft}^3 \cdot \frac{(1 \text{ yd})^3}{(3 \text{ ft})^3} = 2.29 \text{ yd}^3$$

10. Most companies will only allow you to order concrete by the full cubic yard. Find the relative difference between what KJ has to order and what he needs.

$$\frac{3 - 2.29}{2.29} \approx 0.31; \text{ he has to order 31\% more than he needs. Ouch.}$$

11. Each spring, my yard has about 900 square feet of space to cover with mulch. One year, trying to save some cash, I bought cheapo overseas mulch from a gas station, and the packaging said that each bag covered 1.8 square meters. How many bags did I need?

$$1 \text{ ft} = 12(2.54) \text{ cm} = 30.48 \text{ cm or } 0.3048 \text{ m}$$

$$900 \text{ ft}^2 \cdot \frac{(0.3048 \text{ m})^2}{(1 \text{ ft})^2} \approx 83.6 \text{ m}^2; \quad \frac{83.6 \text{ m}^2}{1.8 \text{ m}^2/\text{bag}} \approx 46.4 \text{ bags} \qquad \text{I needed to buy 47 bags.}$$

12. A store has 122 1-quart containers of milk, but the manager wants to pour the milk into gallon containers to sell at a higher price. How many gallon containers can the manager fill allowing 5% extra for spillage?

$$122 \text{ qt} \cdot \frac{1 \text{ gal}}{4 \text{ qt}} = 30.5 \text{ gal}; \quad 0.05 \cdot 30.5 \text{ gal} = 1.525 \text{ gal}; \quad 30.5 - 1.525 = 28.975 \text{ gal}$$

He or she can fill 29 gallon containers if willing to fudge the last 0.025 gallon. I'll go out on a limb and say that this particular manager would not have a problem with that.

13. Measure the room that your class meets in and find the area. Then write that area in square feet, square inches, square meters, and square centimeters.

Answers vary depending on your classroom. It would be a good idea to have students find the dimensions of your class at the end of this lesson. If your class is online, provide the dimensions of an average-sized classroom on your campus to the class.

## 8-2   Applications

Name _____

**14.** The Pentagon in suburban Washington, DC, has total floor area of just about 6,500,000 square feet. If a campus building consisted of 100 identical copies of your classroom, 8 restrooms, each with an area of 320 square feet, and 150 square meters of hallway, how would it compare in size to the Pentagon?

*Answers vary depending on your classroom.*

© Hisham F. Ibrahim/Getty Images RF

**15.** The capacity of a dump truck is listed by the manufacturer as 10 yd³. A construction site requires the removal of 200 m³ of dirt, and the contractor has three identical trucks. How many trips will each need to make?

*First, convert 10 cubic yards to cubic meters:*

$$10 \text{ yd}^3 \cdot \frac{(36 \text{ in.})^3}{(1 \text{ yd})^3} \cdot \frac{(2.54 \text{ cm})^3}{(1 \text{ in.})^3} \cdot \frac{(1 \text{ m})^3}{(100 \text{ cm})^3} \approx 7.65 \text{ m}^3$$

$7.65 \cdot 3 = 22.95 \text{ m}^3$ *per trip.* $\frac{200}{22.95} \approx 8.7$; *they'll need to make nine trips each.*

In 1970, the largest engine available on a Ford Mustang was a 429-cubic inch model that produced 375 horsepower. In 2016, you could top out at a 5-liter engine that produced 435 horsepower.

**16.** Which of the two cars had the bigger engine? How much bigger was that engine by percentage?

$$5 \text{ L} \cdot \frac{1,000 \text{ ml}}{1 \text{ L}} \cdot \frac{1 \text{ cm}^3}{1 \text{ ml}} \cdot \frac{(1 \text{ in.})^3}{(2.54 \text{ cm})^3} \approx 305.1 \text{ in.}^3$$ *The 1970 engine was bigger by 123.9 in.*³

$\frac{123.9}{305.1} \approx 0.406$, *so the 1970 engine was a bit more than 40% bigger.*

**17.** Rate each engine in terms of horsepower per cubic inch of volume.

*1970:* $\frac{375 \text{ hp}}{429 \text{ in.}^3} \approx 0.874 \frac{\text{hp}}{\text{in.}^3}$.

*2016:* $\frac{425 \text{ hp}}{305.1 \text{ in.}^3} \approx 1.393 \frac{\text{hp}}{\text{in.}^3}$     *Technology is an amazing thing.*

# Lesson 8-3   Prep Skills

This is a short review of skills that will come in handy in the next lesson. In each case, answer the question, then rate your confidence level by checking one of the boxes. If you feel like you're struggling with these skills, consult the online resources provided by your instructor for extra practice.

I KNOW IT    THINK SO    UNSURE    NO IDEA

### SKILL 1: USE DIMENSIONAL ANALYSIS

1. Use dimensional analysis to convert 134 yards to inches.

2. Use dimensional analysis to convert 111 centimeters to inches.

3. Use dimensional analysis to convert 4 miles into kilometers.

### SKILL 2: PERFORM METRIC CONVERSIONS

4. How many decigrams are in 84.3 milligrams?

5. How many hectometers are in 94 meters?

6. How many dekaliters are in 431.2 liters?

### SKILL 3: SUBSTITUTE VALUES INTO AN EXPRESSION

7. Evaluate the expression below for $x = 48$.

$$\frac{7}{4}x + 51$$

8. Evaluate the expression below for $t = -4.3$.

$$\frac{4}{7}(t - 40)$$

## Lesson 8-3   **Weighty Matters**  (Units of Weight and Temperature)

### LEARNING OBJECTIVES

☐  1. Convert weight and temperature measurements within the U.S. and metric systems.

☐  2. Convert weight and temperature measurements between the U.S. and metric systems.

☐  3. Demonstrate an understanding of the sizes of measurements in these systems.

*Patience and tenacity are worth more than twice their weight of cleverness.*
            —Thomas Huxley

According to the Nintendo Corporation, the weight limit for the fitness board that can be used with its Wii game system is 150 kg. If you're like the average American, you have no idea exactly how heavy you can be and still safely use the board. This, of course, is because you are so accustomed to weights being measured in pounds. But like any other form of measurement, there are a variety of units that can be used for weight. We will study them in this lesson, then conclude with a quick look at measuring temperatures, like the 150 or so degrees the guy in this picture must be feeling while working out in that getup.

**0.** After reading the opening paragraph, what do you think the main topic of this lesson will be?

© AFP/Getty Images

> No Class portion in this lesson. At this point, the students have learned all the skills they need. It's just applying them to different situations in this lesson.

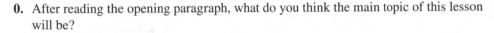

## 8-3   Group

### Conversions for Measures of Weight

Before we begin our study of measuring weight, there's a technical issue we need to deal with. We defined the gram as the standard unit of weight back in Lesson 8-1, but that's not quite accurate: the gram is a measure of *mass,* not weight. The weight of an object is the measure of the gravitational pull on it, so your weight can vary depending on where you are. Mass, on the other hand, is a constant measure of the physical size of an object regardless of location. Fifty kilograms is fifty kilograms, whether it's at the bottom of the ocean, the top of Mount Everest, or orbiting Earth in the International Space Station. While the gravitational pull of Earth can vary slightly depending on altitude, that variance is so tiny as to be mostly negligible anywhere on the planet. Since we all live on the Earth, in this book we'll consider mass and weight to be synonymous. If you don't live on Earth, my apologies, and take me to your leader.

In the English system, weight is most often measured in ounces, pounds, and tons. In the metric system, we know that the base unit for weight is the gram, but this is a very small unit—a dollar bill weighs about a gram, for example. So a more commonly used unit is the kilogram, which is 1,000 grams. There is also a metric equivalent of the ton: a metric ton, sometimes written "tonne," is 1,000 kg. The basic conversions for weight, along with the symbols used to represent units, are shown in the box at the top of the next page.

## Units of Weight

| English Units | Metric Units | English/Metric Conversions |
|---|---|---|
| 16 ounces (oz) = 1 pound (lb) | 1 kg = 1,000 g | 1 kg ≈ 2.2 lb |
| 2,000 lb = 1 ton (T) | 1,000 kg = 1 metric ton (t) | 1 oz ≈ 28 g |

Actually, the first equivalence under Metric Units above isn't necessary, as we've already studied conversions within the metric system. We gave you that one for free. For converting metric units of weight, we'll go back to moving decimal places based on the prefix.

For reference, here's a reminder on the order of metric prefixes going from largest (1,000) down to smallest (one-thousandth): kilo, hecto, deka, base unit, deci, centi, milli

In Questions 1–3, convert each measurement.

1. 150 grams of protein powder to milligrams

   *The prefix milli is three steps below the base unit, so multiply by 1,000 (or move the decimal three places right) to get 150,000 mg.*

### Math Note

Recall that when converting metric units, we multiply or divide by powers of 10. When moving three steps, we multiply or divide by $10^3$, or 1,000. When moving six steps, we multiply or divide by $10^6$, or 1,000,000.

2. 23 grams of salt to hectograms

   *The prefix hecto is two units above the base unit, so divide by 100 (or move the decimal two places left) to get 0.23.*

3. 3.5 kilograms of chicken to pounds

   $$3.5 \, kg \cdot \frac{2.2 \, lb}{1 \, kg} \cdot = 7.7 \, lb$$

## Did You Get It

Try these problems to see if you understand the concepts we just studied. The answers can be found at the bottom of the portfolio page.

1. One of the weight classes in Olympic boxing is 81 kg. How heavy is that in grams? Pounds?
2. An average golden retriever puppy weighs 12½ ounces at birth. How many grams does it weigh?

## Conversions for Measures of Temperature

Temperature is measured in the English system using degrees **Fahrenheit.** On this scale, water freezes at 32° and boils at 212°. The average temperature of the human body is 98.6°. In the metric system, temperatures are measured in degrees **Celsius** (also known as **centigrade**). Like all metric measurements, the Celsius scale is based on powers of 10 in some form: water freezes at 0° and boils at 100°. The average temperature of the human body is 37°.

4. How can you tell from the information in the paragraph above that a change of one degree on the Celsius scale is NOT the same as a change of one degree on the Fahrenheit scale?

*Because the difference between freezing and boiling is not consistent across the two scales.*

5. Compare the difference in temperature Fahrenheit between freezing and boiling water to the difference in temperature Celsius by forming a ratio (and reducing). This will tell you how many degrees Fahrenheit corresponds to one degree Celsius.

$$\frac{212 - 32}{100 - 0} = \frac{180}{100} = \frac{9}{5}$$

© McGraw-Hill Education/ Ken Cavanagh, photographer

Using what you learned in Question 5, it's not too difficult to develop formulas that convert between the two measures of temperature.

---

 **Fahrenheit-Celsius Conversions**

Converting from Celsius to Fahrenheit:

$$F = \frac{9}{5}C + 32$$

Converting from Fahrenheit to Celsius

$$C = \frac{5}{9}(F - 32)$$

---

6. In preparing for vacation, Randy and Catalina check the Internet and find that the average temperature over the next week at their destination is predicted to be 28° Celsius. Should they pack coats or bathing suits?

$$F = \frac{9}{5}(28) + 32 = 82.4°$$

*Swimsuits and sunblock it is!*

In case you're wondering why we didn't lead students through a development of the formulas: they require the assumption that the relationship is in fact linear. Of course this is true, but there's no way to know that in advance. If you'd prefer to use this as an exercise in linear modeling, we support you fully!

## Math Note

It would be nice if there were two separate symbols for degrees in the two systems. It would also be nice if I had a Ferrari. Alas, neither of those things was in the cards. With temperatures, you just have to pay attention to context.

7. A frozen pizza needs a 450° Fahrenheit oven to cook. Suppose you bought a cheap oven on eBay, and found that it had been scavenged from Romania, so the temperatures on the dial are Celsius. At what temperature should you set the oven?

$$C = \frac{5}{9}(450 - 32) \approx 232.2°$$

*You should set the temperature to about 230 degrees.*

---

## Did You Get It

Try these problems to see if you understand the concepts we just studied. The answers can be found at the bottom of the portfolio page.

3. The average high temperature for March in Moose Jaw, Saskatchewan, is −1° Celsius, which sounds dreadful at first if you're not a fan of the cold. Is it? Find the temperature on the Fahrenheit scale, then comment on how cool of a name Moose Jaw, Saskatchewan is.

4. The pizza box from Question 7 recommends 225° Fahrenheit for rewarming. Where should the dial be set for rewarming?

---

8. According to the Guinness Book of World Records, the largest healthy baby ever delivered weighed 360 ounces. How much did he weigh in pounds? How does this weight compare to the average weight of a newborn boy, which is 7.5 lb?

$$360 \ oz \cdot \frac{1 \ lb}{16 \ oz} = 22.5 \ lb$$

*This is exactly three times as heavy as the average newborn boy. Ouch.*

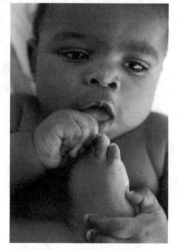

© Creatas/PictureQuest RF

9. Suppose the child was a little older and weighed 50 lb when his parents took him to the doctor, who read his temperature as 40° C. Does he have a fever? If so, how many degrees Fahrenheit above normal body temperature is the poor little guy? (Little being a relative term in this case.) Recall that 98.6° F is considered the normal body temperature for humans.

$$F = \frac{9}{5}(40) + 32 = 104°$$

*Yes, that is one sick little fella: 5.4° above normal.*

**10.** If he has a fever, the recommended dose is 15 mg of acetaminophen per kg of body weight. If there are 160 mg of acetaminophen in 5 ml of children's Tylenol, how many ml of children's Tylenol should the child receive?

$$50 \text{ lb} \cdot \frac{1 \text{ kg}}{2.2 \text{ lb}} \cdot \frac{15 \text{ mg acetaminophen}}{1 \text{ kg}} \cdot \frac{5 \text{ ml Tylenol}}{160 \text{ mg acetaminophen}} \approx 10.7 \text{ ml Tylenol}$$

> This problem can be solved in stages, but it's a GREAT example of the power of dimensional analysis to see it solved all in one calculation. Emphasize that the units do all of the work in deciding how to do the calculation.

**11.** If the entire bottle of liquid children's Tylenol contains 4 fluid ounces, how many mg of acetaminophen are in the bottle? How many grams? How many kilograms?

$$4 \text{ oz} \cdot \frac{1 \text{ qt}}{32 \text{ oz}} \cdot \frac{1 \text{ L}}{1.06 \text{ qt}} \cdot \frac{1,000 \text{ ml}}{1 \text{ L}} \cdot \frac{160 \text{ mg acetaminophen}}{5 \text{ ml}} \approx 3,773.6 \text{ mg acetaminophen}$$

This is 3.7736 g, or 0.0037736 kg.

---

## Did You Get It

Try these problems to see if you understand the concepts we just studied. The answers can be found at the bottom of the portfolio page.

5. How many ounces is a 12-pound bowling ball?

6. The temperature in a bowling alley is important for consistent lane conditions. At 74°F, what is the equivalent temperature in Celsius?

---

**12.** An empty Boeing 747 weighs about 175 tons. How much does it weigh in ounces?

$$175 \text{ T} \cdot \frac{2,000 \text{ lb}}{1 \text{ T}} \cdot \frac{16 \text{ oz}}{1 \text{ lb}} = 5,600,000 \text{ oz}$$

© Royalty-Free/Corbis

**13.** If this same 747 burns about 10 tons of fuel per hour when at cruising altitude, determine the number of gallons per minute this jet consumes (assuming jet fuel weighs about 6.8 lb per gallon).

$$\frac{10 \text{ T}}{1 \text{ hr}} \cdot \frac{2,000 \text{ lb}}{1 \text{ T}} \cdot \frac{1 \text{ gal}}{6.8 \text{ lb}} \cdot \frac{1 \text{ hr}}{60 \text{ min}} \approx 49 \frac{\text{gal}}{\text{min}}$$

> Point out to students that it is ABSOLUTELY silly to weigh a 747 in ounces. The point of questions like this is reminding them why it's so useful to be able to measure things in many different units.

**14.** At \$4.55 per gallon for jet fuel, how much will fuel cost for a 4-hour flight?

$$49 \frac{gal}{min} \cdot 240 \ min \cdot \frac{\$4.55}{1 \ gal} \approx \$53,508$$

**15.** A 747 can carry up to 467 passengers. How much would each have to pay just to cover fuel costs for the flight?

$$\frac{\$53,508}{467 \ passengers} \approx \$114.58 \ per \ passenger$$

**16.** Megan decides that she absolutely will not go to Florida for spring break unless she loses 15 pounds in the next 3 months. She finds an advertisement online for a British weight loss system that guarantees loss of 3 kg per month. If that claim is true, will she reach her goal?

$$\frac{3 \ kg}{1 \ month} \cdot \frac{2.2 \ lb}{1 \ kg} \cdot 3 \ months = 19.8 \ lb$$

If the claim is true (and that's a very big if), Megan should start packing for her trip.

## Did You Get It

Try these problems to see if you understand the concepts we just studied. The answers can be found at the bottom of the portfolio page.

**7.** An average male African elephant weighs about 176,000 ounces. How many tons does he weigh?

**8.** Bart's football coach tells him that he'll start next year if he gains 10 pounds in the 14 weeks between spring practice and summer drills. He hires a personal trainer who promises him a gain of 1 kg every 3 weeks. Will he make his goal?

## 8-3 Portfolio

Name _____

Check each box when you've completed the task. Remember that your instructor will want you to turn in the portfolio pages you create.

### Technology

1. ☐ The bar graph at the end of the applications (page 730) shows the average monthly high temperatures in degrees Celsius (rounded to the nearest degree) for Las Vegas. Read the graph and record the temperatures in a spreadsheet. Use the correct formula to convert each temperature to the Fahrenheit scale, then create a bar graph using those temperatures. Discuss how the graphs compare visually. Which one appears to show a greater variation in temperature?

### Online Practice

1. ☐ Include any written work from the online assignment along with any notes or questions about this lesson's content.

### Applications

1. ☐ Complete the applications problems.

### Reflections

Type a short answer to each question.

1. ☐ Explain the difference between mass and weight. In most applications, weight and mass are treated as if they mean the same thing. Why is it reasonable to do that?
2. ☐ Even though the base unit of mass/weight in the metric system is the gram, kilograms are used far more commonly. Why is that?
3. ☐ Measuring temperatures in metric units is different from the other measurements we studied. How?
4. ☐ Take another look at your answer to Question 0 at the beginning of this lesson. Would you revise your answer now that you've completed the lesson? How would you summarize the topic of this lesson now?
5. ☐ What questions do you have about this lesson?

### Looking Ahead

1. ☐ Complete the Prep Skills for Lesson 8-4 and read the opening paragraph in Lesson 8-4 carefully, then answer Question 0 in preparation for that lesson.

### Answers to "Did You Get It?"

1. 81,000 g, or about 178.2 lb    2. About 350 g    3. 30.2° F
4. About 110° C (107.2° C is exact.)    5. 192 oz    6. About 23.3° C
7. 5 ½ T    8. Yes, by about 0.3 lb.

## Applications

Name _____

In Questions 1–4, which would be the most appropriate unit of weight: gram, kilogram, or metric ton?

**1.** A cruise ship

*metric ton*

**2.** The eight-man rowing crew at Harvard

*kilogram*

**3.** A crew-neck sweater

*gram*

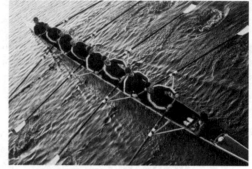

© Purestock/SuperStock RF

**4.** Tom Cruise

*kilogram*

**5.** If the temperature is 26°C, are you more likely to be in Seattle or San Antonio?

*San Antonio*

**6.** If the temperature is 9°C, are you more likely to be in Louisville or Anchorage?

*Anchorage*

**7.** If you step into a bath at 90°F, what will be the result?

*A delightful soak*

**8.** If you step into a bath at 90°C, what will be the result?

*A trip to the emergency room if you're lucky*

**9.** Blaine weighs 112 kg. Is he more likely to be a football player or a golfer?

*Football player*

**10.** Damon weighs 50 kg. Is he more likely to be a school bus driver or one of the kids riding the bus?

*Kid*

## 8-3 Applications

Name _____

11. My favorite recipe (spaghetti pie) calls for 12 ounces of ground sausage. Since it's awesome, everybody wants some, so I decided to make five pies and pass them out to the select few in my inner circle. The sausage comes in one-pound tubes. How many tubes did I need, and how many grams of delicious sausage were left over for my omelet the next morning? (Feel free to email me for the recipe. Seriously dude, it's awesome.)

$$60 \text{ oz} \cdot \frac{1 \text{ lb}}{16 \text{ oz}} = 3.75 \text{ lb}; \text{ I bought four tubes with } 0.25 \text{ lb left over.}$$

$$0.25 \text{ lb} \cdot \frac{16 \text{ oz}}{1 \text{ lb}} \cdot \frac{28 \text{ g}}{1 \text{ oz}} = 112 \text{ g}$$

12. After giving birth to her first child, Tricia was informed that he weighed 111 ounces. Her first thought was "Holy smokes—no wonder it felt like I was carrying around a bowling ball." The average newborn boy in the United States weighs about 7 pounds, 10 ounces, and an average bowling ball weighs 12 pounds. Find the baby's weight in pounds and rate Tricia's first instinct for accuracy.

$$111 \text{ oz} \cdot \frac{1 \text{ lb}}{16 \text{ oz}} = 6.937 \text{ lb}; \text{ not accurate. The baby was less than average, and just more than half the weight of an}$$

average bowling ball.

13. A large construction crane is rated to lift weights up to 16 metric tons. The design for a new building in downtown Houston calls for four large chillers to be placed on the roof, each of which weighs 8,200 pounds. Can the crane handle them all at once?

$$16 \text{ t} \cdot \frac{1,000 \text{ kg}}{1 \text{ t}} \cdot \frac{2.2 \text{ lb}}{1 \text{ kg}} = 35,200 \text{ lb}; 4 \cdot 8,200 \text{ lb} = 32,800 \text{ lb}$$

The crane can handle all of them at once.

14. Before heading to Switzerland for a skiing vacation, Jamel checks a weather report, which predicts temperatures from −3°C to 5°C while he and his family are there. Worried that he's going to almost freeze to death and have to get rescued by one of those St. Bernards with a barrel of wine around its neck, he checks a temperature conversion app. What does he find out about the Fahrenheit temperatures?

$$F = \frac{9}{5}(-3) + 32 = 26.6°; F = \frac{9}{5}(5) + 32 = 41°$$

If anything, that's a little on the warm side for a ski trip. He may find himself shushing slush.

## 8-3    Applications

Name _____

15. The temperature started out at 39°F at 7:30 this morning, and rose steadily at the rate of 3.2°F per hour until noon. What was the temperature in Celsius at noon, and what was the rate of increase in degrees Celsius per hour?

$$4.5 \text{ hr} \cdot \frac{3.2° \text{ F}}{1 \text{ hr}} = 14.4° \text{ F}$$    *The temperature at noon was 53.4°.*

$$C = \frac{5}{9}(39 - 32) \approx 3.9° \text{ F};\quad C = \frac{5}{9}(53.4 - 32) \approx 11.9° \text{ F}$$    *The temperature change was 8°C in 4.5 hours, for a rate of*

*about 1.78°C per hour.*

16. A pharmacist receives a shipment of two-thirds of a kilogram of a prescription powder used to treat early-stage flu. She plans to divide it into 90 bottles for distribution to customers, and the manufacturer recommends 6,000 mg per customer. Does she have enough?

$\frac{2}{3}$ *kg* $\approx 0.667$ *kg, which is 667 grams, or 667,000 mg. Dividing by 90, we get a bit over 7,411 mg per bottle, so she has plenty.*

**Technology**

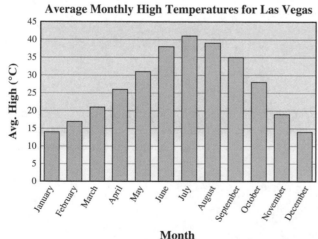

# Lesson 8-4   Prep Skills

This is a short review of skills that will come in handy in the next lesson. In each case, answer the question, then rate your confidence level by checking one of the boxes. If you feel like you're struggling with these skills, consult the online resources provided by your instructor for extra practice.

**SKILL 1: FIND THE AREA OF A CIRCLE**

1. Find the area of a circle with radius 4.5 cm.

2. Find the area of a circle with diameter 11".

**SKILL 2: FIND THE CIRCUMFERENCE OF A CIRCLE**

3. What is the circumference of the circle in Question 1?

**SKILL 3: FIND THE AREA OF A RECTANGLE**

4. Find the area of a rectangle with length 4 in. and width 2 feet.

**SKILL 4: FIND THE VOLUME OF A RECTANGULAR BOX**

5. A rectangular box has the rectangle in Question 4 as its base, and its height is 16 in. What is its volume?

**SKILL 5: WRITE AND INTERPRET A RATIO**

6. Write and simplify the ratio of 48 in. to 8 in. What does the result tell you about the relationship between those two measurements?

# Lesson 8-4   **Stocking the Shelves**   (Evaluating Efficiency in Packaging)

## LEARNING OBJECTIVES

☐ 1. Develop surface area and volume formulas for rectangular solids and cylinders.

☐ 2. Study the volume to surface area ratio for different product packages and identify its significance.

☐ 3. Develop methods for deciding on optimal size and shape given certain goals.

*Sometimes life gives us lessons sent in ridiculous packaging.*
                                    —Dar Williams

When you're at the grocery store looking at a stocked shelf, what makes you choose one product over another? In an ideal world that choice would be based on the quality of the actual product. But in this world, far too many people don't put that much thought into the quality of the product; buying choices are often made based on advertising or the appearance of the container that products are packaged in. Human psychology is a strange thing, and even the shape of packaging can have a subtle effect on how likely you are to notice a given item. When it comes to food packaging, volume has to be the first consideration: packages have to be designed to hold a certain amount of product. But another important consideration is the cost of materials, so it's in the manufacturer's best interest to limit the amount of metal, plastic, or cardboard used in packaging. As we'll see in this lesson, however, efficiency is often sacrificed in the interest of aesthetics because keeping costs down is good, but if nobody buys your product it doesn't really matter what your costs look like—you're out of business, pal.

**0.** After reading the opening paragraph, what do you think the main topic of this lesson will be?

© McGraw-Hill Education/Andrew Resek

> Exhausted? Winding the course down? Want a shorter lesson? Just provide students with the needed surface area and volume formulas, then move on to the Group portion.

## 8-4   Class

### Surface Area and Volume of a Rectangular Box

We'll begin our mathematical study of food packaging with breakfast cereal, and since Count Chocula isn't available at this time of year (don't get me started on THAT), we may as well go with Cocoa Puffs.

**1.** How many sides does a cereal box have?

   *Six.*

Courtesy of David Sobecki

The dimensions of the biggest box of Cocoa Puffs I could find are 24.4 cm by 7 cm by 29 cm.

2. Assign variable names $l$, $w$, and $h$ to represent these quantities. Think about it, and try to assign variable names to each dimension that make the most sense. Looking at the picture of the box will help.

$l = 24.4$ cm, $w = 7$ cm, $h = 29$ cm

3. Find the area of the bottom of this box.

The bottom is 24.4 cm by 7 cm, so the area is $(24.4)(7) = 170.8$ cm$^2$.

4. Is there another surface with the same area? Which one?

Yes, the top.

5. Write a formula for the area of the bottom in terms of $l$, $w$, and/or $h$.

$A = lw$

6. Find the area of the front of the box (the part with Sonny the Cuckoo Bird on it).

$(24.4)(29) = 707.6$ cm$^2$

7. Is there another surface with the same area? Which one?

Yes, the back.

8. Write a formula for the area of the front in terms of $l$, $w$, and/or $h$.

$A = lh$

9. Find the area of the side of the box (the part that usually has the nutrition label).

$(7)(29) = 203$ cm$^2$

10. Is there another surface with the same area? Which one?

Yes, the opposite side.

11. Write a formula for the area of one side in terms of *l, w,* and/or *h.*

$A = wh$

12. At this point, you should be able to use all of the stuff you've thought about up until now to write a formula for the combined area of all of the sides of the box. This is known as the **surface area** of a figure. Write your formula below in the colored box.

## The Surface Area of a Rectangular Box

For a rectangular box with base length *l*, base width *w*, and height *h*, the surface area is

$A = \underline{\quad 2lw + 2lh + 2wh \quad}$

> Needless to say, it's crucial that students have this formula correct before moving on.

13. Use your formula to find the surface area of the Cocoa Puffs box.

$A = 2(24.4)(7) + 2(24.4)(29) + 2(7)(29) = 2,162.8 \ cm^2$

14. The way we compute the volume of a box is pretty straightforward ($V = l \cdot w \cdot h$). You were asked about it in the prep assignment. What is the volume of this box of yummy treats?

$V = 24.4 \cdot 7 \cdot 29 = 4,953.2 \ cm^3$

15. Find the ratio of the volume to that of the surface area. Try to think about what this value represents. You'll discuss it more soon.

$\dfrac{4,953.2}{2,162.8} \approx 2.29$ 　 *Answers vary on what this represents.*

## Did You Get It

Try this problem to see if you understand the concepts we just studied. The answer can be found at the bottom of the portfolio page.

1. Find the volume, surface area, and ratio of volume to surface area for a shipping container that measures 8 ft by 6 ft by 12 ft.

## Surface Area and Volume of a Cylinder

The can in the photo has a radius of 3.6 cm (which is half of the distance across the top) and a height of 11.3 cm.

16. How many sides does a cylinder have? (Legal disclaimer: this is a dumb question but we wanted you to think about it.)

    *One, unless you consider the top and bottom, in which case three.*

Courtesy of David Sobecki

17. Find the area of the bottom of this can. If you don't remember the formula for the area of a circle, look it up or ask your professor nicely.

    $\pi(3.6)^2 \approx 40.7\,cm^2$

18. Is there another surface with the same area? Which one?

    *Yes, the top.*

19. Imagine (or maybe actually do this) cutting off the label by slicing it straight down the side (carefully) and stretching it out. What shape would that be?

    *A rectangle*

20. Find the area of the side of the can. You'll need the formula for the circumference of a circle.

    $2\pi(3.6)(11.3) \approx 255.6\,cm^2$

21. Write a formula for the area of the side of the can if we use $r$ to describe the radius and $h$ to describe the height.

    $A = 2\pi rh$

Use what you've learned to write a formula for the surface area of a cylinder.

### The Surface Area of a Cylinder

For a cylinder with radius $r$ and height $h$, the surface area is

$A = \underline{\quad 2\pi rh + 2\pi r^2 \quad}$

**22.** Use your formula to find the surface area of the soup can.

$A = 2\pi r^2 + 2\pi r h = 2\pi (3.6)^2 + 2\pi (3.6)(11.3) \approx 337\,cm^2$

**23.** The volume of a can is found by first calculating the area of the bottom of the can and multiplying by the height of the can. $V = \underline{\ \ \pi r^2\ \ }\,h$

**24.** Can the volume of the box of cereal be calculated by multiplying the area of the base times the height? What does that tell you in general about volume?

It can. To find the volume of a container with identical cross-sections throughout, you multiply the cross-sectional area times the height.

**25.** Back to the soup can. Find the volume using the formula from Question 23, then the ratio of the volume to that of the surface area. Try to think about what this value represents. You'll discuss it more soon.

$V = \pi (3.6)^2 (11.3) \approx 460.1\,cm^3$

$\dfrac{460.1}{337} \approx 1.37$   Answers vary on what this represents.

> Let students know that since we're comparing two completely different measures, there's not much value in the units for the answer, so it's okay to just use a raw number for the ratio.

**26.** Before moving on to the experimental phase of this lesson, fill in one of the blanks below with "surface area," and one with "volume."

The _____volume_____ of a container is a measure of how much food it can hold.

The \_\_\_\_surface area\_\_\_\_ of a container is a measure of how much material is needed to build the container.

## Did You Get It

Try this problem to see if you understand the concepts we just studied. The answer can be found at the bottom of the portfolio page.

2. A standard soda can is 4.83 in. high and has a radius of 1.3 in. Find the volume, surface area, and volume to surface area ratio.

# 8-4 Group

## LAB: Exploring Efficiency in Food Packaging

**Supplies needed:**

1. Have students and instructors bring in a wide assortment of rectangular boxes and metal cans of food. Better still, plan on donating the food to a local food pantry when you're done.
2. Rulers with centimeter measurements

> Encourage students to set up a spreadsheet to do all of the calculations! This will be the tech assignment, and it helps in class.

**1. Directions:**

1. Carefully measure each package, recording all dimensions shown on the table below.
2. Find the surface area and the volume of each.
3. Calculate the volume to surface area ratio for each product according to type (cans or boxes).
4. Calculate the ratio of length to width for the bases of all boxes.

*Samples from my pantry shown.*

| Length or Radius | Width | Height | Volume | Surface Area | V to SA Ratio | L to W Ratio |
|---|---|---|---|---|---|---|
| 12.5 | 5.4 | 20.5 | 1,383.8 | 868.9 | 1.59 | 2.31 |
| 9.5 | 2.5 | 16 | 380 | 431.5 | 0.88 | 3.80 |
| 19.3 | 5 | 28.5 | 2,750.25 | 1,578.1 | 1.74 | 3.86 |
| 8.6 | 3.3 | 18 | 510.8 | 485.2 | 1.05 | 2.61 |
| 7.5 | 4 | 13.7 | 411 | 375.1 | 1.10 | 1.88 |
| 17 | 9 | 20.7 | 3,167.1 | 1,382.4 | 2.29 | 1.89 |
| | | | | | | |
| 3.7 | | 11 | 473.1 | 341.7 | 1.38 | |
| 3.3 | | 6.8 | 232.6 | 209.4 | 1.11 | |
| 5 | | 5.5 | 432.0 | 329.9 | 1.31 | |
| 4.2 | | 5.6 | 310.3 | 258.6 | 1.20 | |
| 3.9 | | 12.5 | 597.3 | 401.9 | 1.49 | |
| | | | | | | |
| | | | | | | |

**2.** Look at your answers to Question 26 at the end of the Class portion of this lesson. Use them to explain why the ratio of volume to surface area is a measure of how efficient the containers are in terms of cost of production.

*To package a certain amount of food, you need a certain volume, but the amount of material used can change depending on the shape. When that ratio is larger, it means you're getting a larger volume compared to the amount of material used, which is a good thing for efficiency.*

**3.** Which of the containers is most efficient in terms of construction cost? Which is the least?

*Answers vary. Make sure they get that it's the one with the largest ratio of volume to surface area.*

**4.** Are cylinders more or less efficient than rectangular boxes on average? Explain.

*This is a bit of an opinion. At least in the sample, the most efficient boxes were way better than the most efficient cans, but the averages aren't terribly different.*

**5.** Look at the boxes that ranked higher in terms of efficiency. What can you conclude about comparing their height to the size of the base?

*Answers vary. We're just setting up thinking about the most efficient shape, which we'll study shortly.*

**6.** Look at the cans that ranked higher in terms of efficiency. What can you conclude about comparing their height to the size of the base?

*Ditto.*

Now we're going to do some math modeling to study maximum efficiency. We'll begin with cylinders, as that's a bit more straightforward. Using the formulas you developed in this lesson and some pretty darn fancy algebra, I was able to develop a formula that describes the surface area for a cylinder with a given volume $V$ and given height $h$:

$$A = \frac{2V}{h} + 2\sqrt{\pi V h}$$

> Looking for a nice extra credit project for more talented students? Have them try to derive this formula, and the one on page 741.

For maximum efficiency in terms of material cost, we would like to find a height that makes the surface area as small as possible when we know the volume. Finding the height that does that is a classic problem in calculus, which this course is not. We can, however, do the next best thing: graph the function on a graphing calculator and find the lowest point on the graph.

7. The volume of the soup can we studied was 460.1 cm$^3$. Plug this value into the above formula to find a function describing the surface area of a can with that volume.

$$A = \frac{920.2}{h} + 2\sqrt{1,445.4h}$$

8. Graph your answer to Question 7 on a graphing calculator. Set the viewing window so that Xmin = 0 and Xmax is at least 20. Then find the lowest point on the graph, either by using trace or by using the built-in minimum command. Write both coordinates of the lowest point.

   *The minimum is about (8.4, 330.0).*

9. One of those coordinates is the smallest surface area you could possibly have for a can with that volume. What is that minimal surface area?

   *330.0 cm$^2$*

10. Find the ratio of volume to surface area in that case. How does it compare to what we calculated for the actual can? What can you conclude?

    *$\frac{460.1}{330.0} = 1.39$; the ratio we calculated for the can was about 1.37, so the actual can is pretty darn efficient, just not maximally efficient for that volume.*

11. What would the dimensions of the most efficient can be? How do they compare to the Chunky soup can?

    *The height would be 8.4 cm. To keep the volume the same, we'd have to solve $460.1 = \pi r^2 (8.4)$ for r; the result is about 4.2 cm. The Chunky can has dimensions 3.6 cm and 11.3 cm, so the ideal can is shorter and wider.*

12. Look back at your table on page 738. Did any of the cans have a higher ratio than the ideal can with volume 460.1 cm$^3$? If so, what do you think that says about finding the ideal can?

    *If there is one, great, because it's certainly possible. It turns out that the biggest ratio you can get for a given volume depends on the volume; it's not a constant value.*

Now let's model efficiency for the rectangular boxes. This is a little more involved because there are three variable dimensions, as opposed to two for the cylinder. To construct a model, we have to choose a specific ratio of length to width for the bottom of the box, which is why you were asked to find those ratios. If we use $R$ to represent the ratio of length to width (where we always take "length" to mean "the longer of those two dimensions"), then this function describes the surface area of a rectangular box in terms of the volume ($V$) and the width ($w$):

$$A = \frac{2V(1 + R)}{Rw} + 2Rw^2 \qquad \text{(Trust me, I'm a doctor.)}$$

13. The Cocoa Puffs box we studied earlier had a volume of 4,953.2 cm$^3$ and a length to width ratio of 3.2. Use that information to write a function describing its surface area in terms of the width of the base $w$.

    $$A = \frac{13,002.2}{w} + 6.4w^2$$

14. Graph your answer to Question 13 on a graphing calculator. Set the viewing window so that Xmin $= 0$ and Xmax is at least 20. Then find the lowest point on the graph, either by using trace or by using the built-in minimum command. Write both coordinates of the lowest point.

    *The minimum is about (10.1, 1,940.2).*

15. One of those coordinates is the smallest surface area you could possibly have for a box with that volume. What is that minimal surface area?

    *1,940.2 cm$^2$*

16. Find the ratio of volume to surface area in that case. How does it compare to what we calculated for the actual box? What can you conclude?

    $\frac{4,953.2}{1,940.2} \approx 2.55$; *the ratio we calculated for the box was about 2.29, so once again, the actual package is pretty efficient, just not maximally efficient for that volume.*

**17.** What would the dimensions of the most efficient box be? How do they compare to the Cocoa Puffs box?

*We know the width would be 10.1 cm. Based on the ratio of 3.2, the length would be 3.2 times 10.1, or about 32.3 cm. To find the height, solve $4{,}953.2 = 32.3 \cdot 10.2 \cdot h$, to get a height of about 15.0 cm. The Cocoa Puffs box was 24.4 cm $\times$ 7 cm $\times$ 29 cm. The ideal box is quite a bit different: longer and wider, but shorter.*

**18.** Based on what you've learned, do you think the ratio for the most efficient box will change depending on the volume of the box? You'll be checking out some other boxes in the Applications: at this point, we're just asking for your best guess.

*Answers vary.*

**19.** Given that in each case, we found that the packaging was efficient, but not perfectly efficient, what are some other factors that you think go into deciding on the dimensions for packaging? List as many different ideas as you can think of.

*Answers vary.*

## 8-4 Portfolio

Name _____

Check each box when you've completed the task. Remember that your instructor will want you to turn in the portfolio pages you create.

### Technology

1. ☐ If you used a spreadsheet to compute the surface area, volume, and ratios on page 738, then you've already done the tech assignment. Just turn it in! If you didn't, (1) you should have, and (2) do so now. You can use the tech template for this lesson: just enter all of the dimensions for the packages you measured. Then input formulas that will calculate the surface area, volume, and ratios automatically.

### Online Practice

1. ☐ Include any written work from the online assignment along with any notes or questions about this lesson's content.

### Applications

1. ☐ Complete the applications problems.

### Reflections

Type a short answer to each question.

1. ☐ Describe what the surface area of an object is.
2. ☐ Why is the volume to surface area ratio useful in studying the efficiency of packaging?
3. ☐ What did you learn about food packaging from this lesson?
4. ☐ Take another look at your answer to Question 0 at the beginning of this lesson. Would you revise your answer now that you've completed the lesson? How would you summarize the topic of this lesson now?
5. ☐ What questions do you have about this lesson?

### Looking Ahead

1. ☐ Begin preparing for your final exam!

### Answers to "Did You Get It?"

1. Volume: 576 ft$^3$; surface area: 432 ft$^2$; ratio: 1.33
2. Volume: about 25.6 in.$^3$; surface area: about 50.1 in.$^2$; ratio: 0.51

## 8-4  Applications

Name _____

Pick one of the rectangular boxes you measured in class, and write all of the relevant information about it below. You'll be copying this information from the table on page 738.

Length:

Width:

Volume:

Surface area:

Volume to surface area ratio:

Length to width ratio:

> Sorry friends, I get to sit this one out and you're on your own for answers. All of the questions are specific to the packages measured in your class. The good news is that all of the calculations here are the same as the ones done in the lesson: we're just asking students to analyze some different containers in terms of how they stack up (pun intended) to those with maximal efficiency.

1. Recall that the function describing the surface area of a rectangular box for a fixed volume in terms of the width of the base $w$ is

$$A = \frac{2V(1 + R)}{Rw} + 2Rw^2$$

where $V$ is the volume and $R$ is the ratio of length to width. For the box above, use the values of $V$ and $R$ to write the surface area function.

2. Use a graphing calculator to draw the graph, then find the lowest point on the graph and record the coordinates here.

3. Describe what each of the coordinates of that point mean.

4. Find the volume to surface area ratio for the most efficient box with that volume and discuss how efficient you think the box you measured is.

## 8-4   Applications

Name _____

5.  How does the volume to surface area ratio for the ideal box of that volume compare to the ideal ratio for a box with a different volume we found in Question 16 of the Group portion? What do you think that comparison means?

Next, record the information for one of the cans you measured below. Again, you're just copying from the table at the beginning of the Group portion.

Length:

Width:

Volume:

Surface area:

Volume to surface area ratio:

Length to width ratio:

6.  Recall that the function describing the surface area of a cylindrical can for a fixed volume in terms of the height $h$ is

$$A = \frac{2V}{h} + 2\sqrt{\pi Vh}$$

For the can above, use the values of $V$ and $h$ to write the surface area function.

7.  Use a graphing calculator to draw the graph, then find the lowest point on the graph and record the coordinates here.

8.  Describe what each of the coordinates of that point mean.

## 8-4  Applications

Name _____

9. Find the volume to surface area ratio for the most efficient can with that volume and discuss how efficient you think the can you measured is.

10. How does the volume to surface area ratio for the ideal can of that volume compare to the ideal ratio for a can with a different volume we found in Question 16 of the Group portion? What do you think that comparison means?

11. Look at all of the data in the table on page 738, with a focus on the volume to surface area ratio column. Try to draw some general conclusions on some things that make containers more efficient in terms of cost of construction.

## Lesson 1-1

1. 27, 31

2. 32, 64

3. 12, 21, 36

4. 25, 55, 70, 100

5. $2a + 16$

6. $-9y + 34$

## Lesson 1-2

1. Tens place: 8; ones place: 7; tenths place: 2; hundredths place: 3

2. 8,430, 11.5, $85

3. $12 \times 8 = 96$;   $300 \times 6 = 1,800$;
   $25 \times 8 = 200$;   $120 + 80 = 200$;
   $95 + 15 = 110$;   $1,400 + 800 = 2,200$

## Lesson 1-3

1. 32 ft

2. 18″

3. $\frac{32}{3}$ ft, or 10 ft, 8 in.

## Lesson 2-1

1. $\frac{3}{5}, \frac{4}{5}, \frac{17}{7}, \frac{11}{24}$

2. $\frac{3}{5}, \frac{6}{25}, \frac{49}{50}, \frac{33}{100}$

3. 0.12, 0.3, 1.375, $3.\overline{6}$ or 3.666 . . .

4. $x = 7$

5. $y = 700$

6. $x = 383.92$

## Lesson 2-2

1. 40%

2. About 19.2%

3. 125%

4. 30

5. 1,020

6. $34.66

7. $575

8. $12,408

## Lesson 2-3

1. 0.12, 0.04, 0.0299

2. 12.3, $34.66

3. 18

4. 0.75, 1,012

5. $x = 1$

6. $r \approx 0.025$

## Lesson 2-4

1. 0.47, 0.094

2. $264

3. $500(1.03)^4$

4. 720, about 513.34

5. About 33.54

## Lesson 2-5

1. 0.91, 0.0648

2. $204.75

3. $582.30

4. 2,460

## Lesson 2-6

1. $3,240

2. $3,974.73

3. About 9.58, about 17,504.29

4. 0.790957

## Lesson 2-7

1. a. 16 g
   b. 441 mg
   c. 8%

2. 64 g

3. 62.5%

4. 5 g

5. $M = \dfrac{k}{P}$

## Lesson 2-8

1. 23%, 79.4%, 3.5%

2. $860.30

3. $3,519.32

4. $9,300.20

## Lesson 3-1

1. $\dfrac{3}{4}, \dfrac{13}{16}$

2. 0.6, 0.125

3. 60%, 75%

4. 13%, 5.8%

5. 15, 16, 17, 18, 19; 2, 3, 4, 5, 6, 7, 8

## Lesson 3-2

1. 30, 120

2. $\dfrac{1}{9}$

3. $\dfrac{1}{4}$

4. $\dfrac{1}{6}$

5. $\dfrac{2}{3}$

## Lesson 3-3

1. 12

2. 144

3. $\dfrac{9}{19}$ or about 0.47

4. About 5.3%

5. 840, 90

## Lesson 3-4

1. 330, 36

2. 120

3. 79,833,600

4. 210

5. 105

6. 0.625

7. 0.125

## Lesson 3-5

1. $\dfrac{1}{3}, \dfrac{4}{5}$

2. $\dfrac{5}{36}, \dfrac{7}{12}$

3. $\dfrac{13}{21}$

4. $-\dfrac{13}{9}$, or $-1.\overline{4}$

## Lesson 3-6

1. $\dfrac{13}{40}$ or 0.325

2. $\dfrac{3}{40}$, or 0.075

3. $\dfrac{9}{11}$

4. $\dfrac{3}{4}$

5. $\dfrac{31}{80}$

6. $P = 0.31$

## Lesson 3-7

1. $\dfrac{2}{11}, \dfrac{27}{100}, \dfrac{2}{25}$

2. $\dfrac{1}{11}$

3. $\dfrac{1}{13}$

4. $\dfrac{1}{4}$

5. $\dfrac{3}{26}$

6. About 0.165

## Lesson 3-8

1. 1, 495

2. $\dfrac{1}{8}$ or 0.125; $\dfrac{262,144}{1,953,125}$ or 0.134

3. $\dfrac{1}{3}$

## Lesson 4-1

1. 6

2. $348,000

3. $107,000

4. 20

5. It depends on if you do or do not include $150,000: either 2 or 3.

## Lesson 4-2

1. 97.2

2. $66.\overline{6}\%$

3. 12.5

4. 0.75, 1.25, 1.75, 2.25, 2.75, 3.25, 3.75, 4.25, 4.75, 5.25, 5.75, 6.25, 6.75, 7.25, 7.75

5. 0.25, 0.75, 1.25, 1.75, 2.25, 2.75, 3.25, 3.75, 4.25, 4.75, 5.25, 5.75, 6.25, 6.75, 7.25, 7.75

6.

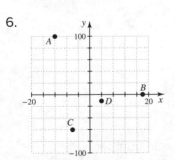

## Lesson 4-3

1. 1.2　1.3　1.3　1.7　1.7　1.7　2.1　2.3　2.4　2.4　2.4　2.5　2.5　2.8　3.1　3.7

2. 35.1

3. $\dfrac{43}{5} = 8.6$

4. 55

5. 1.2

6. 16

## Lesson 4-4

1. 49.5

2. 191

3. 10.58, 121.95

4. 110

## Lesson 4-5

1. 70%

2. 28%

3. 11 were rainy, 20 were not

4. 157

5. It goes up by 1.

## Lesson 4-6

1. $1.00–$1.99

2. 14

3. 0.12

4. About 8 square centimeters

5. About 83.8%

## Lesson 4-7

1. About 15.9%

2. 341,106

3. c

4. Mean = 147.875, standard deviation ≈ 9.44

5.

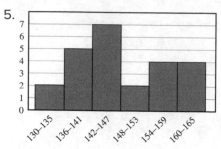

## Lesson 4-8

1. 35.8, 164.8, 75.36

2. $290,340

3.

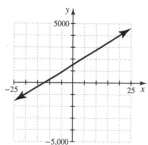

## Lesson 4-9

1. Mean: about 25.9; median: 19; mode: 18; midrange: 53

2. $3.85, about 51.7%

3.

**Depth of Great Lakes**

4.

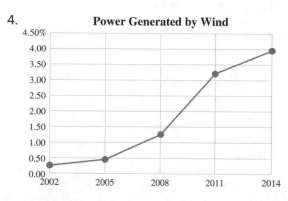

**Power Generated by Wind**

## Lesson 5-1

1. $\frac{7}{10}$

2. $\frac{3}{5}$

3. $\frac{3}{8}$

4. $\frac{9}{2}$

5. 11

6. $x = \frac{15}{4}$

7. $x = \frac{1}{4}$

## Lesson 5-2

1. −8, 12, 32; 700, 595, 370; −15, −3, 57; 400, 200, −400

2. $x = -6$; $x = 2,333.\overline{3}$

3. $x < 140$; $y \le -10$; $4 < z < 12$

## Lesson 5-3

1. (0, 300) and (−25, 0)

2. −12, −27, 428; about −3.778, −39.582

3. The second

4. $3x^2 + 45x$;   $-64x^2 + 160x$

## Lesson 5-4

1. About 813.71, about 33,577.43

2. (0, 70) and $\left(\frac{70}{23}, 0\right)$

3. $y = -12, 12$

4. $x = \sqrt[3]{90}$

6. $x = \frac{28}{3}$

7. $t = -8$

## Lesson 6-1

1. Integer, whole number, odd number

2. Integer, even number

3. Integer, whole number, even number

4. Integer, whole number, even number

5. No

6. No

# Lesson 6-2

1. {Sunday, Monday, Tuesday, Wednesday, Thursday, Friday, Saturday}

2. {6, 8, 10, 12, 14, . . .}

3. $\{x|x \in N \text{ and } 4 \leq x \leq 10\}$ is one potential answer.

4. $\{x|x$ is a letter of the alphabet that comes after d}

5. 128, 256, 512; 90, 110, 130

6. 16, 128

# Lesson 6-3

1. $A = \{9, 11, 13, 19, 21\}, B = \{9, 17, 19, 30\}, A' = \{7, 17, 30, 33, 42\}$

2. $A \cup B = \{9, 11, 13, 17, 19, 21, 30\}, A \cap B = \{9, 19\}, B' \cup A = \{7, 9, 11, 13, 19, 21, 33, 42\}$

3. $n(B) = 4, n(U) = 10$

4. $\dfrac{1}{2}$

5. 1

# Lesson 6-4

1.
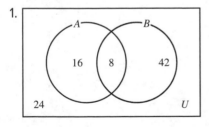

2. $A \cap B'$ or $A - B$

3. $A \cup B$

# Lesson 7-1

1. Yes

2. No

3. No

4. Yes

5. No

6. Yes

7. Yes

# Lesson 7-2

1. Conjunction

2. Conditional

3. Biconditional

4. Negation

5. Disjunction

6. If the patient is in critical condition, then a surgery room is being prepped.

7. The patient is not in critical condition or a surgery room is being prepped.

8. It is not the case that a surgery room is being prepped and the patient is in critical condition.

9. A surgery room is being prepped if and only if the patient is in critical condition.

# Lesson 7-3

1. When $p$ is not true

2. If either or both of $p$ and $q$ are false

3. If either or both of $r$ and $s$ are true

4. It's true unless $r$ is true and $p$ is false.

5. It's false if $q$ and $p$ have different truth values.

6.

| $p$ | $q$ | $r$ | $\sim p$ | $q \vee \sim p$ | $q \vee \sim p \to r$ |
|---|---|---|---|---|---|
| T | T | T | F | T | T |
| T | T | F | F | T | F |
| T | F | T | F | F | T |
| T | F | F | F | F | T |
| F | T | T | T | T | T |
| F | T | F | T | T | F |
| F | F | T | T | T | T |
| F | F | F | T | T | F |

## Lesson   7-4

1. $p \wedge q$; $p =$ I ate an entire side of beef for lunch, $q =$ my stomach does NOT feel good

2. $\sim p \to q$; $p =$ I take some medicine soon, $q =$ I might pass out

3. $p \leftrightarrow q$; $p =$ I'm going to work tomorrow, $q =$ I feel better

4. $p \vee q$; $p =$ Next time I go to that restaurant I'm ordering something different, $q =$ I'll call an ambulance in advance

5.

| $p$ | $q$ | $\sim q$ | $\sim q \vee p$ | $p \wedge (\sim q \vee p)$ |
|---|---|---|---|---|
| T | T | F | T | T |
| T | F | T | T | T |
| F | T | F | F | F |
| F | F | T | T | F |

6.

| $p$ | $q$ | $r$ | $\sim q$ | $p \wedge \sim q$ | $r \to (p \wedge \sim q)$ |
|---|---|---|---|---|---|
| T | T | T | F | F | F |
| T | T | F | F | F | T |
| T | F | T | T | T | T |
| T | F | F | T | T | T |
| F | T | T | F | F | F |
| F | T | F | F | F | T |
| F | F | T | T | F | F |
| F | F | F | T | F | T |

## Lesson   8-1

1. 1,620 minutes

2. About 6.83 hours

3. About 8.08 feet

4. 147.6 inches

5. 8,700 cents

6. $14.93

7. 4

8. $\dfrac{1}{6}$

9. $5z$

## Lesson   8-2

1. 7,040 yd

2. 63.5 cm

3. About 2.61 mi/hr

4. 27,000 ml

5. 3.47 km

6. 900,000 cm

7. 16 sq ft

8. 2.197 cu in

## Lesson   8-3

1. 4,824 in.

2. About 43.7 in.

3. About 6.44 km

4. 0.843 dg

5. 0.94 hm

6. 43.12 daL

7. 135

8. About −25.3

## Lesson   8-4

1. About 63.6 sq cm

2. About 95.0 sq in.

3. About 28.3 cm

4. 96 sq in.

5. 1,536 cu in.

6. $\dfrac{48 \text{ in.}}{8 \text{ in.}} = 6$; The first measurement is six times as big.

# Index